1982

Science Year

The World Book Science Annual

A Review of Science and Technology During the 1981 School Year

World Book–Childcraft International, Inc.

A subsidiary of The Scott & Fetzer Company

Chicago London Sydney Tokyo Toronto

The publishers of *Science Year* gratefully
acknowledge the following for permission to use
copyrighted illustrations. A full listing of illustration
acknowledgments appears on pages 397 and 398.

123 "Computer Tomography Scans of Alcoholics:
     Cerebral Atrophy?," P. L. Carlen et al., from
     Science, © 1979 American Association for the
     Advancement of Science.
233 Drawing by Lorenz; © 1980 The New Yorker
     Magazine, Inc.
245 Drawing by H. Martin; © 1981 The New Yorker
     Magazine, Inc.
266 Photo by Wolfgang Suter. Reprinted by
     permission from *Nature,* Vol. 286, No. 5772, p.
     486 by Olivier Rieppel. © 1980 Macmillan
     Journals Ltd.
287 Drawing by Lorenz; © 1980 The New Yorker
     Magazine, Inc.
305 Drawings adapted from *Science,* © 1980
     American Association for the Advancement of
     Science, from study done at Johns Hopkins
     University, Department of Psychology.
320 Drawing by Ross; © 1980 The New Yorker
     Magazine, Inc.

Preface

A review of some of the articles that have appeared in past editions of *Science Year* can tell us something about the ebb and flow of advances in science, and how understanding of scientific principles develops. Sometimes it appears that nothing happens in a field for long periods of time. But the work does continue in the laboratories and on the drawing boards and, suddenly, another chapter of the story is ready to tell.

Consider the United States manned space program. The moon landings ended in 1972 and the *Skylab* program in 1974. The last Americans in space were those who joined the Russian cosmonauts in the *Apollo-Soyuz* venture in July 1975. There was then a six-year hiatus during which space engineers struggled to make the space shuttle work. The news of the space sciences was marked by failure. But in April 1981, the shuttle was launched and returned with almost perfect results. And *Science Year* had another exciting story to report.

The same record of fits and starts pervades physics and the life sciences. *Science Year* has followed the high-energy physicists, for example, in their search for the fundamental elements of matter. The simple picture of an atomic nucleus of protons and neutrons gave way a decade ago to new heroes — the elusive particles called quarks, recently found to be linked to one another by equally elusive particles called gluons. This work has been the subject of several Special Reports and a constant theme of the Science File entry ELEMENTARY PARTICLE PHYSICS. And while its author this year declares: " . . . particle physics enjoyed a breathing spell during the year . . . " we know that the lull is temporary.

Like their physicist counterparts, the molecular biologists suddenly found two years ago that the DNA world does not behave in ways they had come to expect. The gene-coding system that was continuous and predictable in bacteria does strange things in higher organisms. These genes are split into segments of working parts and other parts whose function is not clearly understood. Again, *Science Year* Special Reports and appropriate Science File articles have tracked the progress and noted the surprises in this fascinating field of science.

For scientists, the challenge of trying to understand these anomalies is the best reason for continuing the work. But it may not be reason enough for many of the rest of us. For it does not answer the question: What, if anything, will understanding these things mean to me? The purpose of *Science Year* is not only to report, but also to explain and interpret the meaning of these scientific searches — and, in so doing, to help answer that question. [Arthur G. Tressler]

Contents

10 Special Reports
Fourteen articles give in-depth treatment to significant and timely subjects
in science and technology.

12 Flight to Saturn   by James B. Pollack
The *Voyager* spacecraft, as they continue their odyssey through the outer
solar system, report on what is new and mysterious about the ringed planet.

26 Rhinos on the Run   by Andrew Laurie
Hounded by hunters and hemmed in by farmers, these big, rugged, jungle beasts
are fighting for survival as a species.

40 End of an Era   by Erle G. Kauffman
The demise of the dinosaurs, along with that of many other species, seems
to have been caused by an unusual, unlucky, combination of events.

54 Image of an Instant   by Harold E. Edgerton
A renowned engineer-photographer describes the techniques he has developed
to capture the steps of high-speed phenomena.

68 Fireworks Mountain   by Peter W. Lipman
The eruptions of Mount Saint Helens have provided earth scientists with a
living laboratory in which to study the forces that drive volcanoes.

84 The Science of Animal Welfare   by Michael W. Fox
It may be necessary for animals to be sacrificed to the dinner table or
the research laboratory, but it is not necessary that they suffer needlessly.

96 Archaeologists in Wet Suits   by George F. Bass
A leading underwater archaeologist describes the special problems
that have to be solved in preserving history from the ocean floor.

112 Alcohol: The Friendly Foe   by Robert B. Millman
A psychiatrist who specializes in drug abuse problems explains how people
can be enslaved by the oldest drug.

126 Pharmacies in the Jungle   by Isao Kubo
Medicine men know, and scientific men are learning, of the healing potential that
resides in the leaves, stems, and roots of many plants.

138 X-Ray Eyes on the Skies   by Stephen S. Murray
The *Einstein* Observatory has taught us much about the power and a little
about the origins of the universe's sources of great energy.

152 The Opening Shot at Hepatitis   by Ben Patrusky
A disease that affects millions of people throughout the world is surrendering
one of its forms to a new vaccine.

166 Using Cancer to Fight Disease by Michael Shodell
The unlikely liaison between a cancer cell and an immune cell may be the most important discovery in the history of medical science.

180 Knowing the Odds by John G. Truxal
Whether tossing a coin or choosing the right tollgate, you can play a winning game if you know the mathematics.

194 Chemistry's Speedy Servants by Lawrence P. Verbit
Catalyst, a word that has come to mean any agent of change in our daily lives, was derived from a chemical phenomenon that is a keystone in much of modern industry.

206 For Further Reading
A list of books and magazines that provides additional information on the subjects of some of the Special Reports.

208 Science File
A total of 40 articles, alphabetically arranged by subject matter, plus 6 *Science Year* Close-Ups, report on the year's work in science and technology.

321 World Book Supplement
Five revised articles reprinted from the 1981 edition of *The World Book Encyclopedia:* "Bacteria," "Brain," "Drug Abuse," "Radiocarbon," and "Videodisc."

337 Science You Can Use
A selection of articles that focus on science and technology as it applies to the consumer.

354 People in Science
This section takes the reader behind the headlines of science and into the laboratories and classrooms to focus on scientists and on lay people who want to share some of the excitement science produces.

356 J. Robert Cade by Noel D. Vietmeyer
A sports-minded kidney specialist applied his specialty to the development of a popular soft drink, and improvements in nutrition in general.

370 The Making of a Doctor by Sherry Baron
A third-year medical student describes the work and rewards of learning the fundamentals for a medical career.

385 Index

Staff

Editorial Director
William H. Nault

Editorial
Executive Editor
Arthur G. Tressler

Managing Editor
Darlene R. Stille

Chief Copy Editor
Joseph P. Spohn

Senior Editors
Patricia Dragisic
Marsha F. Goldsmith
Beverly Merz
Jay Myers
Edward G. Nash

Copy Editor
Irene B. Keller

Editorial Assistant
Lettie Zinnamon

Art
Executive Art Director
William Hammond

Art Director
Roberta Dimmer

Senior Artists
Bernard Arendt
Margaret Smith

Artists
Karen Forch
Margot McMahon

Photography Director
John S. Marshall

Photographer
Stephen Hale

Senior Photographs Editor
Carol A. Parden

Photographs Editor
Karen M. Koblik

Research and Services
Director of Editorial Services
Susan C. Kilburg

Head, Editorial Research
Mary Norton

Head, Research Library
Indrani Embar

Head, Cartographic Services
H. George Stoll

Index Editor
Claire Bolton

Product Production
Director of Manufacturing
Joseph LaCount

Director of Pre-Press
J. J. Stack

Composition Manager
John Babrick

Production Control Managers
Sandra Grebenar
Barbara Podczerwinski

Assistant Product Manager
Madelyn Krzak

Film Separations Manager
Alfred J. Mozdzen

Film Separations Assistant Managers
Ann Eriksen
Barbara J. McDonald

Research and Development Manager
Henry Koval

Editorial Advisory Board

Contributors

Adelman, George, M.S.
Editor & Librarian
Neuroscience Research Program
Massachusetts Institute of Technology
Neuroscience

Ahrens, Thomas J., Ph.D.
Professor of Geophysics
California Institute of Technology
Geoscience, Geophysics

Alderman, Michael H., M.D.
Professor of Medicine and
Public Health
Cornell University Medical College
Medicine, Internal
Public Health

Auerbach, Stanley I., Ph.D.
Director, Environmental
Sciences Division
Oak Ridge National Laboratory
Ecology

Baron, Sherry, B.A.
Medical Student
Case Western Reserve University
The Making of a Doctor

Bass, George F., Ph.D.
President
Institute of Nautical Archaeology
Texas A&M University
Archaeologists in Wet Suits

Bell, William J., Ph.D.
Professor of Biology
University of Kansas
Zoology

Belton, Michael J. S., Ph. D.
Astronomer
Kitt Peak National Observatory
Astronomy, Planetary

Brawley, Susan H., Ph.D.
Research Associate
Marine Systems Laboratory
Smithsonian Institution
Close-Up, Zoology

Capece, Raymond P., B.S.E.E.
Managing Editor, Technical
Electronics Magazine
Electronics

Cohen, Barney, M.A.
Free-Lance Writer
Close-Up, Energy

Cromie, William J., M.A.
Executive Director
Council for the Advancement
of Science Writing
Close-Up, Molecular Biology

Dewey, Russell A., Ph.D.
Assistant Professor of Psychology
Georgia Southern College
Psychology

Edgerton, Harold E., D.Sc
Institute Professor, Emeritus
Massachusetts Institute of Technology
Image of an Instant

Flier, Jeffrey S., M.D.
Assistant Professor of Medicine
Harvard Medical School
Close-Up, Nutrition

Fox, Michael W., D.V.M.
Director
Institute for the Study of
Animal Problems
The Science of Animal Welfare

Gates, W. Lawrence, Sc.D.
Professor and Chairman
Department of Atmospheric Sciences
Oregon State University
Meteorology

Goldhaber, Paul, D.D.S.
Dean and Professor of Periodontology
Harvard School of Dental Medicine
Medicine, Dentistry

Gump, Frank E., M.D.
Professor of Surgery
Columbia University
Medicine, Surgery

Hartl, Daniel L., Ph.D.
Professor of Biology
Purdue University
Genetics

Hester, Thomas R., Ph.D.
Professor of Anthropology and Director
Center for Archaeological Research
University of Texas at San Antonio
Archaeology, New World

Jennings, Feenan D., B.S.
Director, Sea Grant Program
Texas A&M University
Oceanography

Jones, William G., A.M.L.S.
Assistant University Librarian
University of Illinois at Chicago Circle
Books of Science

Kauffman, Erle G., Ph.D.
Professor and Chairman
Department of Geological Sciences
University of Colorado
End of an Era

King, Lauriston R., Ph.D.
Deputy Director
Sea Grant Program
Texas A&M University
Oceanography

Kessler, Karl G., Ph.D.
Director, Center for Absolute
Physical Quantities
National Bureau of Standards
Physics, Atomic and Molecular

Kubo, Isao, Ph.D.
Assistant Professor of Natural Products
Chemistry
University of California at Berkeley
Pharmacies in the Jungle

Laurie, Andrew, Ph.D.
Research Associate
Department of Zoology
University of Cambridge
England
Rhinos on the Run

Lewis, Richard S., B.A.
Free-Lance Writer
Space Exploration

Lipman, Peter W., Ph.D.
Geologist
U. S. Geological Survey
Fireworks Mountain

Lipscomb, David M., Ph.D.
Professor of Audiology and Speech
Pathology
University of Tennessee
Killing your Ears with the Sound of Music

Maran, Stephen P., Ph.D.
Senior Staff Scientist
NASA-Goddard Space Flight Center
Astronomy, Stellar

March, Robert H., Ph.D.
Professor of Physics
University of Wisconsin
Physics, Elementary Particles

McCullough, Elizabeth A., Ph.D.
Assistant Professor
Kansas State University
Insulating Yourself Against the Elements

Meade, Dale M., Ph.D.
Head, Experimental Division
Plasma Physics Laboratory
Princeton University
Physics, Plasma

Merbs, Charles F., Ph.D.
Professor
Department of Anthropology
Arizona State University
Anthropology

Millman, Robert B., M.D.
Clinical Professor of Public Health
Cornell University Medical College
Alcohol: The Friendly Foe

Murray, Stephen S., Ph.D.
Astrophysicist
Smithsonian Astrophysical Observatory
X-Ray Eyes on the Skies
Astronomy, High Energy

Negele, John W., Ph.D.
Professor of Physics
Massachusetts Institute of Technology
Physics, Nuclear

Orbach, Raymond, Ph.D.
Professor of Physics
University of California
Physics, Solid-State

Patrusky, Ben, B.E.E.
Free-Lance Science Writer
The Opening Shot at Hepatitis

Piel, E. Joseph, Ed.D.
Chairman, Department of Technology
and Society
College of Engineering
State University of New York at
Stony Brook
Do you Really Need a Home Computer?

Pollack, James B., Ph.D.
Space Scientist
NASA Ames Research Center
Flight to Saturn

Reidenberg, Marcus M., M.D.
Professor of Pharmacology and Medicine
Cornell University Medical College
Drugs

Roberts, Thomas M., Ph.D.
Assistant Professor
Sidney Farber Cancer Institute
Harvard Medical College
Molecular Biology

Salisbury, Frank B., Ph.D.
Professor of Plant Physiology and Botany
Plant Science Department
Utah State University
Botany

Sforza, Pasquale M., Ph.D.
Professor of Mechanical and Aerospace
Engineering
Polytechnic Institute of New York
Feeling Dry? Humidify

Shodell, Michael, Ph.D.
Associate Professor of Biology
Long Island University-Case Western
Post Center
Using Cancer to Fight Disease

Shuldiner, Herbert, B.A.
Executive Editor
Popular Science Magazine
Rounding Up Facts About Radial Tires

Silk, Joseph, Ph.D.
Professor
University of California at Berkeley
Astronomy, Cosmology

Snyderman, Ralph, M.D.
Professor of Medicine and Immunology
Chief, Division of Rheumatic and Genetic
Diseases
Duke University Medical Center
Immunology

Thompson, Ida, Ph.D.
Research Associate
Center for Coastal and Environmental
Studies
Rutgers University
Geoscience, Paleontology

Tierney, John, B.A.
Staff Writer
Science Magazine
Close-Up, Geoscience

Trefil, James S., Ph.D.
Professor of Physics
University of Virginia
Dressing your Home for Winter

Truxal, John G., D. Eng.; Sc.D.
Distinguished Teaching Professor
State University of New York
Knowing the Odds

Verbit, Lawrence P., Ph.D.
Professor of Chemistry
State University of New York
at Binghamton
Chemistry's Speedy Servants
Chemistry

Vietmeyer, Noel D., Ph.D.
Professional Associate
National Academy of Sciences
J. Robert Cade

Visich, Marian, Jr., Ph.D.
Associate Dean of Engineering
State University of New York
Energy

Ward, Harold R., Ph.D., J.D.
Director, Center for Environmental Studies
Professor of Chemistry
Brown University
Environment

Wenke, Robert J., Ph.D.
Assistant Professor
University of Washington
Archaeology, Old World

Wetherill, George W., Ph.D.
Director
Department of Terrestrial Magnetism
Carnegie Institution of Washington
Geoscience, Geochemistry

Wittwer, Sylvan H., Ph.D.
Director
Michigan Agricultural Experimental Station
Michigan State University
Agriculture

Wurtman, Judith J., Ph.D.
Research Associate
Department of Nutrition
Massachusetts Institute of Technology
Nutrition

Contributors not listed on
these pages are members of the
Science Year editorial staff.

Special Reports

The Special Reports give in-depth treatment to the major advances in science and technology. The subjects were chosen for their current importance and lasting interest.

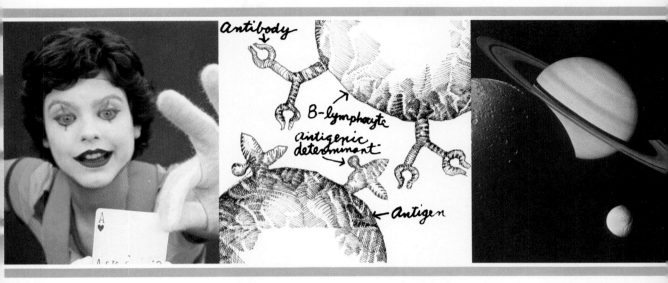

12   **Flight to Saturn**   by James B. Pollack

26   **Rhinos on the Run**   by Andrew Laurie

40   **End of an Era**   by Erle G. Kauffman

54   **Image of an Instant**   by Harold E. Edgerton

68   **Fireworks Mountain**   by Peter W. Lipman

84   **The Science of Animal Welfare**   by Michael W. Fox

96   **Archaeologists in Wet Suits**   by George F. Bass

112   **Alcohol: The Friendly Foe**   by Robert B. Millman

126   **Pharmacies in the Jungle**   by Isao Kubo

138   **X-Ray Eyes on the Skies**   by Stephen S. Murray

152   **The Opening Shot at Hepatitis**   by Ben Patrusky

166   **Using Cancer to Fight Disease**   by Michael Shodell

180   **Knowing the Odds**   by John G. Truxal

194   **Chemistry's Speedy Servants**   by Lawrence P. Verbit

Flight to Saturn

By James B. Pollack

Voyager's visit to the planet named for the Roman harvest god has yielded a rich crop of data on the golden orb, its many moons, and its unique icy rings

As the latest stop on its interplanetary grand tour, the National Aeronautics and Space Administration's (NASA) *Voyager 1* spacecraft visited the Saturn system in 1980. That was three years after leaving Earth on Sept. 5, 1977, and a year and a half after its spectacular fly-by of Jupiter in 1979. Observations of the Saturn system began on August 22, when the spacecraft was still 109 million kilometers (68 million miles) away. They were intensified greatly around November 12, when *Voyager* passed within 126,000 kilometers (78,000 miles) of the planet, and continued for another month.

As a member of the *Voyager 1* imaging team, I was privileged to be among the first to see the excitingly vivid close-up pictures of gold-colored Saturn, most of its 15 moons, and its 7 remarkable rings.

Voyager 1 instruments detected three new moons; provided the first accurate analysis of the atmosphere of Saturn's major moon, Titan; relayed new information about the properties of the ring particles; and made the first detailed measurements of the wind speeds in Saturn's atmosphere.

The Saturn system, located nearly 10 times farther from the Sun than is Earth, is quite different from our water-covered planet and its one satellite, the Moon. Nor does it resemble Mercury, Venus, or Mars, the other planets of the inner solar system — those nearest the Sun. Among the planets of the outer solar system, which include Jupiter, Uranus, Neptune, and little-known Pluto, Saturn is second in size, and most similar, to Jupiter. Because Saturn, like Mercury, Venus, Mars, and Jupiter, is bright enough to be seen without a telescope, it was known to ancient astronomers. But it was only a point of light until the telescope was invented in the 1600s. Italian astronomer Galileo Galilei, gazing at the planet from a rooftop in Padua, Italy, in 1610, was the first person to view Saturn's rings. Observations later in the 1600s by Dutch astronomer Christian Huygens and French astronomer Jean Domenique Cassini and in the 1700s by English astronomer Sir William Herschel and later by others led to further discoveries. After spacecraft flights became feasible in the 1960s, scientists sent unmanned probes to visit all five planets known to the ancient astronomers. Saturn was first visited on Sept. 1, 1979, by *Pioneer 11*. That spacecraft set the stage for the *Voyager* mission.

Even before spacecraft approached the planet, scientists had a fairly good idea of the composition of Saturn. They knew that a rocky object that occupied the same volume as Saturn would weigh about 10 times more than ground-based measurements told them Saturn weighs. In fact, even a body consisting of an equal volume of water would have about twice Saturn's mass. These comparisons suggested that Saturn is made of lighter materials. Because molecular hydrogen (two hydrogen atoms joined) is the most abundant gas in Saturn's atmosphere, scientists suggested that the planet consists mostly of gases having the same proportion of elements as the Sun. That is, Saturn would be almost 90 per cent molecular hydrogen and 10 per cent atomic helium (only one helium atom), with gases containing nitrogen, carbon, oxygen, and less abundant elements making up the remaining few tenths of 1 per cent. However, if it were made up only of gases, Saturn would have somewhat less mass than we know it to have from years of observation and investigation.

These facts and the construction of detailed mathematical models that match Saturn's measured mass and volume have convinced most scientists that Saturn has two major components: a thick fluid envelope made of elements similar to those that are found in the Sun that act like gases near the planet's surface and like liquids at greater depth, and a denser central core made of rocks and perhaps, liquid

The author:
James B. Pollack is a space scientist at NASA Ames Research Center in Moffett Field, Calif. He is a member of the *Voyager* imaging team.

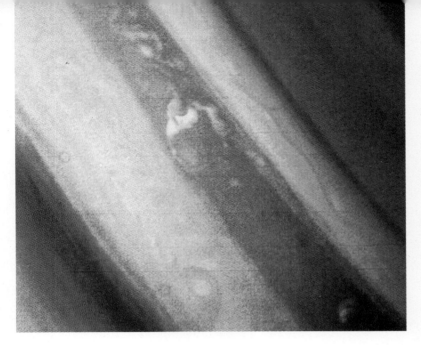

Saturn's northern hemisphere clouds, as seen from a distance of 9.5 million kilometers (5.5 million miles), are hidden by heavy haze. Hydrogen, methane, and ammonia vapors they are made of (colored by traces of hydrocarbons, sulfur, and phosphorus compounds) appear as a variety of swirling waves and eddies.

water, methane, and ammonia. The mass of the core is about 20 times Earth's mass and extends about 12,000 kilometers (7,450 miles) from the center of the planet. The envelope has a mass 75 times that of Earth and ranges from 12,000 to 60,000 kilometers (7,450 to 37,000 miles) from the planet's center.

Pioneer 11 and *Voyager 1* measured the temperature and atmospheric pressure in the upper 1 per cent of Saturn's fluid envelope, the observable part of its atmosphere. They found that the coldest temperature is about −188°C (−306°F.), which occurs at a pressure about 0.1 of that at the surface of Earth. It is so cold also at somewhat lower altitudes in the upper troposphere, Saturn's second-highest atmospheric region, that some gases condense and form cloud layers. There is not enough condensable gas at higher altitudes in the stratosphere, the topmost atmospheric region, for clouds to form there. Two main types of clouds are believed to be in the troposphere — water clouds that form where the temperature is about 27°C (81°F.) and pressure about 20 times that at Earth's surface, and ammonia-ice clouds that form where the temperature is −123°C (−189°F.) and pressure 1½ times that at Earth's surface. There may also be a cloud made of combined hydrogen sulfide and ammonia between the water and ammonia clouds.

Saturn's appearance is determined by a combination of stratospheric smog particles, the ammonia cloud, and chemicals that act as coloring agents within and outside this cloud. The most outstanding feature on Saturn is a set of alternating bright, whitish zones and dark-colored belts that circle the planet parallel to its equator. As seen in ground-based photographs, Saturn's zones and belts do not show much contrast, and *Voyager* photos supported the theory that a thick layer of smog particles partially masks underlying features.

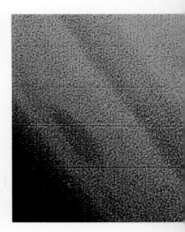

The odd orange oval in the southern hemisphere kept its form throughout four months' observation, proving that some atmospheric features endure despite Saturn's extremely strong winds.

Titan viewed from the side opposite the Sun is a day-lit crescent. A high-altitude haze layer stands out clearly above the lower atmosphere that obscures its surface.

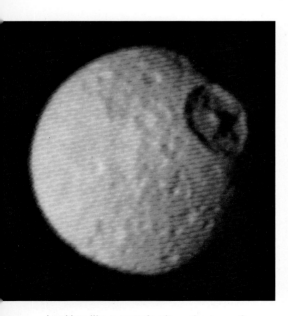

Looking like a cosmic ulcer, the scar of an ancient impact covers one-third of Mimas. A 9-kilometer (6-mile)-high rim rings the 130-kilometer (80-mile)-wide crater.

The smog particles, and perhaps the coloring agents too, form in the stratosphere when ultraviolet sunlight breaks up certain molecules of gas and the molecular fragments then undergo complex chemical reactions. Some scientists now think that these particles come mainly from methane gas, because *Voyager* detected ethane, acetylene, and perhaps propane — gases that may be intermediate products in the methane conversion process — in Saturn's atmosphere. *Voyager* also found phosphene gas, a combination of phosphorus and hydrogen atoms, on Saturn. Sunlight acting on phosphene may produce red phosphorus, which could be responsible for the color of Saturn's red-orange spot, a smaller version of Jupiter's Great Red Spot.

We measured wind speeds near the ammonia cloud tops by tracking the motion on *Voyager* photos of such small features as moving clouds. Near Saturn's equator, the winds blow mainly from west to east at the astonishing speeds of up to 1,770 kilometers (1,100 miles) per hour. This "jet stream" ranges from about 40 degrees south to 40 degrees north of Saturn's equator. At higher latitudes, the winds are much slower and tend to alternate between blowing to the west and to the east. We hope to learn what drives these enormous winds by further study of the *Voyager* data.

Saturn's nine largest moons were known and named by 1900. From largest to smallest, they are Titan, Rhea, Iapetus, Dione, Tethys, Enceladus, Mimas, Hyperion, and Phoebe. Astronomers discovered three smaller moons — 1980 S1, 1980 S3, and 1980 S6 — close to Saturn in 1966 and in 1980, when they viewed the flat, disk-shaped rings edge-on from Earth. Because the rings appeared much dimmer than usual, the moons could be seen. Three additional moons — 1980 S26, 1980 S27, and 1980 S28 — were found on *Voyager* photographs. They are also quite small and lie even closer to Saturn than the first three.

Titan's diameter of 5,140 kilometers (3,192 miles) makes it slightly larger than the planet Mercury and somewhat smaller than Mars. The remaining moons range in diameter from 1,530 kilometers (950 miles) for Rhea down to 30 kilometers (19 miles) for 1980 S28. The moons' distance from Saturn's center ranges from 137,300 kilometers (85,263 miles) for 1980 S28 to 10,583,200 kilometers (6,572,167 miles) for Phoebe.

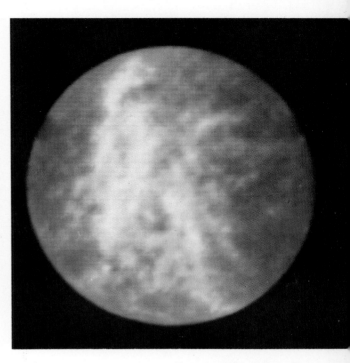

Scientists derive information about the composition of the moons from their *mean density* — the ratio of the mass of a given volume of a substance to that of an equal volume of water. *Voyager* pictures provide accurate information on the size and, therefore, the volume of almost all the moons. We estimated the mass of the larger ones from their slight but measurable gravitational effect on the paths of *Pioneer* and *Voyager* spacecraft as they flew by. Our measurements show that all the moons are made of rock and ice — probably frozen water as well as ammonia and methane for the outer ones.

Like almost all planetary satellites, including our Moon, the surface of Saturn's moons are pocked with craters formed when small stray bodies such as comet nuclei or asteroids struck them. *Voyager* photos transmitted the first data on the Saturn system's crater density — the number of craters per unit area of surface. Scientists use this information to estimate the age of a moon's surface. Generally, the older the surface, the higher its crater density. Also, the smaller the moon, the more likely it is to remain densely cratered because of a lack of internal activity. For example, we found such a high crater density on Mimas — one of the smaller moons, with a diameter of 390 kilometers (242 miles) — that we estimate its surface probably dates back almost to the formation of the Saturn system 4.6 billion years ago. However, we were puzzled to find that Enceladus, which formed at the same time as Mimas and is only slightly larger with a diameter of 500 kilometers (310 miles), has a relatively low crater density. We

From a million miles off, wispy markings on Rhea, *above,* were a clue that ice and rock long ago burst through the moon's crust and melted over it. But a mosaic photo made at 20 times closer range, *above left,* proves that Rhea now is Saturn's most cratered satellite. The many ridges and grooves at right resemble those found on Earth's Moon and on Mercury.

The side of Iapetus that faces Saturn is so much darker than the other that they seem to be made of different matter. Ice may have been deposited, or inner matter ejected, on one side of the moon.

think that some type of internal activity may have recoated the surface of this moon from time to time.

Other *Voyager* pictures provided clear evidence that some of the larger satellites have been "smoothed out." Rhea, whose diameter of 1,530 kilometers (950 miles) makes it the second-largest moon, and Dione, 1,120 kilometers (695 miles) in diameter, showed much lower crater density in some areas than in others. Complex networks of bright, wispy markings that show up against the darker places on these two moons are the clues to what occurred. They show where ice and rock in the moons' interiors, made very hot by uranium and other radioactive elements at work there, were pushed up through large fractures in the moons' crust by internal pressures. As this molten material poured across the surface, it filled craters. Heating due to the decay of radioactive elements probably created most of the resurfacing material during the moons' first billion years, when the elements were most plentiful. Later, as they decayed and produced less heat and the crusts grew thicker, no material could reach the moons' surfaces. Early heating of the larger moons may also have caused some of the heavier rock of which they are made to sink toward their centers and water to rise to their surfaces. So their composition now may vary with depth, with more water and other "icy" components

Dione's distinguishing feature is a series of deep valleys dug out of the crust (bottom right). Intense shock waves caused by the impact of meteorites may have created them, or they may have resulted from internal processes. The bright streaks at Dione's top edge may be ice from the interior.

closer to the surface. Smaller moons are less likely to have undergone such active early episodes because they contained less radioactive material and did not get as hot.

Because Titan is Saturn's largest moon, it held special interest for us. We hoped *Voyager* would get close enough to uncover some of its secrets. For example, we knew from ground-based observations that Titan was the only planetary moon to have a substantial atmosphere, and that methane gas was a part of that atmosphere, but we had no idea which other gases might be found on Titan. Therefore, estimates of the atmospheric pressure on Titan ranged from 0.02 to 20 times that on Earth. By sending radio waves through Titan's atmosphere that were slightly deflected by the atmosphere and by making other measurements when *Voyager* passed within 5,000 kilometers (3,100 miles) of Titan's surface, the *Voyager* radio science team led by Von Eshleman and G. Leonard Tyler of Stanford University in Palo Alto, Calif., answered some basic questions. They learned that Titan is the only body in the solar system besides Earth where nitrogen is the most abundant atmospheric gas. Titan's atmosphere also contains a few per cent of methane, a few tenths of 1 per cent of molecular hydrogen, and traces of ethane, acetylene, and hydrogen cyanide. The atmospheric pressure on Titan is 1.6 times that on Earth.

Voyager's infrared spectrometry team, led by Rudolph Hanel of Goddard Space Flight Center in Greenbelt, Md., made a particularly interesting discovery. They detected hydrogen cyanide — a molecule made of single atoms of hydrogen, carbon, and nitrogen — on Titan. This gas has not been found in any other planetary atmosphere in the solar system besides Earth's atmosphere. Hydrogen cyanide is a key intermediate material in the chemical sequence that may have led to the origin of life on Earth. Further studies of the complex chemical processes that take place in Titan's atmosphere may yield valuable clues about similar processes that occurred in Earth's atmosphere when our planet was young. Science-fiction writers have speculated about the possibility of life on Titan, but one vital ingredient in the life-forming process is lacking there — Titan is too cold for any significant amounts of water to exist either as vapor in its atmosphere or as liquid on its surface.

We were frustrated in our attempt to see what Titan looks like because smog particles, made of carbon, nitrogen, and hydrogen, extend throughout the bottom 300 kilometers (186 miles) of the atmosphere and totally obscure the surface. However, *Voyager* measurements gave us a good idea of what the "climate" is like. The smog particles play an important role in the heat balance of Titan's atmosphere. Because they are good absorbers of sunlight and poor emitters of heat radiation, they keep the middle portion of Titan's atmosphere, above 100 kilometers (62 miles), at about −113°C (−171°F.). But at an altitude of 50 kilometers (31 miles), where little sunlight penetrates, it becomes much colder. At still lower altitudes,

An artist's view, *right,* of the ice particles in Saturn's ring system complements an amazing *Voyager* photo, *below,* of the main body of the rings with 95 ringlets.

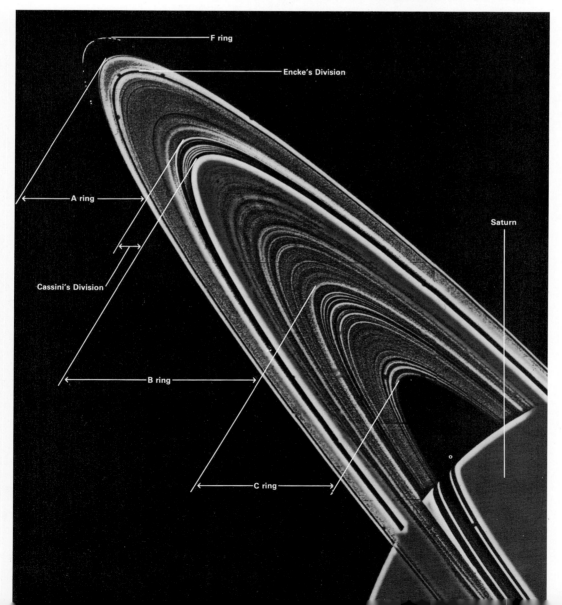

F ring

Encke's Division

A ring

Cassini's Division

Saturn

B ring

C ring

where molecular nitrogen can trap radiating heat, the temperature gradually rises to −180°C (−292°F.).

In addition to the smog particles, the lower 50 kilometers of Titan's atmosphere may contain condensation clouds of methane. Methane may behave on Titan very much like water behaves on Earth. Almost all our water is in the oceans and polar icecaps, and our planet's surface temperature determines the small fraction of water vapor in our atmosphere. Titan's surface temperature is on the borderline between the values at which liquid and solid methane can exist. Both methane oceans and glaciers may be present on different parts of Titan's surface, and methane snow or rain may fall.

In addition to helping us learn more about Saturn's moons, *Voyager* added to our knowledge of Saturn's rings. Huygens in 1655 was the first to realize that they are a thin, flat disk of material lying in the planet's equatorial plane but detached from the planet. For the next 200 years, most scientists believed that the rings were solid or liquid sheets of material. Then British physicist James Clerk Maxwell demonstrated mathematically in 1857 that rings with such a structure would be ripped apart by tidal forces raised by Saturn, and that slight disturbances would keep them from being centered around the planet. Maxwell said that the rings must consist of many small bodies traveling in independent orbits around the planet. Astronomer James E. Keeler of Allegheny Observatory in Pittsburgh, Pa., verified this mathematical deduction in 1895. He measured the velocity of different portions of the rings and found that those in the inside traveled at a higher velocity, proving that the rings were composites of innumerable smaller pieces of matter.

The main body of the rings is divided into the bright A and B rings and the faint C ring. The C ring lies closest to Saturn and the A ring farthest from it. The A and B rings are separated by Cassini's division, a dark zone 3,500 kilometers (2,170 miles) wide named for its discoverer. A gap in the A ring, also named for its discoverer, is called Encke's division. The main region of the rings stretches from about 73,200 kilometers (45,500 miles) from Saturn's center to about 136,200 kilometers (84,600 miles). Recent ground-based and spacecraft photos established that much fainter rings lie both inside and outside the main rings. The D ring, first observed by *Voyager,* begins near the inner edge of the C ring and extends toward the planet's surface. The very narrow F ring, first observed by *Pioneer 11,* is just 4,400 kilometers (2,730 miles) outside the A ring. *Pioneer 11* data also suggested that the G ring existed about 170,600 kilometers (106,000 miles) from Saturn's center, and *Voyager* photos confirmed it. Finally, the extremely faint E ring, which was discovered when the rings were seen edge-on from Earth in 1966, ranges from about 210,000 kilometers (130,400 miles) to 300,000 kilometers (186,000 miles). The letters assigned to the rings reflect the order of their discovery rather than their distance from the planet.

The F ring is not one smooth curve, but three separate rings, each about 20 kilometers (12 miles) wide. Two of the rings twist around each other. The strange configuration has been credited to the gravitational effects of two tiny moons found "shepherding" the ring.

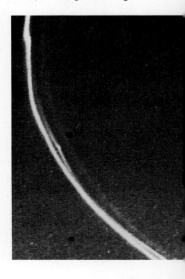

Seen for the first time from their unlit side, the rings give clues to their makeup. Sunlight filtered through the translucent material of the normally dark C ring's curtain imparts a creamy glow, while the B ring's rusty-brown color shows its particles are nearly opaque.

A variety of ground-based observations indicated that the ring particles are made almost completely of water ice and that many particles in the main region of the rings range in size from a few centimeters to a few meters. *Voyager* measured the largest particles more precisely and discovered particles of two other sizes. It found particles about one-thousandth of a millimeter in size in parts of the A and B rings; most of the particles in the F ring are this size. However, much larger bodies, from about one to 100 kilometers in size, appear to be present throughout much of the ring system, and none of the tiny particles are found in the C ring or in Cassini's division.

The fact that the rings contain many bodies has an important effect on their thickness. Collisions that occur among ring particles equalize their speed relative to one another, eliminating variations in velocity and keeping them all circling Saturn at the same velocity and in about the same plane. Therefore, the particles do not disperse and the rings remain only a few kilometers thick.

One of the most surprising discoveries of the *Voyager* mission was the amount of separate detail within the main region of the rings. Rather than shading smoothly from brighter to darker, each region has

Time-separated photos of the B ring's spokes suggest they may be tied to Saturn's magnetic field. Particles rotating with the planet may become electrically charged and then be held above the ring plane by electrical repulsion.

an almost countless number of alternating bright and dark ringlets. These variations in brightness reflect changes in the number and type of ring particles over distances of tens to hundreds of kilometers from Saturn's center.

Prior to the *Voyager* mission, some scientists thought that resonances with some of Saturn's satellites, especially Mimas, determined how the rings were divided. Resonances are greatly amplified gravitational forces that occur when a ring particle's orbital period is a simple fraction of a moon's period. Most of the fine structure seen on *Voyager* pictures cannot be caused by such resonances. We now think that much of it is caused by small moons, perhaps a kilometer in diameter, that are embedded in the rings. Their gravitational effects could push away much smaller particles located near them.

Voyager photos show that the F ring is made up of three ringlets, each about 20 kilometers (12 miles) wide. The outer two look knotted and appear to twist around each other over a part of their circumference. These effects may result from the gravitational impulse that affects sections of the ringlets when they pass close to the "shepherding" moons 1980 S26 and 1980 S27, which lie on either side of the

F ring. Or they may be caused by interactions between Saturn's magnetic field and electrical charges on ring particle surfaces.

Planetary astronomers gained all their information about one phenomenon of the Saturn system solely from spacecraft. No Earth-based telescope could detect the planet's strong magnetic field that deflects the flow of the solar wind around the planet, creating a protected region called the magnetosphere. The solar wind is a high-velocity, rarefied, magnetized, and fully ionized gas that flows out from the Sun to fill the space between bodies in the solar system.

Scientists have developed elaborate mathematical models to explain the possible origin and early history of the solar system. Now we can test and refine these models, using data returned by space probes such as the *Voyager* mission to Saturn. According to a widely accepted theory, all the objects in our solar system formed within the solar nebula, a flattened disk of gas and charged particles that filled the entire solar system some 4.6 billion years ago. The giant planets, including Saturn, originated as regions of greater gas density within the solar nebula, because of either the earlier build-up of their rock-ice cores or an instability within the solar nebula. We think that Saturn's gaseous envelope originally extended several hundred times the planet's present radius of 60,000 kilometers. As more and more material was gathered by the forming planet and it began to contract,

Voyager photos of the ringed planet and six of its moons inspired an artistic grouping of the members of the Saturn system in which Dione rises before Saturn. Tethys and Mimas fade into the distance at lower right, Enceladus and Rhea are to the left, and Titan orbits alone at top right.

temperatures inside the envelope gradually increased, and molecular hydrogen deep within the envelope eventually was changed into hydrogen atoms. As soon as this occurred, the giant gas ball collapsed rapidly. When it had shrunk to a radius of about 300,000 kilometers (186,000 miles), it then contracted very slowly until it reached its present size.

We think all of Saturn's moons except Phoebe formed from a flattened disk of gas and dust that the shrinking planet shed near the end of its collapse. Dust particles and ice that formed from condensing gases as the nebula cooled gradually joined together and formed very large bodies — the moons. The composition of the moons was determined partly by the temperature of Saturn's nebula, which was controlled by the excess heat emitted by the early planet. If this theory is correct, Saturn's inner moons should contain significant amounts of water ice. *Pioneer* and *Voyager* data tended to confirm the theory by showing that Saturn's inner moons have the low mean densities typical of water-ice bodies.

Phoebe, Saturn's outermost moon, may have formed elsewhere in the solar nebula and been captured by the forming planet. We think that Phoebe is a captured moon because it travels around Saturn in the direction opposite to that in which Saturn rotates. Also, its orbit is noncircular and is inclined 30 degrees to the planet's equatorial plane, in sharp contrast to all the other moons.

Saturn's nebula should have been cooler farther from the planet. If water ice could form in the nebula's inner portions, the temperature was probably cool enough at Titan's distance to permit ammonia and methane to be incorporated into some of the ices that condensed there. These ices may have formed the raw material from which Titan's atmosphere of nitrogen and methane was derived.

Finally, Saturn's early nebula may have cooled enough that water ice could condense within portions of the main rings. Because these water-ice particles formed quite close to Saturn, tidal forces prevented them from joining together to form a large moon. Although *Voyager* showed that Jupiter also has a ring, it is much fainter than Saturn's rings and is apparently made of rocky material. This difference may reflect differences in the temperatures of the early nebulae. If the larger particles that *Voyager* reported in Saturn's rings indicate the limits on particle growth close to Saturn, the rings offer us a fascinating snapshot of an intermediate stage in the formation of the planet's major moons.

We who were part of the imaging team, along with many other scientists, will continue to study the information about Saturn returned by the *Voyager* spacecraft. If all goes according to plan, *Voyager 2* will continue its distant travels and send us eye-opening data about Uranus by 1986. It may even continue on to Neptune. That will complete the first interplanetary grand tour — an unprecedented view of the solar system.

Rhinos on the Run

By Andrew Laurie

An enduring belief in the magic of its extraordinary horn and increasing destruction of its habitat combine to imperil the future of a rugged animal

It was dark. A thick mist hid the forest, and dew dripped steadily from the trees as I picked my way through the cold wet undergrowth and emerged onto the open riverbank. I stopped to listen for a moment, then walked silently to the water's edge and waded in the icy river. Only the high-pitched alarm call of an alert chital deer disturbed the quiet gurgling of the river and the peaceful droning of crickets as I headed upstream toward a hidden simul tree. Finding the tree, I climbed up to my *machan* (observation blind) in the crown, then hauled my backpack up on a rope and settled down to wait.

I was in the Chitawan Sanctuary of Nepal, generally called Royal Chitawan National Park, at the southern end of the Chitawan Valley in Nepal, where I lived from December 1972 until July 1976 making the first detailed study of the ecology and behavior of the greater one-horned, or Indian, rhinoceros (*Rhinoceros unicornis*). The valley lies less than 100 kilometers (70 miles) south of the lofty peaks of Annapurna and Dhaulagiri, yet it is only about 120 meters (400 feet) above sea level. This region is now the home of the second largest surviving population of the endangered Indian rhinoceros. Only the

Kaziranga Reserve in the neighboring Indian state of Assam has more of the huge beasts.

An hour passed while I watched from my machan. I heard splashes. Then, unmistakably, came the slow gait and heavy breathing of a rhinoceros. It had crossed the river, paused to sniff my scent at the foot of the tree, and walked on into the forest munching leaves and twigs. I saw nothing, but when the mist lifted, a line of large three-toed footprints showed clearly in the dew-soaked grass.

Twigs snapped in the scrubby forest across the river, and soon a rhinoceros cow and her young calf came into view on the opposite bank. They paused to drink, then crossed the river toward me. Watching through binoculars, I saw the calf hugging his mother's side and struggling to keep his feet on the bottom. The cow led the way to the forest, her nose close to the ground, sniffing loudly at the tracks of the rhino that had crossed earlier. I recorded the entire incident in detail in my notebook, including the identity of the cow and her calf. I recognized them from previous sightings.

After another hour, the sun appeared. To the north, I could see the dark line of hills known as the Mahabharat Mountains, and far in the distance stood the magnificent snow-covered peaks of the Himalaya, crisply outlined and still slightly orange in the morning light. People shouted and cowbells rang across the river, and smoke began to filter up through the grass roofs of village houses. The rhinos had fed during the night in the rice fields of these villagers.

Distracted by the morning din, I hardly heard my transportation approaching. But soon Naran, the driver, brought the elephant Devi Kali to a halt below me. "*Chal* (Let's go)," I called. I lowered my backpack on the rope, and then followed hand over hand to Devi Kali's spacious back. From his seat astride her neck, Naran urged the elephant on with muttered oaths and sharp jabs of his toes behind her ears. I told him how many rhinos I had seen, and with the sun warm on our faces we rode on upstream in search of more.

I had planned the Chitawan study in England at the Pachyderm Research Unit in the University of Cambridge Department of Applied Biology. Swedish naturalist Carolus Linnaeus defined *pachyderms* in the 1700s as "the thick-skinned quadrupeds." His classification included elephants, rhinos, hippopotamuses, tapirs, and pigs. Although the term is obsolete, my colleague Robert Olivier and I resurrected *pachyderm* to describe our research on hippos, rhinos, and elephants, because these large animals share many characteristics that are important in the study of their comparative ecology — their relationship with one another and with their environment — and the practical problems involved in their conservation.

Probably for as long as they have shared their habitat with humans, the large pachyderms have been hunted for meat and for their tusks and horns. But now their habitat itself is being threatened. The forest-dwelling pygmy hippopotamus (*Choeropsis liberiensis*) of West

The author:
Andrew Laurie is a research associate in the Department of Zoology at the University of Cambridge in England.

Chinese bronze figure of an Asian rhinoceros from the 200s B.C., *above left,* its armor once inlaid with gold, attests to the ancient awe this beast inspired. Visions of the proud unicorn, *above,* may have come from travelers' tales about Asian rhinos.

Africa and the Sumatran (*Dicerorhinus sumatrensis*) and Javan (*Rhinoceros sondaicus*) rhinoceroses of the Southeast Asian tropical rain forests are in the most danger. Trees and other vegetation are being cleared to provide new cropland at the rate of 310,000 square kilometers (120,000 square miles) per year, and almost all the remaining forest is already committed to timber harvesting. The African elephant (*Loxodonta africana*) and Asian elephant (*Elephas maximus*); the black rhinoceros (*Diceros bicornis*), white rhinoceros (*Ceratotherium simus*), and Indian rhinoceros; and the hippopotamus (*Hippopotamus amphibius*) survive in slightly larger numbers. But all are threatened by the rapid rate at which their habitat is being destroyed and by the soaring prices of ivory and rhino horn.

For 50 million years, the rhinoceros, that unbeautiful but unique beast, has survived. By the end of this century, it may be extinct. As recently as 1970, tens of thousands of rhinos roamed the forests and grasslands of Africa and Asia. Since then, about 90 per cent of those animals in Kenya, Uganda, and Tanzania have been killed, and the situation in India, Java, and Sumatra is equally grim. In all of Africa there are probably no more than 20,000 rhinos today, and only about 2,000 remain in Asia. Halting or reversing the trend is difficult because of the beliefs held by many people in the countries where these animals live.

Superstition and folklore, which long ascribed magical properties to almost every part of the rhinoceros, have created an immense trade in rhino horns and other parts. Traditional Chinese medicine, still widely practiced in China and throughout Asia, considers rhinoceros

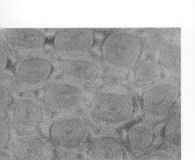

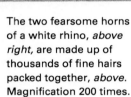

The two fearsome horns of a white rhino, *above right,* are made up of thousands of fine hairs packed together, *above.* Magnification 200 times.

horn, which is made of compacted hair, keratin, and gelatin, a cure-all. Scraped or powdered horn is prescribed for everything from reducing fever to increasing male potency. The Nepalese use rhino urine to treat earache and place a rhino horn under the bed of a woman in childbirth to ease her labor. Rhino blood is also highly valued in Nepal and India.

Obviously, it is extremely difficult to obtain rhino blood or rhino horn without killing rhinos. Because killing rhinos is dangerous and illegal work, the price of rhino parts is high. As more animals are killed, people fear that supplies of rhino parts will run out, and prices go even higher. In 1980, Asian rhino horn retailed in Taiwan and Hong Kong at about $18,000 per kilogram ($8,200 per pound). African rhino horn sells at a lower price in Asia. However, in Yemen (Sana), men rich with new oil wealth buy rhino horn for the handles of their *jambias,* or daggers, instead of the cow or buffalo horn they used when the country was poor. Every adult Yemeni male wears a dagger, and many willingly pay up to $13,000 for a rhino horn handle because of its association with aggressiveness and virility. Between 1969 and 1977, Yemen (Sana) imported 2.7 metric tons (3 short tons) of rhino horn from Africa annually. This quantity represented about 8,000 rhinos killed over 8 years, primarily to provide *jambia* handles.

Until recently, the few laws that existed to restrict trading in rhino horn in Africa and Asia were ignored, and poaching — illegal hunting — was rampant. With disaster at hand, an international Save the Rhino campaign was launched in September 1979 by the Swiss-based World Wildlife Fund and the International Union for the Conservation of Nature and Natural Resources. The campaign aims to stop poaching and to persuade all governments to ban the import and sale of rhino parts and products.

An elaborately carved horn cup, *left,* worth a fortune in medieval China, was an early item of trade in rhino parts. In a modern setting, an African poacher dries rhino meat and skins at his camp after the kill, *top.* Street vendors in Tsavo, Kenya, display rhino horns along with elephant tusks, *above,* before private sale of these items was prohibited in 1977.

As early as 1972, conservationists who cared about maintaining groups of living creatures interrelating in their natural environment were concerned with what was happening to the world's large animals, including rhinos. The alarming trends that seem to portend their end were just starting to accelerate when a grant from the New York Zoological Society enabled me to go to Nepal.

Indian rhinos once ranged from Pakistan to Burma on the flood plains of the Indus, Ganges, and Brahmaputra river systems. Now there are fewer than 1,500 rhinos left, and almost all of these are confined to eight small reserves or national parks with a total area of less than 900 square kilometers (350 square miles). One reserve is in Nepal, two are in India's West Bengal state, and five are in Assam state. The massive reduction in the Indian rhino's range was caused primarily by the loss of most of the wet grasslands where they prefer to live. The grasslands are also the most suitable areas for wet rice cultivation — and therein lies the problem. By the mid-1900s, most of the rhinos were restricted to reserves, and their survival depended on their being protected. Hunters and farmers still threaten them, but now an additional threat stems from the concentration of the few remaining rhinos in a few tiny reserves.

My task was to find out how many rhinos were left in the Chitawan area, what habitat they preferred, and whether they liked to change living areas with the seasons. I had to find out what the rhinos ate, whether their diet changed throughout the year, how far they moved, what type of social organization they had, how often they bred, how long calves stayed with their mothers, and when they became sexually mature. With this information, conservationists hoped to predict rhino population trends, estimate how many rhinos the park's ecosystem could support, and learn the effect on the rhinos of extensive grass-burning, cutting grass for thatching, and grazing domestic livestock within the park.

As I studied the animals, I also had to keep in mind the livelihood of the hundreds of people living close to the park. Many of them complained that rhinos ravaged their crops every year. Ideally, my study would suggest some ways that the people and the rhinos in Nepal and India could share their environment.

The people of India must have been familiar with the rhinoceros for thousands of years, but the first reference to it in Western literature comes from Ctesias, Greek physician to Queen Parysatis of Persia in the 4th century B.C. Ctesias wrote a book about India in which he mentioned the "Indian ass" from whose horn a poison-detecting cup could be made. Through the Middle Ages, people believed that cups carved from rhino horn protected them against poison, because such a cup would cause a deadly drink to effervesce. The belief had some foundation in fact, because many ancient poisons were strong alkaloids that would have reacted and bubbled up when poured into a rhino horn cup.

In ancient times, in pleasant contrast to the present, rhinos were worth as much alive as dead. There are many reports of people taming and even training Indian rhinos. They used the animals to pull plows in Assam, and Assamese and Indian kings used them as "war horses." During the early 1800s, tame rhinos often grazed with cattle in Assam. A washerman in Gauhati, Assam, had a tame rhino that carried the laundry on his delivery rounds in 1900. Recent experiences with Indian rhinos in zoos and circuses confirm that they can be tamed and trained, but they are also unpredictable and can be quite dangerous.

Standing as high as 1.8 meters (6 feet) at the shoulder and weighing as much as 2,100 kilograms (4,600 pounds), the Indian rhinoceros is truly an impressive beast. Folds in the thick, studded, hairless skin, resembling joints in armor, hang as heavy jowls around the neck and as bibs beneath the chin. A single horn grows from the skin of the nose and may be up to 60 centimeters (2 feet) long. The upper lip is prehensile for picking up grass and tearing leaves from bushes. The tiny eyes, which are not very keen, are placed forward near the horn. Two large ears, which make the rhino's hearing better than its vision, stand erect on top of the head. The rhino's most acute sense is smell. A pair of razor-sharp incisor tusks jut forward from the lower jaw and grind against two blunter versions in the upper jaw. Prehistoric in appearance, the rhinoceros is indeed an ancient species. Its ancestors roamed the swamps, forests, and grasslands of the Himalayan foot-hills for millions of years.

Fortified with "book learning" and excited at the prospect of observing real live rhinoceroses going about their daily rounds, I arrived in Chitawan in December 1972. From the royal elephant camp nearby, the Nepalese government provided me with Devi Kali and three men to look after her.

The tall grasslands and dense woodlands of Chitawan made observations difficult, especially during the annual monsoon rains between May and September when much of the study area was flooded. Sometimes I made aerial surveys to locate the rhinos, but most of my work required that I observe the animals up close. An elephant was sometimes indispensable, particularly for journeys of a week or longer, but I also worked on foot and from machans built in trees or on the ground. I used binoculars or a telescope on a tripod to watch rhinos during the day, and at night an image intensifier helped me see them feeding on the riverbanks or in the rice paddies. During full-moon periods, I, like the rhinos, became almost totally nocturnal.

I studied the animals in two ways: Part of the time I traveled over a large area and recorded the number, location, activities, and identity of all rhinos I came across. At other times, I followed selected individuals for longer periods.

Sometimes, in the course of my observations, rhinos would come rather near before I was aware of their presence. But on other

A black rhino in Kenya, *above*, grasps shrubs with its prehensile lips. Strong teeth enable the Indian rhino, *top right*, to tear another diet of twigs and leaves from bushes, while its cousins in Nepal, *above right*, eat water plants.

occasions, they were easily detected from afar by their loud vocalizations. Rhinos make a wide variety of sounds, and I distinguished 10 different types that seemed to be used for communication. I characterized them as: snorts, honks, moo-grunts, squeak-pants, bleats, humphs, roars, rumbles, groans, and shrieks. The first two were by far the most common, both when the rhinos were undisturbed and when they were aware of my presence.

After about six months in Chitawan, I could identify about two-thirds of the 300 or so adults and young animals according to variations in their horn sizes and shapes, skin folds and bumps, scars, ear nicks, and tail cuts. I identified them with the aid of "passports" — cards I made up with photographs and descriptions of each animal.

I tried to identify each rhino I saw, but when I could not, I determined its sex and put it into one of seven age classes on the basis of horn development and estimated shoulder height. I had to estimate ages by size, and I did this by measuring heights photographically. I would take an animal's picture, then — after it left and without moving the camera — have an assistant holding a graduated surveying pole stand in the rhino's forefoot print while I took another picture. Comparing the two photographs later, I could calculate the shoulder height of the rhino.

I gave names to many of the rhinos. Triscar had three parallel scars on his flank; Flapper had a big flap of skin on one fold. Others were Stumptail, Crumplerump, Curvy, Cutear, and Splithorn. I also

A white cow and 3-day-old calf, *above left*, and black cow nursing an older calf, *left*, comprise rhino family units. Young adults hang out together at the local watering hole, *below*, but a white bull, *above*, prefers a solitary life.

learned their individual temperaments, so that I knew I could walk safely past some animals as they lay in a wallow or grazed in a clearing, confident that they would ignore me or run away, lumbering through the undergrowth like tanks. I gave others a wide berth, knowing that they were more aggressive and likely to charge if surprised at close quarters.

The most exciting close encounter I had was with the female I called Crumplerump. I was walking along a narrow path in scrubby forest just outside the park one day when I heard rhinos approaching. I slipped off my backpack and swung up into the nearest tree – a small one about 20 centimeters (8 inches) in diameter with one fork about 2 meters (7 feet) above the ground. I got up just in time. An 18-month-old calf came around the corner ahead, sniffing the air, and Crumplerump, his mother, charged head down from behind him. She smashed into the trunk of my tree and carried my backpack 18 meters (60 feet) down the path on her horn. The slender tree began to bend under my weight while the aroused rhino ground my pack into the earth, left it with the metal frame broken in pieces, and returned to stand with her calf under my tree, sniffing the air with head held high. I waited helplessly as the damaged tree sank slowly toward her. Then, at the last moment, when I was only a few inches above her back, she ambled off, still without seeing me.

On another occasion, Triscar walked up to a hiding place I had built on the ground near a wallow. When they are not eating, rhinos spend a good bit of their time wallowing in mud pools to keep cool. I had my camera ready to record this behavior when Triscar began to lick the lens, which was pointing through a slit in the front wall of my "hide." I waited rather nervously at the far wall, near the back entrance but still only about 1 meter (3 feet) from the rhino, until he tired of the taste of glass.

An old bull I called Stumptail once visited me as I was napping on the veranda of the flimsy house I lived in, waking me from sleep by heavy sniffing with lots of fine spray. He hurried off with a start when I woke up and moved my head.

Gradually, as the years passed and I sat in my thatched house by the river, I learned about the rhinos and the overall ecology of Chitawan. The area is also home to tigers; leopards; sloth bears; gaur, or wild oxen; wild pigs; and four species of deer. Seasonal changes in climate and the shifting streams and rivers greatly influence the vegetation on which all the animals depend.

The rhinos I studied fed on 183 species of plants that belonged to 57 botanical families, but 50 species of grass made up 70 to 89 per cent of their diet, according to the season. They also ate shrubs; the fruits, leaves, and twigs of trees; and submerged and floating aquatic plants. They moved seasonally among various vegetation types to feed on plants that were flourishing. Their range was smallest in areas where vegetation was most diverse and rhino population most dense,

with up to 12 rhinos per square mile. Before Indian rhinos were confined to reserves, their density was typically between 1 per 2 square miles and 3 per 1 square mile, depending on availability.

The Indian rhino's courtship is violent, and the bulls also fight among themselves to establish dominance and claim desirable mates. They sometimes chase breeding females over long distances, while the females utter loud vocalizations – thus possibly attracting other, stronger bulls. Even after an Indian rhino bull succeeds in winning a cow, he treats her roughly. I saw many fights between couples.

In Chitawan, there were more female rhinos than males in the population; perhaps because many males are wounded and some are killed in fights with one another. Other rhinos are killed by poachers, and tigers prey on the calves. However, the population increased slowly during my 3½-year stay. Females have their first calf when they are about 7 years old and give birth at intervals of about three years thereafter. Calves stay with their mothers until they are 3 or 4 years old; then, with other young rhinos, they form small groups until they are about 7 years old. The females are then ready to start their own families while the males set out on the solitary life that seems the fate of bellicose bulls.

Because vegetation varies with the season and is not available everywhere, the rhinos in Nepal developed different distribution, movement, and social organization patterns from those in Africa and Southeast Asia. Over millions of years, the five living species even developed differing physical adaptations to their environment. For example, the small Javan rhino, which weighs up to about 1,300 kilograms (2,860 pounds) and the Sumatran rhino, which weighs about 850 kilograms (1,870 pounds) are adapted for life in the forest. They have prehensile lips for feeding on leaves and saplings. The

A game park ranger gives an antidote to a sedated rhino, *top left*, that will take effect after it is moved, *top right*, to a more hospitable area. Warning signs, *above*, attest to the rigorous rhino conservation efforts of the South African government.

Overcrowding in the tiny rhino reserve in Nepal forces an abnormally large number of animals to use the watering hole. Should an epidemic strike, or food run out, disaster would be the certain result.

large, two-horned white rhino is a short-grassland grazer, using its square lips to crop grass very close. Female white rhinos weigh about 1,600 kilograms (3,500 pounds), while males may reach 2,250 kilograms (5,000 pounds). The savanna-browsing black rhino has a prehensile lip for feeding on shrubs. Like the other browsers, it is smaller, weighing from 700 to 1,300 kilograms (1,500 to 2,800 pounds). Perhaps the browsers are smaller because their food supply is generally more scattered, and larger animals would find it hard to get enough to eat. The adaptable Indian rhino is intermediate in size. The Asian rhinos have apparently retained tusks as weapons, whereas the African species have lost their tusks and developed larger horns. The horns may be more useful as displays to frighten competitors and attract mates in the open habitats of Africa than they would be in the thick forests and grasslands of India and Southeast Asia.

Although poaching is still a great danger to most rhino species, it is less of a threat in Chitawan and in the densely populated Kaziranga Reserve in Assam than in other areas. Rampant during the 1960s, illegal hunting in Chitawan almost completely stopped by 1974 as a result of increased vigilance and excellent protection by the guards throughout the Kaziranga Reserve. Now the biggest danger lies in the concentration of the few remaining rhinos into so few tiny reserves and national parks. More than 1,200 of about 1,500 surviving animals live in Chitawan and Kaziranga, which together contain only 520 square kilometers (200 square miles) of suitable rhino habitat. Any catastrophe, such as an epidemic disease, drought, or food shortage, or a breakdown in protection measures, could drastically deplete the total Indian rhino population. Furthermore, increased flooding and erosion each year, and even small changes in the courses of rivers, may make some of the limited habitat unsuitable. It may be quite difficult to maintain the present variety of suitable vegetation in the small protected areas that remain.

Although land is scarce, my study in Chitawan helped persuade the government to increase the national park in size by 40 per cent by 1981. It will be difficult to expand other refuges because rhinos and rice flourish in the same kinds of places. One possibility is to create buffer zones, forbidding farming and forest-cutting but allowing livestock to graze, and protecting rhinos.

As a safeguard for the future, it seems essential that rhinos should be reintroduced to other reserves within their former range. This would spread out the population and reduce the danger of extinction posed by a sudden catastrophe in any one locality. Several sites in Nepal are suitable for rhinos, and some rhino groups may be moved there after surveys have been done.

An excellent precedent for such an operation is the highly successful white rhino reintroduction scheme in South Africa, which probably saved that species from extinction. The problem was to distribute rhinos throughout various reserves. Modern technology came to the rescue. Rhinos are spotted by helicopter-borne rangers who tranquilize them with shots from dart guns, then transport them by truck to holding paddocks. After six weeks, they are shipped to a new home. In 1980, 500 white rhinos — and 14 black ones — were sent to zoos and reserves around the world. Many of the animals are sent to parts of Africa where poaching is still a problem, but the imports are guarded as closely as possible.

The question of what population the land will support is basic to any discussion of conservation. I am not concerned with saving only the rhino, but rather with saving entire ecosystems of which rhinos are a part. Human populations in the developing countries are growing so fast that at some point they will overwhelm the land. So the question becomes whether we save the remaining forests and grasslands and face the problem of population growth now, or whether we put off the problem until there is no natural habitat left. Ecological diversity is important for the stability of ecosystems, climate, and agricultural productivity. It is also vital as a storehouse of genetic resources for possible future use in breeding domestic livestock, cultivating plants, or even developing drugs.

Rhinos may not seem to be of immediate potential use to everyone in the world, but I regard them as a symbol of the habitats in which they live. I am not interested in saving rhinos in a zoo pen, but in saving the whole community of plants and animals with which they live. If we can save the rhino in the wild, we can save all those other associated animals and plants, and ensure not only their future but also our own.

End of
an Era

By Erle G. Kauffman

Some 70 per cent of all species died out 65 million years ago, and paleontologists now think that there were many unconnected causes for this misfortune

Mankind has always lived with small-scale catastrophe, but only in the last 40 years has the world been threatened with the rapid, widespread annihilation of most life forms that would result from a nuclear holocaust. Humans could quickly become extinct; only a few plants, insects, lizards, and deep sea creatures might survive in an earth rendered nearly uninhabitable by nuclear warfare.

It is hard for us to imagine such a catastrophe and its aftermath. There is nothing in human experience with which we can compare it. We can understand smaller, more restricted catastrophes such as war, earthquakes, floods, volcanic eruptions, and great storms. But we have never experienced a swift, deadly, global catastrophe.

During the Cretaceous Period, dinosaurs held center stage on a warm earth teeming with life. But changes were coming, and the days of the dinosaurs — and many other creatures — were numbered.

Such catastrophes seem to have happened. And paleontologists have studied them since they began to document the history of life on earth. These extinction events lasted, at most, a few thousand years to nearly a million years — scarcely an instant in the 4-billion-year history of the earth. During these times, a significant percentage of all life forms died, to be replaced by new, and often very different, forms.

These extinctions can easily be documented in the fossil record — the remains of plants and animals deposited in layer after layer of sedimentary rocks that began as water-borne mud and sand and hardened slowly under pressure from sediments that settled on top of them. These fossil rocks extend upward from 3.5 billion years ago to the present. Paleontologists measure time by calculating the decay rate of radioactive isotopes in rocks. They measure age by the position of fossils relative to the bottom or the top of the rock record.

The oldest rocks are generally the most deeply buried. A few feet of rock may represent an hour or several million years of deposition. Sedimentary rocks are found everywhere, from cores taken from the ocean bottom, to deposits found high in mountains. In these are the remains of the life of the period when the rocks were formed. The fossils might represent the plants and animals of a dry-land environment, or a shallow-water coral reef or some deep-sea habitat, even within the same rock sequence, telling us that earth's environments have changed through time. The fossils themselves, whether they are the bones of large animals, plant spores, the microscopic shells of tiny sea creatures, or even the delicate casts — impressions — of soft-bodied animals, help the paleontologist piece together the story of life.

For example, a certain kind of animal might be preserved in a sedimentary rock layer millions of years old. Succeeding layers might contain the same animal. But above a certain layer, if paleontologists fail to find the animal no matter where they search in rocks of the same age, the animal is considered extinct. When many kinds of plants and animals on land and in the sea, from single-celled *Protozoa* to higher vertebrates, all become extinct at about the same time, the paleontologist has evidence of a biological catastrophe.

The apparent biological catastrophe that occurred some 65 million years ago has inspired more scientific study and public interest than any other such event. One reason for our interest is that this widespread extinction, which came at about the end of the Cretaceous Period and the beginning of the Tertiary Period, called the C-T boundary, included the disappearance of the dinosaurs. These enormous animals had dominated the land for about 135 million years.

Dozens of theories, ranging from climate change to extraterrestrial events, have been proposed to explain the Cretaceous extinctions. In 1979, geologist Walter Alvarez of the University of California, Berkeley, his father, physicist Luis Alvarez, and associates at Lawrence Berkeley Laboratories announced that they had found unusually high levels of iridium, osmium, and other rare elements in a layer of clay

The author:
Erle G. Kauffman is a paleontologist and the chairman of the Department of Geological Sciences at the University of Colorado in Boulder.

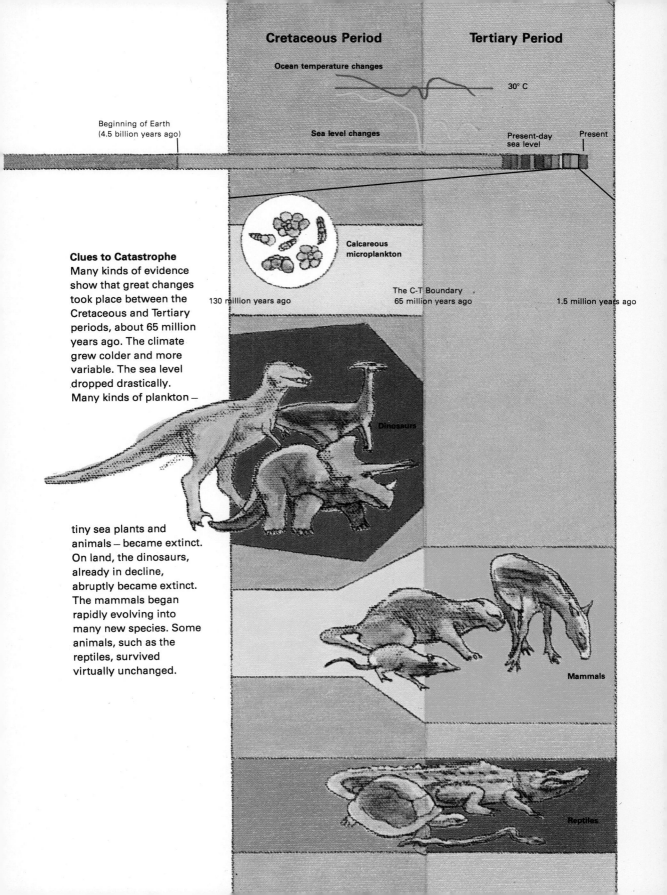

Cretaceous Period

Tertiary Period

Ocean temperature changes

30° C

Beginning of Earth
(4.5 billion years ago)

Sea level changes

Present-day
sea level

Present

Calcareous
microplankton

The C-T Boundary
65 million years ago

130 million years ago

1.5 million years ago

Clues to Catastrophe
Many kinds of evidence
show that great changes
took place between the
Cretaceous and Tertiary
periods, about 65 million
years ago. The climate
grew colder and more
variable. The sea level
dropped drastically.
Many kinds of plankton —

Dinosaurs

tiny sea plants and
animals — became extinct.
On land, the dinosaurs,
already in decline,
abruptly became extinct.
The mammals began
rapidly evolving into
many new species. Some
animals, such as the
reptiles, survived
virtually unchanged.

Mammals

Reptiles

Sea-Level Slump
A drop in sea level of more than 100 meters (328 feet) in the late Cretaceous Period reduced the living space available to the shallow-water species of plants and animals normally found along coastlines. The increased competition for living space killed off many species.

that occurs exactly at the C-T boundary in some areas of Denmark, Italy, and other countries. These elemental levels are very high for earth-made rocks. But they match those found in certain meteorites. The Alvarez group proposed that they were produced by the impact of a gigantic meteorite striking the earth. They suggested that dust and debris thrown into the atmosphere by this impact might have dramatically reduced the amount of sunlight reaching the earth for 10 to 100 years and caused the final Cretaceous extinctions. The death of green plants, which depend on sunlight, would have led to the death of the plant-eating animals. Then, the *carnivores* (meat-eaters), deprived of their prey, would have died. Extinctions in the sea would have followed the same pattern, from the death of tiny one-celled plants called plankton, up the food chain to the carnivores.

The theory seemed to some observers to provide a cause for the Cretaceous catastrophe. The Alvarez findings certainly indicated that something unusual happened at the C-T boundary, and that it probably originated beyond the earth. But was this the sole cause of the widespread extinction, or simply one factor among many? The answers may lie in a close re-examination of the fossil evidence.

The history of the Cretaceous extinction is still incompletely known, partially because of the imprecise way in which extinction data have been reported. Scientists, working with an incomplete fossil record, have often assumed that many of the extinct organisms known to be present at some time during the last 5 million years of the Cretaceous Period survived right up to the C-T boundary and then became extinct. Recent research has shown this to be false for many organisms. Further, many studies did not distinguish groups that were abundant and diverse, with many species just prior to extinction, from those that were already in an evolutionary decline.

Among the many life forms – perhaps 70 per cent of all species – that disappeared during the late Cretaceous were some groups of plants, the dinosaurs, marine reptiles, the many-tentacled ammonoid and belemnoid cephalopods related to the squids, many clams and snails, and the tiny *calcareous* (calcium-shelled) microplankton, one-

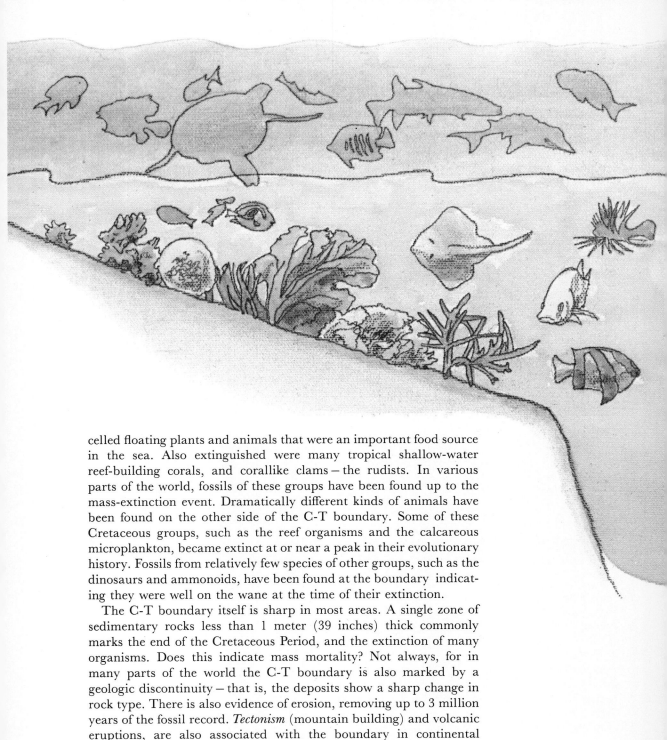

celled floating plants and animals that were an important food source in the sea. Also extinguished were many tropical shallow-water reef-building corals, and corallike clams — the rudists. In various parts of the world, fossils of these groups have been found up to the mass-extinction event. Dramatically different kinds of animals have been found on the other side of the C-T boundary. Some of these Cretaceous groups, such as the reef organisms and the calcareous microplankton, became extinct at or near a peak in their evolutionary history. Fossils from relatively few species of other groups, such as the dinosaurs and ammonoids, have been found at the boundary indicating they were well on the wane at the time of their extinction.

The C-T boundary itself is sharp in most areas. A single zone of sedimentary rocks less than 1 meter (39 inches) thick commonly marks the end of the Cretaceous Period, and the extinction of many organisms. Does this indicate mass mortality? Not always, for in many parts of the world the C-T boundary is also marked by a geologic discontinuity — that is, the deposits show a sharp change in rock type. There is also evidence of erosion, removing up to 3 million years of the fossil record. *Tectonism* (mountain building) and volcanic eruptions, are also associated with the boundary in continental settings, keeping fossils from being preserved. In deeper marine environments, a thin layer of clay occurs at the C-T boundary in some regions. It is in this clay that the Alvarez group found their rare-element concentrations.

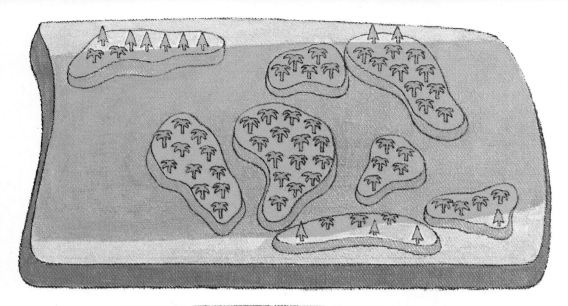

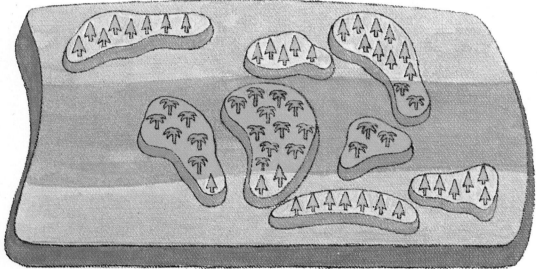

Climate Crunch
The Temperate Zones grew larger and the Tropics shrank as the earth cooled and temperatures grew more varied in the late Cretaceous. Tropical species that could not adapt to the changes in climate became extinct.

The geologic record further indicates that both sea and land environments deteriorated badly during the last 5 million to 10 million years of the Cretaceous Period. The sea level dropped several hundred meters during this time. Shallow continental seas and many coastal areas were drained, eliminating or greatly restricting the best habitats for many marine organisms. Continental environments changed from uniform, moist, warm maritime climates to more variable, drier, and cooler continental climates. Temperate zones increased as the tropics shrank in size. The effect of these changes on plants and cold-blooded reptiles must have been profound. Major changes also occurred in the oceans. Analyses of shells and calcareous sediments suggest that ocean temperatures dropped during the late Cretaceous, with rapid fluctuations of 1° to 3°C (1.8° to 5.4°F.) near the end of the Cretaceous and into the early Tertiary.

There is excellent geologic evidence to indicate that many of these environmental changes which developed during the last 10 million years of the Cretaceous were closely linked to the gradual extinction of organisms once thought to have become abruptly extinct at the end of the Cretaceous. Much biological and environmental change preceded the final catastrophe. In a sense, global life was weakened — "set up for the kill" — by these long-term changes.

The environmental changes had another effect. The drop in sea level left the rock layers on and near continents exposed to erosion that wiped out much of the fossil record of the late Cretaceous and early Tertiary periods. Almost 90 per cent of the known continental rock sequences have gaps ranging from a few hundred thousand years to 5 million years on either side of the C-T boundary. This loss of evidence magnified the apparent catastrophe because it erased many records of the earlier gradual and intermittent extinctions.

Less than a dozen sites have been found where the complete or nearly complete C-T boundary sequence of rocks can be studied. And almost all of these sequences — found in Spain, Italy, Mexico, Haiti, and North Africa — are of tropical and subtropical oceanic microplankton with calcareous skeletons. Few of the larger fossils of organisms we think suddenly became extinct at the end of the Cretaceous, are actually found in layers immediately below the boundary in these complete sequences. Only the calcareous microplankton, living in the ocean's upper levels, clearly became extinct at a peak in their evolutionary history, during the last 10,000 to 100,000 years of the Cretaceous. Noncalcareous microplankton, which also lived in the upper levels of the world's oceans, show much less change.

A complete rock sequence near Zumaya, Spain, first studied in detail by German paleontologist Dietrich Herm of the University of Munich in 1965, is typical of this tropical ocean extinction record and sheds considerable light on what may have caused it. Scientists have found no evidence of large midwater and bottom organisms in strata laid down 1 meter below, or a few hundred thousand years before, the C-T boundary, suggesting that life in the ocean was gradually dying from the bottom up. Throughout the 2 million years or so when large marine midwater or bottom forms such as the ammonoids gradually became extinct, the Zumaya record indicates that the plankton population remained normal. The abrupt extinction of the calcareous microplankton clearly occurs at the C-T boundary at Zumaya and this represents the only real catastrophic extinction in the late Cretaceous record. Paleontologists have found similar patterns in rocks in Brazil and elsewhere.

Thus, both catastrophic and gradual extinction patterns characterize the best-studied, most complete C-T boundary sequences. True catastrophe occurred only among the warm-water calcareous microplankton. Most larger organisms declined gradually, beginning 1 million to several million years before the catastrophic event.

A thin, dark layer of rock, recessed in the cliffs of Denmark just above today's sea level, marks the boundary between the Cretaceous and Tertiary periods. An unusual concentration of rare elements in this layer suggests the earth had an extraterrestrial visitor — perhaps a meteorite or a comet — during that time.

Almost all evidence of Cretaceous reef life, which usually is thought to have suddenly become extinct at the C-T boundary, has been found in areas where the last 1 million to 3 million years of Cretaceous history is missing. The gap is caused by the drop in sea level during the later Cretaceous, which stranded most shallow-reef habitats and left them exposed to erosion. However, in the most complete Cretaceous reef-rock sequences, found in Jamaica and Spain, there is evidence of a marked decline in the reef life 1 million to 2 million years before the end of the Cretaceous. This generally correlates with the demise of normal ocean-bottom life in Zumaya. Beyond this point, only a few species of reef organisms can be found.

The Cretaceous extinction is even less well defined in tropical land areas. Paleobiologist Thomas J. M. Schopf of the University of Chicago compiled data in 1981 indicating that dinosaurs in the tropical and subtropical regions disappeared at least 2 million years before the end of the Cretaceous. Only a few species in North America and western Europe survived long enough to become extinct at the C-T boundary. As far as scientists can tell, tropical land plants suffered no significant change across the C-T boundary.

Species that lived in temperate waters show only a moderate amount of extinction. For example, a remarkable number of molluscan groups in Denmark, Greenland, and along the middle Atlantic coast of the United States cross the C-T boundary with little loss in numbers and types of major groups. South temperate life seems to have followed a similar marine pattern, based on 1981 data from the Antarctic put together by paleobiologist William Zinsmeister of Ohio State University. The C-T boundary layers in northwest Europe, the

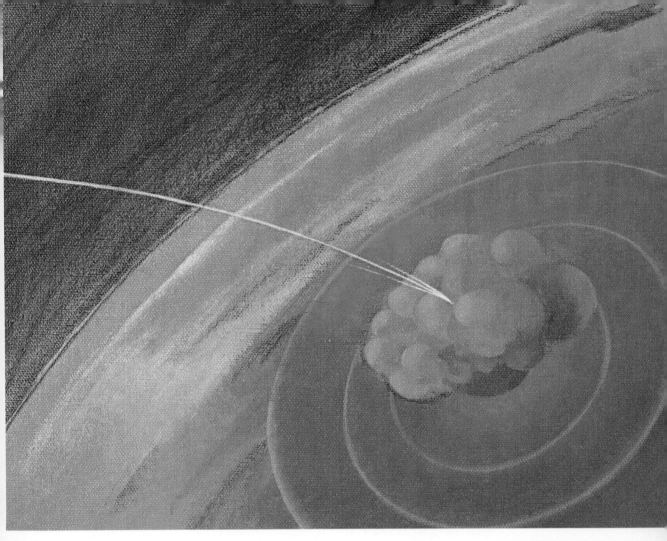

richest and the best studied in the world, show only low to moderate levels of extinction of species, and similar life forms and habitats appear on both sides of the boundary and only the calcareous microplankton became abruptly extinct in temperate waters.

This comparison of global evidence reveals some startling patterns paleontologists had not previously considered in assuming that a biological catastrophe occurred. The C-T extinction does not have an equal global impact. It appears to decline in severity as it moves from equatorial toward polar areas, even in the case of the calcareous microplankton. Only in the tropics were numerous late Cretaceous groups extinguished during peaks in their evolution. All of these extinguished organisms have one factor in common — they lived in the warm upper layers of ocean water for all or part of their life cycles. This suggests that one or more events centered in the upper layers of tropical and subtropical oceans may have caused the final catastrophic part of the Cretaceous extinction.

Ruinous Rendezvous?
A giant meteorite striking the earth and hurling billions of tons of dust and debris into the stratosphere could have blocked sunlight from reaching the earth, killing off plants, then plant-eating animals, and finally, meat-eaters. Such an event may have climaxed the steady decline of life in the late Cretaceous Period.

Early attempts to explain the crisis at the end of the Cretaceous focused on several major causes. Loss of habitats through lowering of sea level and a worsening of climate are both clearly seen in the fossil record. Other explanations were the collapse of the global ecosystem through catastrophic loss of marine and land plants — the base of the food chain — and changes in oceanic water chemistry.

A food-chain collapse is a tempting explanation of any mass extinction, with the extinction of the microplankton causing the demise of the higher creatures that fed on the plankton. Unfortunately, the Cretaceous extinction went the other way; most of the organisms that were high on the oceanic food chain — predators, smaller carnivores, and advanced plant eaters — became extinct or nearly died out before the plankton disappeared. Furthermore, a detailed study of the C-T boundary zone shows that the actual amount of

plankton probably changed little. Other plankton species in near-equal numbers replaced calcareous microplankton as they died out.

Some experts have also suggested that the dinosaurs starved after massive extinction of the land plants. However, paleologist Leo Hickey of the Smithsonian Institution in Washington, D.C., has demonstrated that the dominant flowering plants, a major part of the plant-eating dinosaurs' diet, changed only moderately at this time.

Some biologists have proposed that the world's oceans lost much of their oxygen because of changes in ocean circulation, brought about by the movement of continents across the earth's surface and climatic shifts that significantly slowed deep ocean circulation. Warmer global climates, for example, might reduce the north-south temperature difference across the world's oceans so much that oxygen-rich surface water near the poles might not become cold enough to sink to the

By the Tertiary Period, the dinosaurs were gone and the surviving mammals continued developing into new species. The drama of life continued with a new cast of characters.

bottom in these areas. This would have greatly reduced bottom currents and thus, oxygen supply.

A marked change in ocean-bottom environments caused by a loss of oxygen occurred 1 million to 2 million years before the end of the Cretaceous. The poorly oxygenated water gradually spread upward. During the final 500,000 years of the period, midwater organisms, for example, were severely depleted. The spread of oxygen-poor water and the lowering of sea level were important factors in the widespread marine extinction, but they cannot be the only reasons because marine organisms living in temperate coastal waters as deep as 200 meters (650 feet) were only moderately affected at the C-T boundary, and many shallow-water organisms survived.

Temperature data obtained through carbon and oxygen isotope analysis of fossil shells and calcareous sediments suggest that the temperatures of the oceans dropped sharply near the C-T boundary. Several geologists have mentioned this as the probable cause for extinction, especially among the dinosaurs and warm-water organisms that were sensitive to temperature. There was an overall decline in oceanic temperature of 1° to 3°C. Probably the most important temperature changes were short-term fluctuations of 2° to 4°C (3.6° to 7.2°F.) that occurred over a span of 1 million to 2 million years just before, during, and after the extinction event. But such changes were not sufficient, by themselves, to have caused a true catastrophe.

Thus, there is no compelling evidence that any of these earthbound hypotheses for extinction of land and marine organisms at the C-T boundary were the single primary cause of extinction. But they suggest coinciding widespread environmental change that could have contributed to the gradual extinction of animals and plants over the last few million years of the Cretaceous. Collectively, these effects could have had a profound impact on global life. Many paleobiologists favor the theory that all these forms of environmental decline converged to produce the extinction of most major groups of Cretaceous organisms, and so weakened other groups that the final event, whatever it may have been, was able to push these groups — and the calcareous microplankton — over the brink of extinction.

How then do we explain the catastrophic extinction of the calcareous oceanic plankton and the final demise of other organisms at the C-T boundary? Many scientists suggest extraterrestrial causes. Some say that a solar flare or a nearby supernova — exploding star — bombarded the earth with massive, death-dealing amounts of radiation at or near the C-T boundary. Paleobiologist Dale Russell of the National Museum of Canada in Ottawa has been the main spokesman for radiation hypotheses, and especially for supernova radiation as a principal cause of catastrophic extinction.

After such massive radiation, we would expect to find highly diverse organisms becoming extinct simultaneously and widespread genetic damage resulting in abrupt changes and abnormalities among surviving life forms. The greatest impact would be on land and very-shallow-water organisms unprotected by deep water. However, the pattern of extinction does not reflect this prediction. The Cretaceous extinction was gradual for most land and sea organisms, with less impact on land. Many land plants and shallow-water invertebrates show little or no change across the C-T boundary.

Alvarez' suggestion that a giant meteor, or asteroid, struck the earth at the end of the Cretaceous is the latest extraterrestrial theory. According to the Alvarez group, the impact of a body 10 to 15 kilometers (16 to 24 miles) in diameter striking the ocean would have created a giant tidal wave several kilometers high that would have swept across low-lying land areas and contaminated large areas of the ocean with potentially toxic minerals. In addition, the explosion and impact would have produced a thick cloud of meteoric and ocean-bottom material that would have blanketed the earth for months or years, blocking out much of the sun's light and heat.

But the geochemistry — the concentrations of iridium and other elements at the C-T boundary — is the only evidence for a meteorite impact. There is no giant crater and no deposits have been found reflecting a huge tidal wave. Most damaging to the theory is the fossil record itself, which simply does not show near-instantaneous extinction for most of the organisms that disappeared near or at the end of the Cretaceous Period. Equally important is Hickey's observation that the flowering land plants were not severely affected during this time. They certainly would have been if solar radiation had been blocked for any length of time. The meteorite theory must be dismissed on the bulk of existing evidence.

But we cannot deny that the unusual chemical enrichment at the C-T boundary has an extraterrestrial fingerprint. Geologist Kenneth Hsu of the Technical Institute of Zurich, Switzerland, has another answer. He suggests that the earth may have been hit by a comet, or may have passed through the tail of a comet. This could have produced the unusual chemical enrichment and perhaps partially shocked global life without causing instantaneous extinction.

The evidence suggests a progressive worsening of global land and sea environments. Any single chance event — whether it was a comet, meteorite, or extraterrestrial radiation burst — was clearly not the major cause of the extinction. Rather, it could have been the "straw that broke the camel's back" — the event that pushed already weakened groups over the brink of extinction.

The Cretaceous extinction was like a terrible streak of bad luck lasting millions of years. Imagine a dice game with ones, or snake eyes, as the only losing roll. Roll after roll, snake eyes kept coming up for life during the late Cretaceous as sea-level drop, climate change, and oxygen loss in the ocean thinned out the living. When snake eyes came up on the last roll, that single spot on the die looked very much like a comet or a meteorite on a collision course with earth.

Image of
an Instant

By Harold E. Edgerton

**Stop-action photographs taken with lightning-fast
lamps help scientists and engineers explore
the fleeting world of extremely rapid motion**

An engineer learns how a fan circulates air by studying photographs that have frozen miniature whirlwinds of test smoke in time. A zoologist measures the motions of a hovering hummingbird simply by laying a ruler on a series of pictures that have stopped the bird's beating wings. A tennis coach analyzes a pupil's serve by studying a photograph that contains 40 superimposed images taken $\frac{1}{120}$ of a second apart. Rapidly flashing light from a small gas-filled tube permits such images to be made of phenomena that are too swift for the human eye and mind to perceive directly.

I designed the first such tube — an electronic flash unit called a stroboscopic light, or strobe — in the early 1930s. Other researchers had taken high-speed pictures with light from sparks as early as 1851, but their equipment was large, heavy, complex, and provided barely

A bullet that is traveling 425 meters (1,400 feet) per second is caught by strobe light of 1/2,000,000 of a second as it rips through toy balloons. The instantaneous flash provides details of how balloons burst that could never be perceived by the eye in ordinary light.

enough light. The ordinary flashbulb, introduced in 1929, is brighter but, at an operating speed of $\frac{1}{50}$ of a second, too slow for this kind of photography. The strobe has proved to be the handy, practical device that scientists need to photograph rapidly moving objects.

The first camera could not even photograph slow motion. In 1826, this crude device required eight hours to take a photograph of stationary objects. The camera operated on the same principle as do modern cameras. It admitted light into a dark chamber that held a chemically coated plate — the equivalent of modern film. The light, as reflected from the object being photographed, caused a slow chemical change, creating an image of the object on the plate.

In the 1830s, French inventor Louis Daguerre used faster-acting chemicals to cut exposure time to three minutes. Daguerre's invention enabled photographers to take pictures of people, but the person being photographed had to wear painful head clamps to help him hold still. By 1851, faster films had reduced exposures to a few seconds. By the late 1870s, even faster films, used in conjunction with fast-acting shutters — devices that control the length of time that light falls on the film — permitted pictures to be taken in $\frac{1}{25}$ of a second. By 1930, exposure time had been reduced to $\frac{1}{125}$ of a second or less — fast enough to photograph a moving human being without blurring.

Today's professional photographer, using high-speed film and a camera that operates in $\frac{1}{1,000}$ of a second, can easily freeze the motion of the quickest athlete. But scientists or engineers often study phenomena that require exposures of less than $\frac{1}{10,000}$ of a second. No

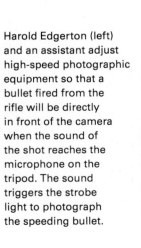

Harold Edgerton (left) and an assistant adjust high-speed photographic equipment so that a bullet fired from the rifle will be directly in front of the camera when the sound of the shot reaches the microphone on the tripod. The sound triggers the strobe light to photograph the speeding bullet.

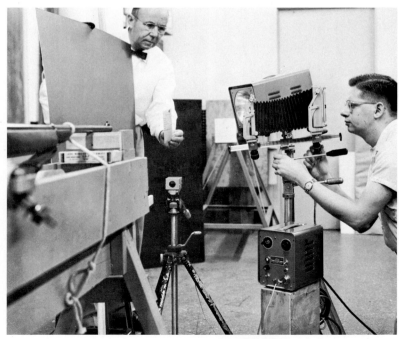

Papa Flash

The hallway leading to Harold E. Edgerton's laboratory at the Massachusetts Institute of Technology (M.I.T.) in Cambridge is known as Strobe Alley. Display cases along the corridor are filled with old strobe lamps, cameras, flashbulbs, and camera and flash controls. Mounted above the showcases are pictures that Edgerton and his students have taken since he entered the world of high-speed photography in 1930.

Edgerton did not begin his career with the idea of becoming the world's foremost authority on strobe photography. His main interest was electric motors, and he pursued this interest until a strange occurrence in an electrical power lab at M.I.T. sent him down the path to Strobe Alley.

As a graduate student in electrical engineering, Edgerton was trying to determine how power changes affect motor and generator speed. He was experimenting with a generator and vacuum tubes that emitted rapid pulses of bright light as they operated. The tubes had been placed close to the generator.

In the midst of his experiment, Edgerton suddenly noticed that the generator's rotor, or rotating part, seemed to stand still when the tubes flashed. Edgerton understood immediately that the tubes' pulse rate matched the generator's speed almost perfectly. Each time the tubes flashed, the rotor was in nearly the same position, creating the illusion that it was almost stationary.

The light also caused a flash of inspiration in Edgerton's mind. He decided to develop a practical device that he could use with a camera to "stop" motion — the modern stroboscope. Edgerton turned onto the new path with tremendous enthusiasm, and the results came quickly. The May 1931 issue of *Electrical Engineering* magazine described his remarkable invention — the mercury flash stroboscope. During the 1930s, Edgerton and two of his students, Kenneth Germeshausen and Herbert E. Grier, formed a partnership that designed and built myriad flashing lamps, cameras, and controls.

Their photographic equipment and expertise revealed a previously unseen world to researchers and commercial photographers. The design partnership had become famous by 1940, when Edgerton and Germeshausen went to Hollywood, Calif., to shoot a movie with their high-speed motion-picture camera. The resulting film, which showed what the camera could do, won an Academy Award for the best feature short of the year.

Edgerton turned his talents to military reconnaissance during World War II and focused his lights and cameras on enemy positions all over Europe and the Pacific theater.

Edgerton and his two partners incorporated their manufacturing and consulting business as Edgerton, Germeshausen, and Grier in 1947. The new company prospered, but eventually Edgerton left its management to the other two founders so that he could continue to teach and do research.

By this time, Strobe Alley had become a mecca for people who wished to learn Edgerton's techniques or have him analyze rapid motion. Edgerton photographed hummingbirds, bats, bareback riders, acrobats, running water, milk drops, and bullets. He helped baseball players, fencers, golfers, and tennis players to analyze their form. Archaeologists, explorers, naturalists, and professional photographers also sought him out. Edgerton made 10 voyages with French oceanographer Jacques-Yves Cousteau between 1954 and 1978 and became known for designing underwater cameras and *sonar* (*so*und *na*vigation *r*anging) devices.

Edgerton formally retired in 1968 at the age of 65, but he continues to probe the world of the unseen. One current project is photographing plankton, the tiny, delicate plants and animals that float and drift in seawater. Papa Flash, as Cousteau calls him, has helped others try to get underwater photographs of Scotland's Loch Ness monster, to settle the controversy about what is in the loch. Would a picture of the legendary monster become Strobe Alley's most amazing exhibit? Perhaps, but it would have to overcome plenty of competition.   [Jay Myers]

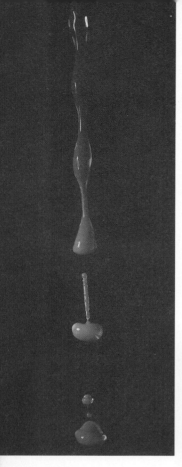

camera shutter can operate fast enough to take pictures at these speeds. The strobe overcomes the camera's mechanical limitations and transforms it into a high-speed scientific instrument.

The scientist-photographer connects the strobe to the camera and sets the shutter at an exposure time long enough for the strobe to complete its flash and let its intense light imprint the image on the film. The picture is "taken" only while the strobe light is on, even though the shutter may be open for a much longer period.

Special single-flash strobes that turn on and off in less than $\frac{1}{1,000,000}$ of a second enable scientists to photograph moving objects as fast as a flying bullet. Multiple-flash strobes that provide up to 6,000 pulses of light per second can trace the bullet's path.

Perhaps philosophers are right in saying that there is nothing new under the sun. Nevertheless, engineers and scientists are discovering worlds of new information under the strobe.

A stream of colored water, *above*, seems to fall like thick oil through strobe light that lasts for 1/50,000 of a second. A splashing milkdrop forms a crown, *right*, that is captured by a 1/10,000-second flash.

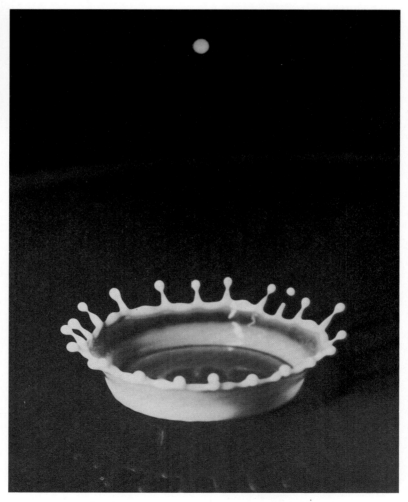

A single burst of light
1/100,000 of a second long
records how a golf ball
distorts at impact, *right*,
while successive flashes
of the same duration
photograph a golf swing as
a multiple exposure, *below*.

A bullet bursts a
balloon whose collapse
is recorded by rapid
motion-picture
photography. Lighting
the scene with flashes
1/1,000,000 of a second
in duration prevents
blurring. Timing the
flashes at 1/4,000-second
intervals keeps the
images from overlapping.

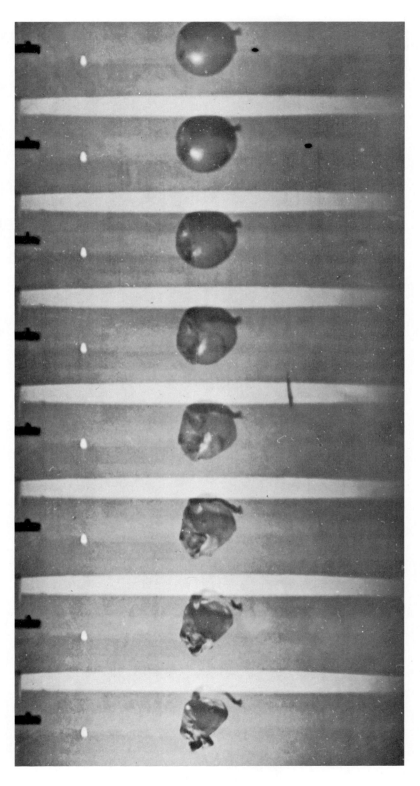

The author photographs tiny ocean plants and animals alive in their natural habitat, *left*, by dropping ocean water onto a sheet of film, then flashing a strobe lamp that prints their shadows on the film. An enlargement, *below*, reveals details of young brine shrimp 1 millimeter (0.04 inch) long.

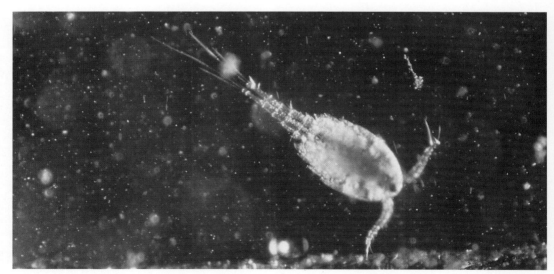

A rapidly fluttering copepod, a sea animal about 1 millimeter (0.04 inch) long, appears to be tranquilized for scientific examination as it swims in aquarium water, illuminated by a 1/10,000-second flash.

A 15/100,000-second flash "stops" blood that pulses through a human eye, providing pictorial information about circulation in small vessels.

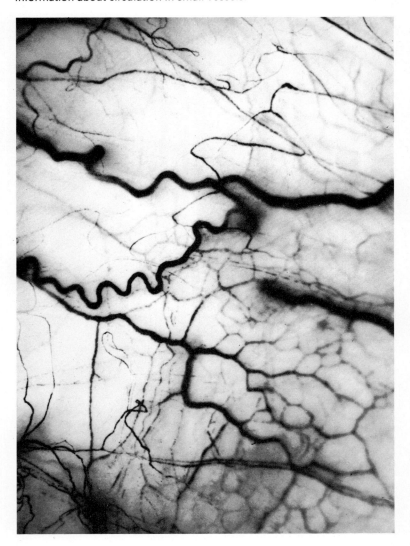

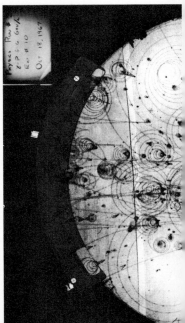

A hummingbird adjusts its wing feathers to direct air downward so that it can hover as it beats its wings 60 times per second. A flash 1/20,000 of a second in duration reveals this detail of flight.

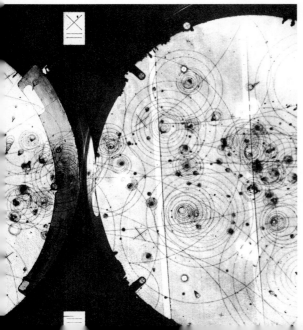

Subatomic particles trigger a brief flash that illuminates particle trails in a bubble chamber before the trails expand and lose their sharpness. Trails give scientists information on particle formation, identity, charge, and velocity.

A dust explosion
inside a tank bursts
a protective metal vent,
releasing pressure that
otherwise would damage
the tank. Pictures taken
1/2,400 of a second
apart prove that the
vent opens as designed so
that dangerous pressure
can escape rapidly.

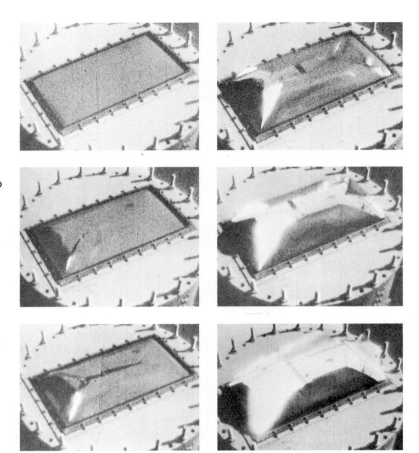

A tank bursts in a pressure-test
rig, setting off a strobe flash
that records the burst even before
escaping high-pressure water reaches
the floor. The image can be used
to analyze the design of the tank.

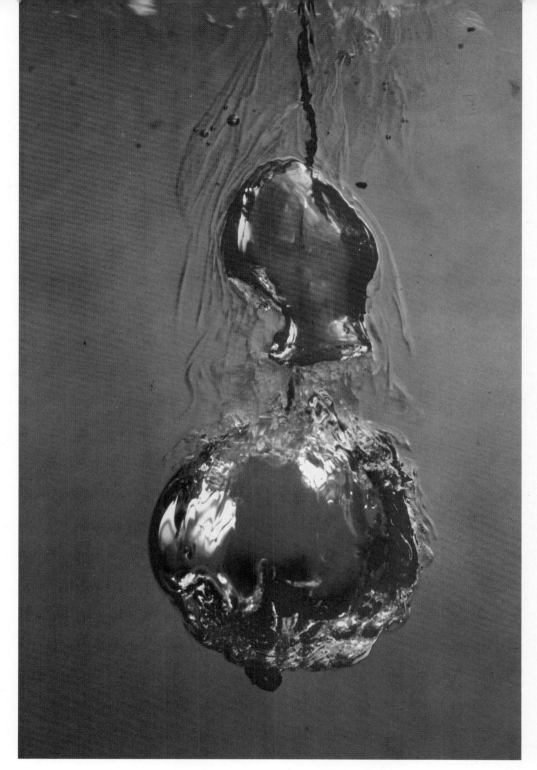

A red-hot nickel ball immersed in oil forms a balloon-shaped bubble of oil vapor. Photographing the bubble with a timed 1/100,000-second flash provides information about the bubble's rate of formation and rate of rise that can be used to measure the oil's ability to cool metal.

A drop of oil strikes a hot surface, spreads, and forms a ring, but does not burn. Images of this impact taken at high speed show how increasing temperatures affect oil's ability to form a lubricating film.

A milling machine's cutting tool takes chips from a metal part. Strobe flashes lasting 1/1,000,000 of a second, 1/50 of a second apart, record chip formation rates and the angles at which chips fall — data that can be used to determine how to adjust the machine.

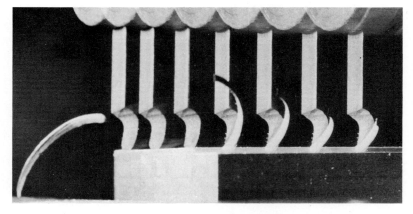

Strobe Without Flashes

You can build a device that shows the stroboscopic effect without a flash unit. Cut a disk out of cardboard about the size of a Frisbee. Next, cut out six windows equally spaced along the rim, large enough to look through when you hold the disk up to your eye. Then draw a thick line from the center of the disk to each window. Punch a hole through the center with a pencil and twist the pencil until the disk will spin on it. Finally, cut out a small retainer disk, poke the pencil through it, and slide it up to the large disk.

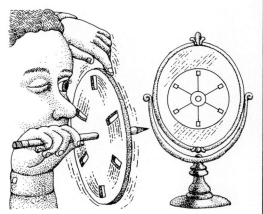

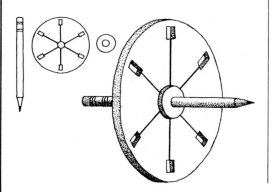

Hold the device up to your eye in front of a mirror so that you can see the reflection of the lines through one of the windows. Spin the large disk and note how the lines seem to stand still. You are actually seeing the succession of moving lines as the windows go by, but your eye and brain blend them into stationary lines.

Fireworks Mountain

By Peter W. Lipman

Mount Saint Helens is serving as a natural laboratory for geologists who study the whys, wheres, and whens of volcanic eruptions

As we approached the desolate remains of once sublimely beauti-ful Spirit Lake early on the morning of May 19, 1980, we found it almost impossible to comprehend the devastation caused by Mount Saint Helens. This was only about 24 hours after the catastrophic eruption of the volcano. During the previous six weeks, my colleagues James Moore, Donald Swanson, and I, geologists for the United States Geological Survey (USGS), had worked on the volcano's north slope almost every day, making geophysical measurements and moni-toring activity inside the mountain. We had come to treasure the beauty of the crystal-clear blue waters of Spirit Lake and the sur-rounding virgin forests of giant Douglas firs.

But the landscape changed drastically on May 18, when the north side of the 2,900-meter (9,677-foot) volcano collapsed in a monstrous landslide under the force of a strong earthquake. The sudden release

Indians of the 19th century watch in awe as Mount Saint Helens erupts, *above left,* in a detail from the 1847 painting, *Mount Saint Helens* by Paul Kane. Geologists of the 20th century, *above,* watch with scientific instruments for movements of the mountain shortly after its 1980 eruption.

of pressure on the mountainside caused the volcano to explode, like a bottle of champagne when the cork is pulled too quickly. The explosion destroyed all life as far as 25 kilometers (15.5 miles) from the volcano. Trees were sheared off and knocked down as if they were blades of grass caught in a giant lawn mower. The blast devastated an area of nearly 600 square kilometers (230 square miles). It clogged the rivers and streams with debris. At least 34 persons are known to have been killed.

We had studied the results of many recent volcanic eruptions in Hawaii, Japan, the Philippines, Iceland, and the Caribbean region, but this one was exceptional. The main eruption was a directed blast, an uncommon and devastating type that is known to have occurred at only a few volcanoes, located in remote places. This volcanic eruption presented us with unusual opportunities to understand what goes on deep inside the earth. Mount Saint Helens has proved to be a natural laboratory for geologists interested in why volcanoes exist in only a few places and the source of their tremendous energy. Also, we were able to experiment with scientific measurements that may help us better predict future volcanic eruptions.

Few Americans outside of Alaska and Hawaii are accustomed to the idea of living with active volcanoes. Not many people realize that the picturesque mountains of the Cascade Range in Washington, Oregon, and northern California consist largely of relatively young, dormant volcanoes – which may become active, or erupt again – nestled among older, extinct volcanoes.

As a volcanologist, a geologist specializing in volcanoes, I have been studying eruptions and their effects for 20 years. I have studied recent and ancient volcanic deposits in most of the Western states of the United States. I worked at the USGS Hawaiian Volcano Observatory for two years studying the active volcanoes Kilauea and Mauna Loa, and I studied in Japan for a year with Japanese volcanologists, learning the ways of a society that lives with especially active and dangerous volcanoes.

Geologists classify volcanoes and their eruptions in various ways, but every volcano is the product of similar processes within the earth. Magma, very hot liquefied rock and dissolved gases, forms by the melting of rocks deep in the earth's crust or in the underlying mantle. As magma forms, it becomes lighter and more fluid than the adjacent rock, and the hot molten material tends to rise. Some magma rises rapidly to erupt at the surface of the earth, but usually it accumulates at depths of a few kilometers beneath volcanic vents to form a magma reservoir, or chamber. In the reservoir, the magma may change further in composition and dissolved gases may begin to separate, in preparation for an explosive eruption. The magma, called lava if it reaches the surface as a flow, or ash if it is erupted explosively, accumulates on the surface of the earth around the volcanic vent, cools, and hardens. Repeated eruptions from the same reservoir

The author:
Peter W. Lipman is a geologist with the United States Geological Survey in Denver.

Steam and ash ascend from Mount Saint Helens, *left.* A bulge gradually forms on its north slope, *below left.* The bulge falls away in landslide on May 18, 1980, *below,* and this sudden release of pressure triggers a major eruption, *bottom.*

can produce layered sequences of lava flows and ash that form cone- or shield-shaped volcanic mountains.

Volcanoes such as Mount Saint Helens are built at or near the edges of about 20 giant tectonic plates that make up the earth's crust. These plates move over the mantle, a deep thick region of heated rock between the crusted plates and the earth's core. When two plates move apart at ocean ridges, magma comes up through the gap between them, enlarging the ridge or forming a new one. As the plates move apart, they encounter other plates at their opposite sides.

Plates meet in three ways: two plates may slide past each other, creating an earthquake zone like the San Andreas Fault in California; they may collide head-on, both thrusting upward to form mountains like the Himalayan range in Asia; or two may collide in such a way that one glides down beneath the other. Friction and internal heat cause the descending plate to partially melt, creating magma. Plate movements are complex and unpredictable. After a volcano has formed in one area, changing plate movements can cause a further build-up of pressure that leads to birth of a new volcano nearby.

In the Pacific Northwest area, the tiny Juan de Fuca Plate is sliding down under the giant North American Plate. As a result, Mount Saint Helens formed near the edge of the North American Plate.

Seismologist Stephen Malone and his associates at the University of Washington in Seattle were the first to realize that something unusual was happening at Mount Saint Helens. They detected a swarm of earthquakes directly beneath the Mount Saint Helens cone beginning on March 20, 1980. For several years, the University of Washington and the USGS had been working together, measuring the normal seismic patterns of Cascade volcanoes in order to evaluate the possibility of a dangerous eruption. Another purpose of the study was to try to evaluate the potential underground energy associated with the volcanoes.

The USGS asked me to work on Mount Saint Helens in 1980 as part of a team of volcanologists and other scientists from state and federal agencies, universities, and industrial research groups. We wanted to learn how to forecast eruptions so that state and local authorities could clear the area if necessary. At the same time, we hoped to learn about processes of volcanism that have rarely been observed before. Our conclusions about Mount Saint Helens are the product of interaction and cooperation among many scientists.

The larger setting for our work was the Cascade Range, a chain of volcanoes that lie in a remarkably straight line. At least 15 of them are potentially active. Straight or curved chains of such volcanoes occur throughout the world, wherever one plate is descending beneath another. In addition to the Cascades, notable examples include the Aleutian Islands of southwestern Alaska, the volcanic belts of Japan, and the great Andean volcanoes of South America. Although generally similar, each area has special characteristics that are probably

How the Earth Builds Volcanoes

The Cascade Mountains, a volcanic chain, formed near the edge of the North American Plate, *below,* one of about 20 plates that make up the earth's crust. The tiny Juan de Fuca Plate moves slowly away from the Pacific Plate and its leading edge is forced down under the North American Plate, *right,* and melts into magma. Heated and pressured by gases, the magma rises under the overriding plate to the surface, forming the volcanic mountains and also fueling their periodic eruptions.

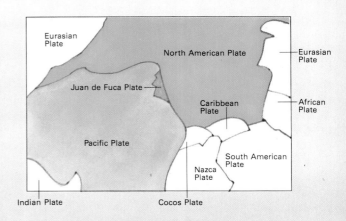

Eurasian Plate

North American Plate

Eurasian Plate

Juan de Fuca Plate

Caribbean Plate

African Plate

Pacific Plate

South American Plate

Nazca Plate

Indian Plate

Cocos Plate

Mt. Garibaldi

Canada

Mt. Baker

Glacier Peak

United States

Mt. Rainier

Mt. St. Helens

Mt. Adams

Mt. Hood

Juan de Fuca Plate

Mt. Thielson

Three Sisters

North American Plate

Pacific Plate

Mt. McLoughlin

Mt. Shasta

Lassen Peak

Magma Chamber

Mantle

Mantle

Melting plate

Magma

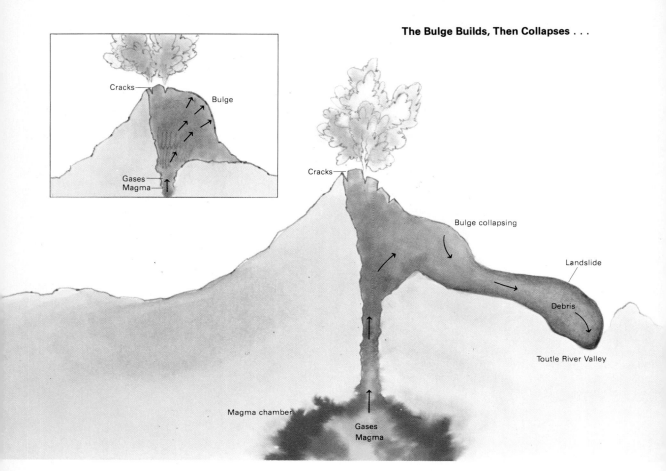

A bulge, *top,* appeared in Mount Saint Helens' north slope in March 1980 as gases and magma rose within the mountain and built up pressure inside the volcano. The bulge failed, *bottom,* on May 18, 1980, causing a huge landslide.

related to such variables as the speed of the moving plates, the thickness and other physical properties of the descending plate, and the composition of the crust through which the magma rises before reaching the surface.

The Cascades stand along a plate boundary that moves very slowly—about 1 centimeter (0.4 inch) per year. Scientists suspect that this slow rate explains why eruptions occur infrequently in the area. Because eruptions are relatively infrequent, Mount Saint Helens' 1980 activity came as a surprise to most people, but some volcanologists had anticipated it. Geologists Donal R. Mullineaux and Dwight R. Crandell of the USGS reported in 1978 that Mount Saint Helens was "probably the volcano most likely to endanger people and property in the Western United States." They forecast that it might erupt before the year 2000, basing their opinion on their geologic studies of prehistoric volcanic deposits on and around the Cascade volcanoes. Before 1980, the most recent eruption in the Cascades occurred in 1915-1916 at Lassen Peak in northern California. Most of the major volcanic cones have erupted at least once in the last few hundred years, and Mount Saint Helens has been an especially frequent performer. In fact, Mount Saint Helens appears to

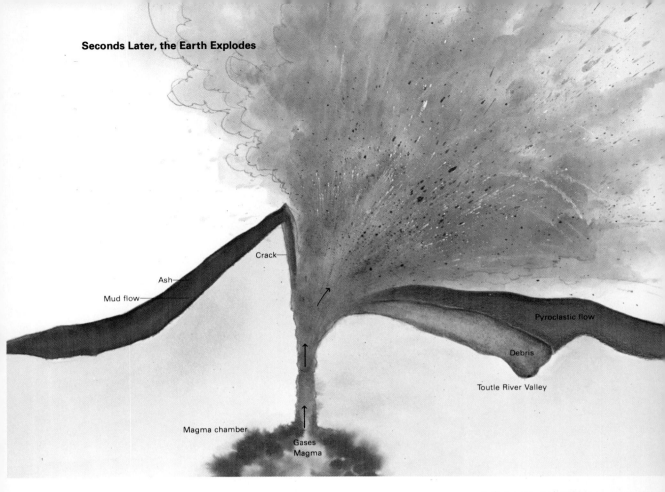

Crack

Ash

Mud flow

Pyroclastic flow

Debris

Toutle River Valley

Magma chamber

Gases
Magma

be the youngest, most recently active volcano in the Cascade Range.

The series of earthquakes in March 1980 included the largest quakes ever recorded near Mount Saint Helens, some registering a magnitude of 4 or more on the Richter scale. Within a few days, quakes were occurring so frequently and with such intensity that the scientists could not distinguish one quake from another on the seismometer nearest the volcano. At the same time, steam was building up within the volcano. It came from ground water, heated by magma, which joined with hot gases released from the liquefied rock itself. The first steam explosions occurred on March 27, sending clouds of steam billowing thousands of meters in the air and leaving a crater about 60 meters (200 feet) wide at the top of the volcano. At the same time, observers flying over the mountain noted that large cracks had appeared in the snow cover near the summit and a bulge had begun to develop high on the volcano's north flank. Earthquakes, steam explosions, and enlarging of the summit crater and bulge went on for six weeks, from late March until mid-May.

The earthquakes continued steadily through this period. The largest measured about magnitude 5 on the Richter scale. The Richter scale is logarithmic; that is, an increase of one whole number equals a

A massive eruption blew away the remainder of the north slope, just seconds after the bulge fell away. The lateral (sideways) blast buried the landscape to the north under tons of debris and pyroclastic flow deposits (rock avalanches) and filled the sky with ash.

After the May 18 eruption, a geologist puts his life on the line to set up markers to help measure further changes in the mountain's topography.

tenfold increase in strength. For example, a magnitude 5 earthquake releases 10 times as much energy as one of magnitude 4. In April and early May, 10 to 40 earthquakes with magnitude greater than 3 were recorded each day, and 3 to 10 of them had magnitudes over 4.

The scientists recording the quakes agreed that this was an astonishing release of seismic energy by Mount Saint Helens, compared with most other carefully studied similar volcanoes.

I began on-site studies on April 2. Working up on the volcanic cone, my colleagues and I felt earthquakes every few hours. At times they were so intense that it was difficult to remain standing. But because the source of the quakes was very shallow — at most a few kilometers below the mountain and in some instances, probably from within the cone itself — even the largest earthquakes were not felt by people living 10 kilometers (6.2 miles) away from the base of the volcano. We watched explosive eruptions occur as frequently as several times per day. They lasted from a few minutes to more than half an hour. These were phreatic eruptions — driven by very hot water that flashed into steam, carrying ash with it. Thin layers of fine gray ash mixed with the snow that fell almost every night and completely coated the cone of Mount Saint Helens. The ash consisted entirely of finely powdered old rock from within the volcano. No new magma had reached the surface so far.

The growing bulge on the north side of the mountain seemed to be an especially significant feature. Cracks and faults were forming on the upper ice-covered slopes of the volcano. At first we could not see them clearly because of the steam and ash eruptions and frequent new snowfall, and we thought just the ice might be cracking because of increased heat from the volcano. But later it became clear that the rock was also breaking as the north side was being pushed up and out at an astonishing rate by molten rock rising within the volcano. Moore, Swanson, and I repeatedly measured the bulge in April and May with precision laser equipment that bounced a light beam off 14 targets with plastic reflectors that we had placed at various points on the mountain near the bulge. We compared our measurements of the changing mountain with contour maps Moore had made at the USGS-Menlo Park office, using aerial photos taken in November 1979 and April 1980. Our measurements demonstrated that rocks within the bulge were moving upward and outward at a rate of 1.5 to 2.5 meters (5 to 8 feet) per day. Some points had moved several hundred meters since the activity began. Similar events have been observed only a few times before at other volcanoes. For example, at Showa Shinsen on Honshu Island, Japan, in 1944 and 1945, Japanese scientists found that lava, pushing out at the base of Usu volcano, raised nearby rice fields as much as 300 meters (1,000 feet) in only a year and a half. Eventually, enough hot sticky lava reached the surface of Usu volcano to form a lava dome that rose up another 100 meters (350 feet).

A helicopter is the scientist's link to safety as he monitors the motions of the tectonic plates beneath the mountain.

Four such lava domes had formed around the north side of Mount Saint Helens in the past 1,500 to 2,500 years, telling us that molten rock had flowed out of this side of the mountain in previous eruptions. So we suspected that another lava dome was developing in the spring of 1980. But there was a special problem at Mount Saint Helens in late April and May. Because of the bulging, the already steep north side of the volcano was becoming even steeper. We were concerned that the north slope of the volcano might slide away. This would endanger the many people using the recreational areas around the north side of the volcano at Spirit Lake. The U.S. Forest Service estimated that several thousand people visited the area each spring weekend. Based on the USGS estimate that the situation was dangerous, the Forest Service and state officials closed much of the area to the general public as a safety precaution. County sheriffs and the National Guard put up roadblocks and evacuated several villages.

The scientists worked long hours manning the seismometers, tiltmeters, and other equipment customarily used to monitor earthquakes. They also experimented with techniques that might give a few days or even a few hours warning of an impending disaster. Most of us were certain that Mount Saint Helens was building toward a major eruption, including a blast of magma and a possible landslide on the north slope. Our instruments did not detect any major changes in the pattern of earthquakes from March 20 to May 18. The rate of growth of the bulge remained the same, as did the quantity of gases escaping in the few days before the May 18 eruption. However, the entire pattern of activity since March 20 had provided clear warning of an impending major volcanic event. Nevertheless, none of the scientists on the scene were prepared for the awesome scale of the events that soon followed.

At 8:32 A.M. on May 18, Mount Saint Helens was shaken by the largest earthquake yet recorded there—a magnitude of about 5.1. Geologists Keith and Dorothy Stoffel were almost directly over the volcano in a small airplane at the time; they could see—and their photographs documented their observation—that the volcano was shaking so intensely that it caused the bulge to fall away. Many ground observers who happened to be up early on that Sunday morning also took spectacular photographs of the eruption. Among the most instructive to geologists was a sequence by free-lance photographer Gary Rosenquist taken in rapid succession from a point about 20 kilometers (12 miles) to the northeast. His photos showed how the north side of the volcano slid away, allowing the pent-up magma and gases inside the peak to explode.

The rocks and debris roared downslope into Spirit Lake and the valley of the North Fork Toutle River, coming to rest as far as 20 kilometers from the volcano. Seconds after the landslide started, the interior of the volcano began to explode and superheated water, previously held in by the weight and pressure of the overlying rock, flashed into steam. These explosions were similar to the earlier steam-blast eruptions, but on a much greater scale. Because the peak's north side had been removed by the landslide, the volcano sent its tremendous blast laterally, or horizontally, to the north. I did not witness the beginning of the great eruption personally, because I was in Denver at the time. But Swanson was in his car driving toward the volcano when it blew. His and other eyewitness accounts — and later analyses of records covering the periods when instruments failed — indicate that the explosion may have hurled material at more than 700 kilometers per hour (kph), or 495 miles per hour (mph).

Heat from the blast melted snowfields and glacial ice on the upper slopes of the mountain, triggering torrential flows of muddy water and debris. Geologists calculated that some mud and debris flowed at velocities of more than 125 kph (75 mph).

After upper parts of the volcano were torn away by the landslide and explosions, magma erupted violently as gases dissolved in the

Mud from the landslide stopped short of farm buildings in the Toutle River Valley, *below.* Washington woman sweeps away some of the ash that blanketed a huge area, *below right.*

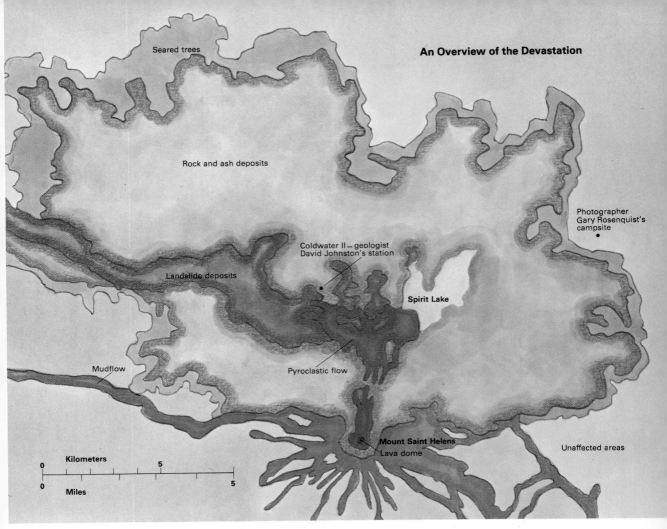

Seared trees

Rock and ash deposits

Photographer
Gary Rosenquist's
campsite

Coldwater II — geologist
David Johnston's station

Landslide deposits

Spirit Lake

Mudflow

Pyroclastic flow

Mount Saint Helens
Lava dome

Unaffected areas

Kilometers

0   5

0   5

Miles

The Mount Saint Helens
eruption concentrated
its force to the north
of the peak, *above.*
Mudflow from the sides
of the mountain clogged
rivers and streams.
Pyroclastic flow (hot
rock avalanches) and
landslide deposits
(older rock that fell
from the bulge)
destroyed all life.
Blast deposits (ash and
rocks) uprooted and
destroyed trees. In the
seared zone, trees died
but were left standing.

79

The crater-marked landscape, devoid of greenery, makes the area around Mount Saint Helens look like a scene from a science-fiction movie.

magma expanded. Much of this magma came out in the form of glassy pumice, a light, frothy, spongelike material resulting from the expansion of the bubbles of dissolved gas. More finely fragmented glassy ash was mixed with the pumice. The fragments of ash and pumice formed hot avalanches, called pyroclastic flows, that rushed down the north slope of the volcano toward Spirit Lake. These flows were much like snow avalanches, but they moved more freely because the rock fragments mixed with the air and heated it — changing the mixture to a liquidlike material.

Within about 30 minutes after the explosion, a column of hot ash and pumice — driven upward by expanding gases and by turbulence, or fluid motion, as the gases mixed with the air — had risen more than 24 kilometers (15 miles) into the atmosphere, the maximum height that can be measured by the radar system at the Portland, Ore., airport 80 kilometers (50 miles) to the south. The pumice and ash soon began to fall out downwind, forming a layer on the ground as thick as 0.5 meter (1.5 feet) within 10 kilometers of the volcano. The eruption gradually diminished late in the afternoon of May 18.

When Moore, Swanson, and I reached the devastated area the next morning, we found that about $1 billion worth of prime timber lay strewn around like matchsticks in the 600-square-kilometer area. Logging trucks and other pieces of heavy machinery were tossed around in topsy-turvy fashion, and many plastic parts were melted by the brief but intense heat that accompanied the blast. Trees at the edge of the area were left standing but dying, their foliage seared gray by the heat.

Muddy ash from the slopes of the peak, mixed with water from snowfields and glaciers and heated to a liquid by the blast, had flowed rapidly down the east and west sides of the volcano, overflowing riverbanks, ripping out roadways and bridges, and trapping unsuspecting drivers in their cars for tens of kilometers beyond the other effects of the eruption. The Columbia River was closed to shipping

A new dome in the massive crater left by the eruption had built up a month later.

when debris from the mudflows clogged its channel at the junction with the Cowlitz River 120 kilometers (75 miles) downstream.

The pumice and ash in the air near the volcano were so thick that they blocked the sun, turning day into night in cities as far away as Yakima, Wash. A layer of pumice and fine ash was deposited as far away as North Dakota, 1,500 kilometers (930 miles) to the east. The dry powdery ash damaged farm crops, blocked roads, choked vehicle engines, disrupted water-treatment plants, and closed airports.

Within the blast zone, in addition to the 34 persons known dead, at least 30 were missing, and many others lay injured or trapped behind blocked roadways. Among those lost was volcanologist David Johnston, my friend and USGS colleague for 10 years, who had been monitoring the composition of volcanic gas coming from the mountain. He was killed when the lateral blast swept away his camp on a high ridge 9 kilometers (5 miles) from the volcano.

Most volcanic eruptions in recorded history have blown skyward. Major lateral eruptions like the one at Mount Saint Helens on May 18 have occurred only rarely — for example, at Bandai-san volcano in Japan in 1888 and at Bezymianny volcano on USSR's Kamchatka Peninsula in 1956. Most of the devastation at these sites, as at Mount Saint Helens, was caused by the force of the initial lateral explosion, rather than by the volume of magma erupted. The May 18 eruption did not spout an exceptional volume of magma or release a great amount of energy, compared with previous eruptions from this same volcano or other famous eruptions in history.

The May 18 events at Mount Saint Helens were only the first and most catastrophic of a series of eruptions that continued throughout the year. The later eruptions were less violent and caused no significant damage. But they were especially interesting to volcanologists because they differed in volume, composition, and force, offering important clues to the nature of the magma chamber beneath the volcano. Also, as we developed increasingly sophisticated monitoring

Life returns to the volcano's slopes as Alpine daisies push their way up through the thick layer of ash.

techniques to measure activity within the volcano, we were able to anticipate most of these events a few hours or days in advance. As a result, observers and equipment could be moved around to areas where we could make unique measurements of volcanic processes.

We have used the events on Mount Saint Helens to investigate the fundamentals of volcano behavior, especially magmas. Many of the procedures we tried had never been used before on an active explosive volcano. Some worked magnificently, while others developed unforeseen problems when exposed to the "real world" environment of an active explosive volcano.

Eruptions of magma occurred on May 25, June 12, July 22, August 7, October 16 to 18, and between December 27 and Jan. 3, 1981. Before most of these eruptions, we detected increases in earthquake activity, changes in the shape of the mountain, and changes in the type or amount of gases rising from the vent. Harmonic tremor — a low-level vibration that could be described as a "seismic hum" that precedes some volcanic eruptions — was a pronounced feature. Seismic instruments detected harmonic tremor within Mount Saint Helens a few hours to a few days before most eruptions. For example, harmonic tremor occurred almost continuously after the May 18 eruption until the eruption on May 25.

When we measured changes in the ground with precise surveying instruments, we found a general collapse or flattening of the mountain from early June through most of the rest of the year. But just before or during eruptions, the volcano swelled, apparently because of increased pressures from the shallow magma body below the crater. These patterns of ground changes differed from those that were recorded before May 18, when the bulge area expanded rapidly but the rest of the volcano did not change detectably.

Before May 18, geochemists had found only low levels of gases issuing from the volcano, indicating that the shallow magma body was well sealed. By contrast, the amounts of gaseous sulfur and carbon dioxide began to increase considerably in early June. The June 12 eruption started with explosive eruptions of ash and pumice similar to those on May 18 and May 25, then concluded with viscous magma that contained little gas flowing to the surface and forming a lava dome within the main crater. Lava domes commonly well up at volcanoes such as Mount Saint Helens late in the eruption cycle.

Another pyroclastic eruption on July 22 blew out the center of the dome formed in June. An eruption on August 7 also began with an explosion of hot ash and provided a high point in my work at Mount Saint Helens. I was fortunate to see and record a major eruption. Based on changes in seismic measurements and the composition of the gas plume — which had been rising from the crater since May 18 — we began to suspect early in the afternoon of August 7 that an eruption was imminent. Work parties were withdrawn, and two groups of observers landed in helicopters.

Accompanied by photographer Terry Leighley and electronics technician Bruce Furakawa, I chose a commanding viewpoint 8 kilometers (5 miles) due north of the volcano and about 500 meters (1,600 feet) above the volcanic plain on a hill that would protect us from any pyroclastic flows that might move toward us. About 20 minutes after we arrived — while we were getting our camera and video-recording equipment in position — we noticed that the gas plume within the crater grew larger and became darker. Within seconds, a dark column moved up from the crater floor, so laden with ash and pumice blocks that it began to spill out to the north as a large hot pyroclastic flow that moved slowly down the north side of the volcano. We watched and photographed it for several minutes. Later calculations indicated that it reached velocities as great as 100 kph (62 mph). As the pyroclastic flow rushed down the north slope, a vertical column of less dense ash developed above the crater, eventually reaching a height of almost 15 kilometers (9 miles). We were forced to leave when ash began to fall on us.

After the August 7 eruption ended, a second small lava dome formed. But that dome was blown out during pyroclastic eruptions in October, and a third lava dome then appeared. That lava dome was enlarged in late December when two additional lobes of thick lava oozed out onto its sides without additional explosions. This composite dome more than doubled in size in early February when another large lobe welled out from the crest of the October dome, nearly burying it and quickly reaching a height of about 200 meters (650 feet) above the crater floor.

A decline in the force and volume of eruptions late in 1980 and early in 1981 suggested to many of us that one phase of Mount Saint Helens activity was ending. Several alternatives remain, however. The volcano may gradually become dormant again within a few years, or domes may continue to grow within the central crater, gradually filling it and restoring the former shape of the volcano to some degree. Some lava-dome complexes at other volcanoes have grown for 20 years or more, and the eruptions at Mount Saint Helens in the 1800s may have continued on and off for 23 years.

We know from the geological record of the area that major eruptions comparable to the 1980 Mount Saint Helens activity have occurred every few thousand years in the Cascades. So we can expect another devastating eruption in the area, but probably not in our lifetime. Nevertheless, the Cascades' volcanoes are now being monitored more closely so that we can warn the industrialized, heavily populated Pacific Northwest area if another major eruption threatens. As scientists, we gain invaluable experience in studying volcanoes such as Mount Saint Helens. But we also have an awesome responsibility in advising the authorities who, in turn, must make hard decisions about protecting the people who live and work in the shadow of volcanoes.

The Science of
Animal Welfare

By Michael W. Fox

**Ensuring the well-being of our pets and
the animals used in research and agriculture
can be beneficial to humanity as well**

He spends his days in darkness punctuated by light only when his meals — a liquid formula — are delivered. He is confined in such tight quarters that he cannot turn around, so he exercises his legs by bracing them against the slats of the floor. He cannot see, touch, or communicate with any of his fellows. He will leave these confines only when the time comes for him to be killed.

He is a 2-month-old veal calf and unaware that, only a few feet from his narrow stall, the sun is streaming down upon the Wisconsin countryside where his great-grandparents once played, grazed, and nuzzled each other. While his forebears enjoyed many natural freedoms, today's veal calf is one of the billions of animals used in science, industry, and agriculture that have been deprived of these rights — often unnecessarily.

Like many people, I once enjoyed eating veal, blissfully ignorant of the deplorable conditions under which most veal calves are raised. Like some scientists, I once welcomed the latest research reports, oblivious to the degree of animal suffering that may have been necessary to produce them. Although trained as a veterinarian and animal psychologist, I had not thought much about animal rights until the early 1970s. At that time, I was studying the behavior of wolves at Washington University in St. Louis. I had come to feel indebted to my subjects for their contribution to my professional success, and when I learned that wolves were being destroyed in Alaska, I realized that I was being given an opportunity to repay them. I mounted a campaign to preserve their packs. As my work with the wolves began to receive publicity, people contacted me with reports of abuses to other animal species. I began to devote more of my time to animal welfare work. In 1976, I left St. Louis to become the director of the Institute for the Study of Animal Problems in Washington, D.C., the scientific branch of the Humane Society of the United States.

At the institute, we are working to develop a science of animal welfare — a system that will provide for the maximum well-being of animals in the wilds, in laboratories, on farms, and as pets. I feel that this sense of well-being depends upon an animal's ability to meet its needs and pursue its interests — in effect, upon its ability to enjoy its natural rights. Ideally, all animals have the right to life, to humane treatment, and to experience *telos,* the intrinsic nature of their species. While a pig's telos may lead it to root in the mud, a raccoon's telos may require it to wash its food before each meal.

In reality, however, the rights of animals are relative. In nature, the rights of each species are cast in a broad ecological framework. The lion's right to life necessitates violating the antelope's right to life. In turn, the antelope's survival as a species may depend upon the lion's ability to kill certain of their numbers so that they do not become too numerous and deplete their own food supply.

Domesticated and captive animals have their rights restricted even further. Endangered species such as the panda have had their right to roam freely exchanged for the protection of zoos and game preserves; pet dogs and cats have lost the right to reproduce without limit; livestock have lost the right to live out their natural life span; and some laboratory animals have even lost the right to avoid pain. However, because humans have come to dominate other animals and deprive them of some of their rights, we must preserve as many of the remaining rights as possible. Even doomed laboratory animals and livestock should have the freedom to stand up, lie down, and turn around easily; to groom and preen; to enjoy some social contact with their own species; and the right, finally, to a humane death.

Laws regarding the rights of animals used in research and education differ throughout the world. In Canada, Great Britain, and

The author:
Michael W. Fox is director of the Institute for the Study of Animal Problems in Washington, D.C.

Research animals often endure unnecessary discomfort. Rats grapple for space in a crowded cage, *above.* A baby rhesus monkey gasps following a soap toxicity test, *right.*

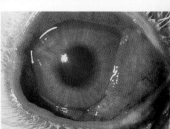

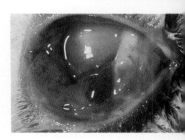

Rabbits held in stocks await their turns as subjects of eye toxicity tests, *above.* Substances such as new cosmetics dropped into a rabbit's eye may result in damage such as membrane irritation, *top right,* a clouded cornea, *middle right,* or severe ulceration, *bottom right.*

Sweden, laws prohibit students from causing animal suffering as part of their science education. But in the United States, some degree of animal suffering is rationalized in the name of learning.

At the 1976 International Science and Engineering Fair for high school students, I stopped at one of many experiments involving live animals and took a deep breath. Emaciated, wild-eyed rats darted about fitfully in a small cage. A poster announced the project as "The Effects of Caffeine Poisoning" and detailed how the rats, given high concentrations of caffeine, deteriorated and developed eye infections, diarrhea, insomnia, weight loss, and breathing difficulties. The rats were clearly in distress and for no good reason – the project taught us nothing new. The harmful effects of caffeine had long been documented in textbooks. Other exhibits at that fair reported the sickness and slow, agonizing death of guinea pigs injected with a drug that caused a heart attack, and a kitten's hearing loss after hair spray had been sprayed repeatedly into its ears. All of these projects were needless – demonstrating effects that had already been detailed in medical textbooks and research reports.

In Canada, such projects are forbidden. Regulations for animal experimentation in science fairs, adopted in 1975, allow only those projects that involve observations of the normal living patterns of animals; forbid using vertebrates in exhibits; and encourage projects involving bacteria, fungi, protozoans, and cell cultures. In contrast, U.S. guidelines for science fair projects suggest only that projects involving animals be "supervised" – not screened for their worth or the degree of pain inflicted.

Scientists and concerned laymen are now questioning the necessity of making laboratory animals suffer in the development and testing of products that are not essential for human well-being, such as cosmetics. The eyeshadows advertised as inspired by the Tahitian tropics actually originated in a large factory and, long before they adorned a fashion model's eyelids, they were tested in the eyes of laboratory rabbits. A procedure known as the Draize test, developed in 1944 by pharmacologist John Draize, entails putting the test substance into the eyes of rabbits held motionless in stocks and then evaluating the degree of damage to the eye.

The Draize test is also used to test any product that might accidentally come into contact with the eyes of human beings. Although some test substances such as nose drops may have no effect, or cause only a mild reddening, others, such as oven cleaner, can produce painful inflammation or even blindness. Federal regulations require companies that make such products to use the Draize test to ensure that their products are safe for human use.

The Draize test may be on the way out, however. Guidelines issued by the U.S. government in 1980 stipulated that acids and other known irritants should not be tested in animals' eyes, and in December 1980, Revlon, Incorporated, a major cosmetics firm, under pressure from a coalition of humane societies, announced a $750,000 grant to Rockefeller University in New York City for the development of an eye-irritancy test that does not involve animals.

Another toxicity test used by the manufacturers of countless household products, from paint thinners to window cleaners, results in even greater animal suffering than the Draize test. Known as LD-50, it is designed to test the effects of swallowing or inhaling these products, or absorbing them through the skin. It determines what concentration of a given product is high enough to kill half of a group of laboratory animals tested — in other words, the Lethal Dose for 50 per cent. This test destroys thousands of laboratory mice and rats each year. Scientists have come to question its value, because the effect of a substance on a rodent is not likely to be the same as its effect on a human. Like the Draize test, LD-50 may also be replaced by a test conducted on human cell cultures rather than on live animals, or with procedures using fewer animals.

One such test that has alleviated a great deal of animal suffering is the Ames test, developed by biochemist Bruce Ames of the University of California, Berkeley, in 1975. The test involves adding a particular substance to a culture of *Salmonella* bacteria. If a certain number of bacteria show significant genetic changes or mutations, the substance is considered carcinogenic, or capable of causing cancer. The Ames test has shown itself to be remarkably accurate when used with known human carcinogens such as coal tars. It has eliminated procedures in which scientists injected varying doses of a suspected carcinogen into mice and waited to see a significant number develop tumors. It is both faster and less expensive than using laboratory animals in preliminary procedures and requires fewer animals for subsequent tests.

Industry is not alone in its abuse of animals in product testing. The United States military, in developing a "rubber bullet" for riot control, bombarded baboons with water-filled ping-pong balls. The baboons were anesthetized and strapped into chairs. They were then hit on the front, sides, and back of the head with the missiles. Those who were severely injured were killed immediately and autopsies performed to assess the degree of damage inflicted, but the others were put back into cages to allow the anesthesia to wear off. As they regained consciousness, the baboons crouched in pain without the benefit of as much as an aspirin to relieve what must have been an unimaginable headache.

Theoretically, baboons are protected from such suffering by the Animal Welfare Act of 1966, which stipulates that such research animals should receive adequate veterinary care and be given anesthetics and analgesics during surgery or painful procedures. However, one clause in the act virtually nullifies these provisions. It states that drugs need not be given if administering them might interfere with the experiment. Supposedly, those in charge of the project needed to

Poultry and livestock
suffer undue stress when
kept in poorly designed
facilities. Egg-laying
hens in battery cages
have their beaks blunted
to keep them from
injuring each other.
Cattle herded through
slatted chutes, *above
right,* may balk at
shadows and other
distractions and injure
themselves. But curved,
opaque-walled chutes,
above, with no tight
turns, give them a sense
of security and make
them easier to herd.

witness the animals in pain to determine that the rubber bullets had
been truly effective.

The use of animals in medical research is also regulated by a set of
guidelines set forth by the National Institutes of Health (NIH) in
Bethesda, Md. The NIH guidelines, last revised in 1978 and essentially the same as the provisions of the Animal Welfare Act, stipulate
specific conditions for the care, feeding, and housing of laboratory
animals, prohibit unnecessary suffering, and detail methods of humane killing. Scientists who receive government grants for research
must agree to abide by these guidelines. Their grant applications are
screened by panels of scientists, and may be rejected if the proposed
research does not promise any significant advance in human health or
scientific knowledge. In essence, the scientists must determine whether the possible benefits to society of a given research project will
justify the degree of animal suffering involved. In my opinion, introducing a new color of eye shadow does not justify injuring rabbits'
eyes, although the development of the heart pacemaker did justify
years of preliminary tests — many of them unsuccessful — on many
animals, including primates.

Pigs on factory farms may live out their lives confined in steel and concrete stalls, *left,* even though pigs allowed to move about freely, *below left,* have healthier young and produce better meat.

The rights of farm animals, on the whole, have not received as much attention and concern as have those of laboratory animals. Aside from general protection under state anticruelty laws, farm animals are protected only by the Humane Slaughter Act and the Livestock Transportation Act. Farmers can be prosecuted under anticruelty statutes for abusing or neglecting their stock, but these laws are difficult to enforce against large-scale industrialized systems of livestock production. Thus, while it would be illegal to keep dogs or cats confined to quarters so narrow that they cannot turn around, sows and veal calves are commonly kept under such conditions in many factory-farm operations.

On many pig farms, breeding sows are kept in narrow stalls, some chained to concrete slats on the floor, often for several years. They eat, sleep, and may be artificially inseminated in the pens — leaving them only long enough to give birth. Similarly, veal calves are taken from their mothers at birth and live their 15 to 16 weeks of life chained and alone in dark, narrow stalls. They are fed twice a day on a milk formula purposely deficient in iron so that the calf will become anemic and produce the highly prized white meat. (Healthy calves

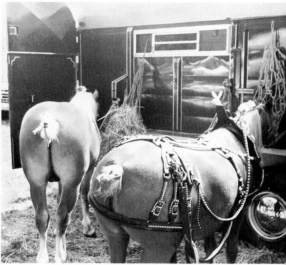

Many animals are mutilated in the name of sport or grooming. The black cock draws blood from the white in a "sporting" fight to the death, *top left*. Cropped tails deprive show horses of their only weapon against flies, *top right*. A Doberman pinscher, *above,* is swathed in bandages after an ear-docking operation that is cosmetic, but quite painful.

produce some red meat.) They are given no straw bedding because, in exercising their natural impulse to chew, they might eat some of it, which would darken their meat.

Many justifications have been offered for such extreme violation of farm-animal rights, the most common being that it is both easier and cheaper to raise animals in smaller spaces. However, there are alternative systems that do not violate the animal's basic rights and are nonetheless productive and profitable. One of the largest veal producers in Great Britain has abandoned the system of keeping veal calves isolated in single pens and now houses them in communal pens of 20 to 30 calves. The pens are equipped with straw bedding and milk dispensers that the calves can suck whenever they wish. This system is more profitable, and the calves are healthier, requiring only half as much veterinary treatment as did calves that were isolated in separate pens.

A study reported by J. L. Albright of Purdue University in West Lafayette, Ind., in 1978 indicated that even a simple improvement in a cow's quarters can yield a striking increase in productivity. Albright's study showed that cows moved from concrete to dirt floors gave an average of 1.4 kilograms (1.5 quarts) more milk each day; had 55 per cent fewer cases of clinical mastitis, an inflammation of the udders; and suffered 56 per cent fewer leg and foot injuries.

While the veal calf and the sow, both highly social animals, spend their lifetime in solitary confinement, the lot of the chicken is just the reverse. Approximately 90 per cent of the eggs sold in the United States come from laying hens kept in so-called battery cages — 30- by 45-centimeter (12- by 18-inch) wire boxes shared with three or four other birds. The cage mates have no perches and are continually at war for standing room. Even though their beaks have been blunted by burning them with a hot iron, they still injure and sometimes kill one another as they fight for space.

The reason for the overcrowded cages is obvious. It is easier to maintain, clean, and collect eggs from one large henhouse lined with cages than from 30 to 40 small coops, each housing hens free to perch and lay eggs wherever they choose. Yet the hens' condition could be improved substantially by a relatively minor change in cage design. A study conducted in Canada indicated that merely providing perches improved the birds' overall condition and increased the productivity of laying hens.

The stress of living in crowded conditions or in confinement is considerable, and it increases as farm animals are sent to market. Stress accounts for more than $1 billion in annual losses due to bruising, sickness, or death as animals are shipped to or held for slaughter. Some $50 million of this amount is due to losses from bruises inflicted shortly before slaughter as the animals are slammed against the sides of trucks, stumble down loading ramps, or fight for space in crowded pens. Bruised meat is inedible and must be cut from the carcass before it is sold.

Some simple engineering has helped to reduce bruising and other injuries. Temple Grandin, a livestock-handling consultant from Tempe, Ariz., has designed systems for transporting and housing slaughter-bound livestock. Her designs — based on the individual species' perception of distance, response to fear, and need for personal space — blend common sense with sophisticated engineering techniques. Grandin has taken photographs of chutes and holding pens at steer's-eye, sheep's-eye, and pig's-eye levels and has used them to detect and eliminate distractions that might not be noticeable to humans. For example, photographs may reveal shadows of fence rails that startle livestock, causing them to balk as they pass through the chute. The shadows can be eliminated by lining the fences with an opaque material, giving the illusion of solid walls and providing the animals with a sense of security. To relieve transportation injuries, she has designed ramps that slope gently up to truck doors. The doors have rounded edges to prevent cattle from bruising themselves as they enter the vehicle.

Grandin has also proposed solutions to one of the greatest causes of bruising — fights among animals. Unacquainted pigs and cows often fight to establish dominance, but fighting can be eliminated by segregating animals into groups that have been raised together and have already established a social hierarchy. These animals will also fight for space, however, and may actually do battle over a spot near a wall or fence even when the center of the pen is deserted. Because wall space is so highly prized, Grandin suggests long narrow pens to satisfy the animals' personal-space requirements and reduce fighting.

Grandin and other researchers have also found that many animals are bruised by rough herding practices in which pigs are struck with

A red fox, snared in a fur-trader's steel leg trap, helplessly awaits its fate.

sticks, sheep are grabbed by the leg wool, and animals' noses or heads are jabbed with electric cattle prods. She proposes using soft canvas slappers to herd pigs, noisemakers to guide sheep, and a simple plastic bag attached to a pole to shoo cattle into pens.

Grandin's studies also showed that diffused lighting and soft music in holding pens helped to calm animals. She recommends that the music be piped at a slightly higher volume into the chutes that lead the animals to the slaughter, to mask the sounds of the slaughterhouse. Like humans, livestock respond well to a gentle touch, low lights, and soft music.

Grandin's proposed changes in livestock-handling systems not only provide more humane conditions for the animals, but also improve the efficiency of moving them from holding pens to slaughter. Moreover, these changes can be made relatively easily and inexpensively in existing facilities.

As with farm and laboratory animals, the law grants pets the right to humane treatment and decent care. However, many of their other natural rights have been exchanged for the comforts of home. Their right to reproduce is restricted by the need for pet-population control; their need to roam free is limited for public safety and the possibility of their being injured in traffic; and their right to bark or caterwaul without restraint must be balanced against the neighbors' right to peace and quiet. Because we have deprived our pets of so many of their natural rights, we must take special care to preserve those that they can still enjoy — the right to play and affection, exercise, training, medical care, a balanced diet, and — when the time eventually comes — to a humane death.

Even these remaining rights are often needlessly violated. Breeders of thoroughbred animals perpetuate genetic disorders to keep pedigrees pure. Thus, German shepherds are plagued by hip disorders and bulldogs by breathing difficulties. Other animals may be mutilated in the name of good grooming or convenience. Cropping dogs' ears — one of the most sensitive parts of the puppy's body — to make the ears stand upright is a common practice in the United States but it is outlawed in Great Britain. Cats are often declawed when a simple scratching post would allow them to experience the pleasure of scratching without destroying furniture. The owners of some dogs may choose to have their pets' vocal cords severed to prevent them from barking, when an effective training program might accomplish the same purpose.

In a sense, pets have also become products of industry. Millions of pet animals are bred and sold every year. One of the pet industry's most questionable innovations is the so-called puppy mill — a breeding farm that produces puppies in confinement systems similar to those used on livestock farms. Dogs raised in puppy mills are kept in small cages, deprived of normal contact with other dogs and humans, and do not get enough exercise. Most are shipped to pet shops in shopping malls, where they are held in equally small cages and may be teased by shoppers. By the time they are sold, these dogs are likely to be psychologically as well as physically stunted and they may make very poor pets.

Pet shops may also sell wild animals that have been captured or bred in captivity, such as fox cubs and raccoons. In contrast to domesticated animals like cats and dogs, which have been selectively bred over many generations, these species do not adapt well as pets. They usually make poor companions and are difficult to control, to feed properly, and to treat when they are sick.

I knew a family who adopted an orphan raccoon cub that they named Bandit. As a baby, Bandit was a wonderful pet. He was friendly and affectionate and would ride around the neighborhood on the children's shoulders. However, as he reached maturity, Bandit became more difficult to live with. He raided the closets, tore up books, and killed the family's pet canary. Finally, Bandit had to be taken back into the mountains and set free. To this day, the family wonders whether Bandit was able to survive in the wilds after growing up in captivity.

Our treatment of animals — be they wild or tame, laboratory animals, livestock, or house pets — reflects the attitudes and values of our society. While we once held the view that animals existed only for our use, we are coming to recognize that we should protect them rather than exploit them. We are beginning to assume this responsibility for practical as well as ethical reasons, because we have found that humane treatment of animals can produce psychological, economic, and scientific benefits. Animals make more satisfying pets when they are cared for responsibly; laboratory animals provide more accurate data when they are treated humanely; and farm animals raised under less stressful conditions yield greater profits for producers. We are beginning to see that by protecting animal rights we can benefit humanity as well.

Archaeologists in Wet Suits

By George F. Bass

The scientific search for sunken treasure calls for special techniques to collect facts about ancient ships and the people who ran them

Pig bones? What were more than a dozen pig bones doing on a ship that may have been manned by a Muslim crew? Would Muslim sailors 950 years ago have ignored the teachings of the Koran, Islam's sacred book, and eaten pork? I was faced with a puzzle.

I reread archaeologist Gail Carlson's detailed account of the dozens of animal bones that my staff and I had brought up from a medieval shipwreck lying 34 meters (112 feet) deep in Serçe Liman, a natural harbor on Turkey's southwest coast. Carlson, an American at the British Institute of Archaeology in Ankara, specializes in identifying animal remains. She wrote that her identification of the pig bones was "positive." When she made her report in 1979, at the beginning of our third and final summer of excavation, the nationality of the ship was unknown. We are still not sure of it.

Those broken and discolored bones we found on the floor of the Mediterranean Sea are as valuable to me as the filigreed gold jewelry, silver rings, and intricately engraved glassware we also found on the wreck. (All of these artifacts, incidentally, have remained in Turkey). I value them all equally as clues to the mysteries of a voyage that ended in tragedy about A.D. 1025. It is my job as excavation director, often working with reports written by specialists like Carlson, to solve such mysteries of underwater archaeology.

At many points in this research project — which I expect to continue for many years — we have been "certain" that the ship was operated by Islamic people. But then a new look at the evidence would suggest that the officers and crew might have been Greek Christians. The Byzantine Empire ruled various lands along the Mediterranean, including Greece and Turkey, from the A.D. 300s to 1453, and Christianity was the state religion. Muslims, based in the Near East and Middle East, battled the Christians of the Byzantine Empire for control of the area for hundreds of years.

The ship's nationality is of special importance historically, because we think it is the earliest known example of a seagoing vessel built in the modern manner. The remains of the wooden hull show us that the ship's builder fastened stem and sternpost to the ends of a keel, then constructed a skeleton of frames, or ribs, onto which he nailed the ship's side planks. This is the sequence shipbuilders follow today. Earlier Greek and Roman shipwrights built ships quite differently. They constructed hulls without skeletons, or interior framing, by fastening side planks edge to edge with hundreds of individual mortise-and-tenon joints. The tenon was a small piece of wood that fitted into mortises — or slots — carved in the two planks. In early ships, at least through the A.D. 300s, pegs were pounded through the plank and tenon to hold them together. Shipbuilders then attached frames to the insides of the hull to strengthen it. By about 600, shipbuilders refined the basic structure by eliminating the pegs and nailing the planks to frames.

No one knows who first built the new type of hull we found at Serçe Liman, the type that carried explorers, traders, and colonists across the Atlantic Ocean from Europe to North America and around the world. Slowly, we are piecing together the picture of how modern hulls evolved from earlier Greek and Roman hulls. But shipbuilding archaeology is still a relatively new science.

People have been dredging shipwrecks from the sea for centuries — often damaging them and scattering or destroying their artifacts in the process. Their efforts have been destructive, whether their intentions were to reclaim a ship of historic importance or to recover valuable gold treasures.

Underwater archaeology became a serious scientific discipline only in the early 1960s. I began my underwater work then with American journalist Peter Throckmorton, an amateur archaeologist. At that

The author:
George F. Bass is president of the Institute of Nautical Archaeology and Alumni Professor of Anthropology at Texas A&M University in College Station.

time, divers who were not archaeologists were working underwater around the world.

Like archaeologists who work on land, those who work underwater must study each site in detail. An underwater site is usually a shipwreck; a land site is often a village or part of one. Archaeologists photograph and map the site, and make notes on what it looks like and where the artifacts are positioned. They construct metal mapping grids that divide the site into identifiable working areas. Then they remove each item for study, carefully recording the grid in which it was found. By establishing dates for the items and comparing the site with other known sites, archaeologists can draw conclusions about what life was like for early peoples.

Underwater archaeology gives us the chance to paint a portrait on a much larger canvas, however. We study each ship to find out what it carried and where it was going, of course. But we also look for valuable clues to what was going on elsewhere in the world. Ships were the main form of transportation in world trade for thousands of years. So the artifacts we find on a ship may tell us about trading patterns, customs, and culture.

I became involved in diving and underwater work more or less by accident. I was a graduate archaeology student at the University of Pennsylvania in Philadelphia in 1959, specializing in the Mediterranean Bronze Age, the period between about 3000 and 1000 B.C. Department Chairman Rodney S. Young asked if I would learn to dive in order to direct the excavation of a Bronze Age shipwreck Throckmorton had just discovered at Cape Gelidonya in Turkey. I had learned how to dig on land as a student assistant on excavations in Turkey and Greece, but I had no experience underwater.·

The shipwreck that Throckmorton and I excavated at Cape Gelidonya in 1960 was the first to be excavated entirely on the seabed. We

A shipwreck at Serçe Liman, Turkey, *top left,* yielded ancient treasures that included the rusted hilt of a Greek Byzantine sword, *top right,* and Islamic weights used on a scale, *above,* that date to about A.D. 1025.

An underwater archaeologist prepares to remove remains of the ship's wooden hull from the seabed, *right,* after marking the area with grid squares so that all pieces can be identified. Student Sheila Matthews then traces each piece on plastic, *below.* Her tracings are used to build a scale model of the wreck, *bottom.*

were determined to work as precisely at a depth of 30 meters (100 feet) as we would on dry land. We mapped the site in minute detail as we removed the ship's cargo of scrap bronze and copper ingots from the thick rock that had built up around them. Then we carried the pieces to the surface.

At that time, our methods of mapping with measuring tapes and handheld underwater cameras were primitive but accurate. I was concerned about some of the problems involved in working at great depths, however. The main problem was the inconvenience of having to use hoses for our air supply. Divers must breathe compressed air to keep from being crushed by the weight, or pressure, of the surrounding water. As the diver breathes compressed air, the nitrogen in the air dissolves in the blood. The longer the diver is underwater, the more nitrogen enters the bloodstream. When the diver ascends, he must do so gradually, making scheduled stops to permit the nitrogen to reconvert to its gaseous form and be eliminated through breathing. Otherwise, he is in danger of getting the bends, or decompression sickness, a paralyzing illness that can kill its victims. Throckmorton and I could work underwater only an hour or so a day on our first expedition.

Despite the difficulties in diving, we found stone, pottery, and metal artifacts on the Cape Gelidonya wreck that added to our knowledge of the Bronze Age. Intrigued by my first experience with underwater antiquities, I took up the challenge of developing better methods for working underwater.

During a 13-year period from 1961 to 1974, I experimented with underwater techniques on two shipwrecks off Yassi Ada, a small Turkish island. One wreck dated to the A.D. 300s; the other, to about A.D. 625. We experimented with various underwater techniques as we worked. Some of our techniques were variations on other techniques developed by commercial divers. We also experimented with different types of metal for mapping grids and with the size of the grid squares. We learned to secure metal grid pipes by driving stakes into the seabed and fastening the grid to the stakes with wires. We also designed and tested metal photographic stands on which we could place the cameras used to record the site.

We developed many techniques ourselves. For example, we had built a submersible decompression chamber in which divers can rise slowly to the surface in dry comfort, and we evolved a mapping technique that imitates the aerial surveyor's art by making three-dimensional maps from stereophotographs. Archaeology student Michael Katzev invented an underwater "telephone booth," since adopted by the United States Navy and several commercial diving concerns. It allows divers to stand inside an air-filled plastic dome and talk to one another or to workers on the surface by telephone. This is helpful for on-the-spot communication, and it also gives the diver a convenient way to get fresh air in an emergency without having to resurface. Perhaps our ultimate device was the *Asherah,* a two-person submarine launched in 1964 that we used to inspect and map shipwrecks with stereocameras. Using sonar, we had located a wreck more than 100 kilometers (100 miles) west of Serçe Liman on the Turkish coast at a depth of 91 meters (300 feet), too deep for us to work safely with normal compressed-air diving equipment. We used the *Asherah* to explore the site. We learned enough to know that we want to excavate the wreck in the future.

By the late 1960s, we had developed a standard system for studying wrecks as deep as 46 meters (150 feet). First, we remove sea growth from visible cargo, often using ordinary scrubbing brushes. Next, we build a scaffolding of angle iron or plastic tubing over the site to divide it into a grid of manageable 2-meter (6.5-foot) squares, which are then labeled for identification. We draw and photograph the artifacts in place, label the artifacts for identification, and excavate the squares one at a time.

We raise the artifacts to the surface in wire baskets attached to lifting balloons. To fill the balloons, we use air tanks or run a hose to an air supply on the surface. Our larger balloons can lift about 907 kilograms (2,000 pounds).

The wooden hull parts that we find have been buried by shifting sand or mud. The rest of the hull, unprotected by this covering, was destroyed long ago by shipworms and other small animal borers, which thrive in warm salt water. The remains of the wooden hull are fragile and need special handling. We begin by gently fanning away the protective sand. Often we pin the hull fragments to the seabed with sharpened bicycle spokes so the pieces cannot float while we label them and record their location on the site map.

Frederick H. van Doorninck, Jr., my colleague and an archaeologist with the Institute of Nautical Archaeology (INA) in College

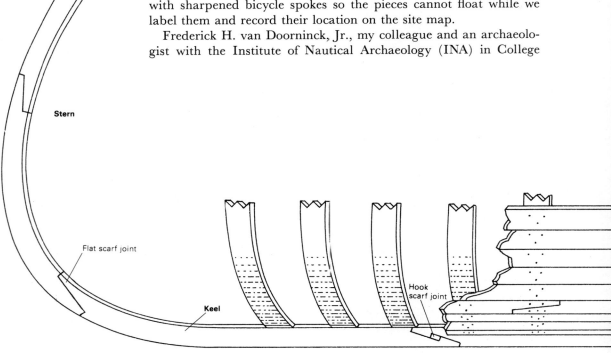

Stern

Flat scarf joint

Keel

Hook scarf joint

Station, Tex., has studied the fragile wood from our wrecks. He has demonstrated that ancient ships can be reconstructed accurately on paper even if we find only scanty remains on the seabed. His reconstructions showed us that the change in ship construction from ancient to modern times came about very slowly, over several hundred years. Shipbuilders gradually depended less and less on mortise-and-tenon joints for strength, and made the joints smaller and farther apart. The Yassi Ada ship of around A.D. 625 was built in the more ancient "shell-first" manner only up to about the water line, then the frames were inserted and fastened in place. Above the water line, the planks were simply nailed to these frames without any type of joining. We suspect that this change, a technical improvement, was also made for economic reasons. The new method required less labor, so it was considerably cheaper.

A new research field was growing up around us. Van Doorninck and I were joined, informally at first, by J. Richard Steffy. Steffy was an electrical contractor, but his great love since boyhood has been wooden ships, and he spent his vacations visiting and working in libraries, shipyards, and naval museums. After reading a magazine article about our work, he wrote to me, offering to build a research model of the Yassi Ada ship from about 625 in order to test and refine our theories.

Steffy eventually built a series of ship models, each one to establish a specific point. He eventually left his business in order to help Katzev

A cast of the ship's anchor was made from an impression left in sand and rock. The anchor itself had rusted away long ago.

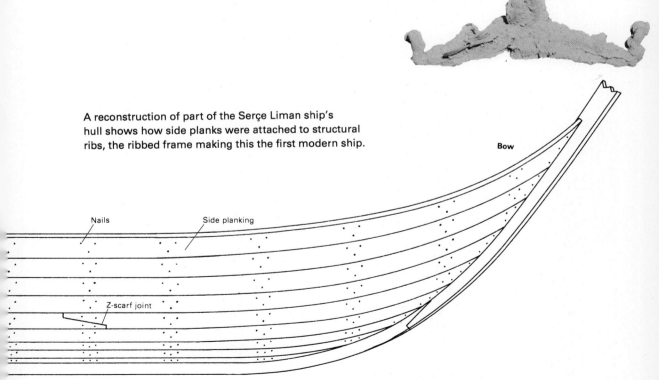

A reconstruction of part of the Serçe Liman ship's hull shows how side planks were attached to structural ribs, the ribbed frame making this the first modern ship.

Bow

Nails

Side planking

Z-scarf joint

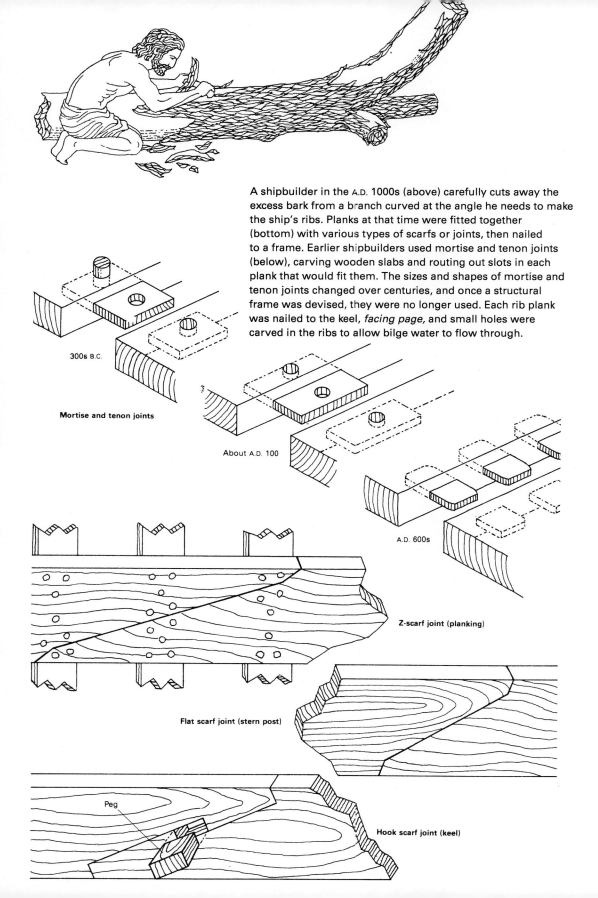

A shipbuilder in the A.D. 1000s (above) carefully cuts away the excess bark from a branch curved at the angle he needs to make the ship's ribs. Planks at that time were fitted together (bottom) with various types of scarfs or joints, then nailed to a frame. Earlier shipbuilders used mortise and tenon joints (below), carving wooden slabs and routing out slots in each plank that would fit them. The sizes and shapes of mortise and tenon joints changed over centuries, and once a structural frame was devised, they were no longer used. Each rib plank was nailed to the keel, *facing page,* and small holes were carved in the ribs to allow bilge water to flow through.

300s B.C.

Mortise and tenon joints

About A.D. 100

A.D. 600s

Z-scarf joint (planking)

Flat scarf joint (stern post)

Peg

Hook scarf joint (keel)

A scale-model replica of the hull, *right,* is made to determine how the ship was built.

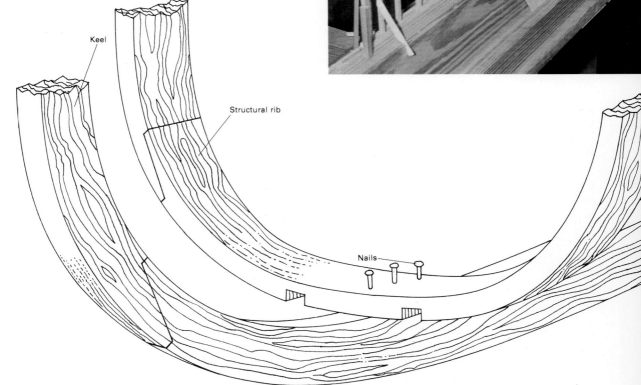

Keel

Structural rib

Nails

restore a 2,300-year-old Greek ship that Katzev had excavated off the island of Cyprus in the late 1960s.

I left the University of Pennsylvania in 1973 to form INA, an institute devoted to the history of seafaring and later affiliated with Texas A&M University. Katzev, Steffy, Van Doorninck, and a few other colleagues soon joined me on the INA staff.

Although I had not become a true hull expert, I was anxious to find wrecks that might show when, where, how, and why the final transition to modern skeletal hull construction took place. By good fortune, Turkish sponge diver Mehmet Ashkin in 1973 showed me a scattering of broken glass that he found on the floor of Serçe Liman. I dived in the area and brought up from the deep sand an amphora, an ancient two-handled storage jar. I sent a photograph of the find to archaeologist Virginia Grace, an amphora specialist at the American School of Classical Studies in Athens, Greece. Grace dated the jar by its shape to the A.D. 1000s.

It is risky to start work on a site — to raise funds, assemble staff and equipment in a distant land, and build a camp and work facilities for up to 45 persons — on the strength of scanty archaeological evidence. But in this case, the glass and especially the date, which represents an apparently critical but little-known period in the history of ships, were enough for me. We decided to commit ourselves and began a full-scale excavation of the site in 1977.

The wreck proved to be well preserved and rich in artifacts. We traced the outline of a ship about 16 meters (52 feet) long lying on its port, or left, side with a pair of Y-shaped anchors at the bow. Six spare anchors had been stored in the forward part of the hold.

A small gold ornament, possibly an earring, found at the Serçe site suggests women may have been aboard, or merchants were carrying jewelry to trade or as gift offerings for merchants they hoped to do business with.

When we began to examine the wreck's artifacts, we found many indications that the ship had been manned by Muslims. The wreck contained ceramic tableware, including bowls glazed in imitation of Chinese T'ang dynasty pottery, which was popular in Islamic nations, and ceramic jugs that probably came from Egypt. We also found about 80 intact glass vessels — cups, bowls, bottles, pitchers, and tumblers — from living quarters at the bow and stern. This was probably cargo being exported by merchants, rather than shipboard tableware. The shapes and engraved decorations of these pieces are typical of medieval Islamic glassware.

In the center of the wreck, we uncovered a solid mass of sharp glass fragments that sliced our fingers when we first tried to extract it. Eventually, we broke much of the mass into lumps weighing up to 45 kilograms (100 pounds) and carried them to the surface. In our lab in Turkey, we separated each lump into hundreds of glass shards. We placed the glass in plastic bags, each labeled with its position on the wreck within 50 centimeters (20 inches). Eventually, we had about a ton of shards stored in 2,000 bags. Cleaning the shards required weeks of rinsing to remove the seawater salt. Then we dried them slowly, over a period of many months.

Two castles or rooks were among the chess pieces found in the Serçe Liman shipwreck.

Careful inspection showed that this broken glass was a collection of factory rejects and domestic sweepings—probably destined to be reused. It demonstrated clearly that recycling materials is a time-honored idea. The glass was placed in the ship's hold, perhaps in baskets, and then tamped down and crushed into still smaller pieces so that it would take up less space. Bases of some broken vases show signs of long use. However, we think that other pieces were warped during manufacture and discarded. The styles, shapes, and designs of these pieces also seemed to be Islamic. Mixed in with this glass were about 1.8 metric tons (2 short tons) of cullet, chunks of raw glass ranging from tiny slivers to jagged blocks up to 50 centimeters (19 inches) long.

The tableware and broken glass were not the only clues suggesting that the ship had carried an Islamic crew and cargo. We also found a terra-cotta, or clay, oil lamp of a known Arab type and a pair of copper buckets, one bearing an Arabic inscription.

The cargo provided other clues, however, that led away from the idea of an Islamic ship. There were nearly 100 terra-cotta amphoras on board, probably once filled with wine. And these jars are inscribed with Byzantine Greek letters that, in some cases, spell Greek names. Were Greek merchants traveling on the ship?

We also found four Byzantine *bullae*—lead disks pierced with holes for string and used by merchants to seal documents or packages. After a package was tied, the ends of the string were run through the hole. The disk was then pressed onto the string with giant pliers, not only sealing the package but also leaving an impression in the soft metal. One of the bullae we found is blank, but two others bear impressions of Greek letters and Christian religious scenes. One depicts the Virgin Mary holding the Christ child, and the other shows the meeting of Saint Peter and Saint Paul. Were Muslim and Christian merchants traveling together peacefully on the ship during this time of Arab-Byzantine hostility?

We plan to pinpoint the national origin of the glass cargo in greater detail, but we have scarcely begun mending the half-million or more fragments. Six of us worked on the glass from 1979 to 1980 at the Bodrum Museum of Underwater Archaeology in Bodrum, Turkey, which houses finds from the wreck. We first wrote identifying numbers on the fragments and then sorted them into 18 categories based on color, thickness, and type of decoration. Each category was then

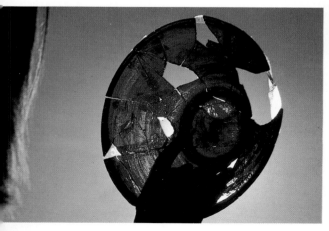

Archaeologists sort glass fragments by color in a laboratory in Bodrum, Turkey, *above,* as the first step in rebuilding some of the artifacts, *left.* A fragile glass jar, *above, near left,* is one of several pieces that survived intact. Graduate student Netia Piercy re-creates designs from fragments of decorated pottery bowls, *top left,* while graduate student Jay Rosloff separates fragments from a jumbled mass of glass, *above, far left.*

broken down into subcategories. For example, all plain purple shards were separated from the rest. Then, darker and lighter purple fragments were separated from one another. Dark purple was next divided into varying shades. Eventually, we had manageable groups of similar shards and we could look for matching pieces from single vessels. At the end of that year, we had put together parts of about 100 new types of vessels, yet we had studied less than one-tenth of the glass from the wreck.

When we have mended, drawn, photographed, and cataloged all the types of vessels found on the wreck, we will compare their shapes and decorations to those that have already been presented in publications and museums. However, noting similar pieces in Egypt, for example, will not necessarily mean that Egypt was the source of our cargo. Glassmakers traveled widely throughout the medieval Islamic world, manufacturing identical types in such countries as Egypt, Persia (now Iran), and Syria.

It has been suggested that chemical analyses of our glass might help identify its source, but the nature of the Serçe Liman cargo indicates how questionable the uses of such analyses are. Our cargo proves that broken glass was shipped from country to country as material for new items. In this way, a bottle blown in Syria, perhaps by an itinerant Egyptian glassmaker, could be made from glass originally manufactured in Persia. However, I believe that chemical analysis of the cullet — the unused raw glass — might prove more useful in determining the ship's route.

We looked at other clues that might tell us where the ship came from. Money found on board did not help us, because we found gold coins that were minted in Islamic nations, as well as copper Byzantine coins.

We identified 16 glass weights, small disks of varying weights that were used on balance-pan scales to estimate the weight of precious materials, such as the flakes of gold we found on the wreck. Fourteen weights bear Arabic inscriptions. Michael Bates, curator of Islamic coins at the American Numismatic Society in New York City, identified our weights from photographs and plaster casts we had made of them in 1977 and 1978, and translated their Arabic inscriptions. The inscription on each weight gives the name of the Egyptian ruler — three reigns are represented — and the year in which it was made. Bates dated three weights to 1024-1025, or possibly 1021-1022, and found none later than that.

We estimate that this ship sank about 1025 because the latest dated coins and glass weights are from that year, and there seems to be nothing more recent on the wreck. Written documents of that time describe the capture of an Arab ship by Byzantine pirates only a few years earlier and a few kilometers away. Could the Serçe Liman ship have suffered a similar fate? Weapons may eventually help us provide an answer.

We found evidence of 7 or 8 swords, 7 lances, and about 50 javelins. But all except a single bronze sword hilt were made completely of iron, so they rusted away long ago. Luckily, the weapons were covered with rock and sand soon after they sank to the bottom. The rock and sand thickened into hard, accurate molds of the weapons corroding inside. In the laboratory, we can break open, clean, and fill each cast with liquid rubber, which hardens into a perfect replica of the original sword or lance.

Some of the best detective work on the weapons — and in other areas — is done by students in my seminar on medieval seafaring at Texas A&M University. For example, Joseph Schwarzer recently wrote a controversial but convincing paper tentatively identifying the bronze sword hilt as Byzantine by its shape and style of decoration. He plans to identify the other weapons on board, comparing them with known artifacts from the 1000s. The weapons are of great importance in understanding the ship's origin.

Steffy and Van Doorninck must wait for the slow processes of conservation before they can complete their restoration of the ship's hull. Waterlogged wood cannot be taken directly from the sea for study and museum display because its cells have been filled with seawater over the years. When the hull remains are raised into the air, unprotected waterlogged wood shrinks and warps beyond recognition as the water inside the cells evaporates and the cells collapse. The wood then falls apart.

Working in our lab in Turkey for more than a year, Texas A&M graduate student Sheila Matthews temporarily removed each piece of wood from the tank of water where the remains were kept. She then traced each piece at full scale with grease pencils on sheets of clear plastic. She used color-coded markings to indicate bolt-holes, nail holes, tool marks, cuttings, damage by marine life, and stains. As soon as Matthews finished working on a piece of wood, she returned it to its water bath.

A number of conservation methods have been devised for waterlogged wood. We use polyethylene glycol (PEG) in the most common and time-honored treatment. We dissolve the PEG, a water-soluble petroleum product, in a tank of water and place the waterlogged wood in the tank in our lab in Turkey. We carefully monitor the wood over the months or years required for it to become saturated with the water containing the dissolved PEG. When the wood is removed from the solution and it begins to dry, the PEG hardens so that the cells hold their original shape.

The PEG treatment of the wood on the Serçe Liman hull began in 1980 and took slightly more than a year to complete. But research on the hull continued in both Texas and Turkey, even while the wood was being treated.

At INA headquarters at Texas A&M, Steffy used the tracings made by Matthews and the site map in 1979 to construct a three-dimensional wooden model on a scale of 1 to 10 of the wreck as it lay on the harbor bottom. This model allows us to see the entire wreck, which was not possible on the seabed.

Steffy then began a sort of dress rehearsal for his eventual reassembly of the conserved wood in Turkey, where he will fasten the thousands of fragments together with stainless steel wire. After carving replicas of all of the fragments to scale, he has begun the long, slow process of fitting them together as they were on the ship to determine the hull's shape and dimensions. He will use this model to draw up plans of the ship and to write formal descriptions for other experts to examine and review.

In the process of reproducing the hull, Steffy will learn a lot about the working habits of a shipwright from the Middle Ages. For example, Steffy has already learned that the shipwright used tree limbs of about the same size — curved at about the same angle — for the ship's ribs.

This look at real people who lived in ancient times often gives us the greatest satisfaction. Kenneth Cassavoy, one of our students, identified small, crudely carved pieces of wood as part of a chess set. A backgammon piece was found, too, so we can imagine the crew or passengers playing these games in their leisure hours. We also hope to determine more exactly the areas where the crew and passengers lived, to get a complete picture of shipboard life.

From 900 lead net weights found in two clusters, we can picture the crew fishing to supplement the ship's diet. A plate found in 1977 still held fishbones, perhaps from a final shipboard meal. Did the diner also eat the nuts and fruits whose seeds we found, or were they only cargo? Where was he from and where was he bound? Did he escape the wreck? Did he leave behind the pouch of jewelry we found? Do women's wooden combs and bone spindle parts for spinning mean that women were on board?

The material we excavated in only three summers of diving will require years of study before we can understand and publish the complete story of this ship. Meanwhile, French colleagues are studying wrecks of a similar type and date off the coast of France.

We have located a wreck off the coast of Turkey that apparently dates from before 1025 — the date of the Serçe Liman wreck we are working on now — but after 625, the date of a ship we excavated at Yassi Ada. We plan to study this wreck in the future, therefore, as a means of increasing our knowledge of the evolution of shipbuilding and of trade on the high seas.

Archaeologists from INA are also exploring sites off the coasts of Maine, Grand Cayman Island, Jamaica, and Kenya. We look forward to examining the evidence from many cultures and many eras. And we think that through underwater archaeology, shipwrecks and other underwater sites will continue to yield fascinating secrets of our common past.

Alcohol: The Friendly Foe

by Robert B. Millman

The favorite drug of millions throughout history, alcohol can warm the heart and sharpen the wit, and create a living hell for its addicts

The patient is a high-ranking bank executive, 50 years old, with a wife and two children, a house in a prosperous suburb of a large city, and a summer home in the country. He tells his doctor he is losing weight, feels chronically tired and depressed, and has difficulty getting his work done at the bank. He does not sleep well, often awaking at 4 or 5 A.M., unable to go back to sleep. He complains of tingling and numbness in his toes and stomach pains.

The doctor's examination shows that he has a ruddy complexion, slightly elevated blood pressure, an enlarged and tender liver, some numbness in his legs, and his hands tremble. Laboratory tests reveal anemia and signs of liver damage. In response to the doctor's questioning, the patient reveals that he has been drinking more heavily lately because of work, family, and health problems. He says he usually buys a pint of vodka on his way to the train in the morning and has his first drink on the train. He then continues to drink small amounts steadily throughout the day until the bottle is empty. He also has several drinks with friends or business associates at lunch, several more in the club car of the train going home in the evening, a cocktail before dinner, and several nightcaps before going to bed.

When the physician suggests that alcohol may be causing some of his problems, the patient angrily denies it. He protests that he is drinking *because* of his problems, that he is not drinking any more than his friends and contemporaries, and that he can stop at any time.

This man is abusing alcohol; his excessive drinking has adversely affected his health and how he functions socially. He is not alone. Between 5 million and 9 million Americans are hooked on the psychoactive drug *ethanol* (ethyl alcohol), the active ingredient of any alcoholic drink. They are high school students and senior citizens, ordinary people and public figures. Rock star or sports star, doctor or

pilot, these men and women share a bond with the skid-row derelict. They are alcoholics. Their personal struggles and tragedies add up to an international problem of enormous proportions.

Although alcoholism may take years to develop, it can strike even the young. A 1978 report by the Department of Health and Human Services estimated that more than 3 million 14- to 17-year-olds in the United States were problem drinkers. Some of these were already alcoholics. Others ran a serious risk of developing the disease.

Alcohol abuse is considered to be the primary cause of more than 200,000 deaths annually in the United States. It is involved in one-third of all suicides, half of all murders and traffic deaths, and up to 40 per cent of all industrial accidents. In recent years, scientists have found alcohol to be the third leading cause of birth defects involving mental retardation. Alcohol-related costs are estimated at more than $50 billion per year in accidents, lost production, medical bills, and other expenses in the United States alone.

Alcohol is the most widely used, most easily obtained, and most socially acceptable of the mind-altering drugs. Its use to heighten pleasure and dull pain probably goes back beyond the beginning of history. Like any drug, it can be abused. Accounts of drunkenness are found in Genesis, the first book of the Bible, and other early writings. The Greek physician Hippocrates, the father of modern medicine, described symptoms of alcohol withdrawal in the 400s B.C.

Most people who drink can handle alcohol reasonably well. But alcohol can become a life-threatening problem for some 10 per cent of the estimated 100 million social drinkers in the United States. And despite many years of scientific research, alcoholism is still a complex, controversial, and poorly understood affliction – part physical, part psychological. Some regard it as a disease; to others, it is a character weakness, or even a sin. Its victims endure more than physical torment and mental anguish, they must suffer the scorn of those, luckier than they, who do not understand.

Many alcoholics do not know they have a problem – at least in the early stages. The banker's refusal to admit that he has a problem with alcohol comes in part from the fact that there is no sharp line that distinguishes the moderate use of alcohol – social drinking – from problem drinking and alcoholism. An early alcoholic also tends to deny his preoccupation with liquor, or attempts to rationalize his need by assertions that he drinks no more than his friends. These denials are often unconscious in the drinker.

Because of conflicting social, cultural, religious, and political perceptions of how people should use this mind-altering drug, it is difficult to define normal drinking in terms of how much people drink. Problem drinking can be defined, however, as use of alcohol in a manner that significantly impairs biological, vocational, or social function. Problem drinking or alcohol abuse varies in intensity from intermittent episodes to the full-blown disease of alcoholism.

The author:
Robert B. Millman is a psychiatrist and clinical professor of public health at Cornell University Medical College in New York City. He specializes in treating drug addiction.

An alcoholic is one who becomes physically dependent on alcohol and overwhelmingly involved in getting and using it. Four clinical features are essential to the diagnosis of alcoholism: loss of control, "craving" or drug-hunger, tolerance, and physical dependence. Loss of control describes the inability to regulate alcohol intake after starting to drink. Many alcoholics tell of occasions when they resolved to have just one drink at a bar with friends, only to remain long after their friends had left, drinking until their money was gone or the bar closed. Others recall buying a bottle of liquor with the intention of having a few drinks, and then finishing the bottle at one sitting. Craving, the continual and overwhelming desire to drink alcohol, occurs whether the alcoholic is drunk or sober. It is marked by dreams about drinking, and ingenious rationalizations that excuse renewed drinking after a period of abstinence.

Tolerance to alcohol results mainly from the relative resistance of central nervous system cells to the effect of a given concentration of alcohol in the blood. Many heavy drinkers and alcoholics can consume large amounts of alcohol without significantly impairing their behavior or coordination. The level of alcohol in their blood may be twice the amount that authorities use as the legal limit in drunk-driving cases, for example. Thus, people who hold their liquor well may just drink too much too often.

Repeatedly using alcohol, or certain other drugs, produces physical dependence. This requires the alcoholic to continue drinking in order to prevent the characteristic symptoms of withdrawal, or abstinence. After a bout of acute intoxication, a person usually suffers a hangover — general discomfort, headache, nausea, diarrhea, agitation, tremulousness, depression, and inability to sleep. Hangovers are similar to the first symptoms of the withdrawal syndrome. Continued heavy drinking for prolonged periods will increase the severity of this syndrome. The drinker's hands begin to tremble as early as six hours after he stops drinking. He may have auditory and visual hallucinations. In severe cases, grand mal seizures similar to major epileptic seizures may occur from 12 to 24 hours after drinking ends. In even more extreme cases, delirium tremens (DTs) may occur, marked by confusion, disorientation, delusions, hallucinations, agitation, and high fever and may culminate in collapse of the heart and other major organ systems. Delirium tremens is a potentially lethal disorder that requires hospitalization and intensive care.

Acute, or short-term, alcohol withdrawal usually occurs when a person suddenly stops drinking after several years of heavy intake. Withdrawal may last four to six days, after which most patients are discharged from the hospital or treatment program. Their physical dependence on alcohol is believed to be over and they are cautioned not to begin drinking again. Unfortunately, most of them relapse to alcohol abuse. Doctors and other observers formerly believed that, once the withdrawal syndrome is over and presumably much of the craving is diminished, people relapse because of moral or psychological weakness, lack of will, or mental illness.

However, recent evidence suggests that a protracted withdrawal stage follows the acute stage. During this period, the patient experiences tremulousness, anxiety, depression, and insomnia. Abnormal brain-wave activity shows up on electroencephalograph readings. During this time — for perhaps as long as six months — some people experience *anhedonia,* the inability to feel pleasure. Scientists do not fully understand these prolonged withdrawal symptoms, but some believe that they may be the basis for persistent alcohol craving and may be important stimuli for the patient to begin drinking again.

Some scientists suggest the existence of a feedback system between nerves and hormones to explain these findings. They point out that if a patient takes a thyroid hormone drug, for example, the body senses that there is sufficient thyroid hormone present and the thyroid gland slows down or stops producing the hormone. Continued use of the hormone drug may cause the gland to atrophy, permanently impairing natural hormone production. The same sort of problem may exist with some neurotransmitters. The neurotransmitters are chemicals that carry nerve messages, such as the dopamines, which are involved in many brain functions, and the endorphins, the morphinelike brain substances discovered independently in the 1970s by several groups, including neuropharmacologist Solomon H. Snyder and his associates at Johns Hopkins University in Baltimore.

Many scientists believe that some neurotransmitters control or moderate emotional states such as calm, optimism, anxiety, or depression. The continued use of alcohol or opiates may turn off the production of certain neurotransmitters by a complex feedback system. For example, alcohol may enhance the power of the neurotransmitter gamma-aminobutyric acid (GABA) to inhibit anxiety.

Personal insecurity, heavy emotional demands by others, and the general pressures of life may help drive some people to seek relief in drinking, *below.* Many teen-agers experiment with alcohol because their friends are doing it, *below right.*

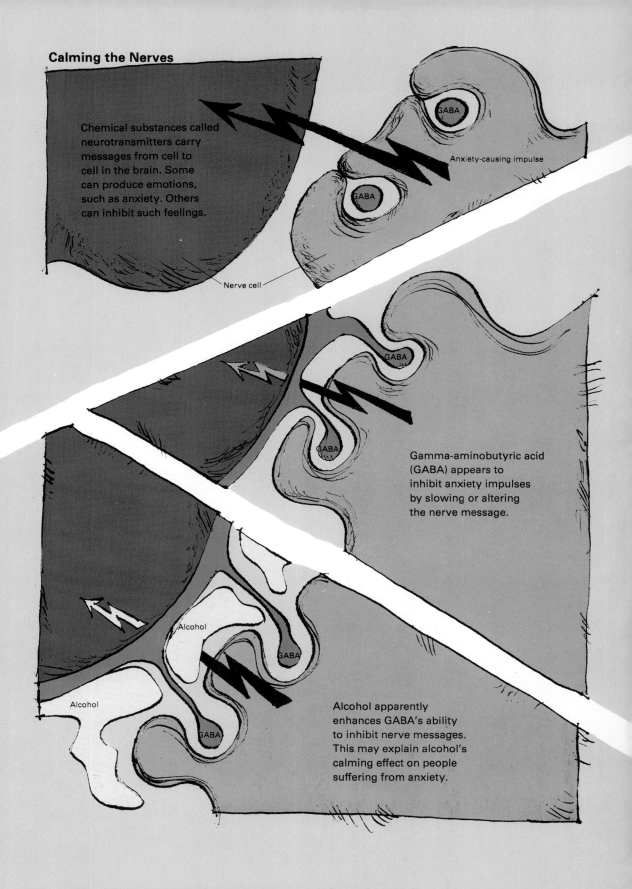

Calming the Nerves

Chemical substances called neurotransmitters carry messages from cell to cell in the brain. Some can produce emotions, such as anxiety. Others can inhibit such feelings.

Anxiety-causing impulse

Nerve cell

Gamma-aminobutyric acid (GABA) appears to inhibit anxiety impulses by slowing or altering the nerve message.

Alcohol apparently enhances GABA's ability to inhibit nerve messages. This may explain alcohol's calming effect on people suffering from anxiety.

A nameless fear seems to surround the alcoholic, paralyzing the will, shattering self-respect, and crushing hope.

Continued heavy drinking may lead to decreased production of GABA. Then, when the drinking stops, the body may be depleted of the transmitters, leading to acute withdrawal. It is also possible that these emotional control systems do not return to normal for long periods of time, leading to protracted withdrawal.

The progression from harmless social drinking to problem drinking varies greatly with individuals. Most people begin drinking in a controlled and social fashion. They then slip imperceptibly, without conscious intent, into excessive drinking. Increased drinking frequently occurs during periods of unusual stress. A person takes a few extra drinks to unwind, to forget, or to sleep. In some cases, repeating this practice leads to both psychological and physical dependence and the compulsive use of alcohol. The bank officer fits this pattern.

The neurological and psychiatric disorders that appear during alcohol withdrawal are only part of the medical cost of excessive drinking. Alcohol affects nearly every system in the body. Its misuse is related to a bewildering number of afflictions, including heart attacks and cancer, muscle deterioration, and anemia. Perhaps the most serious problems occur in the stomach and intestines.

"Use a little wine for thy stomach's sake," wrote Saint Paul in his Epistle to Timothy. It was a counsel of moderation. In excess, alcohol has far-reaching effects, including inflammation and cancer of the esophagus, stomach inflammation, and chronic diarrhea. Alcohol

Unable to cope with
the ordinary events
of daily life at work
or at home, the alcoholic
withdraws, *left*. The
ability to work well
depends on memory,
which alcohol can impair.

abuse causes the small intestine to absorb nutrients poorly, which can lead to vitamin deficiencies and such nutritional diseases as beriberi, pellagra, and scurvy. Fat levels in the blood may be elevated and sugar levels depressed by heavy drinking.

The most common and serious damage occurs in the liver. One major role of this chemical factory, the largest internal organ in the body, is to deactivate drugs and foreign chemicals – including ethanol. An overload of ethanol over a long period of time produces fatty liver, a degeneration of liver tissue. In many cases this can lead to alcoholic hepatitis, a liver inflammation, and cirrhosis, in which scar tissue forms throughout the liver. Cirrhosis is now the fifth leading cause of death in the United States. In fact, the incidence of cirrhosis in various countries appears to be linked closely to rates of alcoholism and alcohol consumption. Epidemiologists Jan DeLint and Wolfgang Schmidt at the Alcohol and Drug Research Foundation in Toronto, Canada, noted an increase in alcohol consumption in the United States between 1950 and the mid-1970s. Cirrhosis deaths, in both males and females, increased during the same years. Cirrhosis of the liver may now be the most rapidly increasing cause of preventable premature death.

Other countries have reported similar findings. France, Portugal, and Italy, where wine is popular, have extremely high per capita alcohol-consumption rates and the highest cirrhosis rates in

the world. Interestingly, Ireland, with a reputation for a high rate of alcoholism, has a low cirrhosis rate and, presumably, the actual alcoholism rate is similarly low.

Biochemist Charles S. Lieber and his co-workers at the Veterans' Administration Hospital in the Bronx, N.Y., reported on the nature of liver damage in chronic alcoholism in November 1977. They administered a nutritious liquid diet to a group of baboons in which alcohol comprised 50 per cent of the total calories. Over a period of nine months to four years, the entire range of liver injuries seen in human alcoholics was produced in the animals. Lieber found that there was a progression from fatty liver to alcoholic hepatitis and alcoholic cirrhosis and that these diseases resulted from the direct toxic effects of alcohol rather than from poor diet, as many had formerly thought.

Use of such animal models may permit researchers to study many of the unsolved problems related to alcohol abuse and addiction, as well as to trace the mechanisms of tissue damage. Research with rat liver cells by pathologist Francis A. X. Schanne and others at Temple University School of Medicine in Philadelphia, for example, has provided a clue to how alcohol damages liver cells. The Philadelphia researchers suggested in April 1981 that alcohol may weaken cell membranes so that they are more susceptible to injury.

Despite many costly and painstaking studies, no test has ever been devised that can accurately predict how, or when, a person becomes an alcoholic. Many psychological, biological, and social factors are associated with alcohol abuse and alcoholism, but no research has proved that these factors are clear-cut causes of alcoholism.

Nonetheless, some factors indicate at least a statistical vulnerability to the disease. For example, individuals in certain occupations are apparently more vulnerable to alcoholism. Bartenders, waiters, longshoremen, writers, musicians, and reporters have relatively high cirrhosis rates; account-

Death comes early to many alcoholics. Some, trapped in despair, find release in suicide. Others die in accidents, murders, or from diseases brought on by drinking too much alcohol, for too long a time.

Because it impairs
judgment and reactions,
alcohol is involved in
more than half of all
traffic-accident deaths
in the U.S., *left*. Alcohol
abuse can damage
almost all the body's
systems, *below*. The most
serious injury is to the
liver and heart, but
the brain, muscles, and
digestive tract can
also be damaged.

ants, mail carriers, and carpenters have relatively
low rates.

Personality characteristics in alcohol-abusing
persons vary considerably. Alcoholics run the
gamut from the severely disturbed to the reasonably normal. Some use alcohol as self-medication for
painful psychological conditions that existed long
before they began to drink excessively. In others,
the psychological disturbance may be a result of
compulsive alcohol abuse in a society that con-
demns the drug-dependent life.

A family history of alcoholism significantly increases the risk that an individual will develop the
disease. According to several studies, about 25 per
cent of the fathers and brothers of alcoholics were
themselves alcoholic. Family studies also show
other psychiatric illnesses associated with alcoholism. There may be an excess of depression, crimi-
nality, antisocial behavior, and abnormal personality traits in the families of alcoholics. Depression
seems more common in the female relatives of
alcoholics and alcoholism or antisocial behavior in
the male relatives.

In such studies, it is often difficult to distinguish between the influence of "nature," or genetic

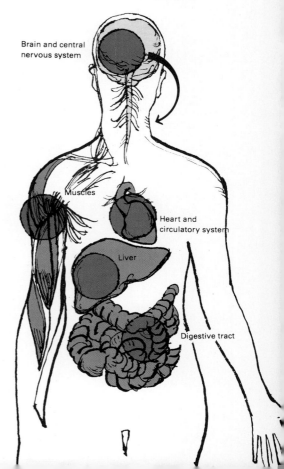

Brain and central
nervous system

Muscles

Heart and
circulatory system

Liver

Digestive tract

Alcoholics must help themselves, but they also need the help of others to overcome their affliction. For some, individual therapy, *above,* may be valuable. Family or group counseling, *right,* may help other alcoholics and their loved ones to understand and deal with this disease.

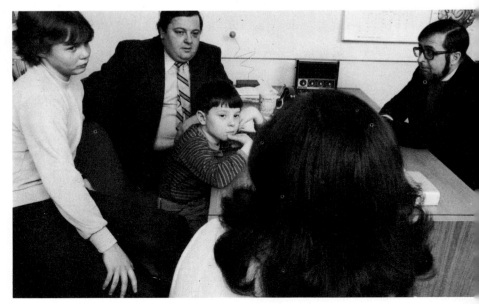

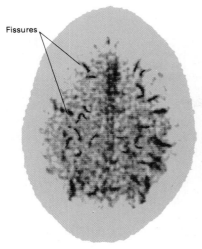

Fissures

**Brain scan taken one
month after patient's last drink**

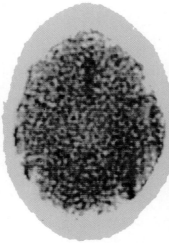

Brain scan eight months later

In X-ray brain scans of an alcoholic, made four weeks after his last drink, *left,* the dark lines around the edges are enlarged brain furrows, indicating alcohol damage. The furrows are less prominent in scans made eight months later, *right,* indicating that the brain may have reversed much of the damage done by alcohol.

factors, and "nurture," or learned factors, because most people — including alcoholics — are raised by their biological parents. More-over, it is likely that children who see adults drinking excessively in order to cope with stress or anxiety will themselves abuse alcohol as adults, even though they have experienced the destructive effects of alcohol-related behavior. In an attempt to distinguish between nature and nurture, scientists have undertaken studies of twins because of genetic similarities, and of adoptees because they are reared by nonbiological parents.

A twin study done by psychiatrist L. Kij at the University of Lund in Sweden in 1960 found that *monozygotic* (single-egg, or identical) twins with identical genetic makeup were approximately twice as likely both to become alcoholics as were *dizygotic* (two-egg, or frater-nal) twins of the same sex. Another twin study, conducted in Finland by epidemiologist J. Partanen and associates at the University of Helsinki, found that while the quantity and pattern of drinking was more alike among monozygotic than among dizygotic twins, both twin types were equally likely to become alcoholic pairs.

A series of pioneering studies on adopted people in Denmark conducted in 1973 by psychiatrist Donald W. Goodwin and his co-workers at the Washington University School of Medicine in St. Louis, Mo., served to clarify these issues further. Goodwin's group studied 133 Danish men who had been separated from their biological parents within a few weeks of birth, and then adopted. The research-ers found that the sons of alcoholics raised by unrelated nonalcoholic adoptive parents were four times more likely to become alcoholic by an early age than were adopted sons of nonalcoholics. But they were no more likely to have other psychological disturbances and no more likely to be classified as heavy drinkers. These findings suggest that there is a genetic component to alcoholism. Other studies confirmed these findings and indicated, conversely, that simply being raised by an alcoholic parent, whether a biological parent or a foster parent, does not necessarily increase the risk of alcoholism.

Daughters of alcoholics, both those raised by their alcoholic parents and those raised by nonalcoholic adoptive parents, had higher rates of alcoholism than the population as a whole. Studies by Goodwin in 1977 also found that the daughters of alcoholics raised by their own parents had higher rates of depression, suggesting that the home environment may cause depression in children of alcoholics.

Apparently, both genetic and environmental factors help to determine who will abuse alcohol. Some alcoholics probably inherit a number of traits that increase their susceptibility to alcoholism, rather than one metabolic or psychophysiological characteristic. Of course, many people who become heavy drinkers do not have a family history of alcohol abuse or alcoholism.

Like many other medical illnesses such as diabetes or schizophrenia, alcoholism is a chronic disease marked by remissions and relapses. No real cure is known. Many people resume drinking despite the best intentions. Treatment must involve short-term measures, long-term follow-up of "recovering alcoholics," and rapid intervention in the event of relapse.

The first step is to help the alcoholic appreciate that he has a problem with drinking and that he will probably need help. This is often difficult, given the extent of denial that is commonly present. After drinking has been ended, the short-term effects of alcohol withdrawal must be managed. This may require hospitalization, tranquilizers to control severe symptoms, and diet supplements to improve nutrition. Other diseases brought on by alcoholism, such as liver disease and pneumonia, must be looked for and treated.

Controlling the disease over the long run is a much different problem. The recovering alcoholic needs the support and understanding of family and friends, and trained health-care personnel.

Long-term treatment may require individual, group, and family therapy; specialized care centers for alcoholics; behavior-modification techniques; and, rarely, long-term drug therapy. The degree of commitment of the treatment team, the amount of time they spend with each patient, and the care with which they follow the patient for long periods may be as important as the treatment method.

Alcoholics Anonymous (A.A.), a voluntary self-help organization, is an important form of group treatment for alcoholics. It was developed by two "recovering alcoholics" in 1935, and now has an estimated membership of 1 million in thousands of local groups all over the world. Many groups have their own focus and some are comprised of particular ethnic, social, or vocational group members. In New York City, for example, there is a physicians' A.A. group, several groups made up of homosexuals, and one comprised of people who work in the advertising industry.

Although A.A. is nonsectarian, it places great stress on spiritual values. The support of the group is particularly important because many alcoholics are typically people who drank alone as a means of solving personal problems. Instead of depending on alcohol, A.A. members are encouraged to depend upon one another. Through helping others, members reinforce their own sobriety and build up self-esteem.

Drugs may be used in the long-term treatment of alcoholism. Disulfiram (Antabuse) is often a valuable aid in the treatment process. If a patient drinks alcohol within three to five days after an Antabuse dose, the liquor causes a violent reaction, including nausea, facial flushing, vomiting, and cramps. Patients taking Antabuse daily will not drink, or even be tempted to drink because of the anticipated effects. Some people may continue this aversion therapy for many months, and in some cases, for years.

On occasion, severe psychiatric problems are uncovered when patients withdraw from alcohol. In these cases, the patient may need drugs such as strong tranquilizers or antidepressants.

Alcoholism-prevention programs have generally focused on educating the drinker to the risks that alcoholism poses for him. Other social programs try to provide reasonable and attractive vocational, educational, and recreational alternatives to alcohol abuse for those most at risk, the young and socially disadvantaged.

Some theorists suggest increasing taxes on liquor to raise the price significantly or restricting its distribution so that fewer people will drink. Interestingly, in recent years, the price of alcohol in Western countries has not kept pace with the increased prices of other items.

Others suggest that all societies through the ages have had intoxicants and people will use them whatever the cost. Those who abuse alcohol are also likely to develop illegal systems to obtain it.

The abuse of alcohol is an enormous public health problem, yet society and the medical profession cannot agree on how to deal with it. Alcoholism has been described at various times as a spiritual, moral, psychological, and medical problem. The disease itself has often been confused with its medical and social consequences — the damage to mind and body, the traffic accidents, the divorces and broken families, and the murders. These effects of alcoholism must be understood in order to provide appropriate treatment for the disease, but the effects are not the disease.

The disorder should be seen in terms of its main clinical features — loss of control, craving, tolerance, and physical dependence — and research efforts must be concentrated in these areas. Alcoholism is behavior determined by the complex interaction of social, psychological, and neurochemical factors. These, too, need further study.

But as our knowledge continues to grow, treatment will remain specific to each individual. The struggle of the recovering alcoholic is an intensely personal one.

Pharmacies in the Jungle

By Isao Kubo

By tapping the secrets of folk healers from Africa and the Amazon, chemists are learning to extract drugs and other chemicals from the areas' plants

It was a clear, sunny day — perfect for a plant-collecting trip in the Kenya bush near the Serengeti National Park. I was searching for *Kigeria africana,* a rare tree with sausage-shaped fruit that is used to make folk medicines. I spotted a clump of *K. africana* trees and, feeling lucky, eagerly climbed up on the first big branch to collect some fruit. After a few moments, I had the feeling I was being watched. Glancing over to the next tree, I looked directly into the menacing eyes of a leopard.

A chill ran up my spine. I broke out in a cold sweat, and my legs trembled. But the leopard

evidently dismissed me as a possible treat. Before I could try to flee, the cat jumped out of the tree and disappeared into the bush. Although it happened in 1974, I remember it vividly.

I have had other equally terrifying experiences while searching for plants. Once in Kenya, I became so engrossed in collecting leaves from the upper branches of a tree that I did not notice about 100 wild buffalo that had surrounded the tree and my land cruiser. I was trapped in the tree for several hours until they left.

I am often asked why a chemist puts himself into such dangerous situations. In my work as a natural products chemist, I have to travel to jungle areas of Africa and the Amazon River Basin in South America to collect plants used by the natives. Plants provide many chemicals that can be useful to humans, especially for drugs and insecticides. Natural products chemists find out which drugs from plants have already been tested by humans as folk remedies and analyze why they are chemically effective. Once we have isolated the active plant chemicals in the laboratory, we can duplicate them and manufacture them for commercial use.

Most anthropologists think that the use of plants to cure various ills goes back to the dawn of humanity, long before written history. The earliest-known written record of prescribed drugs appears on a set of clay tablets that were used by ancient Sumerians in the Middle East at least 4,000 years ago. Most of the drugs listed on the tablets were made from plants. Ancient records from China and Egypt give instructions for preparing drugs from plants. Various cultures in Africa have also used plant preparations as drugs for thousands of years, but the information has been passed down through generations of medicine men by word-of-mouth, rather than by written records. One purpose of my work in Africa has been to help assemble a written record of these drugs.

In 1981, up to 60 per cent of the prescription drugs on the market contained either natural plant chemicals or chemicals made in the laboratory to mimic them. For example, ipecac, a drug used to cause vomiting in patients who have swallowed poisons, is made from the root of a Central American plant. Synthetic codeine, widely used as a painkiller, is prepared chemically to duplicate the codeine taken from opium poppy plants. Quinine, used to treat malaria, is prepared both ways — directly from the bark of the cinchona tree in Asia and Africa, and made synthetically in many Western countries.

Many medical or scientific researchers have experimented with drugs taken from plants after seeing folk healers use them. For example, British physician William Withering noted in the 1700s that some Shropshire villagers used the leaves of foxglove plants that have purple flowers to make a preparation for people with heart problems. Withering decided to test the plant preparation himself, and he reported the results in *An Account of the Foxglove* (1785). We now know which active ingredient in the leaves alleviates heart-dis-

The author:
Isao Kubo is associate professor of natural products chemistry at the University of California, Berkeley.

ease symptoms. It is digitalis, one of the drugs used most frequently by heart patients today.

For at least 10 years, I have been studying how medicine men in Africa and the Amazon area use herbs, leaves, and other plant parts to treat their patients. I had not planned to specialize in chemicals from plants when I began my scientific career. I received my doctorate in organic chemistry from Osaka City University in Japan in 1969 and became an assistant professor there in 1972, expecting a quiet career as a typical organic chemist working in a lab. But the Japan Society for the Promotion of Science asked me to go to Kenya in 1973 for field work, and that experience transformed me into a natural products chemist. At the International Centre of Insect Physiology and Ecology (ICIPE) in Nairobi, I worked with an international team of chemists and biologists doing field work and lab work on such topics as the relationship between insects and plants.

In my 20 months with ICIPE, I helped classify plants and their possible uses. It was a massive job, because many tribes use different names for the same plant and different tribes use the same plant for different purposes. Chemist Carl Djerassi of Stanford University in Palo Alto, Calif., who organized ICIPE in 1970 with cooperation from African scientists and funding from the United Nations and other bodies, was convinced that the many plant species native to Kenya were an untapped gold mine for chemical researchers. We interviewed local Bwana Mganga, or medicine men, to find out which plants they used, how they used them, and where they found them. We then collected samples of the plants to take home for analysis and study.

I have returned to Kenya once or twice a year on collecting trips since that first visit. Thus far, I have collected about 200 species of African plants.

I have learned that the key to collecting plants in Kenya is finding a Bwana Mganga and earning his trust. The Kenya government has outlawed the occupation, so medicine men who still practice are naturally very reserved with strangers, especially foreigners. As I went from village to village, I learned that it was best to approach the local schoolteacher first; he was likely to be most receptive in discussing medical research. Once I gained

The Greek herbalist Dioscorides shows a student a plant used for making drugs in this illustration from an ancient Arab manuscript, *Materia Medica* (1229), *top*. Most historical accounts of plants that yield drugs mention the foxglove, *above*. Digitalis, a substance taken from the foxglove, has been used by doctors since the 1700s to treat heart problems.

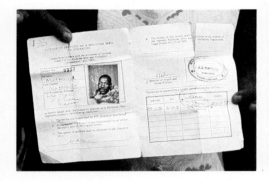

By issuing a license for herbalists to practice, *above,* African nations such as Lesotho recognize the value of folk medicine. This Liberian medicine man, *above right,* is an important person in his local village.

his trust, I asked to be introduced to the chief, who could then introduce me to the medicine man. Even then, some Bwana Mganga were still secretive and reluctant to talk about their work and gave me incomplete or false information — whether out of ignorance or caution, I do not know.

The medicine man who taught me the most was Abdulla. Actually, I learned he was a medicine man only after I had known him for several months. I was tracking down *Warburgia* plants when I met Abdulla. After doing research on *Warburgia ugandensis,* a plant containing a natural insecticide, I was convinced that related *Warburgia* species might be of some value. I went to the village of Vanga near the Tanzanian border to look for *W. sthulmanii,* which I heard was used there for healing. The villagers' Swahili name for the plant is Mukaa. Many people had heard of Mukaa, but no one could show me any samples. Finally, I heard about trees with hot-tasting bark and leaves that might be Mukaa, located in the village of Ukunda.

In Ukunda, I hired Abdulla and several other villagers to help me collect Mukaa bark and leaves. All the villagers kept a respectable distance from me on that first visit. I was a foreigner with skin of a different color, and most of them spoke only Digo and Swahili, which I did not. But I returned to the village many times, and eventually I gained their trust. Between visits, I studied Swahili so that I could communicate with the villagers. As my Swahili improved, I became more at ease, and they began to tell me about the local plants and how they were used. Then one day, while talking with Abdulla about plants, I asked him who the village's Bwana Mganga was — and without hesitation, he said he was.

Abdulla, a Muslim, had two wives and nine children. He and his family lived some distance from the village, as do most medicine men. This separation helps to underline their special role in tribal society and also helps to isolate them, it is thought, from disgruntled family members of patients they cannot help.

The patients come to Abdulla's home for treatment that may include a mixture of drugs and spiritual or exorcistic rites — the "casting out of demons." Abdulla collects part of the fee when he treats the patient, and he gets the remainder only if the patient recovers. He collects nothing from cases he thinks are hopeless.

Information is passed from one generation of Bwana Mganga to another as it has been for thousands of years — by word-of-mouth, usually from father to son. However, the father may tell a daughter how to deal with female reproductive problems. When I met Abdulla, his children were quite young, so he had not yet passed on any information to them. If he were to die suddenly, all the special expertise that he had inherited and acquired through his own practice would be lost.

I asked Abdulla some of the standard questions I had developed for finding out medicine men's secrets. Abdulla is not formally educated, and he does not know the technical names for his patients' symptoms or diseases. So, rather than asking him how he treats "inflammation," for example, I asked what he does when the patient's face or arm swells up, pointing to the appropriate body part and pantomiming the swelling. Then I asked him to show me the drugs he used and how he prepared them. I learned that medicine men the world over prepare most drugs from plants the same way — the plant part is dried, chopped, and boiled in water.

To avoid confusion over plant names, I asked Abdulla to show me the plants he used. I learned that Abdulla used trees more than any other type of plant in his healing. Of these, the bark and the exposed portions of the root were used most often. I then took samples of the plants or appropriate parts of the plant, putting each in a plastic bag and labeling it.

I came to realize that there is a wide range of uses for plants in folk medicine. For example, when I complimented Abdulla on his tremendous memory — having no more in mind than a friendly remark — he explained that he used a memory-aid drug extracted from *K. africana* bark. He claimed that the same drug is also effective in treating headaches. And, somewhat contradictorily, it is used both as a birth-control pill and — mixed with beer or changa, a local alcoholic drink — as an aphrodisiac, a substance that supposedly increases sexual desire.

In addition to my work in Africa, I have done similar field work in the Amazon River Basin, making field trips there in 1976, 1978, and 1980. I hope to work there even more frequently in the future, because there are many exciting plants to investigate in the area.

Much of the Amazon Basin consists of lush jungle that has not been well explored. Because there are many kinds of plants growing together in abundance, I and other natural products chemists hope to discover many useful new medications there.

I naturally began comparing the use of drugs prepared from plants in Africa and the Amazon. The drugs used with the greatest effectiveness in the Amazon seem to be those that work on the nervous system. By contrast, in East Africa, drugs are most effective on the circulatory

A medicine man shows
the author how to prepare
a drug from a plant in
his hut in Kenya, *right.*
The home and hospital of
a medicine man, *top,* are
usually set off from the
rest of the village in
East Africa for reasons
of privacy and status.

system. Interestingly, the poisons traditionally used in tribal warfare in both areas affect those same body systems.

Unlike the medicine men in Kenya, folk healers in Brazil work openly at public stands in the market places. They hang up the plants and herbs they use, so that the patients can see them.

Abdulla's counterpart in the Amazon region was Joao, probably the most knowledgeable and helpful folk healer I found in the area. I met Joao in Belém, the ocean gateway to the Amazon region. I had heard about sacaca, a drug reputed to have wonderful medicinal properties for treating kidney problems, so I went to the market place and shouted repeatedly in Portuguese, "Where is sacaca?" Joao yelled back, "Right here!" He was selling it at a stand. I spoke little Portuguese and he spoke little English, but nevertheless we still managed to communicate.

Joao explained which plant preparations he uses and showed me the plants. He uses veronica, the bark of *Dalbergia monetaria,* to treat blood diseases. He told me that other Amazon healers prescribe veronica for schistosomiasis, a parasitic disease caused by flukes, a type of worm that lives in blood vessels. The larvae of flukes live in aquatic snails. Humans are infected when the larvae leave the snails, swim through the water, and bore through the skin of a person wading or bathing in the water. Schistosomiasis is a major disease in many parts of Latin America, Africa, and Asia. Prescription drugs made from synthetic chemicals are available to treat schistosomiasis, but these are so strong that they may damage or destroy essential healthy body tissue, too.

I was very excited at the possibility of using veronica, a natural substance with no side effects, not only for making a drug to treat schistosomiasis, but also for making an insecticide that would prevent this worldwide public health problem. I am experimenting with veronica to develop an antifeedant, a chemical compound that makes insects avoid eating certain species of plants. An animal pest will not eat a plant containing a chemical that repels it. Scientists believe that many plants have evolved such chemicals as a means of survival — a defense against predators looking for food (see NATURE'S CHEMISTS, *Science Year,* 1981).

I am trying to find out which chemical in veronica the snail cannot tolerate. When the substance has been identified, we must then find a way to make that chemical into a spray that can be applied to the plants the snail eats, or into an additive, such as chlorine, that could be released into the water supply in affected areas such as the Amazon Basin. The snails would then have to leave the area or starve to death. Naturally based antifeedants are preferable to insecticides such as DDT that harm other animals, plants, or the water.

I have decided to specialize in plant chemicals that can be used for insecticides. But I keep in touch with many scientists at other universities and drug companies who specialize in plant chemicals

The bark of the "upside-down tree," *above,* is used by East Africans to make a painkilling drug. The leaves of the *Warburgia* plant, *above right,* are used by East Africans for healing and by the author to prepare an insecticide spray.

that can be used for drugs; sometimes we work with the same substances. And we use similar methods in the laboratory.

I did my first laboratory work on plant chemicals at Columbia University in New York City, beginning in 1975. Chemist Koji Nakanishi of Columbia, an ICIPE colleague, invited me to visit him and use his department's sophisticated lab equipment. I stayed at Columbia for four years, analyzing specimens.

The University of California, Berkeley, then offered me an assistant professorship in entomology, the study of insects. I accepted and moved to California in 1979.

In my lab at Berkeley, I follow a standard method for analyzing the plant samples that I have collected during my field trips. First, I extract the dried plant parts with alcohol. Then I separate the liquefied plant material into the various chemicals it contains. In a trial-and-error process, I test each chemical on insects, usually by applying it to an insect's food. If the insect responds to the chemical — by refusing to eat the food, for example — I break down the substance into even smaller parts. Then I test each in turn until I discover the specific chemical substance — for example, a hormone — that the animal responds to strongly.

I used this method to analyze *Ajuga remota,* an East African plant, after witnessing a striking scene in 1974. I visited a field there after a large number of desert locusts, *Schistocerca gregaria,* had swept through and devoured most of the foliage. Several plants, all members of the species *A. remota,* survived untouched amid the remains of the locusts' feast. Naturally, I was extremely curious about why the locusts ignored these plants, and I took several *A. remota* samples back to my Berkeley lab.

With no *S. gregaria* available in California, I tested the *A. remota* on African army worms, *Spodoptera exempta,* which normally feed on maize. I broke down *A. remota* into its various chemical components and applied a solution of each to the maize leaves. I gave the army worms maize leaves coated with various *A. remota* chemicals until I found one they would not eat. This indicated that the substance contained the effective ingredient, so I tested the substance further.

Bark from the cinchona tree, the source of quinine to fight malaria, is gathered in South America, *top left.* Africans collect medicinal roots, *top right;* lily stems, the source of a drug to reduce fevers, *above;* and branches that contain a cancer-fighting substance, *below.*

Ajuga remota, above, an African plant, is the source of a chemical substance extracted in the author's lab, *above right.* When fed to the fall army worm, the substance caused the insect to grow three tough skin layers one over another, *right.* The skins covered the army worm's mouth, and it starved to death.

A. remota has a strong effect on another African pest, the Egyptian cotton army worm, or *Spodoptera littoralis.* The Egyptian cotton army worm is a caterpillar that molts, or sheds its outer skin as it develops into another life stage, eventually becoming a moth. *A. remota* contains ecdysterone, a hormone that disrupts the insect's normal molting sequence; I am certain the plant evolved the hormone as a defense against insects. Subsequently, I tested ecdysterone in my lab in 1980 by feeding it to another insect, fall army worms, *Spodoptera frugiperda,* in various stages of development. To get around the insect's distaste for *A. remota* — and ecdysterone in particular — we made up a liquid food in the lab that mixed ecdysterone with the flavors of cotton and other plants the insect likes. We have also found that *A. remota* is effective against the fall army worm that attacks cotton crops in the Southern United States.

At one stage of molting, the caterpillar normally grows a tough, cuticlelike new skin to replace the skin it is about to shed. When I fed ecdysterone to the insect as it grew the new skin, the skin hardened before it normally does and trapped the old skin in place. The ecdysterone also caused the animal to grow a third skin. The three skins covered the animal's mouth, and it starved to death.

Ecdysterone and cyasterone, another hormone from *A. remota,* also disrupted the molting process in *Bombyx mori,* a silkworm, and *Pectinophora gossypiella,* the pink bollworm. The *A. remota* substances were ineffective against tobacco pests, however. I am now experimenting with other insect pests to see if they are affected by *A. remota.*

Farmers in the United States, Africa, and elsewhere whose crops have been devastated by pests like the fall army worm would surely welcome the development of a natural development inhibitor to control them.

Electrophysiologist Wei-chun Ma of The Netherlands performed experiments at ICIPE in the 1970s showing that *W. ugandensis* also is a natural antifeedant. Many of us at ICIPE noted that few insects in Kenya seem to feed on the plant, even though it grows abundantly in areas where voracious insects live. Wei-chun Ma found that successive doses of warburganal, a chemical derived from *W. ugandensis,* blocked the taste buds of the *Sexempta* army worm that eats not only maize, but also sugar cane and rice. He used highly sensitive electrodes to measure the reaction of the insect's taste buds to sugar. Before warburganal is applied, the taste buds react strongly to sugar. But with each dose of warburganal, the taste buds' response to sugar decreases until they fail to respond at all, and the insect starves.

Warburganal has great possibilities as an insect antifeedant. It also fights certain disease-causing bacteria and fungi. Three colleagues and I tested 72 plant species, including two *Warburgia* species. We found 40 substances from this group that checked the growth of the organisms. Substances taken from the *Warburgia* plants were among the most effective.

This plant is so promising that no fewer than 16 teams of scientists had reported on their ongoing work with warburganal by 1981. Drug researchers have found that warburganal fights tumors and are testing it further, with an eye toward using it to check cancerous tumors in humans. Warburganal also appears to boost the human immune system in some way.

Several colleagues and I developed an antifeedant spray using a substance from *Azadirachta indica,* the Indian neem tree, and tested it in Africa in 1977. Our tests were successful; locusts in the area sprayed by the antifeedant starved to death. However, we could test only a small land area because of the expense and time required to extract the chemical from *A. indica.* The next step is to isolate the chemical, so that we can make it in quantity and test a much larger land area.

Nature is still the greatest chemist. We hope to use our sophisticated biological and chemical techniques to learn how nature does its work. When we do, we should be able to develop new drugs and other chemicals that can benefit us in nature's way.

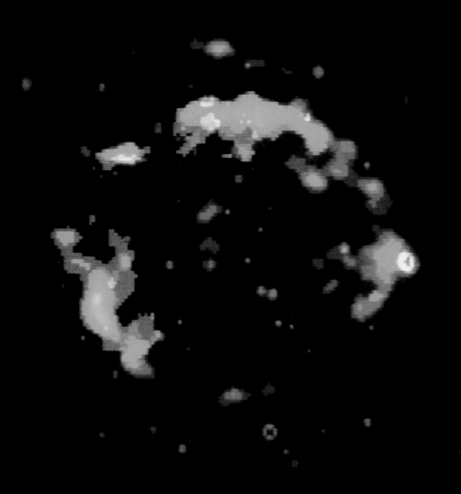

CAS A   SUPERNOVA REMNANT

X RAY

OPTICAL

RADIO

X-Ray Eyes
on the Skies

By Stephen S. Murray

**Astronomers using the *Einstein* Observatory's unique
telescope search deep space to learn the extent
of high-energy events throughout the universe**

Several hundred people anxiously await the moment under the clear night sky at Cape Canaveral, Fla. At the National Aeronautics and Space Administration's (NASA) Kennedy Space Flight Center blockhouse AE-1, last-minute checks confirm that "all systems are go." The result of years of hopes, dreams, and hard work is on the line. Standing beside my 9-year-old son, Jeffrey, who is bobbing up and down with excitement, I reflect that 10 years earlier both he and the event we are about to witness were wonderful ideas waiting to happen.

Suddenly, at 12:23 A.M., the sky around us lights up and a voice blares over the loudspeaker, "We have ignition!" The rocket rises and we can see the second stage ignite. Some time later, when the voice announces that orbit has been achieved, cheers go up and our tension vanishes in exultant handshakes, backslapping, and rejoicing. We are as thrilled as were people all over the world when *Apollo 11* first put men on the moon. And we are certain that this space flight will bring us as much or more scientific knowledge.

What we had just watched, early on Nov. 13, 1978, was an Atlas-Centaur rocket carrying 3,175 kilograms (7,000 pounds) of experiment-loaded spacecraft into a nearly circular orbit 500 kilometers (300 miles) above the earth. The payload was the second High Energy Astronomy Observatory (HEAO-2) — also called the *Einstein* Observatory — the first telescope capable of photographing X-ray sources beyond our solar system.

After the cheering stopped and all the champagne corks had popped, fellow astrophysicist Ethan J. Schreier and I, both of the Harvard-Smithsonian Center for Astrophysics in Cambridge, Mass., flew to the Goddard Space Flight Center in Greenbelt, Md., where we were to turn on the orbiting *Einstein.* There we began the complex sequence of steps necessary to awaken the observatory and start it amassing useful scientific data.

I have devoted most of my scientific career to the *Einstein* Observatory, the most sophisticated instrument yet devised for studying X rays in space. It was designed to locate sources, measure energy, and analyze spectra of objects throughout the universe.

The *Einstein* Observatory is much more than a telescope equipped with sensitive detectors. It includes a complex spacecraft that holds these parts together, controls the pointing of the telescope, provides operating power, and regulates the temperature and operation of the instruments. Named to commemorate the 100th anniversary, in 1979, of Albert Einstein's birth, this newest astrophysical investigating instrument was scheduled during its three-year lifetime to seek answers to many of the cosmic questions posed by Einstein in his theories of relativity and cosmology — the study of the universe.

Until about 1950, most people pictured the universe as a giant clockwork of stars and galaxies in serene and steady motion. Astronomers looking through their optical telescopes saw galaxies, aglow with the light from their stars, swirling through the sky in fixed, static patterns that never changed. But now, using new ground-based or spaceborne nonoptical instruments, we see a dynamic universe. With radio and X-ray telescopes, we find many signs of violent activity.

Starting with the big bang — the cosmic explosion that resulted in the rapidly expanding fireball of radiation that became the universe — high-energy processes seem to have always directed the course of the cosmos. Stars and galaxies and all the elements of which they consist were made from hydrogen and helium, the first materials of the universe. The universe evolved as the original gases were heated to very high temperatures and charged particles were accelerated to high energies. These processes are still going on.

Astronomers learn about the dynamics of the universe by observing the energy given off by objects in space. Various types of telescopes have been devised to observe activity across the entire spectrum of electromagnetic radiation. But all telescopes work essentially the same way. They collect photons, bundles of electromagnetic energy, and reflect them to a focal point where they are perceived by a detector that makes their data accessible to observers. For example, optical telescopes collect photons from the visible light range of the spectrum and focus them onto a photographic plate or television tube that produces an image. Astronomers then analyze the photo or television image with the aid of a computer. In much the same way, photons from the radio range or the X-ray range of the spectrum are collected, reflected, detected, and analyzed.

The energy levels across the electromagnetic spectrum are also measured by the wavelength and frequency of the radiation. At the

The author:
Stephen S. Murray
is an astrophysicist
at the Smithsonian
Astrophysical Observatory
in Cambridge, Mass.

low-frequency, long-wavelength end of the scale, a relatively small amount of energy is needed to produce the photons. Radiation at higher frequencies and shorter wavelengths requires much greater energy. Low-frequency radio waves are produced by the least energetic cosmic processes; high-frequency X rays and gamma rays, by more energetic processes.

Only radio, near-infrared, and visible light waves can be studied within the earth's atmosphere. To detect these waves, astronomers use several kinds of large ground-based telescopes. For example, a 5-meter (200-inch) optical telescope, such as the one operated by the Hale Observatories on Palomar Mountain in California, can take excellent pictures in the medium-wavelength, medium-energy visible light range of the spectrum. To detect shorter wavelengths, astronomers must put instruments above the earth's atmosphere.

Radio and optical signals usually come from the outer regions of the stars, galaxies, and quasars — intense energy emitters that are the brightest and most distant objects known. However, some X rays originate closer to an object's core, and are more directly related to the basic processes involved in its behavior. X-ray emissions allow astronomers to extend the energy range over which we observe the sources and study the power that drives these cosmic engines.

Astronomers can also learn much about objects in space by analyzing their electromagnetic radiation with spectrometers. Each of the chemical elements that make up the objects radiates at its own characteristic wavelength. Bright or dark lines in the spectrum are caused by elements either emitting or absorbing radiation.

The first observation of X rays in space came in 1949 when astrophysicist Herbert Friedman of the Naval Research Laboratory in Washington, D.C., detected X-ray emissions from the sun with detectors mounted on a V-2 rocket. But not until June 1962 did Riccardo Giacconi and his co-workers at American Science and Engineering Incorporated (ASE) in Cambridge, Mass., also using rocket-borne detectors, find X rays from beyond our solar system — in the constellation Scorpio. Those early experiments made astronomers aware for the first time of a pervasive background of X rays from outside the Milky Way Galaxy. It is so bright that if we had "X-ray vision," the night sky would look almost as bright as day.

Excited by the possibilities of X-ray astronomy, Giacconi and his group worked to develop a satellite that could make better observations over longer time periods than could instruments mounted on rockets. On Dec. 12, 1970, *Uhuru,* the first satellite devoted exclusively to X-ray observations, was launched, and astronomers used it to conduct the first all-sky survey of possible X-ray sources. The richness of the X-ray sky became apparent with the publication in February 1974 of a list of more than 300 sources that had been discovered by *Uhuru* and previous detectors. Two important findings, the discovery of binary (double) star X-ray sources and the detection

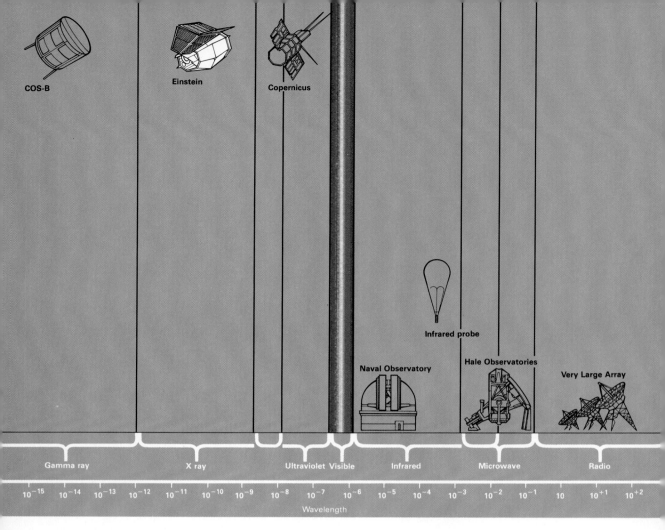

| Gamma ray | X ray | Ultraviolet | Visible | Infrared | Microwave | Radio |

| 10^{-15} | 10^{-14} | 10^{-13} | 10^{-12} | 10^{-11} | 10^{-10} | 10^{-9} | 10^{-8} | 10^{-7} | 10^{-6} | 10^{-5} | 10^{-4} | 10^{-3} | 10^{-2} | 10^{-1} | 10 | 10^{+1} | 10^{+2} |

Wavelength

Eyes on the Universe

Differences in frequency at which data-carrying waves of electromagnetic radiation are transmitted require that observing instruments be positioned at different altitudes. High-frequency gamma, X and ultraviolet radiation must be detected above the earth's atmosphere. Lower-frequency visible and near-infrared light waves and microwave and radio emissions use only ground-based equipment, but balloons are sent aloft for some types of infrared observations.

of hot gas in clusters of galaxies, increased interest in the investigation of stellar evolution and the changing clusters of galaxies.

Several other X-ray satellites, sponsored by scientific groups in the Netherlands and Great Britain as well as in the United States, followed *Uhuru* in the early 1970s. Some continued to survey the sky and monitor particularly interesting objects, while others were designed to pinpoint locations for sources discovered by *Uhuru* or to obtain better data on the objects' spectra or behavior.

Despite spectacular results, the low sensitivity of their equipment kept astronomers from detecting dim or distant objects. All the X-ray detectors were basically proportional counters. This is a gas-filled tube with a window that permits only X-ray photons to pass and detects each one individually. This detector was unable to determine the location from which the X rays came, and was subject to a high background noise from radiation at higher frequencies.

As early as 1960, Giacconi and astrophysicist Bruno B. Rossi, both then at the Massachusetts Institute of Technology (M.I.T.) in Cambridge, had discussed using a collecting device for X-ray astronomy directed beyond the sun. Such a device would concentrate the incoming photons and form an image of the object observed, instead of simply telling the direction and intensity of a detected source.

Just as in an optical or radio telescope, a great many photons must be collected and focused at an X-ray detector to produce high-resolution images. But devices that would reflect X rays did not exist. Unlike visible light and radio waves, the short X rays cannot be reflected by flat, dishlike mirrors because when they strike the surface at perpendicular or steep angles they penetrate the glass. X rays can be collected if they are permitted to strike a smooth surface at very shallow angles and "skip" off it toward the focal plane—a *grazing reflection*. Giacconi and Rossi shared their problem with their colleague Leon P. Van Speybroeck. Together, they designed mirrors that look like polished cylinders or barrels rather than dishes, and are extremely smooth. The system adapted for *Einstein* can accommodate four pairs of mirrors nested one inside the other. This increases the collecting area and makes the instrument more useful.

The mirrors, however, are only one part of the X-ray telescope. Something must detect the X rays focused by the mirrors. The *Einstein* Observatory carries five different instruments to detect X rays. Four of them are arranged on a carousel that can position any one at the telescope focus. One operates independently of the telescope.

Two of the four instruments that can be placed at the focus are imaging devices, or cameras, which produce pictures, and two are spectrometers. One of the cameras detects X-ray images at high resolution—that is, in extremely fine detail—but over a rather restricted field of view. The observatory records on magnetic tape the position and arrival time of each photon as it is detected. After each orbit, these data are transmitted to a ground tracking station. The data are stored in a computer, then photon counts accumulated over a period of minutes to hours are translated into an X-ray image of the sky on a television screen. Scientists photograph these images to produce the spectacular X-ray pictures.

Einstein's second camera takes in a wider field, but it has less ability to distinguish detail. It is

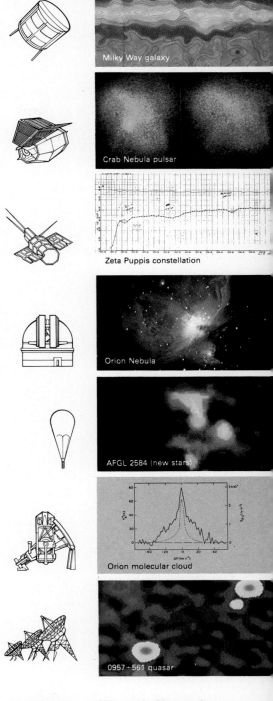

Milky Way galaxy

Crab Nebula pulsar

Zeta Puppis constellation

Orion Nebula

AFGL 2584 (new stars)

Orion molecular cloud

0957+561 quasar

A Full Spectrum of Heavenly Observations
Information perceived from objects that radiate at different wavelengths varies from visual images to computer-generated graphics. This difference in the data's appearance depends on the frequency at which the observing telescope operates.

equipped with an imaging proportional counter that permits us not only to record the position and arrival time of detected photons, but also to measure the approximate energy of each one. More accurate observations of photon energy are made by a solid-state spectrometer with medium resolution. Precise spectral measurements are made by the fourth *Einstein* instrument, a focal-plane crystal spectrometer. The observatory's fifth detector is a monitor proportional counter, which views space independently of the telescope. It studies a much wider area and looks for observable changes in the X-ray emission over time periods of less than one second.

Our study of the supernova remnant Cassiopeia-A (Cas-A) shows how all of *Einstein*'s detectors helped clarify our understanding of this source of X-ray emission. Giuseppina Fabbiano of the Smithsonian Astrophysical Laboratory (SAO) and I observed Cas-A with both imaging detectors on *Einstein* in January 1979. The medium resolution of the imaging proportional counter showed us the circular shape of this source and three brighter areas within it. Because that instrument also tells us something about the spectrum of X rays detected, we noticed that different sections produce different types of emission. However, all these results were crude and qualitative. We were "just looking," not measuring anything.

When we focused the high-resolution imaging detector on Cas-A, what had been indistinct became finely structured. For the first time, we could compare the X-ray structure with radio and optical data to help understand the processes that occur there.

Robert H. Becker and his colleagues at Goddard used the solid-state spectrometer to obtain a spectrum of Cas-A that showed emission lines of many elements. Particularly clear are those representing silicon and sulfur. Magnesium, aluminum, argon, and calcium are also present. When considered along with the imaging data, which show that the X rays come from ejected material, this spectral information confirms that the material comes from the interior of the star that exploded. We know the material originated there because it is the energy released by the transformation of primordial hydrogen and helium into other elements by means of the nuclear reactions inside stars that makes them shine.

Thomas Markert and his colleagues at M.I.T. used the focal-plane crystal spectrometer to study the detailed shapes of some of these elemental emission lines. The structure they found in the lines led them to conclude that the X-radiating material is traveling at a velocity of about 3,000 kilometers (1,860 miles) per second, a rate consistent with explosive ejection from such an object as a supernova.

Astronomers taking part in the *Einstein* Guest Observer Program have compared pictures of Cas-A taken in visible light, at radio wavelengths, and in X rays. By combining the data from various *Einstein* instruments and those operating at other wavelengths, we can increase our information, better interpret all our observations,

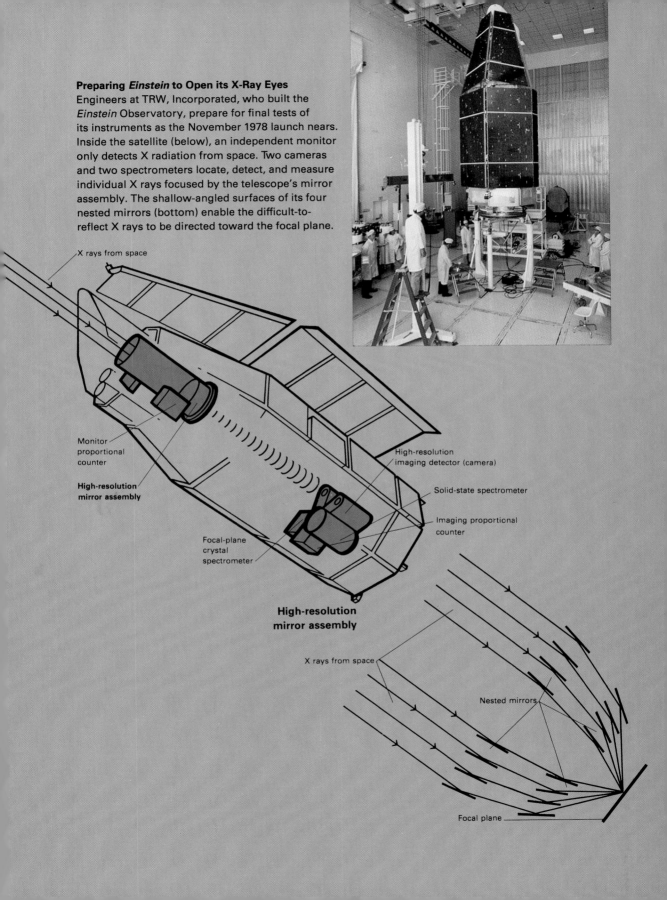

Preparing *Einstein* to Open its X-Ray Eyes
Engineers at TRW, Incorporated, who built the
Einstein Observatory, prepare for final tests of
its instruments as the November 1978 launch nears.
Inside the satellite (below), an independent monitor
only detects X radiation from space. Two cameras
and two spectrometers locate, detect, and measure
individual X rays focused by the telescope's mirror
assembly. The shallow-angled surfaces of its four
nested mirrors (bottom) enable the difficult-to-
reflect X rays to be directed toward the focal plane.

X rays from space

Monitor
proportional
counter

**High-resolution
mirror assembly**

High-resolution
imaging detector (camera)

Solid-state spectrometer

Imaging proportional
counter

Focal-plane
crystal
spectrometer

**High-resolution
mirror assembly**

X rays from space

Nested mirrors

Focal plane

and so gain a greater understanding of the object being studied. Radio astronomer John Dickel of the University of Illinois in Urbana-Champaign obtained computer images at Kitt Peak National Observatory in Arizona and the National Radio Astronomy Observatory in Greenbank, W. Va. With the help of Jeffrey D. Morris of SAO and Donald Wells at Kitt Peak, we combined the separate images into a false-color picture. This allowed us to see common features and to note the places where one form of emission dominates another.

By pooling all our results, we learned that Cas-A was originally a star with a mass 10 to 100 times that of the sun. We see the outward moving blast wave from the supernova explosion as the outermost edge of radio and X-ray emission. The regions of intense X rays, which look extremely bright in photos, within the shell of the supernova remnant may be material ejected from the exploding star and heated by shock waves from the primary blast.

Some scientists have used *Einstein* data to try to learn more about the formation of neutron stars, which they had long believed to be the dense collapsed remnants of exploded supernovae. They had theorized that these remnants are initially very hot because they are formed in the cores of stars. Then after an explosion blows away the outer layers of the original star, it starts to cool very rapidly by radiating energy. Astronomers have predicted the cooling rate theoretically, using concepts of nuclear and atomic physics. After several hundred years, the temperature of a neutron star should be a few million degrees C. It would give off much of its energy as X rays.

Before *Einstein,* it was not always easy to detect these objects. But an X-ray picture of the Crab Nebula, a supernova remnant in our galaxy that exploded about 900 years ago, clearly shows a neutron star that also happens to be a pulsar — that is, it emits pulsed radio waves in short bursts at regular intervals. Frank R. Harnden, Jr., of SAO decided to see if the temperature of the Crab's neutron star agreed with predictions.

Einstein's extreme sensitivity enabled Harnden to directly measure the temperature in the area around the pulsar at its time of minimum emission. He found that the neutron star's highest temperature was 2.5 million °C, which was consistent with predictions. However, when other *Einstein* observers studied other supernova remnants, they failed to find the expected neutron stars. This made them question their theory. Either it is not true that neutron stars always result from supernova explosions, or it is not true that neutron stars always have a certain predictable temperature, or both ideas are wrong.

Other remarkable findings that resulted from the *Einstein* data are helping us understand more about clusters of galaxies. Astronomers have long wondered how these collections of hundreds or thousands of galaxies formed. Did the immense clusters or the individual galaxies come first? One view is that protogalaxies, masses of gas from which the galaxies may have developed, were the first objects that formed when the primordial "cosmic soup" of hydrogen and helium atoms started to cool after the big bang. These objects then floated throughout the universe until gravitational attraction pulled many of them together into the great clumps that we call clusters. Other cosmologists think that the cosmic soup was filled from its start with gaseous clumps the size of clusters. Then as gravity caused these clumps to contract, each one broke into smaller units, which became the star-filled galaxies.

William Forman and Christine Jones, both of SAO, have been studying the structure of X-ray emission from clusters and have shown that the gas in clusters of galaxies comes from the galaxies, indicating that galaxies had to form first. Jones has even found examples of clusters that appear to be still forming in areas where galaxies coalesce.

Forman has also studied galaxies in the Virgo Cluster, a nearby collection of thousands of galaxies, and has shown how gas produced in galaxies as a result of supernovae and stellar winds can be transferred to the cluster. That is, the gas that was between the stars in the galaxy becomes the gas between the galaxies in a cluster. The process, called *ram pressure stripping,* occurs when a galaxy moves through a region that contains some gas which produces pressure that pulls off gas that is part of the galaxy. In one *Einstein* picture of galaxy M86, we can see a plume of X-ray emission that has detached itself from the galaxy. This might well be an example of ram pressure stripping in progress.

Support for Forman and Jones's work comes from another study. Spectral data had already shown astronomers that the hot gas contained in clusters was more than just hydrogen and helium. With the more sensitive spectrometers on *Einstein,* Richard F. Mushotsky of Goddard and Claude R. Canizares of M.I.T. have detected iron, magnesium, sulfur, silicon, and oxygen in several nearby clusters. Their observations show that the cluster gas comes from galaxies where nuclear reactions in the stars have converted hydrogen and helium to heavier elements.

In addition to enabling scientists to gain more knowledge about individual X-ray sources, *Einstein* has provided the key to a puzzle that began with the first X-ray-detecting rocket flights. They discovered, and *Uhuru* confirmed, that a background of intense X radiation existed in every direction in space in which they looked. The radiation did not come from any of the identified sources, so what was causing it? Two theories have been proposed.

One view is that the radiation comes from a thin hot gas, similar to the gas inside clusters of galaxies but less dense and even hotter, that is spread throughout space. The other view is that the background could come from many sources that are too faint to be detected individually but add up to produce the observed radiation. Objects such as undetected quasars have been suggested as possible sources.

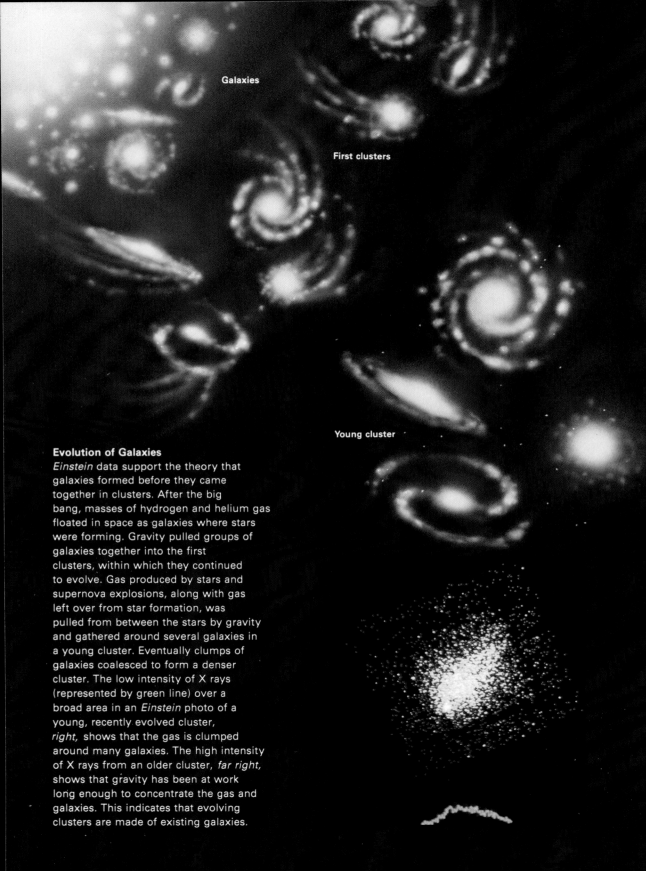

Galaxies

First clusters

Young cluster

Evolution of Galaxies

Einstein data support the theory that
galaxies formed before they came
together in clusters. After the big
bang, masses of hydrogen and helium gas
floated in space as galaxies where stars
were forming. Gravity pulled groups of
galaxies together into the first
clusters, within which they continued
to evolve. Gas produced by stars and
supernova explosions, along with gas
left over from star formation, was
pulled from between the stars by gravity
and gathered around several galaxies in
a young cluster. Eventually clumps of
galaxies coalesced to form a denser
cluster. The low intensity of X rays
(represented by green line) over a
broad area in an *Einstein* photo of a
young, recently evolved cluster,
right, shows that the gas is clumped
around many galaxies. The high intensity
of X rays from an older cluster, *far right,*
shows that gravity has been at work
long enough to concentrate the gas and
galaxies. This indicates that evolving
clusters are made of existing galaxies.

Old cluster

When they considered the implications of their theories, the astrophysicists were confronted with a basic cosmological question: Is the universe open or closed? That is, will the expansion that began with the big bang go on forever, or will something stop it and make the universe collapse? If the observed X-ray background comes from spread-out gas, so much would be required that it would exceed the mass of everything else in the universe. The pull of gravity among the parts of such a massive universe would stop its expansion and cause it to collapse. The universe would be closed. However, if the X-ray background comes from many individual sources, and not from distributed gas, the universe will continue to expand forever. The universe would be open.

Using the high sensitivity of *Einstein*'s X-ray telescope and its fine ability to locate sources accurately, Giacconi, Tommaso Maccacaro of SAO, and I have been trying to answer both the astrophysical and the cosmological questions — we have been counting separate sources to see if there are enough to make up the background. The search for very faint individual sources contributing to the X-ray background requires careful detective work. In order to be sure that it is outside the galaxy, we must not only detect a source, but must also find out what it is. To do this, we compare X-ray observations with optical and radio studies of the same regions. Clues to the nature of a source have to be investigated and evaluated. Often several suspected objects on an optical photographic plate are located near an X-ray source, and each must be examined in order to decide which one is the true source. Some objects turn out to be normal stars. Other times we find a galaxy, a quasar, or what appears to be empty space.

The result of this process is an accurate list giving the location and brightness of presumably extragalactic X-ray sources. Then, by adding up all of these sources, we can measure how much of the background they contribute. By early 1981, we had learned that these X-ray sources amount to at least one-third of it.

Harvey D. Tananbaum and Gianni Zamorani of SAO have been studying the X-ray properties of quasars. They have found a correlation between the X-ray emission and optical brightness of these objects that lets them predict how much all these

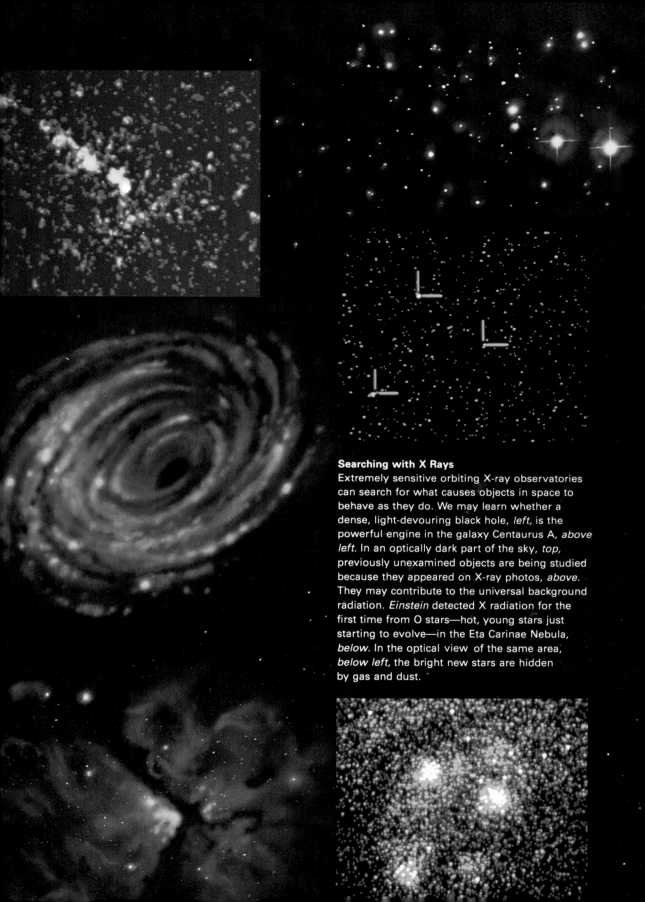

Searching with X Rays

Extremely sensitive orbiting X-ray observatories can search for what causes objects in space to behave as they do. We may learn whether a dense, light-devouring black hole, *left*, is the powerful engine in the galaxy Centaurus A, *above left*. In an optically dark part of the sky, *top*, previously unexamined objects are being studied because they appeared on X-ray photos, *above*. They may contribute to the universal background radiation. *Einstein* detected X radiation for the first time from O stars—hot, young stars just starting to evolve—in the Eta Carinae Nebula, *below*. In the optical view of the same area, *below left*, the bright new stars are hidden by gas and dust.

sources contribute to the X-ray background. Because optical telescopes have explored more of the sky than has *Einstein,* Tananbaum and Zamorani have used the results of their surveys to predict how much X-ray emission comes from all the quasars. Their data and our survey data were in close agreement as to the number of sources seen and the number expected just beyond the present sensitivity limit of our X-ray observatory. We therefore concluded that at least two-thirds, if not all, of the X-ray background must come from individual sources, with quasars being the dominant class of emitting objects.

This result makes it highly unlikely that the universe contains large amounts of hot gas in the empty regions between clusters of galaxies. If this is true, there is too little mass to allow the universe to be gravitationally bound, or closed. There are only a few places left where the material required for a closed universe could be hiding. Such mass might be hidden in black holes — regions of collapsed stars so dense that not even light can escape from them. Another site might be in the centers of galaxies. Future observations in X rays as well as at other wavelengths may show whether such is the case. But, for now, the universe appears to be open.

Those of us whose lives were involved for so long with the *Einstein* Observatory were saddened on April 26, 1981, when it reached the end of its active life. We knew it would start to plummet toward the earth and burn up some time in 1982. But today we find ourselves asking, "Now what?" Our appetites have been sharpened. We have seen how much there is to learn through X-ray astronomy, particularly with an X-ray telescope. Astronomers and astrophysicists throughout the United States agreed long ago that a new X-ray space satellite must be ready to go beyond *Einstein.* As of the summer of 1981, NASA was studying the possibility of launching an Advanced X-ray Astrophysical Facility (AXAF) during the 1980s. AXAF, more than twice as big as *Einstein,* will be in orbit for at least 10 years. Present plans call for launching the facility from the Space Shuttle.

Various scientific groups are developing improved instruments to be used with the AXAF telescope. New types of measurements will be possible, such as simultaneous high-resolution imaging and spectroscopy. This will enable astronomers to see separate spectra from each individual structure, and to isolate for study different processes that are going on at the same time. This satellite will be used as a national observatory, just as Kitt Peak National Observatory and the National Radio Astronomy Observatory are now and as the Space Telescope will be after it is launched, probably in 1984.

With an observatory like AXAF, astronomers will continue to make detailed studies of stars, galaxies, quasars, and clusters. We will be able to probe even further back in time as AXAF extends the range of X-ray observations. Perhaps someday we will be able to see the formation of galaxies, probe the mystery of the quasars, and penetrate the curtain that obscures the early history of the universe.

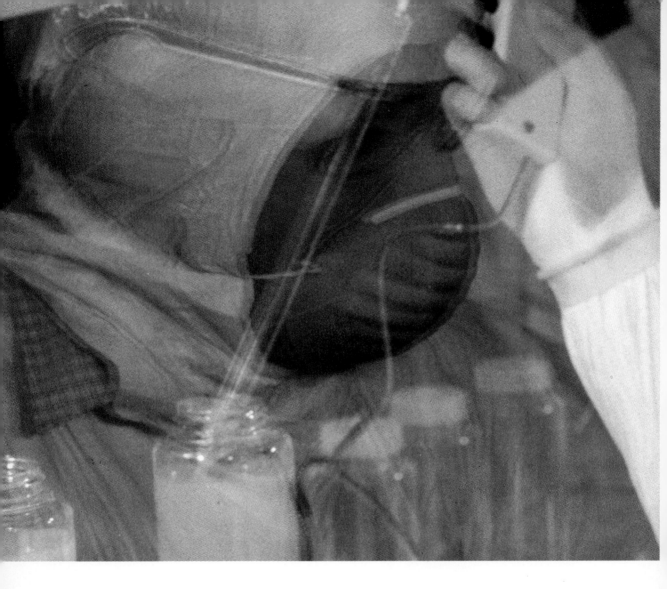

The Opening Shot at Hepatitis

By Ben Patrusky

**Targets of a vast research effort, the several
forms of this viral liver disease may soon
be retreating in a world health battle**

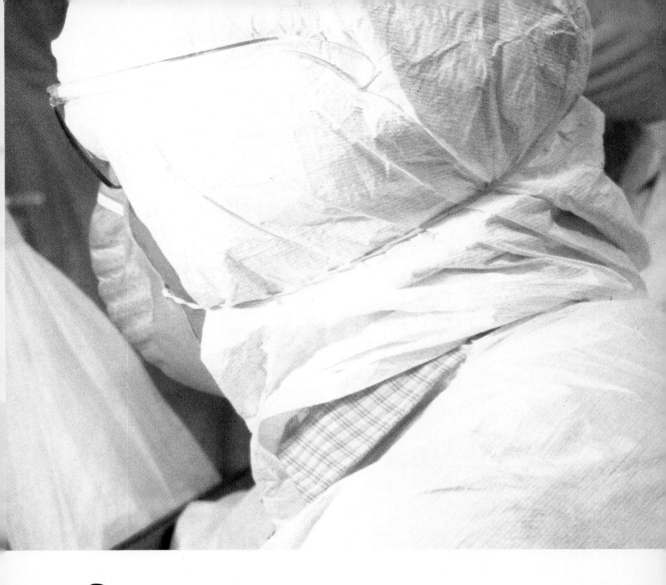

Sometime in late 1981 or early 1982, barring any last-minute hitches, a vaccine against hepatitis B — a sometimes fatal liver disease caused by a virus — will go on sale in the United States. This vaccine represents the first major victory in a campaign against several kinds of viral hepatitis that began nearly 20 years ago. It gives promise of other vaccines that will help control this serious public health problem, which affects millions of people throughout the world. Although the new vaccine will control only one form of hepatitis, it may also limit primary hepatocellular cancer (PHC), a deadly form of liver cancer that has been linked to hepatitis B.

The symptoms of any form of hepatitis (the word means liver inflammation) are generally the same — fatigue, weakness, loss of appetite, vomiting, skin itch, and coffee-colored urine. The most telling symptom is jaundice, a yellowing of the skin and the whites of the eyes. This discoloration indicates that bile — a substance manufactured by the liver to help digestion — is being improperly processed and has backed up into the bloodstream, coloring the victim's skin and eyes with its yellow-orange hue. Almost anything that impairs liver function can cause hepatitis. Long-term overuse of alcohol, for example, can cause alcoholic hepatitis. And, by inflaming the liver, hepatitis can adversely affect dozens of life processes.

Scientists knew for many years that certain kinds of hepatitis were transmitted from person to person. They recognized two such forms of the disease — infectious hepatitis (now called hepatitis A); and serum, or transfusion, hepatitis (hepatitis B). Each, researchers thought, was caused by a different virus; certainly, they spread in different ways.

World War II medical studies showed that hepatitis A was spread when the suspected virus, excreted in the feces of a hepatitis victim, entered the digestive tract of another person, either through poor hygiene — traces of fecal matter on the hands of food preparers, for example — or by eating raw shellfish or other uncooked fish taken from polluted waters. Hepatitis B, by contrast, seemed to be a blood-borne disease communicable only through direct transfusion with virus-tainted blood, or unsterile injections, as in the case of drug addicts sharing the same contaminated needle.

Hepatitis A takes about 15 to 40 days to incubate. But for hepatitis B, the time between exposure and onset of illness is about 60 to 160 days. Once they strike, however, it is hard to tell one from the other.

In the early 1960s, hepatitis research was stalled. Scientists sought a marker in victims' blood, a viral fingerprint that could be readily detected. Such a marker could help them differentiate between serum and infectious hepatitis, explain how the diseases spread, and enable blood banks to devise a screening test to weed out tainted blood. What was needed, perhaps, was some good luck.

The lucky break came from an unexpected quarter in 1963. Geneticist Baruch S. Blumberg certainly was not thinking much about viral hepatitis as he worked in his laboratory at the National Institutes of Health in Bethesda, Md. But he stumbled on a curious thing as he was examining thousands of blood samples to map genetic variations in the proteins found in blood serum, or fluid, around the world. A sample taken from an Australian Aborigine yielded a mysterious agent that Blumberg had never seen before. He dubbed it the Australia (Au) antigen. (An antigen is any foreign substance that provokes the body's immune system to produce antibodies to fight it.)

His curiosity aroused, Blumberg began a search to identify the Au-antigen. He started by tracking its global distribution. Checking his extensive collection of blood samples, he uncovered a perplexing geographic bias: The Au-antigen was rarely found in the serum of North American and Western European peoples, but it was frequently found in serum taken from individuals living in Asia and Africa.

The author:
Ben Patrusky is
a science writer
who often covers
medical subjects.

Eventually, this distribution made sense; it paralleled the incidence of hepatitis B — much higher in Africa and the Far East than in the West. Blumberg had to wait until 1967, however, for the first strong hint that the Au-antigen was somehow linked to hepatitis. That clue came when a laboratory technician, who had been working with the Au-antigen, became ill. Her initial symptoms were suspicious — loss of appetite, general fatigue, and dark urine. She was watched closely, her blood monitored regularly, and one day the Au-antigen made a fleeting appearance. Not long afterward, the technician developed a full-blown case of hepatitis with jaundice.

In 1968, virologist Alfred M. Prince of the New York Blood Center discovered the same antigen in the blood of patients with known, or suspected, hepatitis B — but not in patients with hepatitis A. Whatever it was, the Au-antigen was an unequivocal sign of one species of virus, the agent responsible for hepatitis B. This gave scientists a clear-cut marker to differentiate between the two diseases.

Prince was also quick to see how the Au-antigen could serve as the basis of a blood-bank test to screen out virus-tainted blood or to catch apparently healthy, would-be donors who were carriers of hepatitis B. Carriers — about 10 per cent of hepatitis B victims — remain potentially infectious to others for many years. Prince decided to challenge the blood specimens with antibodies against the Au-antigen. If the antibody reacted, the blood was tainted and should be discarded. Such screening is now nearly 100 per cent accurate, and is mandatory in all blood banks. Hepatitis B was eliminated as a serious transfusion peril by the late 1970s.

With its link to hepatitis B established, the Au-antigen forced a major revision in thinking about how the disease is transmitted. The foundation for that shift was a series of studies conducted in the late 1950s at the Willowbrook State School for retarded children in Staten Island, New York, where hepatitis was widespread. New students at Willowbrook almost invariably contracted hepatitis within two years after admission. Pediatrician-virologist Saul Krugman of the New York University School of Medicine had collected blood samples from a number of children soon after their arrival at Willowbrook. After learning of the hepatitis and Au-antigen connection in the 1960s, Krugman went back and re-examined the carefully preserved blood samples. He detected the Au-antigen in a number of these samples, including some from children who had no history of injections or transfusions. These children must have contracted hepatitis B at Willowbrook in some other fashion.

Prince puzzled over similar observations in a study of close relatives of hepatitis patients. Even though these relatives had not had any transfusions or injections, they tested positively for the Au-antigen far more frequently than did the general population. Prince concluded that the needle was not the only means of transmission. Apparently, close contact was enough. By sharing the same fork,

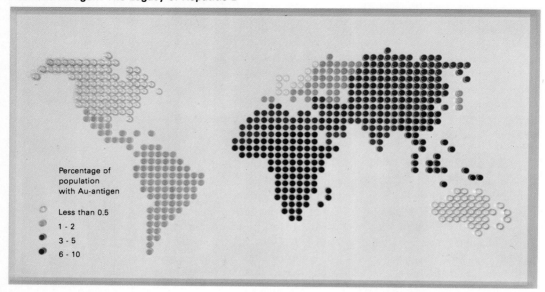

Percentage of
population
with Au-antigen

○ Less than 0.5

◐ 1 - 2

● 3 - 5

● 6 - 10

The Australia antigen appears most frequently in the blood of people who live in Africa and Southeast Asia, where hepatitis B is most prevalent. Primary hepatocellular cancer, a liver cancer, is also common in these areas.

razor, or toothbrush, for instance, or by intimate sexual contact, people could pass on hepatitis B. Mucous membranes or breaks in the skin were likely alternative entryways into the body. Eventually, the Au-antigen was found in a variety of body fluids, including sweat, tears, breast milk, saliva, and semen.

But what was the Au-antigen, now clearly defined as the hepatitis B calling card? How was it linked to the disease-causing virus? Was it part of the virus, or a by-product of the virus' invasion of the liver?

Vital clues came from electron microscopy, which revealed the typical presence of three distinct kinds of particles in the serum of hepatitis B patients: spherical particles measuring 22 nanometers in diameter, the most abundant by far of the three; rodlike cylindrical units of the same diameter; and Dane particles, which were discovered in 1970 by British virologist D. S. Dane. These particles have an inner core measuring 26 nanometers and an outer envelope measuring 42 nanometers. (A nanometer is one-billionth of a meter.)

Other experimental studies — at the Wellcome Research Laboratories in England and in the United States at Baylor College of Medicine, Stanford Medical Center, and the National Institutes of Health — established the roles played by each particle. The Dane particle is the complete virus. Its core contains the genetic machinery, the deoxyribonucleic acid (DNA), of the virus. Wrapped around the core is a viral coat or envelope. When the virus invades the liver, it converts liver cells into factories that make more virus particles. However, the Dane particles show a streak of manufacturing extravagance. The viruses prompt liver cells to produce much more coat than

Hepatitis B: The Virus Leaves its Markers

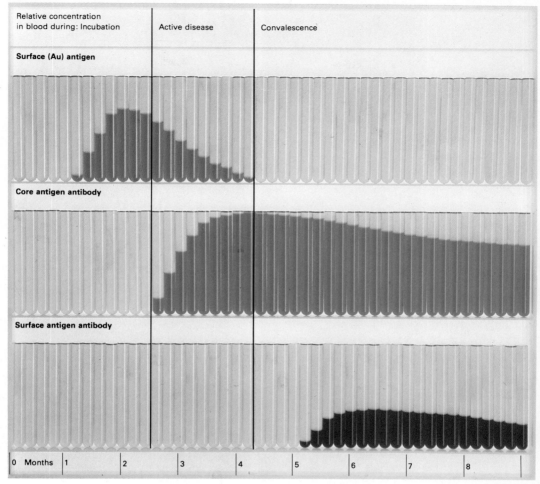

Relative concentration in blood during: Incubation	Active disease	Convalescence

Surface (Au) antigen

Core antigen antibody

Surface antigen antibody

0 Months 1 2 3 4 5 6 7 8

core. The spheres and rodlike particles are excess wrapping material, each made of exactly the same protein as the Dane particle envelope. Blumberg's Au-antigen — now known as the hepatitis B surface antigen (HB$_s$Ag) — was this common surface or envelope protein.

This common factor held the key to developing a vaccine to prevent hepatitis B. Vaccines work by provoking antibody response without causing disease. Normally the virus itself — either totally inactivated (killed) or weakened (attenuated-live) — is injected into the body. This stimulates the production of antibodies to protect the body against the disease. But researchers have to grow a virus in large quantities to prepare an effective vaccine, and all attempts to grow the hepatitis B virus in the laboratory failed.

The body's immune system does not discriminate between the full hepatitis B virus and the overproduced packaging. It marshals the

Various markers appear in blood samples of hepatitis B victims at different stages of the disease. The surface antigen appears before the symptoms do, thus permitting blood banks to screen for infected blood. The antibody to the core antigen appears after the disease is full-blown, and is a less useful marker. When the surface antigen's antibody appears, the victim is recovering.

157

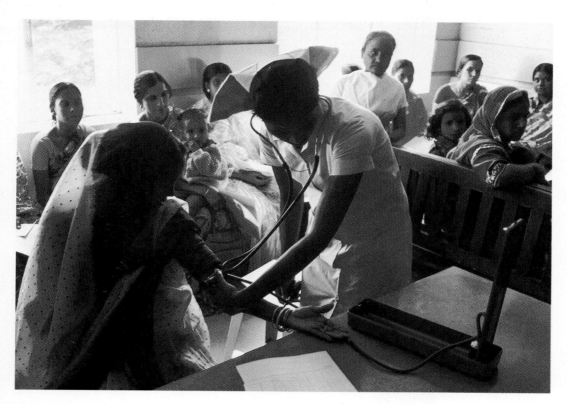

A young woman is
examined in a public
health clinic in India.

same antibody response to each. Blumberg suspected this and proposed to use the excess coat material as a substitute for the virus.
Introduced as a vaccine, the HB_sAg wrapping-only protein ought to
stimulate the production of antibodies that would also neutralize the
whole virus. Blumberg reasoned that long-term hepatitis B carriers,
who carry the antigen in their blood, could serve as "donors," and the
antigen extracted from their blood would be used in a vaccine.

There was evidence that such an unconventional approach might
work. In 1970, Krugman and his colleagues had immunized some
Willowbrook children with a crude "vaccine" produced by boiling
serum taken from carriers. ("Nothing fancy," said Krugman. "We
just heated the serum up on a kitchen stove.") The boiling was
intended to inactivate the virus without depriving the antigen particles of their ability to provoke an antibody response. The preparation
proved surprisingly effective. About 70 per cent of the children
inoculated with this adlib vaccine stayed free of the disease, even
when exposed to the live virus.

Krugman's results spurred efforts to develop a pure vaccine. Several investigative teams settled on essentially the same approach. They
set about preparing a vaccine made up of only the spherical, 22-
nanometer coat particle extracted from donors' blood. By 1975, two
U.S. teams—virologist Maurice R. Hilleman and his colleagues at

the Merck Institute for Therapeutic Research in West Point, Pa., and virologist Robert Purcell and his associates at the National Institute of Allergy and Infectious Diseases (NIAID) in Bethesda — were testing their vaccines in chimpanzees, the only laboratory animal found to be susceptible to the human hepatitis B virus. Both of the vaccines proved safe and effective in fighting off inoculated live virus in the chimps.

After preliminary small-scale human tests, the New York Blood Center — the largest blood collection agency in the United States — launched a large-scale test of the Merck vaccine in 1978. Under the direction of epidemiologist Wolf Szmuness, the study followed more than 1,000 male homosexuals, who, for reasons of sexual promiscuity, run a risk of contracting hepatitis B that is perhaps 50 to 100 times greater than that of the general population. Half the men received the vaccine and the other half were given a placebo, or dummy injection. Each received three shots over a six-month period in a double-blind trial — that is, neither the doctors nor the participants knew who was getting which injection. This was done to eliminate the danger of experimental bias. The findings, reported late in 1980, showed that the vaccine was 96 per cent effective in triggering the production of antibodies to HB_sAg and 92 per cent effective in protecting against the disease. With confirmation of the vaccine's effectiveness, and imminent license approval by the U.S. Food and Drug Administration (FDA), the Merck product will probably become available in 1982.

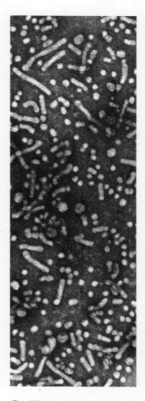

Rodlike and circular particles of the virus that causes hepatitis B (magnified 120,000 times) are used to make hepatitis B vaccine.

Meanwhile, research efforts to design safer, if not more effective, inoculants continue. Scientists worry about vaccines that depend on antigens collected from the serum of carriers. "No biological separation is 100 per cent perfect," says Purcell. It is always possible that unwanted serum proteins or other contaminants might inadvertently slip into the preparations and cause adverse reactions later. For that reason, Purcell and his colleagues continue to test the NIAID vaccine on a small scale in hopes of refining it more. Others are trying an alternative strategy, chopping the purified HB_sAg antigens — the spherical viral coats — into smaller protein subunits called polypeptides, which can still provoke antibody response. The extra step would increase the margin of safety by further purifying the vaccine.

The ideal, however, is to eliminate dependency on hepatitis B carriers as donors. One course would be to find a way to grow viruses in the laboratory and produce weakened- or killed-virus vaccines. Barring that, scientists are also turning to recombinant DNA, or gene-splicing, techniques. They want to isolate the viral gene that carries instructions for the manufacture of HB_sAg and insert it into *Escherichia coli*, a common bacterium. These *E. coli* — all bearing the newly acquired genetic information — would become miniature HB_sAg factories. In 1980, John L. Gerin of Oak Ridge National Laboratory's Rockville (Md.) Molecular Anatomy Laboratory succeeded in coaxing a colony of *E. coli* to accept a viral genetic fragment

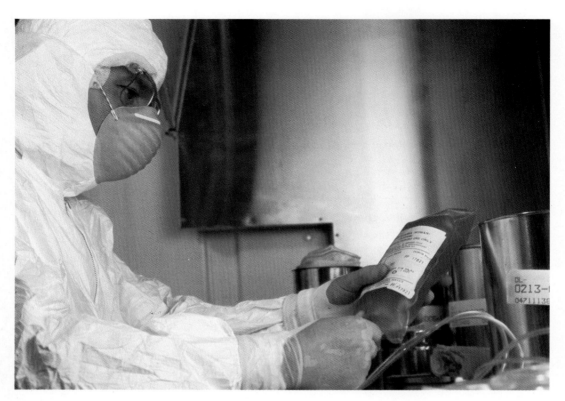

Masked, gloved, and wearing a protective suit to avoid infection, a pharmaceutical worker checks the blood plasma taken from hepatitis B carriers that is the raw material used to make a hepatitis B vaccine.

containing the gene that programs for the hepatitis B surface antigen, and to actually produce HB$_s$Ag proteins. Purcell expects that HB$_s$Ag harvested from bacteria will be the standard vaccine in five years.

Whatever vaccines ultimately become available, there is no question that such preventives are urgently needed. Administered to high-risk candidates, such as spouses of hepatitis carriers, male homosexuals, patients on artificial kidneys, hospital and laboratory personnel, infants born to hepatitis B carriers, and pregnant women, vaccines will undoubtedly make a big dent in the hepatitis B toll. The Centers for Disease Control (CDC) in Atlanta, Ga., which keep count of disease incidence in the United States, record about 15,000 hepatitis B cases per year. But there is little doubt that the true tally is considerably higher. On the basis of a 1980 national survey, investigators at CDC's hepatitis laboratory in Phoenix estimate that at least 50,000 people contract hepatitis B with jaundice annually, while several times that number may be infected with milder symptoms. Even though it may take as long as six to 12 months for the disease to run its course, most patients eventually recover completely. Their livers return to normal, and their blood contains antibodies to HB$_s$Ag that make them immune to repeat bouts.

Unfortunately, some hepatitis B victims can have further problems. Perhaps 5 per cent of all hepatitis B victims develop some degree of

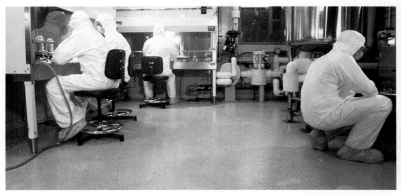

chronic hepatitis, a long-term, debilitating form of the disease. This may make them more susceptible to the progressive degeneration of the liver that ends in cirrhosis. Cirrhosis and liver failure caused by hepatitis B account for about 3,500 deaths in the United States annually. Currently, the United States has about 800,000 hepatitis B carriers. By reducing the number of new carriers, the vaccine should greatly reduce the incidence of cirrhosis as well as hepatitis.

Far more impressive, perhaps, is the impact vaccines could have throughout the world. About 200 million persons, perhaps 5 per cent of the world's population, are hepatitis B carriers. Most of these people live in Africa and Asia. In Taiwan, for instance, 1 in every 5 or 6 persons has chronic hepatitis B viral infection. Szmuness began a trial in Taiwan in 1981 to determine if the Merck vaccine is effective in stopping hepatitis B in children between 2 and 7 years old. He plans another study on infants born to HB_sAg carrier mothers.

An exciting and no less significant added benefit of the vaccine is the likelihood that its protection against hepatitis B will ultimately cause a sharp decline in primary hepatocellular cancer (PHC). This generally fatal liver cancer is one of the two or three most common cancers in the world. A large, still-growing body of evidence suggests that hepatitis B infection sets the stage for many cases of PHC. A worldwide survey, for example, showed a striking correlation between

A technician checks the control panel, *top left,* as the process of producing pure Australia antigen from blood plasma begins. After most contaminants are removed chemically, other workers examine samples of semipurified antigen in a "hot" lab under stringently sterile conditions, *above left.* In another purification step, a high-speed centrifuge, *above,* separates the last of the whole viruses and concentrates the antigen for later stages in the manufacture of vaccine.

the incidence of hepatitis B and PHC cases. In the United States, where the incidence of hepatitis B is relatively low, only about 5,000 cases of PHC turn up annually, but Taiwan, with about 18 million people, reports 10,000 PHC cases each year. Moreover, about 90 per cent of those who develop PHC in high-incidence areas have HB_sAg in their blood. A study of Taiwanese civil servants showed an incidence of PHC 40 times greater among hepatitis B carriers than among control subjects whose blood contained no HB_sAG. After studying Japanese railway workers for several years, scientists reported finding 3 cases of PHC among 341 hepatitis B carriers and none among 17,843 controls. Supporting evidence comes from virologist Jesse Summers, a colleague of Blumberg's at the Institute of Cancer Research, who discovered a viral infection in woodchucks that bears a striking resemblance to that seen in human hepatitis B. The woodchuck disease has a carrier state, and results in a high incidence of liver cancer among the carrier-woodchucks.

Vaccines hold rich promise in preventing future hepatitis infections and subsequent liver cancers. But what about those already infected? In general, scientists have not been very successful in doing battle with the viral disease once the infection has begun. But there may be a chance of cure for those who now have chronic hepatitis. That glimmer of hope springs from a limited study in which carriers were treated with a combination of two antiviral drugs — interferon and adenosine arabinoside (ara-A). Immunologist Thomas C. Merigan and his associates at Stanford Medical Center in California reported in 1980 that they had successfully treated the carrier state in 44 per cent of a small group of hepatitis patients. NIAID is now considering a full-scale trial of this treatment.

The avalanche of research stirred by Blumberg's discovery was hardly confined to hepatitis B alone. Inevitably, there was spillover, and before long scientists were also learning enough about hepatitis A that a vaccine against it now seems imminent.

The pivotal advance came in 1973. Using electron microscopy, Stephen M. Feinstone of NIAID saw the virus for the first time. Feinstone found it in feces samples from human volunteers who had been experimentally inoculated with serum from hepatitis A patients. The hepatitis A virus is about half as large as the hepatitis B virus and it also differs markedly in structure. That was to be expected. The A virus, transmitted by feces, can survive passage through the digestive tract. But the B virus is destroyed in the tract and must find other ways to enter the body. And, unlike B, the A virus produces no excess coat material, no excess antigen. In hepatitis A, the virus and the surface antigen are all of a piece; the virus is its own marker, its own fingerprint. The identification of the virus soon led to a sensitive detection test — not for the virus itself, because it is not always easy to spot in blood, but rather for antibodies to the virus, which are readily found circulating in the blood soon after infection begins.

With such antibody markers now known, scientists have been getting better at monitoring the scope and patterns of hepatitis A infections. From all indications, hepatitis A is on the decline in the United States and Western Europe as a result of improved sanitary conditions and hygienic practices. The number of cases is still far from insignificant, however. CDC officially recorded about 30,000 cases last year. But, as with hepatitis B, the true tally is much greater than that. Based on their 1980 survey, Donald Francis and his co-workers at the CDC hepatitis lab in Phoenix estimate that at least 150,000 cases of severe hepatitis A with jaundice occur per year, plus several times that many with milder symptoms. Hepatitis A is far more benign than hepatitis B, however. There is no carrier state and no chronic condition that progressively destroys the liver. The disease can be extremely distressing, but it is self-limiting. Once well, a patient will suffer no recurrences. As a result, hepatitis A-related deaths are rare — perhaps 50 per year in the United States.

The origin of most hepatitis A infections continues to puzzle investigators. They have been able to trace the source in fewer than 40 per cent of reported cases. Recently, however, the CDC Phoenix team identified day-care centers as a major infection source — particularly those centers that accept children still in diapers. The team surveyed thousands of day-care centers in more than 20 states in 1980. "We saw a clear pattern," says CDC's Francis. "Those in the Northern states, which generally do not accept infants in diapers, had a much lower incidence of hepatitis than those in the Southern states, where diapered infants are generally admitted." According to Francis, as many as 10 per cent of all hepatitis A cases in the United States may be traceable to day-care centers. Diaper-changing is thought to be the critical factor. Generally, the hepatitis A infection is benign in infants. Many show no symptoms. It is the adult day-care employees and their families who appear to be most at risk.

Not long ago, the Phoenix team helped to quash an outbreak in the area by improving hygienic practices in day-care centers and by administering gamma globulin to all individuals associated with the centers. Gamma globulin, or immunoglobulin, offers short-term protection against hepatitis A. It is not a vaccine. While vaccines stimulate the body to make protective antibodies, gamma globulin, a blood extract distilled from the contributions of many blood donors, provides passive, or "borrowed" protection. Scientists presume that many adults had mild forms of hepatitis A during childhood, so at least some of the blood combined from many donors and used to make gamma globulin should contain antibodies against hepatitis A. But scientists do not know if gamma globulin provides protection against hepatitis B.

Scientists may soon be able to offer hepatitis A protection. The possibility of a vaccine arose in 1979 when NIAID's Purcell succeeded in growing the hepatitis A virus in cell culture. Merck's Hilleman

The Vaccine: A High-Grade Pass on Test

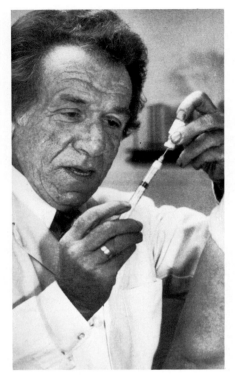

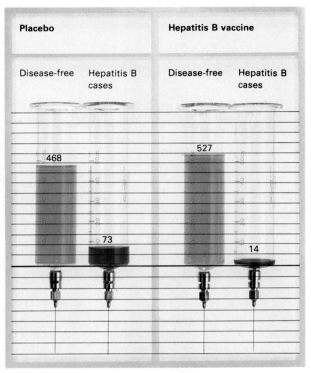

Placebo		Hepatitis B vaccine	
Disease-free	Hepatitis B cases	Disease-free	Hepatitis B cases
468	73	527	14

Epidemiologist Wolf Szmuness prepares to inject a volunteer with hepatitis B vaccine, *above.* The vaccine was remarkably successful in tests on a group of high-risk men. Only 2.6 per cent of those given the vaccine contracted the disease, *above right,* while 15.6 per cent of those who received the placebo, or dummy, injections were infected.

has since done the same. Human trials of an attenuated-live-virus vaccine developed by Merck may begin in 1982.

Currently, the hottest research activity centers around a newly discovered form of post-transfusion hepatitis. This form surfaced in the mid-1970s soon after mandatory screening had all but eliminated hepatitis B as a blood-bank peril. Tests showed that the new illness was neither hepatitis A nor hepatitis B, so it was named for what it was not — non A/non B (NANB) hepatitis. NANB accounts for at least 90 per cent of all current cases of post-transfusion hepatitis.

In 1978, two research groups independently produced NANB hepatitis in chimpanzees by inoculating them with serum taken from patients suffering from post-transfusion hepatitis, or from persons with a history of transmitting the disease to others. These studies proved that an infectious agent was involved and that, like hepatitis B, the new disease produced a carrier state. Medical researchers Edward Tabor and Robert J. Gerety of the FDA's Bureau of Biologics also demonstrated that the disease was probably caused by a virus. When they treated a hepatitis-infected blood sample with formalin, a chemical that weakens or kills viruses, the serum lost its power to produce disease.

The guilty virus has yet to be identified. The most promising prospect seems to be viruslike particles, ranging in size from 25 to 33 nanometers, observed by virologist Daniel W. Bradley and his associates at the CDC in Phoenix. But, as FDA's Tabor warns, "It's very easy to find things that look like viruses in serum or liver tissue."

Moreover, there is a strong likelihood that two different viruses may be to blame. One piece of evidence comes from experimental trials in which chimpanzees developed NANB hepatitis twice, after having been inoculated with serum from different blood samples. Normally, recovery from a viral infection prevents a subsequent attack by the same virus. And epidemiologist James W. Mosley and liver researcher Allen G. Redecker of the University of Southern California School of Medicine reported in 1975 that they found a number of patients who experienced two distinct episodes of NANB hepatitis, in addition to previous bouts with hepatitis A and hepatitis B. Again, one NANB attack should have conferred immunity against any later infection — unless NANB is caused by more than one virus. NANB's incubation period — the time between the transfusion and the appearance of the symptoms — also varies in a way that suggests two diseases. NANB hepatitis has been found to fall into two different time frames — very short incubation (2 to 4 weeks) and long incubation (8 to 12 weeks). These distinctly different patterns seem to support a two-virus theory.

At present, the main research aim is to find blood markers — antigens characteristic of the NANB virus or viruses, or antibodies to those antigens. Once identified, these will be used to screen out blood capable of transmitting post-transfusion hepatitis. Such a test will certainly help to reduce the incidence of NANB hepatitis, which is hardly insignificant. The six-year federally sponsored Transfusion-Transmitted Virus Study, comparing the incidence of disease among hospitalized surgical patients who received transfusions with that of surgical patients who did not, found that from 5 to 15 per cent of donor-blood recipients may develop NANB hepatitis. About 3 million Americans received transfusions in 1980.

Until a blood marker, or specific fingerprint, for NANB hepatitis turns up, scientists plan to use some sort of nonspecific test to screen for the disease. One possibility is to measure blood levels of alanine-aminotransferase (ALT), a liver enzyme. Damage to liver cells, whatever the cause, discharges ALT into the blood. According to the Transfusion-Transmitted Virus Study, monitoring for elevated blood levels of ALT in blood donors might prevent 30 to 40 per cent of NANB hepatitis cases. Many blood centers will soon begin to screen for ALT — at least until something better comes along.

The remarkable advances in knowledge since 1963 have brought scientists to a new era in the war on viral hepatitis. If the preceding decades were a period of enlightenment and mobilization, the coming decades are likely to be an era of conquest. Scientists are now on the verge of controlling, if not erasing, a group of debilitating liver diseases that represent one of the world's greatest health menaces.

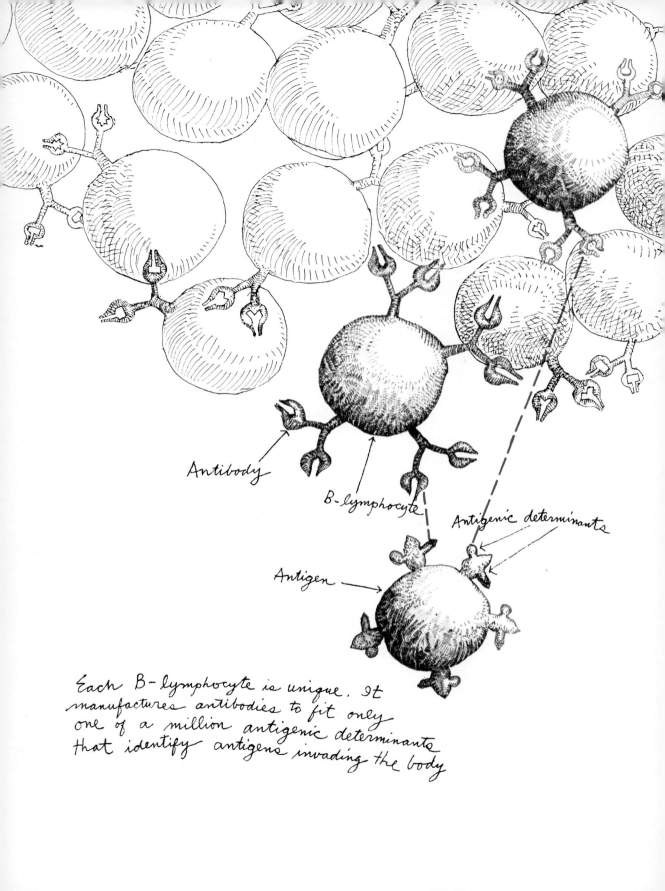

Antibody

B-lymphocyte

Antigenic determinants

Antigen

Each B-lymphocyte is unique. It manufactures antibodies to fit only one of a million antigenic determinants that identify antigens invading the body

Using Cancer to Fight Disease

By Michael Shodell

**Scientists have conferred the immortality of the
tumor cell upon a unique blood cell to create a
potential weapon against a multitude of illnesses**

A new form of cancer is running rife throughout the world. Surprisingly, physicians and researchers are greeting it with enthusiasm rather than apprehension. In fact, scientists themselves created it. In doing so, they harnessed the runaway growth of the tumor cell to expand the disease-fighting power of a unique body cell. The result is a potential weapon against diseases such as influenza and malaria, and even cancer itself.

This new cancer is called a hybridoma because it is a hybrid of a cancer cell and a B-lymphocyte — a white blood cell active in the body's immune system. The immune system is composed of several types of cells and molecules that combat disease and infection. The B-lymphocyte produces antibodies — molecules designed to search out and fasten themselves to other molecules called antigens. An antigen is any molecule that, upon entering the body, can trigger the immune response.

For a first-hand view of such an immune response, picture yourself shrunk to the size of a bacterium and entering someone's bloodstream. You are swept along briskly at first, but the pace of your journey slows as the blood enters a cavernous region solidly packed with boulder-sized cells. You are entering the spleen, an abdominal organ that filters impurities and dead cells out of the blood. The spleen is one of several organs in the body that contains very dense accumulations of blood cells, including lymphocytes.

Your journey has been slowed because the blood is being forced to percolate through this densely crowded throng of lymphocytes. As the tiny you gets pushed and squeezed between these cells, you notice that the surfaces of some of these cells are studded with molecules shaped very much like lobsters, with their tails fastened onto the B-lymphocyte surface and two arms sticking out. These are the antibody molecules. The ends of these arms are equipped with claws held in an open position.

As you move slowly through this region, you can see that the inside of the claws of all the antibodies studded around the surface of any one B-lymphocyte have exactly the same pattern of grooves, lumps, and wrinkles. Scientists call this claw shape the antibody molecule's *idiotype*. There are probably over a million different idiotypes in the body. Each B-lymphocyte and all of its offspring manufacture just one variety. One of them is waiting for you.

As you travel slowly through this thicket of claws, you become painfully aware of your own collection of lumps and bumps — your knees, thumbs, nose and toes. Sooner or later one of your protruding parts will slip into a waiting open claw which exactly matches its shape. The fit is so precise that barely a space exists between the bumps and crevices of the claw and the lumps and hollows of that part of your body.

Fortunately for you, you are the only antigen of your type. The chances of your passing through the spleen undetected by any of your idiotypic matches is actually quite good. However, if your numbers began to increase — as happens in the case of real bacteria — your presence would be picked up. The protruding parts of an antigen, which so neatly slip into waiting antibody claws, are called antigenic determinants. In your case, you would be an antigen displaying — in your facial features, limbs, and various body contours — a large number of complex antigenic determinants.

When the antibody claws on a B-lymphocyte surface meet their antigenic match, the B-lymphocyte is transformed into action. First it grows larger; then it divides into two cells. These cells continue to divide again and again, until the original B-lymphocyte has made a small crowd of itself — a clone of B-lymphocytes. These activated B-lymphoctyes synthesize antibody at an enormous rate. Instead of

The author:
Michael Shodell is associate professor of biology at Long Island University, C. W. Post Center, in Greenvale, N. Y.

staying on the cell surface, the antibody is excreted into general circulation where it can travel to all parts of the body. All of the cells of a B-lymphocyte clone are specialized in making antibody of precisely the same idiotype as the antibody produced by the original B-lymphocyte.

The antibody molecules continue to circulate freely until they encounter their matching antigenic determinant, wherever in the body it might be. When this happens, their claws stick fast to it. Now, however, the antibody molecule's tail is left wagging freely behind as a signal to the body's heavy hitters — two other types of white blood cells, leucocytes and macrophages, and a series of enzymes known as complement. Anything with antibody clinging to it is soon engulfed and digested by these components of the immune system, leaving only traces of unrecognizable debris to mark the spot where the antigen was obliterated.

Because they mark antigens for destruction, antibodies are obviously powerful disease-fighting tools. Until recently, however, scientists were unable to make full use of antibody power. It was extremely difficult to identify the B-lymphocyte that produces a specific antibody — for example, the antibody to the measles virus — among a million B-lymphocyte types in a blood sample. Moreover, even if a laborious trial-and-error procedure turned up the right B-lymphocyte, researchers did not know how to keep the precious cells alive in the laboratory long enough to produce antibodies in quantities that could be used in research or to treat disease.

Then in 1975, immunologists Cesar Milstein and Georges Köhler of the Medical Research Council laboratories in Cambridge, England, found a solution. They "cancerized" a B-lymphocyte by fusing it with a malignant B-lymphocyte known as a myeloma cell, to create a hybrid that not only produced antibody but could also grow and divide indefinitely in laboratory culture. The scientists began by selecting a specific antigen — in this case, one carried on sheep red blood cells, because it stimulated production of an antibody that they could recognize easily. They repeatedly injected these blood cells into a mouse for several weeks and the antigen stimulated the mouse's B-lymphocytes to produce antibodies. Then the scientists removed the mouse's spleen. The spleen, of course, is a major source of B-lymphocytes making antibodies. The scientists knew that some of these antibodies would be specific for sheep's blood antigens. They broke the spleen into individual cells, some of which were active B-lymphocytes that produced mouse antibodies to sheep red blood cells.

The scientists mixed the spleen cells with mouse myeloma cells in a culture containing Sendai virus, which caused some of the cells to fuse. In subsequent experiments, they used a more efficient cell-fusion medium — a solution containing polyethylene glycol, a chemical that is the major ingredient in antifreeze. The polyethylene glycol causes cells to melt together like two snowballs rolled into one.

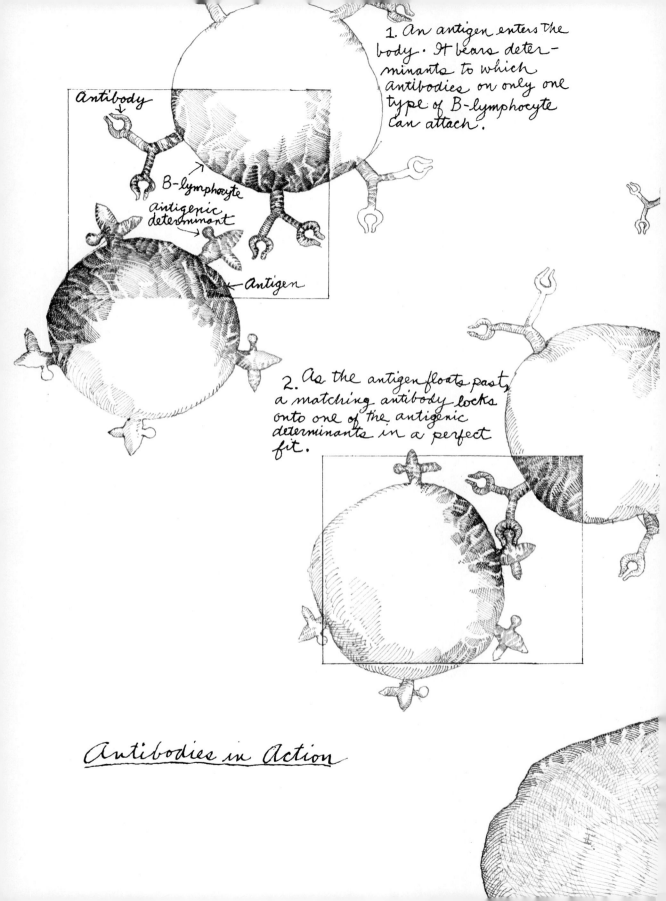

Antibody

B-lymphocyte

antigenic
determinant

Antigen

1. An antigen enters the body. It bears determinants to which antibodies on only one type of B-lymphocyte can attach.

2. As the antigen floats past, a matching antibody locks onto one of the antigenic determinants in a perfect fit.

Antibodies in Action

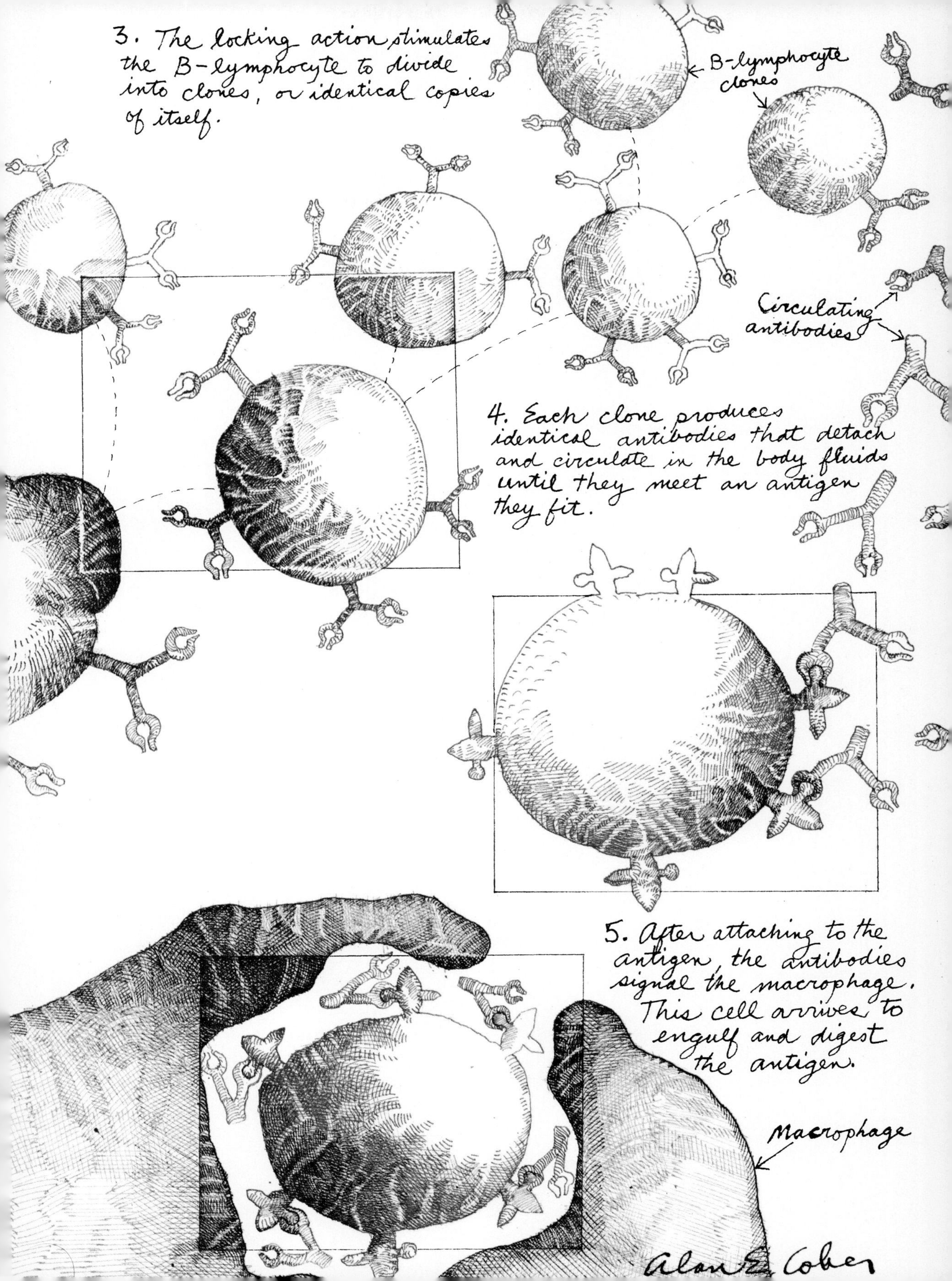

3. The locking action stimulates the B-lymphocyte to divide into clones, or identical copies of itself.

B-lymphocyte clones

Circulating antibodies

4. Each clone produces identical antibodies that detach and circulate in the body fluids until they meet an antigen they fit.

5. After attaching to the antigen, the antibodies signal the macrophage. This cell arrives to engulf and digest the antigen.

Macrophage

Alan E Cober

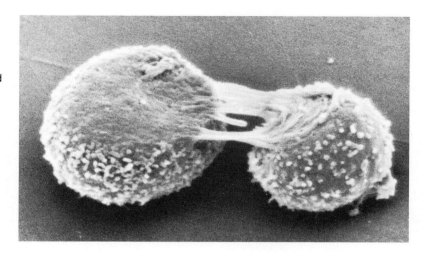

A cancer cell and a B-lymphocyte (magnified 10,000 times) melt together to form a hybridoma — a rapidly proliferating, antibody-producing hybrid.

They used a mouse cancer cell because it would be compatible with the mouse B-lymphocytes and a myeloma cell in particular because it is, in fact, a malignancy of a B-lymphocyte itself. The myeloma cell alone does not produce useful antibody but, fused with the normal B-lymphocyte, it does not interfere with the production of normal B-lymphocyte antibodies.

Milstein and Köhler then removed the hybrid, or hybridoma, cells from the virus medium and placed them in laboratory cultures. These individual cultures grew large numbers of cells — each one a clone of hybridoma cells. The scientists added sheep red blood cells to each of the clones, and found that the antibodies attached to the blood cells in several of the cultures. They concluded that the hybridomas in these cultures were formed from B-lymphocytes that secreted the antibody to sheep red blood cells.

By this procedure, Milstein and Köhler developed a hybridoma that made a specific antibody. They called this type of antibody *monoclonal* because it was produced by a clone of one type of B-lymphocyte. (*Monos* is a Greek word meaning *one*.)

There can be as many types of monoclonal antibodies as there are types of B-lymphocytes. For example, one type of monoclonal antibody may be specific for an antigenic determinant on the surface of a malarial parasite; another type might stick only to an antigenic determinant found on a particular bacterium; a third type might adhere to one type of virus. It may also be possible to obtain monoclonal antibodies that act against human cancer cell antigens. The possibilities are practically endless.

Because a monoclonal can be specific for cancer cells, it could be used to track these cells, allowing physicians to monitor the progress of the disease in patients. By using monoclonals to take a "head count" of the cancer cells that remain after radiation or drug therapy, physicians could determine the most effective treatment or combina-

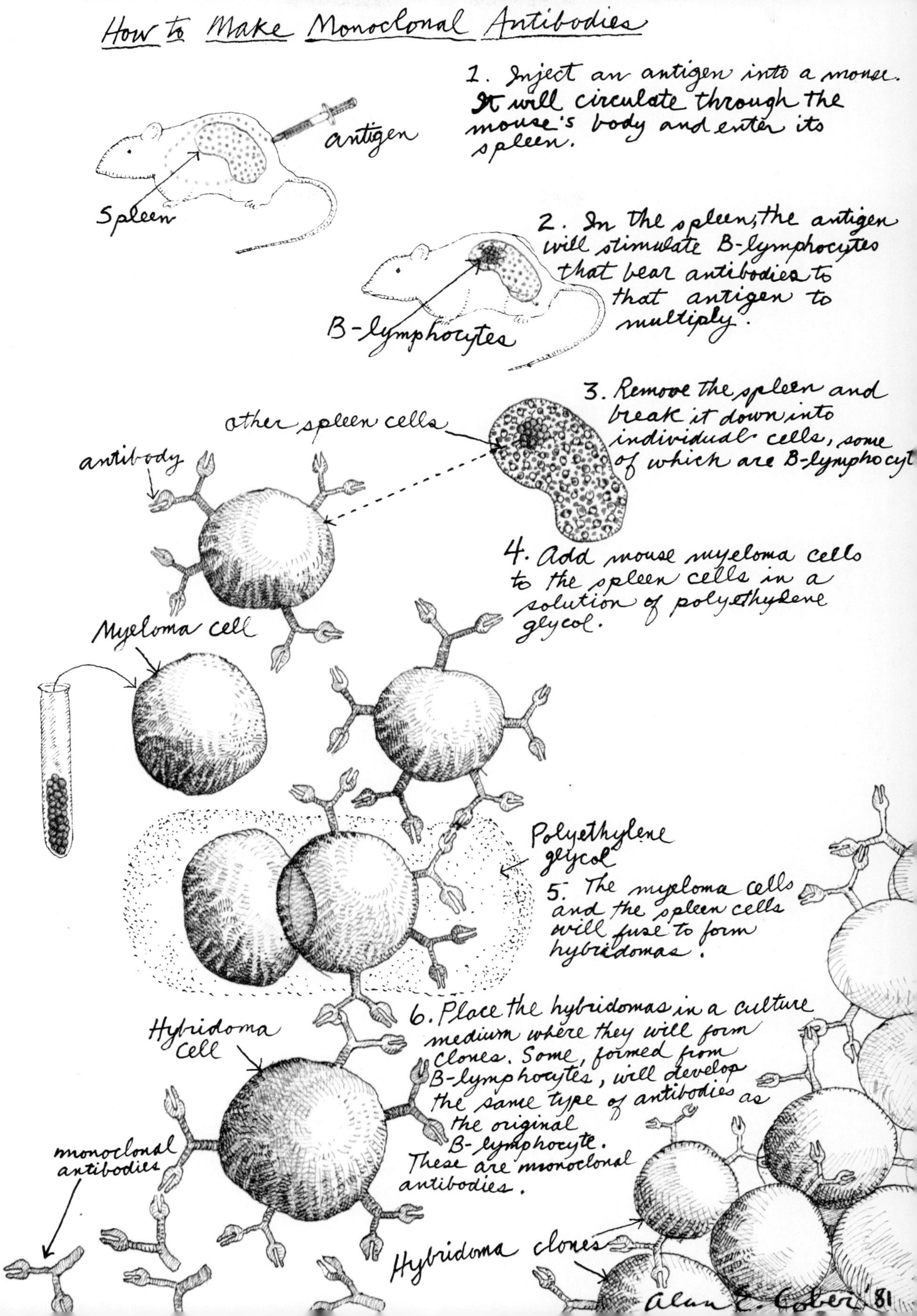

How to Make Monoclonal Antibodies

1. Inject an antigen into a mouse. It will circulate through the mouse's body and enter its spleen.

antigen

Spleen

2. In the spleen, the antigen will stimulate B-lymphocytes that bear antibodies to that antigen to multiply.

B-lymphocytes

other spleen cells

antibody

3. Remove the spleen and break it down into individual cells, some of which are B-lymphocyt[es]

4. Add mouse myeloma cells to the spleen cells in a solution of polyethylene glycol.

Myeloma cell

Polyethylene glycol

5. The myeloma cells and the spleen cells will fuse to form hybridomas.

Hybridoma Cell

6. Place the hybridomas in a culture medium where they will form clones. Some, formed from B-lymphocytes, will develop the same type of antibodies as the original B-lymphocyte. These are monoclonal antibodies.

monoclonal antibodies

Hybridoma clones

Alan E. Cober '81

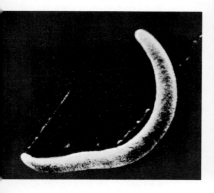

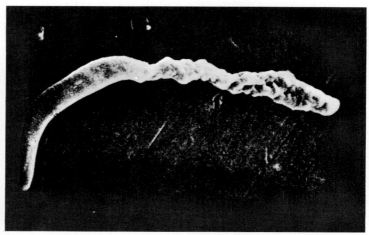

The smooth-bodied malaria parasite, *above,* when incubated in a serum containing antibodies, *above right,* sheds its wrinkled protein coat. By stripping it of its coat, an antibody has made the parasite ineffective (magnified 9,000 times).

tion of treatments for each patient. Using hybridoma technology, scientists have developed monoclonals not only to a variety of cancers, but also to some of the proteins that certain cancers make. These monoclonal antibodies may prove invaluable in detecting extremely early stages of the disease during which cancer cells are not yet evident but the proteins that they produce have begun to appear in the bloodstream.

Scientists have also used monoclonal antibodies to "see" hidden tumors. Researchers at the University of Pittsburgh and the Wistar Institute in Philadelphia reported in November 1979 that they had collaborated to produce a monoclonal specific for teratocarcinoma, a rare type of cancer, and used it to track a mouse tumor. To do this, the scientists first surgically implanted a small teratocarcinoma tumor in the thigh of a mouse. Soon after, they tagged the monoclonal antibody with radioactive iodine molecules and injected it into the mouse's circulatory system. They scanned the animal for radioactivity each day after the injection. Scans taken on the first four days following the injection showed radioactive points throughout the mouse's body. But, on the fifth day, a single radioactive spot remained, precisely at the site of the small tumor. The antibody had homed in on its cancerous target.

This homing property also has important implications for what is called targeted drug therapy. If the monoclonal antibodies can travel to cancer cells within the body, scientists may be able to attach some highly effective anticancer drugs to them. The monoclonal antibody would carry these drugs directly to the cancer cells, leaving the healthy body cells untouched. Because the targeted drugs would not damage healthy cells, the unpleasant side effects of many anticancer drugs would be minimized.

A team under the direction of immunologists Robert C. Nowinski and Irwin Bernstein at the Fred Hutchinson Cancer Center in Seattle

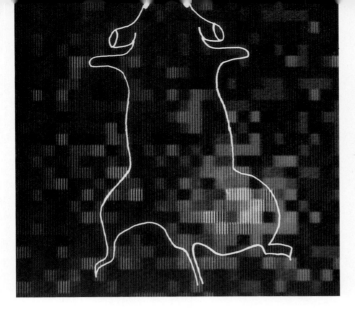

Radioactive monoclonal antibodies to cancer cells produce a patch of bright color on a computerized body scan of a mouse, indicating the site of a malignant tumor.

has reported promising results in using monoclonal antibodies not as drug carriers but as direct agents against cancer cells. The scientists implanted lymphoma tumors in two groups of mice, then injected one group with monoclonal antibodies to the lymphoma cells each day for seven days. They did not treat the other group. On the 10th day they removed the tumors from mice in both groups. They gave no further treatment to either group.

Within 21 days of the original tumor implant, all six of the mice in the group not treated with antibodies had died — a result of the spread of the lymphoma. Of the six animals treated with monoclonal antibodies, one lived 31 days, one lived 36 days, and the remaining four showed no signs of cancer after 45 days. The monoclonal treatment had apparently kept the cancer from spreading.

However promising these results may be, they do not mean that a cancer cure is just around the next hybridoma corner. Decades of research have shown that cancers respond to antibodies in strange and often unpredictable ways. Some, as in the mouse lymphoma case, may regress and eventually disappear. Other cancers seem to be stimulated by the presence of antibody to grow even more vigorously. Still others disguise themselves by changing their surface antigens and simply go on growing — apparently oblivious to the antibody. Clearly, more research is needed as to how antibodies interact with cell surface antigens before monoclonals can be applied to treat cancer directly.

Hybridoma approaches are not limited to the treatment of cancer, of course. Researchers at the New York University Medical Center are experimenting with this technique to control malaria, a common parasitic affliction in parts of Central and South America, Asia, and Africa. Despite decades of research, there is neither a completely reliable cure nor any effective vaccine to control the pernicious malaria parasite, *Plasmodium*.

Parasitologist Ruth S. Nussenzweig and her husband, Victor, each heading a research group, have combined efforts to isolate a hybridoma that produces monoclonal antibody against the critical sporozoite stage of the malaria parasite. At this stage, the parasite is transmitted to humans by the bite of the *Anopheles* mosquito. Sporozoites circulate in the victim's bloodstream for barely half an hour, then disappear into the cells of the liver, where they multiply and change into another form — called a merozoite. The merozoites are then ready to begin the deadly business of invading and breaking down the host's red blood cells.

The antisporozoite monoclonal reacts with a specific antigen, Pb44, which appears to coat the parasite's entire surface. The Pb44 coat enables the parasite to enter the liver cells. When sporozoites are mixed with monoclonal antibody to Pb44, the Pb44 coating is stripped from their surfaces, making them look somewhat like peeled hot dogs trailing their skins behind them. This stripping renders the sporozoites ineffective.

The Nussenzweigs have found that experimental animals given injections of the monoclonal antibody followed by inoculation with large numbers of sporozoites do not develop malaria. It may be possible to use the monoclonal antibodies to isolate and purify large amounts of the Pb44 antigen, which could then be used to produce a safe and effective vaccine.

Monoclonal antibodies are also beginning to play an important role in the drive to produce an effective vaccine for another ancient affliction, influenza. Current flu vaccines are of only limited value because they are developed to combat a virus that is extraordinarily changeable. The major antigen on the surface of one type of flu virus, type A, is hemagglutinin (HA), an enormous protein with several antigenic determinants, each calling for a specific antibody. There is no single standard form of the HA protein, however. To evade existing antibodies, the virus may change one or several of these antigenic determinants. Thus, the antibodies you make to the HA of this year's strain of flu virus may not be able to recognize the HA of the strain of virus that arises next year.

A team at Wistar Institute has been keeping track of these changes in the flu virus by growing the virus in the laboratory and developing monoclonal antibodies to the various types that arise. As each new type is confronted with antibodies to match, it must change its HA form to evade detection. Although this mutation process may take years in nature, the rapid development of monoclonals to each new HA form in the laboratory takes only weeks. Thus, by pursuing each new strain of virus with a matching monoclonal antibody, scientists are able to force HA mutations much more rapidly, and by charting the particular sequences of antigenic determinants in each new HA form, they can witness patterns of mutations that are likely to arise naturally in the future, and can develop vaccines against them.

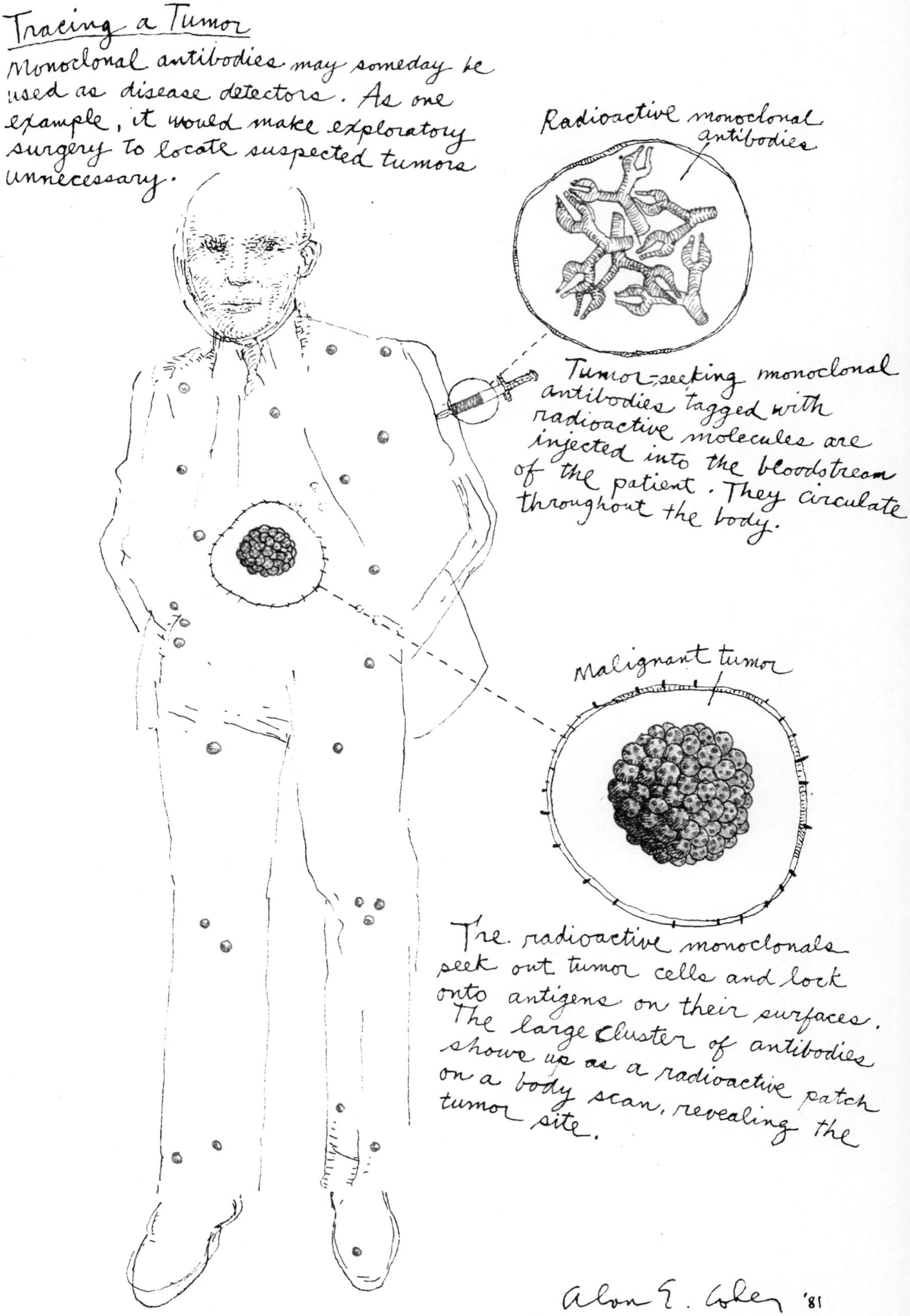

Tracing a Tumor

Monoclonal antibodies may someday be used as disease detectors. As one example, it would make exploratory surgery to locate suspected tumors unnecessary.

Radioactive monoclonal antibodies

Tumor-seeking monoclonal antibodies tagged with radioactive molecules are injected into the bloodstream of the patient. They circulate throughout the body.

Malignant tumor

The radioactive monoclonals seek out tumor cells and lock onto antigens on their surfaces. The large cluster of antibodies shows up as a radioactive patch on a body scan, revealing the tumor site.

Alan E. Cober '81

It is also possible that some of these monoclonals may recognize antigenic determinants in regions of the HA protein that remain constant from one flu strain to the next. Scientists might then develop a vaccine from antigenic determinants in these stable regions of the otherwise changeable HA antigen that would be effective against all flu virus strains.

Until recently, only rat or mouse spleen and myelomas have been used for constructing hybridomas because no human spleens were available. Obviously, researchers cannot remove healthy human spleens merely for research purposes. That has blocked the development of monoclonal antibodies for treating cancer, malaria, influenza, or any other human disease. Unfortunately, large amounts of rat or mouse antibody cannot be injected into humans without causing serious, even fatal, reactions. However, this problem appears to be close to solution.

In July 1980, a team of physicians and researchers led by immunologists Henry S. Kaplan and Lennart Olsson of Stanford University Medical Center announced the creation of a human hybridoma. To construct the hybridoma, the scientists used human spleens removed in a standard procedure in treating Hodgkin's disease, a cancer of the lymphatic tissue. Physicians sometimes remove the Hodgkin's patient's spleen to eliminate it as a tumor site, and to test it for cancer cells to determine how far the disease has spread.

Before the spleen is removed, however, the patient undergoes a variety of other diagnostic tests. One of these tests involves injecting patients with a chemical, 2-dinitrochlorobenzene (DNCB), to determine whether the patient's immune system is producing any antibodies. Spleens later removed from these patients are thus likely to contain B-lymphocytes that have been stimulated to produce antibodies to DNCB. Kaplan and Olsson used only those spleens that were found to be cancer-free as a source of activated human B-lymphocytes. They broke down these spleens into individual cells and fused the spleen cells with human myeloma cells to construct human hybridomas. Some of these hybridomas produced human monoclonal antibodies to DNCB.

Of course DNCB monoclonals made by these hybridomas are not about to cure anybody of anything. They are made to fit a harmless set of test antigens. Nor is it ethical or desirable to sensitize victims of Hodgkin's disease with harmful antigens such as flu viruses, streptococcus bacteria, or other strains of cancer cells to make monoclonal antibodies against these diseases.

However, the Stanford team is now trying another approach — exposing human spleen cells obtained from Hodgkin's patients to the desired antigen in the laboratory. These spleen cells can then be fused to human myeloma cells. Some of the human hybridomas that result will be formed from B-lymphocytes that produce the desired antibody. In this way, it may become possible to establish a library of human hybridomas that produce monoclonal antibodies against a wide range of harmful antigens.

While human hybridomas offer hope in combating a wide spectrum of disease, mouse hybridomas are still the best source of monoclonal antibodies for research. Because mice can be injected with an endless array of antigens, there is no limit to the types of antibodies their B-lymphocytes can produce.

In June 1980, immunologists Derek C. Burke of Warwick University in England and David Secher of the Medical Research Council laboratories reported that they had used monoclonal antibodies to purify interferon — a substance in the body that protects cells against viruses and may perhaps be useful in treating cancer. Interferon occurs only in minute amounts in the body and, because extractions of the substance contain many other proteins, it is difficult to purify by conventional methods.

To purify the substance by the monoclonal antibody method, the researchers first injected mice with human interferon, removed their spleens to extract spleen cells, and fused these cells with mice myeloma cells to create hybridomas from B-lymphocytes that produced antibodies to interferon. They used these monoclonal antibodies to trap interferon molecules from a solution as the mixture passed through a tube. The resulting interferon harvest was 5,000 times purer than interferon extractions previously used in research.

Scientists also expect mouse hybridomas to yield antibodies to other important human proteins — human leucocyte antigens (HLA). HLA molecules act as a biological monogram, identifying the surface of every cell in the human body as the property of that individual. Thirty-two HLA types have been identified, and each cell bears eight of these types, accounting for an enormous number of combinations of HLA types.

Because the body recognizes tissues and organs with an HLA makeup different from its own as "foreign," the immune system of a patient who has received an organ transplant often rejects the new organ. For this reason, it is very important that the HLA makeup of transplant donor and patient be as similar as possible. The development of monoclonal antibodies to each tissue type would make HLA identification and matching much easier and increase the success rate of organ transplants.

Whether a product of mouse or man, the monoclonal antibody appears to have a boundless future in research and medicine. In the years to come, monoclonal antibodies may be used to protect us from disease, to diagnose our ailments, to deliver drugs to specific cells in our bodies, and even to purify those drugs. Monoclonal antibodies may predict the next form of influenza, present a new means for controlling malaria, and aid in combating cancer. Even if they fulfill only a fraction of their promise, they are likely to benefit each one of us in some way.

Knowing
the Odds

By John G. Truxal

**A better understanding of probability can help to
make our lives easier, safer, and even more fun**

It is 6:45 A.M. Candida Jones is awakened by the weather report on
her clock radio: "Temperature, 63 degrees Fahrenheit; probability of
rain, 30 per cent." Candida takes this into account as she dresses for
school, choosing a light cardigan sweater, and leaving her raincoat
behind in the closet.

It is now 8:15. Candida boards the school bus. Her sweater smells
of damp wool and her hair hangs in limp, soggy strands. She has run
the last four blocks to the bus stop through a sudden cloudburst.
"There was supposed to be only a 30 per cent chance of rain today,"
Candida thinks to herself as she takes a seat. "Now that I think about
it, I don't even know what that means. Does it mean that rain is
supposed to fall on 30 per cent of the city, or that rain will fall 30 per
cent of the day? Whatever it means, I feel like I have just played the
odds and lost."

Although neither of her interpretations of the weather forecast was
correct, Candida's feelings were justified. The weather forecaster
meant that it had rained on 30 of every 100 days when similar weather
conditions had prevailed in the past. While this day could have been
one of the 70 dry days out of 100, it turned out to be one of the 30
rainy days instead.

Weather forecasting, like so many other things in life, depends on
probability — the chance that something might happen. Actuaries
calculate the probability of an individual's having an accident to
determine automobile-insurance rates. Political pollsters calculate the

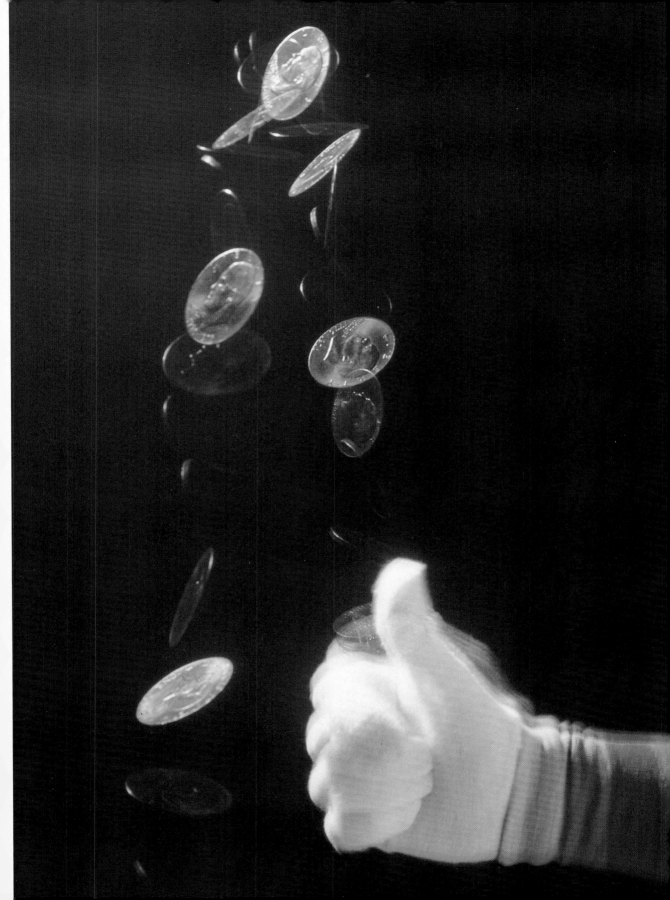

probability of each candidate winning an election. Airport managers calculate the probability of two planes arriving at the same time, in order to set up landing patterns. Thus, whether or not we decide to wear a raincoat, the price we pay for insurance, the slate of candidates we choose from at the polls, and whether the next airline flight we take will circle the airport for hours before landing are, to a great extent, influenced by someone's understanding, analysis, and calculations of probability.

Calculating probability can be a simple matter involving only basic mathematics or it can be an involved process, taking thousands of factors into account. Calculating the probability of getting heads in a coin toss requires the simplest formula — the number of results representing success (heads) divided by the total number of equally likely possibilities (heads and tails). This means that the probability of getting heads is $\frac{1}{2}$, or 1 chance in 2. Like all fractions, probability can be expressed as a decimal (0.5) or a percentage (50 per cent).

Similarly, the chance of drawing the ace of spades from a deck of 52 playing cards is $\frac{1}{52}$. There are 52 equally likely outcomes, but success corresponds to just one of these. However, the chance of drawing any ace from the deck is higher — $\frac{4}{52}$ — because there are four aces, hence four possibilities for success. This fraction can also be reduced and expressed as $\frac{1}{13}$.

While we can compute these probabilities mathematically without tossing a coin or drawing a card, we can also compute them by actually conducting trials. In this case, we are determining probability based on experience, in much the same way as a weather forecaster determines the likelihood of rain. This formula is also quite simple. It says that if an experiment or test is run N times and there are S successes, the probability of success in future trials is s/N. For example, if we toss a coin 100 times, we will get heads about 50 times, so the probability of getting heads is $\frac{50}{100}$, or $\frac{1}{2}$. The more times we toss, the closer the probability comes to $\frac{1}{2}$.

Candida was about to have another brush with probability in her first class, English. For homework, she had been asked to read the novel *Gadsby* by Ernest Vincent Wright. The book was assigned to Candida's English class with the notation that it was a remarkable work, but Candida found it so dull that she could hardly keep from falling asleep. However, today she noticed something peculiar — there were no Es on the page before her. Indeed, E, the most common letter in the English language, does not appear once in the entire 50,000-word novel.

Candida recognized that this was extraordinary when she tried to duplicate the author's feat and found that she could not write even one paragraph without using the letter E. *Gadsby*'s E-less prose was no accident. The author had obviously labored mightily to avoid using Es. The probability that this letter was omitted by chance, for even one page, is as close to zero as we can come.

The author:
John G. Truxal is professor of engineering at the State University of New York at Stony Brook and a former member of the *Science Year* Editorial Advisory Board.

How do we know that the probability is so slight? To compute it, we first need to know the probability that any single letter will be an E. If we count the frequency of letters in various books or newspapers, we are likely to find that in 1,000 letters, each letter appears a certain number of times as the chart indicates.

These frequencies indicate that if we pick a letter at random from any written work, the probability that it is an E is $^{132}/_{1000}$ or 0.132. In other words, we will pick an E 132 times out of 1,000. But we will not pick an E on our 868 other tries, so the probability that it is not an E is $^{868}/_{1000}$, or 0.868.

The probability of the two independent events happening is the product of their individual probabilities. If we select any two letters, the probability that neither is an E is 0.868 x 0.868 or 0.753. The page from the novel contains about 780 letters. To find the probability of no Es, we would have to multiply 0.868 by itself 780 times. While this is much too tedious, we can use a calculator to find that the answer is approximately:

1/1,000,000,000,000,000,000,000,000,000,000,000,000,000,000,000,000

or one chance in 10^{48}.

When we find that a certain event has a very small probability, we can conclude that the event will almost never happen by chance. But

The probability of drawing an ace of hearts, or any other particular card, from a deck is $^1/_{52}$ — the number of ways to succeed divided by the total number of equally likely possibilities.

what do we mean by a "very small probability"? Obviously, the $\frac{1}{1048}$ in our example is so small we can conclude that *Gadsby* was not a product of chance.

When the bell sounded, signaling the end of her English period, Candida moved down the hall to one of her favorite classes, biology. This semester her class was studying genetics, which deals with the principles of heredity. She likes this topic because it helps her to understand how color deficiency, or color blindness, is inherited. Like all other genetic traits, the inheritance of color deficiency is governed by basic principles of probability.

Color deficiency affects about 12 per cent of the males in the United States. Candida's father is one of them. Like most color-deficient

The probability that *E*, the most commonly used letter in the English language, was omitted from the novel *Gadsby* by chance is as close to zero as we can come.

persons, Ralph Jones sees shades of red and green, but cannot distinguish them easily and consistently. He once embarrassed Candida by chaperoning a school dance in a blue suit, green shirt, and red tie, so she now helps him select his clothes.

Color deficiency was first studied in the early 1800s by John Dalton, an English chemist, who was himself color deficient. The disease is called Daltonism in France. However, no one knew how the world looks to a color-deficient person until the 1960s when ophthalmologist Clarence Graham of Columbia University in New York City studied a woman who was color deficient in one eye and had normal vision in the other. Graham's patient was able to describe accurately what a color-deficient person sees.

Color deficiency, like all of the traits that we inherit from our parents, is transmitted by genes — segments of deoxyribonucleic acid (DNA) that determine what our bodies look like and how they function. The genes are organized into rodlike forms in the cell nucleus called chromosomes. Because the gene for red-green perception is located on the X, or female, chromosome, color deficiency is referred to as a sex-linked trait.

Males inherit one X chromosome from their mothers and one Y chromosome from their fathers. Females have two X chromosomes, one inherited from each parent. Because the gene for normal vision is dominant over the gene for color deficiency, the female must have both X chromosomes with the color-deficient gene to be color deficient. If only one X chromosome has the color-deficient gene, she is a carrier — that is, she will have normal vision herself but will be able to pass the gene to her children. The male's vision, whether color deficient or normal, is determined by his single X chromosome, because the Y chromosome lacks a gene governing color vision.

Candida's class is trying to determine the probability that, in a hypothetical family, the children of parents with normal vision will be color deficient. The students know that 12 per cent of all males in the United States are color deficient. Since each male has only one X chromosome, presumably 12 per cent of all X chromosomes carry the color-deficiency gene and 88 per cent carry the normal gene. The students also know that in this family the father has normal vision, so his X chromosome is normal.

The next step is to determine the probability that the mother, who also has normal vision, is a carrier. This is the same as the probability that she could have inherited one color-deficient X chromosome. The class knows that the probability of two events occurring is the product of the probabilities of either occurring independently. Therefore, the probability that the mother inherited a color-deficient gene from her mother and a normal gene from her father is 0.12 x 0.88 or 0.1056. The probability that she had inherited a normal gene from her mother and a color-deficient gene from her father is the same — 0.88 x 0.12 or 0.1056. Because there are two ways to inherit a color-deficient gene, the probability that one of them occurred is the sum of the two — 0.1056 + 0.1056 or 0.2112 — about 21 per cent.

Now the students must look at the next generation. They know that a daughter inherits one X chromosome from her father, and the other from her mother. Because she must have two color-deficient genes to be color deficient, and because her father's X chromosome carries the normal gene, she can inherit only one color-deficient gene — from her mother. The probability that the daughter will be color deficient is 0.

A son will inherit his only X chromosome from his mother, however, and there is a 21 per cent chance that his mother is a carrier. If the mother is a carrier, there is a 50 per cent chance that the son will inherit the color-deficient gene. Therefore, the probability that a son of parents with normal vision will be color deficient is 0.21 x 0.50 or 0.105.

Because both of Candida's paternal grandparents have normal color vision, she realizes that there was only a 10.5 per cent chance that her father would be color deficient. She also concludes that she is a carrier of the trait because she has most certainly inherited his X chromosome. Fortunately, color deficiency is not a serious medical problem. But this case illustrates how probability can be used in the genetic counseling of individuals with severe inherited diseases.

Candida thought that she had left probability analysis behind when she left her biology class; little did she know that she would encounter it again when she got home. That evening before dinner, her brother Seymour, a business student at the community college, challenged Candida to a game.

Seymour asked her to select a triplet from the eight possible outcomes of three successive coin flips — HHH, HTH, THH, TTH, HHT, HTT, THT, and TTT. (H indicates heads and T, tails.) Candida chose HTH and Seymour chose HHT. The object was to flip a coin until one of the triplets appeared in sequence. The person whose triplet appeared first would win.

On the first few flips, the sequence H T T T T H T H appeared. Candida won because the last three flips yielded HTH. For each subsequent game, Candida and Seymour chose different triplets. Candida's luck soon deserted her and Seymour won seven of the next 10 games. She did not know that Seymour was using a strategy based on probability analysis, so that he always played with at least 2 to 1 odds in his favor.

If Candida selected a triplet beginning with either TT or HH, Seymour picked HTT or THH. The last two choices in his triplet were the same as her first two, but his first choice was different. If Candida selected a triplet beginning with either TH or HT, he picked TTH or HHT, respectively. He took the side that she had selected first as both his first and second choice and took her second choice as his third. Seymour had given Candida the first choice of triplets because his strategy depended upon it, not out of brotherly charity.

The Secret of Seymour's Strategy

Seymour's success depended on letting Candida make the first choice of triplets. Then, if Candida selected a triplet in which the first two tosses were the same — either heads or tails — Seymour picked a triplet in which the last two tosses were the same as her first two, but the first toss was different from hers.

To find out why he did this, let us indicate Candida's choices by the notation XXX, which can represent either HHH and TTT, or XXY, which can represent either HHT or TTH. Seymour's related choices, either THH or HTT, are represented as YXX.

Next we construct two branching diagrams. The first indicates the possible results when the first toss is X.

The first toss here would appear to favor Candida. However, it only favors her as long as the second toss also yields X. If it does, she gains ground. If she has chosen XXY, she wins with the next toss that yields Y.

If she has chosen XXX, she wins if the third toss yields X. However, if the third toss yields Y, she loses control of the game because Y is the first toss in Seymour's triplet.

If the second toss yields Y, however, the game, in effect, becomes Seymour's because he chose Y as the first toss in his triplet. If the next toss yields Y, he neither gains nor loses ground but remains in control. And if the next toss yields X, he is close to

completing his triplet and winning. Candida now has no chance because she needs two Xs in a row, and two Xs in a row, preceded by a Y, wins the game for Seymour.

Thus, if the first toss yields X, Seymour has 1 chance in 2 of winning the game, because there is 1 chance in 2 that the second toss will yield Y.

A second branching diagram, in which the first toss yields a Y, makes it obvious that Seymour will certainly win this game.

As long as Y appears, Seymour controls the game. As soon as two Xs appear in succession, he wins. Since any series of Xs will be preceded by Y, Candida has no chance.

You can see from studying the two diagrams that after two tosses there are four equally possible outcomes — XX, XY, YX, and YY — and that Seymour is certain to win in three of these cases. The odds are 3 to 1 that he will win the game.

If Candida chooses XY (HT or TH) for the first two tosses of her triplet, Seymour can counter by choosing XXY. His odds of winning are somewhat less than in the first example, but they are still decidedly in his favor. A more detailed branching diagram can be constructed to illustrate this. Nevertheless, as long as Candida chooses first, Seymour can always respond with a choice that will put the odds on his side.

First toss   X
Second toss   X   Y
Third toss   X Y   X Y
Fourth toss X Y X Y X Y X Y

First toss   Y
Second toss   X   Y
Third toss   X Y   X Y
Fourth toss X Y X Y X Y X Y

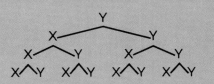

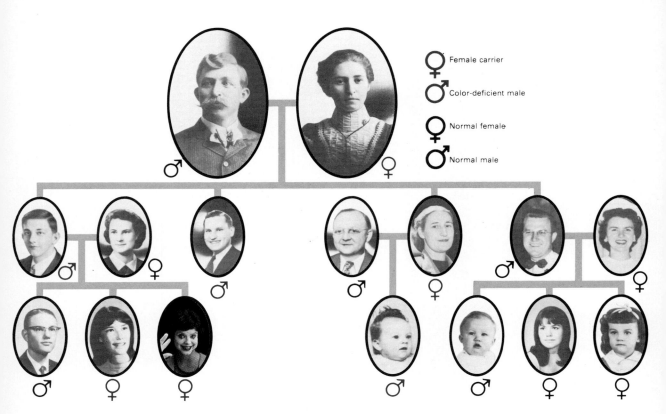

Female carrier

Color-deficient male

Normal female

Normal male

Handing Down
Color Deficiency

A woman with the gene for color deficiency marries a man with normal vision. Three of their four children inherit the gene. Two of the sons are color deficient; the daughter is a carrier. The third son, who has normal vision, marries a woman with normal vision and has children with normal vision. A color-deficient brother and the carrier sister choose spouses with normal vision. The brother has a son with normal vision and two carrier daughters. The sister has a son who is color deficient.

Seymour tried another game on the entire family, using two identical brown shopping bags and a large number of poker chips. He put 14 white chips and 6 blue chips into one bag and 14 blue ones and 6 white ones in the other bag. He called the first bag W because it had more white chips, and the second bag B. Then he told Candida to take the two bags into another room and return with only one. Seymour did not know which bag she brought back, and he did not look inside the bag. He pulled a chip from the bag and noted that it was blue. He replaced this chip, shook the bag, and drew another. After repeating this procedure 10 times he had drawn 7 blue chips and 3 white chips.

Seymour asked his family to guess the probability that he had been drawing from the B bag — that is, the bag with 14 blue and 6 white chips. Candida guessed 50 per cent and Seymour snickered. However, 50 per cent is the same answer Seymour gave that morning when the professor posed the question to his industrial-management class. Other students gave a wide range of answers.

A few, Seymour among them, insisted that the probability was 50 per cent. They argued that the testing was inconclusive — that this sequence of colored chips could have come from either bag. A few more estimated 60 per cent, stating that the sampling favored the B bag, but not by much. The majority of students guessed 70 or 80 per cent. Scientists and students who have taken a course in probability commonly pick about 80 per cent. A few who believed that the sample strongly favored B selected 90 per cent.

The correct answer, reached through an involved series of calculations, is a startling 97 per cent. Moreover, these 10 trials are enough to demonstrate that it is almost certain that Candida had brought back bag B.

Seymour's "game" teaches two important lessons. The first is that surprisingly small samples are adequate to estimate accurately behavior that can only be determined precisely by very extensive measurements. The second lesson is that human intuition, even in fairly simple probability questions, is just not very good.

After dinner, Candida set out for the supermarket to buy some chocolate. She had been delegated to bring brownies to a homeroom party for two classmates whose birthdays fall on the same day. Candida thought it very unusual that two birthdays in a class of 25 students coincided, but actually the odds favor this.

To determine these odds, we start with a given student's birthday. It makes no difference what it is. The probability that a second student's birthday is different is 364 (number of ways we can have success)/365 (number of possible answers). The probability that three students will have different birthdays is $^{364}/_{365}$ x $^{363}/_{365}$, and of four different birthdays is $^{364}/_{365}$ x $^{363}/_{365}$ x $^{362}/_{365}$.

Whe n there are more than 22 people in the room, the odds favor at least two identical birthdays. With 25 students in the class, the probability of all birthdays being different is 0.43. Hence, $1 - .43$ or .57 is the probability at least two birthdays are identical. In other words, the odds for identical birthdays are .57 to .43 or about 4 to 3.

This may seem like a backwards way of calculating the odds that two birthdays would fall on the same date. However, calculating the odds that all students have different birthdays is a much simpler process. As the number of students increases, the number of possible combinations that would produce two birthdays on the same day escalates. For example, although there is only one way in which two students — A and B — can share a birthday, there are six ways in which four students — A, B, C, and D — can do so: A with B, A with C, A with D, B with C, B with D, and C with D. But in calculating the odds favoring all different birthdays, as each additional student is taken into account we merely eliminate one day from the number of possible different birthdays.

At the supermarket, Candida chose the shortest checkout line. However, the line did not move because a customer ahead of her was arguing with the clerk over a blurred price marked on a jar of olives. Candida had once again become an unwitting participant in a game of chance — this time the problem involved queues or waiting lines.

In working through queuing problems, analysts study the likely length of the queue and how long people will have to wait to be served under different conditions. In this way, they can design a service

Intuition and common sense are no better than blind guesswork in computing some odds. The probability that the red chip was drawn from a bowl containing more red chips than blue chips rather than more blue chips than red chips, can only be determined through involved calculations.

system to control waiting time. All queuing problems — whether at banks, supermarkets, or tollgates — have the same general characteristics. Candida's father, returning from a sales convention, was involved in another such problem — the arrival and landing of airplanes at a busy airport late on Friday afternoon.

While Candida's delay at the checkout counter was merely aggravating, the delay in a crowded sky of the jumbo jet carrying Ralph Jones may have been life-threatening. If the planes arrive at regularly spaced intervals — for example, a minute apart — and if each plane needs the same amount of time on the runway — say 54 seconds — such delays can be easily avoided. In theory, a plane arriving at 4:04 uses the next 54 seconds to land, and the runway is free for 6 seconds before the next plane arrives. There is never a queue; the runway is used $^{54}\!/_{60}$ of the time and is clear the rest of the time.

Unfortunately, the real world never behaves so perfectly. In practice, most planes either are delayed or arrive slightly ahead of schedule. Thus, on a normal Friday afternoon, there will be occasional queues. The more tightly the airport is scheduled, the worse the queues will be. For example, if we schedule an arrival every 54 seconds, we can expect to have long queues; if we schedule an arrival every two minutes, we can expect few queues, and they will be short ones.

Because every airline wants to land as many planes as possible on Friday afternoons, the airport manager and the Federal Aviation Administration must decide how many planes can be scheduled between 4 P.M. and 7 P.M. without risking a queue so long that an airplane might have to circle until it ran out of gas or until the worried pilot decided to go to a different airport.

There is no simple solution to the math problem of estimating whether queues will form and how severe they will be, because arrivals occur randomly. For example, there is no mathematical formula the airport manager can use to determine the chances that a queue of seven planes will form.

The manager must use an educated form of trial and error in deciding how many landings can be scheduled from 4 P.M. to 7 P.M. He might simply make a guess, say 180, and test that figure for a few months to see what happens. If 180 seems to cause no serious problems, he could then try 200 and keep increasing the number until a problem arises. But rather than involve actual planes and airline passengers in this experiment, the manager turns to a simulation — a mathematical analysis of a system with the same characteristics as the airport.

First, he sets down all the facts involved. He knows that every plane requires 54 seconds to land. He also knows that planes arrive at random, but at an average rate of one every 60 seconds. If he looks at an interval of 6 seconds, the probability of one plane arriving is $\frac{6}{60}$ or $\frac{1}{10}$, and the interval is so short there is hardly any chance that two planes will arrive at the same time. He could also try 5-second, 3-second, or 1-second intervals. As the interval shortens, his simulation becomes more accurate, but the calculations also become more tedious. An interval of $\frac{1}{10}$ the average time between arrivals is a good compromise.

He now breaks the three hours from 4 P.M. to 7 P.M. into 1,800 6-second intervals. Because there are 10,800 seconds in the period, there are 1,800 such intervals. Henceforth, time is measured by the interval number from 1 to 1,800.

The next step in simulating traffic on one hypothetical Friday afternoon is to find the arrival time of each plane. Because the probability of an arrival in each interval is $\frac{1}{10}$, the manager sets up a situation that also has a probability of $\frac{1}{10}$. He finds a book of random numbers in the library. The numbers in the book were selected by a person or computer by some chance process, such as drawing numbers out of a hat. Because the book contains only double-digit numbers and he is looking for single-digit numbers, he will look at each digit individually. He decides that each digit will represent one interval and that only one number — 6 — will correspond to an arrival. He picks a page that begins with this line:

29 14 16 35 67 22 08 19 40 65

Because the airport manager had decided that the number 6 represented an arrival, the first number, 2, means there will be no arrival in the first 6-second interval. In fact, there are no arrivals until the sixth interval, when a 6 appears. He

Two members of a diverse group may have more in common than a taste for colorful attire — they may share a birthday. In fact, whenever 23 people get together, the odds that 2 will have the same birthday are greater than 50 per cent.

The impatient candy store customers, *above,* cannot predict how quickly the line they choose to stand in will move. In a take-a-number system, *right,* they are handled on a first-come, first-served basis, thus reducing the element of chance.

notices that arrivals occur also at intervals 9 and 19. He continues until he has picked out all of the 6s in the first 1,800 numbers, simulating all the arrivals between 4 P.M. and 7 P.M.

Now he can construct a diagram. Plane A arrives at interval 6 and is on the runway for 54 seconds, or nine intervals. Plane B arrives at interval 9, waits until interval 15 to land and is on the runway from intervals 15 to 24. B is still on the runway when C arrives.

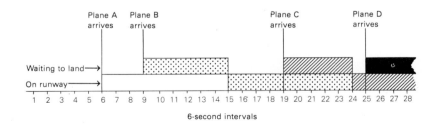

After he completes the diagram for the full 1,800 intervals, he has a picture of the queue at all times during the three-hour period. He can then find the average waiting time and the total length of time that a given number of planes — for example, three — could be stacked up waiting to land, and visualize how the system works.

Once he has completed this simulation "run," he has the information for just one possible Friday afternoon. This may well be a particularly lucky Friday with very few short queues, or it may be unusually crowded. In reality, he has established one schedule for arrivals and tested it only once. He does not have enough evidence to decide whether to adopt this scheduling system.

So he repeats the experiment, using an entirely different set of random numbers. After several dozen runs, he should be able to decide if this scheduling system will work. If it will not, he may then try a different scheduling plan — perhaps one in which a plane is scheduled to arrive every 57 seconds.

The simulation allows him to test various features of a system. He can easily modify the simulation to represent traffic-controller slowdowns or jumbo planes that may require 65 seconds to land and get off the runway. As he makes these changes in his simulation, he can see how the queues of planes waiting to land change.

This probabilistic simulation is used for all kinds of queuing problems, such as designing supermarket checkout counters and highway tollgates. The manager of a facility constantly faces the problem of finding the best compromise between two extremes — having no queues and providing the greatest degree of customer satisfaction, or cutting costs by having only one service channel and a long queue of disgruntled customers. A supermarket manager can continuously adjust the system in his store and open additional checkout counters when the queues seem to be growing too long.

There are many techniques to decrease customer annoyance with long waiting times. In some bakeries and candy stores, for example, customers are asked to take a number and are dealt with on a first-come, first-served, basis. Many airline ticket counters and banks have established a single queue feeding into several clerks' or tellers' stations. If Candida's supermarket had used this system, she would not have been tied up behind the complaining customer.

Until the 1900s, probability analysis was used primarily by gamblers to calculate their prospects in games of chance. However, scientists, medical specialists, and engineers have also started to play the odds. They use probability analysis to predict earthquakes, to assess a patient's chances of having a heart attack, and to determine the number and placement of tollbooths on a turnpike. In the future, we can expect probability analysis to play a part in allocating energy resources, in selecting recipients of artificial hearts, and in designing more complex computer games.

We cannot control random events — the whims of the weather, the flip of a coin, or the accidents of human beings and nature. But probability analysis may make our world safer, more understandable and productive — and perhaps even more fun.

Chemistry's Speedy Servants

By Lawrence P. Verbit

Catalysts serve industry and the consumer by helping chemicals react to form valuable materials swiftly while decreasing manufacturers' energy requirements

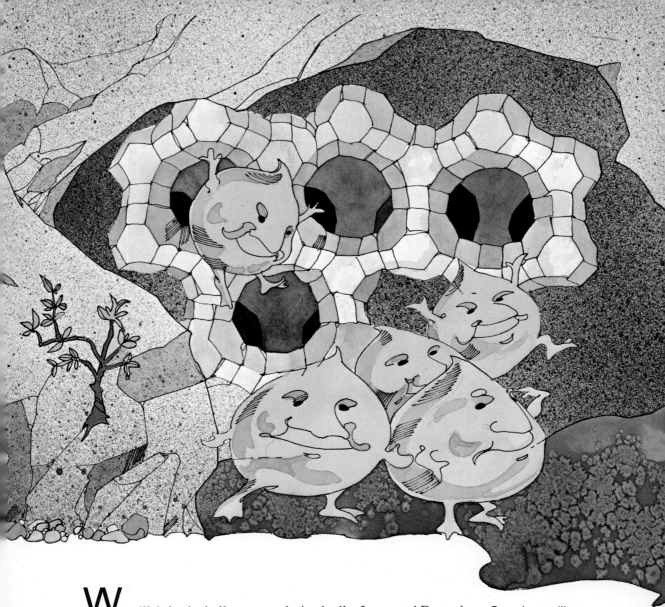

Westville's basketball team was losing badly. Larry and Dave, the guards, could not get the ball to Mel, the center and scoring leader. Coach Henderson motioned to a small figure at the end of the bench. "Hey, Little Joe," he yelled, "get in there for Larry and move that ball around." Little Joe then used his quickness and agility to elude the defense and pass the ball to Mel time after time. Mel began to pile up points, and Westville rallied to win the game. Coach Henderson congratulated Little Joe after the game. "The scorebook shows that you didn't score a point," he said, "but the team would not have won without you. You were the catalyst."

The coach picked a good word to describe Little Joe. A catalyst is a person or thing that brings about some change without being directly affected itself. Little Joe brought about a change in the team's scoring rate without scoring himself.

Pores in cavelike crystals of zeolite are the scene of catalytic reactions that turn methanol into high-octane gasoline.

Just as the coach used a human catalyst to change his team's scoring rate, chemists and engineers use catalysts to regulate the rate of chemical reactions. These reactions are changes in the atomic makeup of chemicals that transform one or more substances into a new substance or substances. Catalysts can speed up or slow down chemical reactions, but the most dramatic catalytic reactions are those that accelerate change. In fact, without such reactions, the drama of life itself would not be possible.

Enzymes, for example, are a special class of catalysts that accelerate vital chemical reactions in plants and animals. The human body contains more than 1,000 kinds of enzymes, each with its own job to do. Without them, the reactions would occur too slowly or not at all, and we could not breathe, digest food, or move any part of our bodies.

Catalysts that speed up industrial processes have brought us foods and other products that enrich our lives. Nickel catalysts promote the hardening of corn oil to form margarine and a reaction that thickens peanut oil in peanut butter. Many medicines are products of catalysts. For example, L-dopa, a drug that treats Parkinson's disease, forms during a reaction with a catalytic salt of the metal rhodium. Two catalysts help to manufacture polyethylene, a plastic used in products such as garbage bags, appliance parts, automobile steering wheels, and children's swimming pools.

A catalyzed reaction consists of two or more steps, each actually a chemical reaction itself. In the simplest case, the catalyst first reacts with the original substance to form an unstable substance — one that soon reacts again, either to form another unstable substance or the final products. Although the catalyst may participate in the last step, it will not appear in the final products of the overall reaction.

Chemists knew about some of the functions of catalysts long before science produced a theory that bound them together. For example, experimenters had discovered by the late 1700s that potato starch reacted with distilled water and cream of tartar, a sour substance, acquiring a sweet taste after several months. But adding acetic acid, which is also sour, to the mixture made the mixture even sweeter in the same period of time. In 1817, English chemist Sir Humphry Davy found that alcohol vapor mysteriously burned at low temperatures in the presence of a heated platinum wire.

Swedish chemist Jöns Jakob Berzelius explained in 1835 that substances such as acetic acid and platinum activated chemical attractions that were dormant, or inactive, at low temperatures. The starch, water, and cream of tartar could react to form a sweet product without a catalyst in a shorter period of time if the temperature were raised, but the acetic acid catalyst permitted this without adding heat energy. Berzelius' explanation also covered chemical reactions that people had put to practical use for centuries. He said, for example, that malt acted as a catalyst in converting starch to sugar during a fermentation process used in making beer. We know now that malt

The author:
Lawrence P. Verbit is a professor of chemistry at State University of New York at Binghamton.

brings about this conversion by releasing an enzyme called diastase that acts as a catalyst. Fermentation also makes bread dough rise and helps us digest food.

German chemist Wilhelm Ostwald, who won the 1909 Nobel prize for chemistry, expressed the present view of catalysis in 1901. He said that every reaction brought about by a catalyst is already proceeding by itself, perhaps immeasurably slowly; that the catalyst speeds up the reaction by reducing the amount of energy needed to bring the reaction about; and that the catalyst does not appear in the final products of the reaction.

Industry wasted little time in putting these characteristics to work. German chemist Fritz Haber, winner of the 1918 Nobel prize for chemistry, invented one of the first important industrial catalytic processes between 1907 and 1909. The Haber process produces ammonia (NH_3) by combining nitrogen (N_2) and hydrogen (H_2) at the surface of a solid catalyst. The catalyst is iron, with small amounts of oxides of aluminum and potassium. The relatively inexpensive ammonia that this process made possible is used in fertilizers that have contributed to greater agricultural productivity. In 1981, the United States produced about 16.8 million metric tons (18.5 million short tons) of ammonia.

Chemical reactions transform substances by breaking and forming chemical bonds that link atoms to one another. Certain electrons of the reacting substances actually break or form the bonds when energy is added.

The simplest reactions start with just one substance and take one step. For example, heating sucrose, a sugar that consists of carbon (C), hydrogen (H), and oxygen (O) atoms, makes it decompose into carbon and water (H_2O). An alternate simple reaction is a combination reaction, the reverse of decomposition, in which two or more substances unite to form another substance. Electrons form a bond in a combination reaction, while one or more bonds break in a decomposition reaction.

In a more complex one-step reaction, bonds both form and break. For example, when acetic acid ($C_2H_4O_2$) is mixed with ethanol (C_2H_5OH), water (H_2O) and ethyl acetate ($C_4H_8O_2$) are formed. A large portion of the water and ethyl acetate then recombine in a reverse reaction to form the starting substances, so the overall reaction produces a mixture of all four chemicals. After several days of reacting, the composition of the mixture no longer changes. The reaction has reached equilibrium and the mixture will retain its composition indefinitely.

The time that a reaction takes to achieve equilibrium depends upon how quickly the reacting substances reach the energy level at which chemical bonds break and form. Energy is like a mountain that separates the reacting substances from the products of the reaction. As the reacting substances absorb energy — almost always heat ener-

Glossary

Aromatic: A molecule that contains one or more benzene rings.

Benzene ring: Six carbon atoms that are connected in the shape of a hexagon.

Catalyst: A substance that speeds up or slows down a chemical process while itself undergoing little or no permanent change.

Heterogeneous catalysis: Regulation of a chemical reaction by a catalyst that is not in the same state of matter — solid, liquid, or gas — as the reactants.

Homogeneous catalysis: Regulation of a chemical reaction by a catalyst that is in the same state of matter — usually a gas or a liquid — as the reactants.

Hydrocarbon: A chemical compound made up of hydrogen and carbon atoms.

Ion: A charged atom.

Paraffin: A hydrocarbon made up of a chain of carbon atoms and more than twice as many hydrogen atoms.

Product: A substance that is obtained from the chemical reaction of one or more other substances.

Initial ingredients of an ordinary chemical reaction slowly climb a mountain of energy to reach their transition state and turn into reaction products. But chemicals in a catalyzed reaction can travel along a low-energy path and reach the reaction goal more quickly.

gy in industrial processes — they climb the energy mountain. When they reach their transition state at the mountaintop, the reaction occurs. The products then go down the other side of the mountain. Some of the products get up enough energy to reverse the process and go back over the mountain, passing newly forming products on the way. Eventually, the mixture of initial substances and products reaches equilibrium.

A manufacturer can save valuable processing time by bringing a reaction to equilibrium more rapidly. A simple way to do this is by turning up the heat. The reacting substances then climb to the same mountaintop, but they do so more quickly. But turning up the heat increases the manufacturer's energy bill. A cheaper way to accelerate the reaction is to add a catalyst that provides a new and lower energy pathway along the mountainside. The starting chemicals no longer have to go over the mountaintop to reach the other side. Nearly all of them take advantage of this easier route, so the catalyzed reaction is much faster than the noncatalyzed change. For example, adding a drop of hydrochloric acid to a solution of acetic acid and ethanol causes the mixture to form exactly the same amounts of the four final chemicals within hours rather than days.

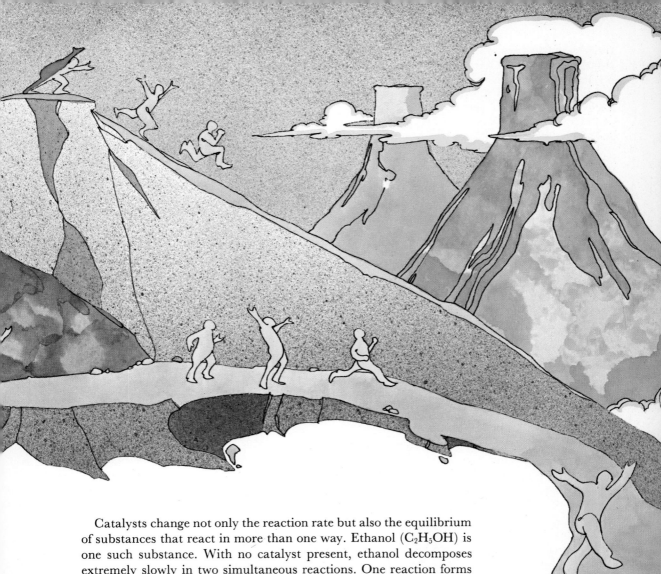

Catalysts change not only the reaction rate but also the equilibrium of substances that react in more than one way. Ethanol (C_2H_5OH) is one such substance. With no catalyst present, ethanol decomposes extremely slowly in two simultaneous reactions. One reaction forms ethylene (C_2H_4) and water (H_2O), while the other forms acetaldehyde (CH_3CHO) and hydrogen gas (H_2). These two reactions compete with each other in the beaker and proceed at about the same rate.

But when you drop pellets of aluminum oxide in one beaker of ethanol and copper in another, a surprising thing happens. The aluminum oxide catalyzes the first reaction so that nearly all of the ethanol decomposes into ethylene and water, while the copper catalyst makes acetaldehyde and hydrogen gas form in the second beaker. Chemists call a catalyzed reaction that overwhelms a competing, noncatalyzed reaction in this manner a *kinetically directed* reaction.

Chemists divide catalysts into two main types. *Homogeneous catalysts* are in the same state of matter as the reacting substances. They may be liquids, solids, or gases that are dissolved in liquids. The catalyzed reaction of acetic acid and ethanol is a typical example of homogeneous catalysis. These two chemicals and the hydrochloric acid catalyst are liquids.

Hours Versus Minutes

Heating a noncatalyzed mixture of acetic acid and ethanol to a certain energy level, *top row*, causes a chemical reaction that forms ethyl acetate and water in three hours. But adding hydrochloric acid as a catalyst, *bottom row*, cuts the time needed to obtain an identical mixture to five minutes.

Legend:

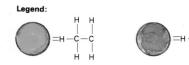

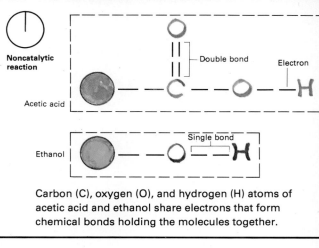

Carbon (C), oxygen (O), and hydrogen (H) atoms of acetic acid and ethanol share electrons that form chemical bonds holding the molecules together.

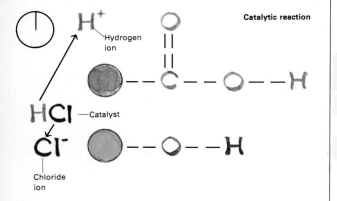

Catalyst HCl first separates into a negative chloride ion, which does not take part in the catalytic reaction, and a positive hydrogen ion.

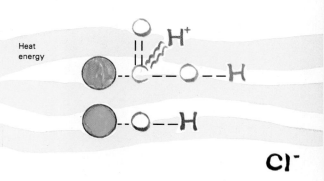

Attraction between positive ion and negative electrons of acetic acid's double bond causes the hydrogen ion to approach acetic acid rapidly.

Heterogeneous catalysts such as the iron catalyst in the Haber process make up the other major group. A heterogeneous catalyst is a solid that catalyzes the reaction of liquids or gases. Chemists do not understand heterogeneous catalysis as well as they understand homogeneous catalysis, partly because of the problems involved in studying reactions that occur between materials of different states. But they know that many processes taking place on the surface of heterogeneous catalysts occur in three steps. First, electrically charged regions in the catalyst attract opposite charges in the gas or liquid molecules. The attracted substances approach the catalyst and eventually stick to its surface. There, the chemical bonds of one or more of them may break, allowing the substances to react with one another. Finally, the catalyst releases the products of the reaction. The process repeats itself until the chemicals reach equilibrium.

Many processes that are essential to the chemical industry use heterogeneous catalysts. For example, a heterogeneous process that two German chemists discovered nearly 60 years ago is well on the

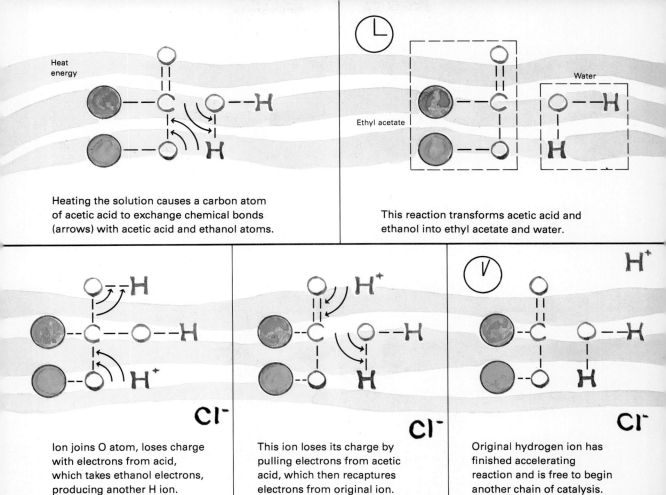

Heating the solution causes a carbon atom of acetic acid to exchange chemical bonds (arrows) with acetic acid and ethanol atoms.

This reaction transforms acetic acid and ethanol into ethyl acetate and water.

Ion joins O atom, loses charge with electrons from acid, which takes ethanol electrons, producing another H ion.

This ion loses its charge by pulling electrons from acetic acid, which then recaptures electrons from original ion.

Original hydrogen ion has finished accelerating reaction and is free to begin another chain of catalysis.

way toward solving the energy problem of at least one nation. In 1923, Franz J. Fischer and Hans Tropsch discovered that heating hydrogen (H_2) and carbon monoxide (CO) gases under pressure with a catalyst formed a mixture of organic liquids. Since then, chemical firms have learned to distill these liquids to give a 60 per cent yield of a low-grade gasoline. Other organic chemicals in the liquids become diesel fuel, lubricating oils, synthetic fats, and soap. The hydrogen-carbon dioxide mixture, called synthesis gas, can be obtained by heating coal in the presence of steam and oxygen, but almost any carbon source, including oil, natural gas, plant material, even garbage, can generate synthesis gas.

A typical Fischer-Tropsch catalyst is a mixture of cobalt, magnesium oxide, and thorium oxide dispersed as fine particles on the internal surfaces of pellets of a porous material called a support. Kieselguhr, a type of diatomaceous earth that is formed from the fossilized remains of animals called diatoms, is often used as a support. Kieselguhr holds the catalytic substances within its pores. A

blast of hot synthesis gas agitates the pellets, which are contained in a chamber. Gas molecules that blow through the pores of the swirling pellets form organic vapors which are permitted to cool to the liquid state in other chambers and are then collected in tanks.

Germany in the 1940s was the first country to put the process to work on a large scale. Germany has a plentiful supply of coal to make synthesis gas, so that nation used the Fischer-Tropsch process to help fuel its military machine when its petroleum supply was curtailed during World War II. But the process was so costly that its products could not compete with gasoline and other synthetic chemicals refined from the relatively cheap Middle East oil that became available after the war ended.

However, South Africa, a country rich in coal but lacking petroleum, now uses the process on a massive scale. Two huge plants convert coal from nearby mines to synthesis gas and then transform this gas into products such as gasoline, diesel fuel, alcohol, coal tar chemicals, liquefied natural gas, ammonia, and sulfur. South Africa expects a third Fischer-Tropsch plant to be operating in 1982. The country would then be able to produce most of its transportation fuel catalytically from coal.

The United States and other industrial countries use the Fischer-Tropsch process on a large scale to convert synthesis gas into methanol, or methyl alcohol (CH_3OH). The directed reaction that they use produces only methanol so that costly separations are avoided. They obtain the synthesis gas from petroleum and natural gas.

This process is efficient and vast production facilities are available, so some energy experts are considering methanol as a gasoline substitute that would relieve U.S. dependence on gasoline refined from Middle East petroleum. Since synthesis gas can also be obtained from coal, an economical, large-scale process that would produce methanol in a sequence beginning with coal has great potential for the United States, which is rich in coal.

But automobiles that run on gasoline cannot use methanol as a fuel, so their engines would require major changes. Moreover, 1 liter (0.26 gallon) of gasoline contains as much energy as 2 liters (0.53 gallon) of methanol, so twice as much methanol would have to be produced, transported, and pumped into automobiles' fuel tanks if methanol were to replace gasoline. But if chemists found an efficient method of converting methanol into gasoline, they would avoid many problems of using methanol as a transportation fuel.

Coal is transformed into gasoline in three steps. First, heat turns coal into synthesis gas. A catalyzed reaction stream then transforms this gas into methanol, which passes through the catalytic caverns of a special zeolite crystal and emerges as a high-quality gasoline.

A heterogeneous catalyst called a zeolite may provide such a method. In a landmark achievement, scientists at Mobil Oil Corporation laboratories in Paulsboro, N.J., used zeolite crystals in 1975 to convert methanol directly into a mixture of fluids that have the same composition as a high-grade gasoline, and water.

Zeolites are made up mainly of a framework of silicon, oxygen, and aluminum. They occur naturally, but scientists also make them in the laboratory. Zeolites have pores, or cavities, with interconnecting channels that can trap molecules of the reacting substance. Only molecules of certain shapes and sizes can enter the catalyst's pores and only products of these shapes and sizes can leave the pores.

Electrical charges in the zeolite channels break and form bonds in the molecules trapped in the zeolite. Mobil uses a zeolite named ZSM-5 in its methanol-to-gasoline process. The pores are so small that molecules larger than those of ordinary gasoline cannot leave the zeolite. Such molecules must break down into smaller molecules that can slip through the pores.

The most important molecules in gasoline are hydrocarbons, which are made up of carbon and hydrogen. These include paraffins, which have more hydrogen atoms than carbon atoms, and aromatics, with more nearly equal numbers of these atoms. Paraffins have closed or open chains of interconnected carbon atoms, while aromatics have six interconnected carbon atoms arranged in a hexagon shape that is called a benzene ring.

Methanol is transformed inside the zeolite, so the reactions are difficult to study. But researchers have proposed a theory that explains how methanol forms these particular molecules. Scientists suspect that positive charges in the zeolite structure first break down two methanol molecules ($2CH_3OH$) into water (H_2O) and dimethyl ether (CH_3OCH_3). This ether reacts further to produce olefins, molecules that are made up of two to five carbon atoms and twice as many hydrogen atoms. Some of these olefins leave the zeolite as paraffins, while others remain in the zeolite, where they react to form products that have more than six carbons. Mobil chemists believe that these long molecules then undergo complex reactions that form aromatics. These reactions continue until the largest product is the aromatic tetramethylbenzene, which is made up of 10 carbon atoms and 14 hydrogens. The aromatics then pass out through the zeolite pores and mix with the paraffins to form gasoline.

The Mobil process provides a narrow range of products, unlike the Fischer-Tropsch process that South Africa uses. About 75 per cent of the molecules have five or six carbon atoms, and almost none has more than 11 carbons.

The ZSM-5 catalyst operates continuously without losing its effectiveness for three to five weeks, but eventually chemicals clog its pores. Mobil researchers renew zeolites by injecting air that reacts with these chemicals and removes them. Renewal extends the average catalyst's life to about one year, during which each kilogram of catalyst can convert about 6,000 kilograms (13,000 pounds) of methanol to gasoline.

Gasoline produced by this process in the United States is much too expensive to compete with gasoline obtained from petroleum refining. But as oil prices continue to rise, methanol may become an important source of gasoline.

Other scientists are developing techniques for producing substances that may replace both methanol and gasoline as automotive fuels. For example, chemist Michael Grätzel and his team at the Swiss Federal Polytechnic Institute laboratory at Lausanne have used a heterogeneous catalyst to help the energy of sunlight split water into hydrogen, a potential fuel, and oxygen. The catalyst is made up of tiny spheres of titanium dioxide with ruthenium dioxide and platinum deposited on them. Another chemical, a ruthenium salt to which several organic groups of atoms have been attached, helps the catalyst do its job.

The scientists put the catalyst and the salt in a beaker of water and expose the beaker to sunlight. The heterogeneous catalyst first attracts the salt to its surface and holds it there. Next, the light contributes energy to electrons in the salt. Some of these electrons flow to the platinum which, in turn, contributes them to water molecules. These molecules break up and recombine to form hydroxide ions (OH^-) and hydrogen gas (H_2). At the same time, the ruthenium dioxide takes electrons from other water molecules, which react to form hydrogen ions (H^+) and oxygen gas (O_2).

The ruthenium oxide then transfers these electrons to the salt, converting it back to its original form; and the hydrogen ions combine with the hydroxide ions to form water. Finally, the researchers collect the gases that bubble to the surface.

Heterogeneous catalyzed reactions such as this are years away from practical large-scale use, but they may provide us with important sources of energy in the future. Meanwhile, as we continue to burn ordinary gasoline and other fuels, catalytic reactions help to protect our environment from pollutants that they produce. For example, a catalytic reaction called hydrodesulfurization removes potentially harmful sulfur impurities from oil, coal, and natural gas before they are burned. Another important catalytic process takes place in your automobile. Exhaust gases from the engine pass through a catalytic converter that decreases the amounts of carbon monoxide, hydrocarbon, and nitrogen dioxide pollutants in them.

The future looks promising for chemical catalysis as scientists continue to find new catalysts that can help produce a wide variety of useful chemicals. The future will see catalysts do even more to keep our environment safe and clean. Catalytic fuel cells powered by the sun's energy will be important, and so will fuels produced catalytically from coal, plant material, and other yet-to-be-imagined sources.

For Further Reading

Additional information on some of the subjects covered in the Special Reports may be found in these books and magazine articles.

Flight to Saturn

Beatty, J. Kelly. "Rendezvous with a Ringed Giant," *Sky & Telescope,* January 1981.

Berry, Richard. "Voyager 1 at Saturn," *Astronomy,* January 1981.

Berry, Richard. "Voyager: Science at Saturn," *Astronomy,* February 1981.

Smith, Bradford A. et al. "Encounter with Saturn: Voyager 1 Imaging Science Results," *Science,* April 10, 1981.

Smith, Bruce A. "Voyager 1 Finds Answers, New Riddles," *Aviation Week & Space Technology,* Nov. 17, 1980.

Smith, Bruce A. "Saturn Science Data Continue to Grow." *Aviation Week & Space Technology,* Nov. 24, 1980.

Rhinos on the Run

Beard, Peter. *End of the Game.* Doubleday, 1977.

Martin, Esmond B. "The Conspicuous Consumption of Rhinos," *Animal Behavior,* February-March and April-May, 1981.

Raloff, Janet. "Stealing a Horn of Plenty," *Science News,* Nov. 17, 1979.

Verney, Peter. *Animals in Peril: Man's War Against Wildlife.* Brigham Young University Press, 1980.

End of an Era

Alvarez, L. W., Alvarez, W., Asaro, F., and Michel, H. V. "Extraterrestrial Cause for the Cretaceous-Tertiary Extinction," *Science,* June 6, 1980.

Davis, M. "Apocalypse Then," *Discover,* November 1980.

Newell, N. D. "Crises in the History of Life," *Scientific American,* February 1963.

Image of an Instant

Edgerton, Harold E. *Electronic Flash, Strobe.* MIT Press, 1979.

Edgerton, Harold E., and Killian, James R., Jr. *Moments of Vision.* MIT Press, 1979.

Mili, Gjon. *Photographs and Recollections.* New York Graphic Society, 1980.

Stuart, Gene S. *Hidden Worlds.* National Geographic Society, 1981.

Fireworks Mountain

Decker, Robert, and Decker, Barbara. "The Eruptions of Mount St. Helens," *Scientific American,* March 1981.

Kerr, Richard A. "Mount St. Helens: An Unpredictable Foe," *Science,* June 27, 1980.

"Mount Saint Helens Update," *Science News,* Dec. 20 and 27, 1980.

The Science of Animal Welfare

Gorman, James, "Burden of the Beasts," *Discover,* February 1981.

Morris, R. W., and Fox, Michael W. *On the Fifth Day: Animal Rights and Human Ethics.* Acropolis Books Ltd., 1978.

Nevin, David. "Scientist Helps Stir New Movement for 'Animal Rights'," *Smithsonian* Magazine, April 1980.

Singer, Peter. *Animal Liberation.* Random House, 1975.

Archaeologists in Wet Suits

Bass, George F. *Archaeology Beneath the Sea.*
Harper & Row, 1976.

Burgess, Robert F. *Man: Twelve Thousand Years under the Sea.* Dodd, Mead & Company, 1980.

Goodwin, Derek V. "Blackwater Wreck,"
Science 81, January-February 1981.

Alcohol: The Friendly Foe

Kinney, J., and Leaton, G. *Loosening The Grip: A Handbook of Alcohol Information.*
C. V. Moseby, 1978.

Mendelsohn, J. H., and Mello, N. K. (eds.) *The Diagnosis and Treatment of Alcoholism.*
McGraw-Hill, 1979.

Pharmacies in the Jungle

Aikman, Lonnelle. *Nature's Healing Arts: From Folk Medicine to Modern Drugs.* National Geographic Society, 1977.

Hanlon, Joseph. "When the Scientist Meets the Medicine Men," *Nature,* May 24, 1979.

Meinwald, Jerrold, and others. "Chemical Ecology: Studies from East Africa," *Science,* March 17, 1978.

Myers, Norman. "Witch Doctors Are Good Guys Again," *International Wildlife,*
January-February 1981.

X-Ray Eyes on the Skies

Giacconi, Riccardo. "The Einstein X-Ray Observatory," *Scientific American,* February 1980.

Hartline, Beverly K. "Einstein Explores High Energy Astrophysics," *Science,*
June 29, 1979.

Hartline, Beverly K. "Einstein Pictures the X-Ray Sky," *Science,* July 6, 1979.

Maran, Stephen P. "Two Satellites in Search of X-Rays," *Natural History,* March 1980.

Overbye, Dennis. "X-Ray Eyes of Einstein," *Sky & Telescope,* June 1979.

"X-Ray Pictures from Space," *Astronomy,* June 1979.

Using Cancer to Fight Disease

Milstein, Cesar. "Monoclonal Antibodies,"
Scientific American, October 1980.

Schloen, Lloyd Henry. "Immortalizing Immunity," *The Sciences,*
July/August 1980.

Shodell, Michael. "Enlisting Cancer,"
Science 80, September/October 1980.

Knowing the Odds

King, Almy C. *Pathways to Probability.* Holt Library of Science, 1963.

Weaver, Warren. *Lady Luck, The Theory of Probability.* Anchor Books, 1963.

Science File

Science Year contributors report on the year's major developments in their respective fields. The articles in this section are arranged alphabetically by subject matter.

Agriculture
Anthropology
Archaeology
  Old World
  New World
Astronomy
  Planetary
  Stellar
  High-Energy
  Cosmology
Books of Science
Botany
Chemistry
Deaths
Drugs

Ecology
Electronics
Energy
Environment
Genetics
Geoscience
  Geochemistry
  Geophysics
  Paleontology
Immunology
Medicine
  Dentistry
  Internal
  Surgery
Meteorology
Molecular Biology
Neuroscience
Nutrition

Oceanography
Physics
  Atomic and Molecular
  Elementary Particles
  Nuclear
  Plasma
  Solid-State
Psychology
Public Health
Science Awards
Space Exploration
Zoology

Agriculture

The eruption of Mount Saint Helens on May 18, 1980, profoundly affected that region's agriculture. This was reported in January 1981 by plant pathologist Robert J. Cook and a team of soil scientists from the United States Department of Agriculture (USDA) in Pullman, Wash., and their associates from Washington State University in Pullman. The volcanic eruption deposited up to 30 kilograms per square meter (55 pounds per square yard) of volcanic ash over the Columbia Basin area to the north, west, and east of the volcano. Crop losses in eastern Washington were about $100 million, or 7 per cent of the annual crop value.

The scientists attributed the losses to varied effects of the ash. Ash on plant leaves stunted growth by reducing *photosynthesis* — the process plants use to convert water and carbon dioxide into carbohydrates — as much as 90 per cent, and it crushed alfalfa hay under its weight. It also proved lethal to certain beneficial insects.

The ash had one possible benefit, however. Gas bubbles in the ash left holes that store large amounts of water for plant use. In combination with the ash particle size and shape, the holes enable 0.45 kilogram (1 pound) of Mount Saint Helens' ash to hold 0.28 kilogram (8 ounces) of water. The typical silt loam soil of the Columbia Basin region stores only half that amount.

Jojoba breakthrough. Scientists in 1981 reported progress toward replacing the oil of the endangered sperm whale with jojoba (*Simmondsia chinensis*). The jojoba plant grows in desert climates. It has seeds that contain a wax that is chemically almost identical to whale oil, which is used in soaps, varnishes, and cosmetics.

Jojoba normally produces male and female flowers on different plants. However, only the female flowers produce the wax-bearing seeds, so a high percentage of female plants is essential for high wax yields.

Two groups of researchers reported in 1981 on ways to eliminate the necessity of growing the male plant, which is only used for pollination. Geneticist Demetrios M. Yermanos of the Uni-

An agricultural engineer checks the tape holding a miniature radio transmitter that relays a pig's heartbeat to a data station as the animal is readied for market. The heartbeat indicates the degree of stress the pig suffers during sorting, penning, and shipping, which could affect its ability to gain weight.

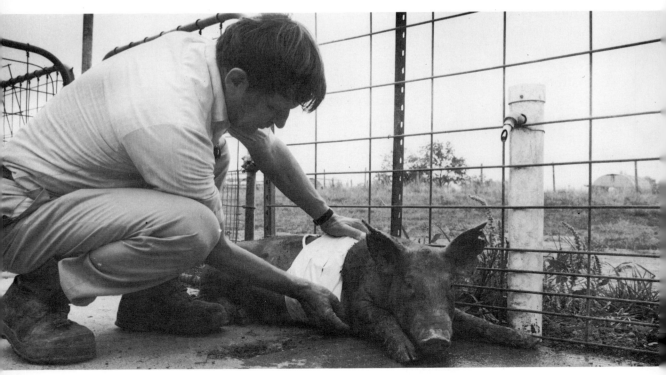

Agriculture

Continued

versity of California, Riverside, announced in January that he had developed a jojoba strain that produces self-pollinating flowers containing both male and female parts. Horticulturists Clifford B. Low and Wesley P. Hackett of the University of California, Davis, reported in March that jojoba can be grown from stem cuttings made during the spring and summer, and that some female varieties had a high potential for putting out roots.

Biological nitrogen fixers. USDA plant physiologist Gary H. Heichel of the University of Minnesota at St. Paul reported in December 1980 on the results of a two-year comparative study of the nitrogen-fixing abilities of three crops — alfalfa, red clover, and bird's-foot trefoil. Nitrogen-fixing plants play host to root-dwelling bacteria that convert atmospheric nitrogen to ammonia. When the bacteria die, the plants absorb the ammonia. These plants need no nitrogen fertilizers and leave the soil rich in nitrogen.

Heichel planted the crops in fields enclosed in polyurethane tents and replaced atmospheric nitrogen with N^{15}, an isotope of nitrogen that is particularly easy to identify. After harvesting the crops, he tested them for nitrogen content. He knew that N^{15} would have been fixed from the atmosphere and all other nitrogen absorbed from the soil or water. He found that alfalfa was the top nitrogen-fixer with 330 kilograms per hectare (295 pounds per acre), followed by red clover with 245 kilograms per hectare (218 pounds per acre), and trefoil with 195 kilograms per hectare (173 pounds per acre).

Steven N. Talley and Donald W. Rains, agronomists at the University of California, Davis, reported in April 1980 that up to 50 per cent of the nitrogen requirement for rice currently grown in California could be supplied by planting another nitrogen-fixing crop, *Azolla,* for one growing season. *Azolla* is a genus consisting of at least six species of fast-growing, floating miniature ferns that grow abundantly in tropical and temperate fresh waters. Under favorable conditions, it doubles its mass every two days.

Anabaena, a blue-green algae that contains a cyanobacterium capable of refixing atmospheric nitrogen, grows on the *Azolla* and sends threadlike filaments into the fern. The two live in symbiotic harmony, with *Anabaena* furnishing nitrogen for *Azolla.*

Successful cultivation of *Azolla* in rice fields or as a dual crop with rice requires phosphorus fertilization. Talley and Rains fertilized the *Azolla* plantings with phosphorus, harvested the crops 35 days after planting, and analyzed the elements the plants contained. They extracted more than 5 kilograms (11 pounds) of nitrogen for every 1 kilogram (2.2 pounds) of phosphorus they applied to the crops.

A new plant-growth regulator, aminoethoxyvinylglycine (AVG), was extensively tested during 1980 and 1981 with a variety of favorable results. For example, USDA horticulturists at the University of Wisconsin in Madison reported in June and October 1980 that AVG concentrations as low as 50 parts per million produced male flowers on female cucumber plants and produced flowers containing both male and female parts on female muskmelon plants. These results eliminate the need for planting cucumbers and muskmelons of both sexes in the same area to obtain seeds for future generations.

Maurice Liebermann and Robert Hardenberg of the USDA in Beltsville, Md., reported in February 1981, that they had used AVG to prevent or inhibit the synthesis of ethylene, a chemical that promotes ripening, in apples. The scientists sprayed apples with AVG shortly before harvesting them in the fall of 1980. They found that AVG delayed or prevented apples kept at room temperature from ripening and thus increased the length of storage time.

The Beltsville team also applied AVG to apples by vacuum infiltration. They placed the apples in a sealed chamber, removed the air from the chamber, and pumped in AVG, thus forcing the AVG into the apples. This method completely inhibited ethylene synthesis. However, AVG is expensive and not yet available commercially.

Crop irrigation developments. A team at the University of Idaho in Boise and the USDA's Snake River Conservation Research Center in Kimberly, Ida., reported the development of an energy-efficient, labor-saving, automated crop-irrigation sys-

A chemist uses a liquid nitrogen vacuum system to collect air samples from a commercial potato bin, *right*. Then a lab technician analyzes the collected samples by gas chromatography, identifying each gas in the samples, *below*. High proportions of certain gases indicate the presence of bacterial soft rot in a stage that can be easily arrested.

tem. Agricultural engineers Williams H. Heinemann and Dennis C. Kincaid and their associates call this new system "cablegation." It uses a single pipe with round holes on the upper surface. Water flows through each hole to irrigate a single furrow. A traveling plug, controlled by a cable on a battery, moves down the pipe at a specified rate, blocking off some holes and allowing the water to flow through others. Thus, irrigation can be regulated to give each furrow the amount of water needed. The use of a single cable rather than a network of cables significantly reduces equipment costs.

Lamb transplants. The first purebred Suffolk lambs to have developed from transplanted embryos in the United States were born at Michigan State University's sheep research center in February 1981.

Veterinarian Darold McCalla of Williamston, Mich., transferred eight embryos from two yearling ewes into four other ewes. Two sets of twins and two single births resulted from the transfer. Five of the lambs were transferred from the same donor ewe and all the lambs were sired by the same ram.

Embryo transplant involves treating the female with hormones that trigger superovulation, or the release of more than the normal number of eggs. The eggs are customarily fertilized by artificial insemination and the resultant embryos transplanted into the wombs of a number of other females. See TRANSFERRING THE CELL OF LIFE, *Science Year,* 1980.

Embryo transfer, which was responsible for the births of 20,000 cattle in 1980, is very difficult with sheep. While cattle embryos can be flushed from the womb, sheep embryos have to be surgically removed because of the ewe's small cervix. In addition, ram semen has not been successfully frozen, so ewes have to be naturally bred. Because sheep usually breed only in the fall, the time in which embryo transfer can be carried out is limited. Agriculturists expect, however, that embryo transfer will become a popular and practical method of sheep breeding because it allows prize animals to produce far more offspring and increases the rapidity of genetic improvements in the breed. [Sylvan H. Wittwer]

Anthropology

An expedition led by paleoanthropologist Woo Ju-kang (Wu Rukang) of the Chinese Academy of Sciences discovered a broken but complete skull of *Ramapithecus* in southern China in December 1980. Thought by many anthropologists to be a hominid — an ancestor of humans, rather than apes — *Ramapithecus* was found first in India and more recently in Kenya, Greece, Turkey, Hungary, and Pakistan. However, those finds were limited to jaw parts and loose teeth.

The new *Ramapithecus* skull came from a lignite bed about 100 kilometers (62 miles) west of K'un-ming (Kunming), the capital of Yunnan Province. Although not yet dated precisely, the lignite is believed to be about 8 million to 14 million years old. The skull was broken into many pieces but generally well-preserved and researchers believe it can be accurately reconstructed.

The expedition scientists found other specimens of *Ramapithecus* — upper and lower jaws with teeth in place, skull fragments, and hundreds of teeth — along with the remains of more than 30 kinds of mammals — in the same area. Using these new finds, anthropologists will be able to compare *Ramapithecus* with another hominid, *Australopithecus afarensis,* which lived at least 4 million years later in East Africa.

Anthropologists from the Chinese Academy of Sciences also made an unusual find in November 1980 at the Dragon Pool Cave site in Anhwei (Anhui) Province in southern China. They found a human cranium, complete except for the face; part of a lower jaw with two molars in place; and several loose teeth, all apparently from the same individual — whom the Chinese classified as *Homo erectus.* They said the skull has a thick, flat, frontal bone with a distinct ridge down the center and unusually thick brow ridges that nearly meet over the nose.

The Chinese also said the skull, about 400,000 years old, is more primitive in appearance than that of the famous Peking Man, the *Homo erectus* fossil found near Peking. They said the skull resembles more closely the Lan-t'ien skull found in Shensi (Shaanxi)

Symbols found carved on rocks in Guyana may represent a tally system used by prehistoric hunters and gatherers 7,000 years ago to keep track of such food sources as game animals.

Province in the 1960s and the Java Man fossils found on the island of Java, Indonesia.

Croatian finds. A number of important human fossils have been found in the Hrvatsko Zagorje region of northwest Croatia in Yugoslavia. The finds include Neanderthal (*Homo sapiens neanderthalensis*) remains from Krapina, and more modern (*Homo sapiens sapiens*) remains from Velika Pećina and Veternica. The fossils were described by Mirko Malez, Jahov Radovĉić, and Darko Rukavina of the Institute for Paleontology and Quarternary Geology, Yugoslav Academy of Sciences and Arts; anthropologist Milford H. Wolpoff of the University of Michigan in Ann Arbor; and Fred H. Smith of the University of Tennessee.

They reported in April 1981 on fossils recovered from this area beginning in 1974 at Vindija Cave, about 55 kilometers (34 miles) northeast of Zagreb. The limestone cave measures about 50 meters (164 feet) long and contains about 8 meters (26 feet) of ancient layered deposits. The layer dating from 40,000 to 59,000 years ago produced the most interesting material, according to the scientists. About 40 human fossils were found there, along with stone tools.

The researchers said that the fossils are definitely Neanderthal, but have a smaller face, smaller brow ridges, and thinner skull bones than are usually seen on Neanderthals. The Vindija remains also point toward the early development of a chin. In these respects, the fossils resemble modern humans. The researchers think that all of the Hrvatsko Zagorje fossils may represent the evolutionary history of a single human lineage.

Tetracycline in old bones. Anthropologists reported in September 1980 that they had found the antibiotic tetracycline in ancient human bones from the Nubian region of northern Sudan. Everett J. Bassett, Margaret S. Keith, George J. Armelagos, and Debra L. Martin of the University of Massachusetts in Amherst, and Antonio R. Villanueva of Henry Ford Hospital in Detroit said that the bones came from a cemetery dating from A.D. 350 to 550 on the west bank of the Nile River near Wadi Halfa. They studied thin sections

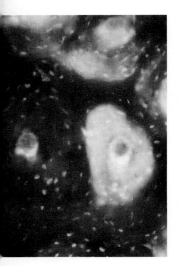

Tetracycline shows up as light spots on human fossil bones viewed under fluorescent light in a microscope. The bones, which date to about A.D. 350, were found in a fertile farming area in the Sudan. The antibiotic apparently grew on stored grain and may have provided the person with natural protection from disease.

of femora, or thigh bones, under ultraviolet light through a microscope and observed yellow-green fluorescent areas, the distinctive sign of tetracycline bound to bone. The people who lived in the area then were farmers who grew wheat, barley, and millet and stored their crops in mud bins.

The scientists think that the tetracycline was produced by streptomycetes, or moldlike bacteria, living on the grain. Streptomycetes flourish in a very dry, warm, alkaline environment, and they account for 60 to 70 per cent of the bacteria found in Sudanese desert soils. Because tetracycline is effective against some bacteria, rickettsias, spirochetes, and viruses, its presence in the bones may explain the extremely low rates of infectious diseases during that time in the Sudan.

Tracking sickle cells. Yuet Wai Kan and Andrée N. Dozy of the University of California, San Francisco, reported in July 1980 on how they used a technique for identifying genes to determine at what locations throughout the world certain mutations, or changes, in the hemoglobin gene occurred to produce sickle cell anemia. Hemoglobin is the oxygen-carrying element in red blood cells. Persons who inherit abnormal hemoglobin genes from both parents have sickle cell anemia.Their blood cells are stiff and misshapen, blocking blood flow. Those who inherit one gene do not have the disease, but are carriers who can pass it on to the next generation.

The University of California researchers took blood samples from people in Africa and India, where malaria is a major health problem, as well as from people in the United States whose ancestors had lived in these areas. They found that concentrations of three kinds of molecules, or markers, around the sickle cell gene were related to different geographic areas. Based on the present-day distribution of sickle cell markers, the researchers concluded that the genetic mutation that changed normal hemoglobin into sickle cell hemoglobin occurred not once, as previously thought, but at least twice. The mutation occurred in West Africa, again in southern India, and perhaps even a third time in East Africa. or Saudi Arabia.   [Charles F. Merbs]

Archaeology

Bone and stone tools from the Hadar region of Ethiopia are about 2.6 million years old. These oldest artifacts yet found pose new questions about when the human brain developed.

Old World. Archaeology begins with mankind's oldest tools, and laboratory research in 1981 determined that the earliest tools yet found may be about 2.6 million years old. Archaeologist John W. K. Harris of the University of Pittsburgh found 18 crudely chipped stone tools in the Afar region of Ethiopia in 1977. Harris and physical anthropologist Donald C. Johanson of the Cleveland Museum of Natural History reported in February 1981 that they used two chemical dating methods to estimate the age of the volcanic rock surrounding the tools. One method measured potassium-argon atoms in the rocks; the other, uranium-238 atoms in volcanic glass. The earliest tools previously reported are about 2.1-million years old.

Anthropologists believe that hominids evolved large brains about 2 million years ago and that their increased brain capacity enabled them to learn to use complex tools. However, if these tools are dated correctly, they were made and used at least 500,000 years before that. So the tools present archae-

ologists with another puzzle: Were there large-brained hominids between 2 million and 3 million years ago who made these tools? Or did tool use stimulate brain development?

Ancient Asia. Anthropologist Richard S. Davis of Bryn Mawr College in Pennsylvania and two Russian colleagues reported in December 1980 that they had discovered two types of stone tools dating to at least 250,000 years ago in 12 areas of the central and eastern Soviet Union. This casts doubt on one of the oldest beliefs in archaeology — that the use of improved stone tools, which started in Africa about 250,000 years ago and spread to Europe, did not penetrate far into Asia.

Davis, archaeologist Vadim A. Ranov, and geologist Andrey E. Dodonov found the tools buried under 60 meters (200 feet) of loess, a silty soil containing fine mineral particles.

Davis reported that the use of "choppers," stones with one or both sides chipped off to form a cutting edge, and flake tools, made by splitting a stone into a wedge shape, showed that tool-

215

Archaeology

Continued

A wall, *above right*, uncovered in the City of David in Jerusalem's Old City, *above*, may have been part of the palace of King David or his son King Solomon around 1000 B.C.

making 250,000 years ago was much more diverse and complex in these areas than previously thought.

Origins of farming. Anthropologist Mark Cohen of the State University of New York at Stony Brook reported in November 1980 that his studies support the theory that population growth forced people to develop new food sources. Archaeologists know that organized farming started in many parts of the Old World at about the same time – 8000 B.C. to 5000 B.C. But they do not know the reasons for this simultaneous development.

Cohen studied Old World and New World skeletons and found evidence of malnutrition and disease in many of the skeletons from the earliest days of farming. He says a society that was not feeding people properly would be pressured into finding new ways of producing adequate nourishment.

Many scientists now disagree with Cohen, however. Anthropologists Fred Wendorf of Southern Methodist University in Dallas and Romuald Schild of the Polish Academy of Sciences in

Warsaw reported in September 1980 on their studies of Egyptian sites about 20,000 years old. They attempted to learn why people gathered in the Nile Valley about that time and began cultivating wheat and barley. Some researchers had thought that drought in what is now the desert had spurred this move. But Wendorf and Schild said their studies ruled out weather and population pressure as possible causes for the growth of farming on the Nile. They plan further work in the area to try to pin down the factors responsible.

Prehistoric art. Archaeologist Tom Rogers of the Stone Age Studies Research Association of Canada reported in January 1981 that animal figures on the walls of caves in the Wye Valley in England were probably used as magic symbols, intended to increase the hunters' luck. The paintings may date to 15,000 B.C.

While on a field trip, Rogers found the painted outline of an animal similar to a deer in a cave near his camp. He then found several similar cave paintings in the area. [Robert J. Wenke]

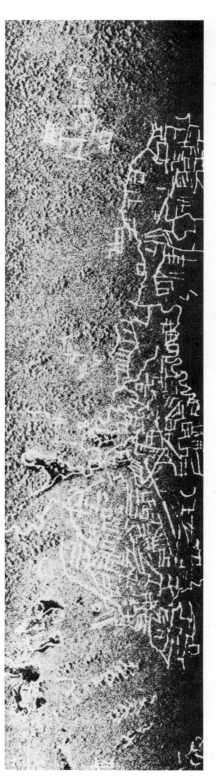

Lines drawn on a radar image made by a satellite outline a network of canals built by the ancient Maya in what are now the jungles of Guatemala.

New World. Archaeologist Richard E. W. Adams of the University of Texas at San Antonio reported in May 1980 that he and his colleagues used a sophisticated radar system designed for mapping the surface of Venus to identify an extensive network of ancient Maya canal systems in Central America. The canals evidently were used to irrigate fields and to drain swampy areas that could be used as farmland. Apparently the canals helped agricultural output that reached its height about A.D. 600.

Adams and scientists from the Jet Propulsion Laboratory in Pasadena, Calif., used the radar system, mounted in a National Aeronautics and Space Administration jet, to scan about 37,000 square kilometers (14,285 square miles) of jungle in Guatemala and northern Belize. Adams used the stored radar images to map the area.

Archaeologists previously thought that one factor in the collapse of the Maya was that the Mayan civilization failed to develop a good irrigation system. But Adams reported that the canals were distributed over land that could have produced enough food to support at least 1.2 million persons.

The earliest Americans. Archaeologist Dennis J. Stanford of the Smithsonian Institution in Washington, D.C., reported in April 1981 on an unusual experiment he performed. He showed that 50,000-year-old mammoth and mastodon bones from the Old Crow site in Canada's Yukon Territory could have been tools. Archaeologists agree that the ancestors of the American Indian came to North America from Siberia across the Bering Strait. But controversy continues over when this occurred.

If the bones were used as tools, they are evidence that humans lived in the Yukon area 50,000 years ago. But some scientists have wondered if the bones were simply broken by accident.

For the experiment, Stanford and two colleagues cut up the carcass of Ginsberg, a 23-year-old African elephant that died at the Boston Zoo. Elephants are the closest modern relatives of ancient mammoths and mastodons. The scientists were able to make crude tools from several of Ginsberg's bones that looked like the tools found at the Old Crow site.

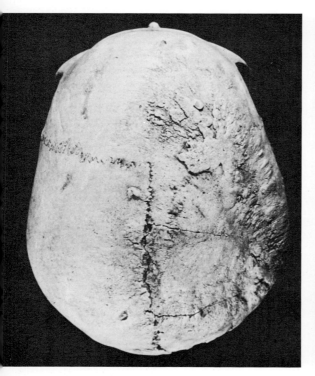

Archaeology

Continued

Skulls found on the Crow Creek Sioux Indian Reservation in South Dakota, *above right,* are part of the evidence for a massacre of about 500 persons in the 1300s. The skull of one victim, *above,* shows evidence that he had survived an earlier scalping.

To determine whether the ancient hunters used fresh bones or bones that had been cured, or dried, Stanford also attempted to make tools from an African elephant *femur* (thighbone) that had been dried for four years. When he split the femur, it shattered. This experiment reinforced the idea that the Old Crow hunters did not dry the bones they used for tools. They simply used bones from their latest kill.

The scientists then used the tools to cut apart sections of Ginsberg's flesh, as a prehistoric hunter might have used them to butcher a freshly killed mastodon. They found that these bone tools cut the carcass effectively.

The tools lost their sharp edges quickly, and this may shed light on why prehistoric hunters in grasslands butchered their kills on the site. Stanford thinks that prehistoric hunters discarded their cutting tools when the tools became dull, and made other tools when they needed them from the bones of freshly killed animals.

Early melting pot. Archaeologist Kathleen Deagan of Florida State University in Tallahassee reported in October 1980 that artifacts from the 1500s reveal that St. Augustine, Fla., was a blend of Spanish, Latin American, Mexican, and Florida Indian peoples. So the city was apparently America's first melting pot.

Deagan analyzed charred plant remains from abandoned water wells used as trash receptacles. The food she found there helped determine the various cultures represented by the diet of the early settlers. Some items, like peaches and red peppers, were imported from Europe. Deagan thinks the settlers received native foods — including maize, gourds, squash, and melons — from the Indians in exchange for such items as pottery.

She found pieces of Indian pottery with designs borrowed from Spanish pottery. Houses in the area showed the same mixing of influences.

Deagan also found evidence that St. Augustine was a trading town. Pieces of Chinese pottery, Spanish ceramics, and some Venetian glass were found on the site. [Thomas R. Hester]

Astronomy

Planetary Astronomy. Uwe Fink and his associates at the University of Arizona in Tucson reported in October 1980 that they had discovered a thin atmosphere on Pluto. The astronomers used a charge-coupled device, a new instrument that detects light rays more efficiently, attached to a conventional spectrometer. By analyzing the spectral lines in the light coming from distant objects, astronomers can determine which materials the objects are made of. Earlier observers who detected methane on Pluto interpreted it as frost covering the planet's surface. But Fink showed that the spectrum contained lines characteristic only of gaseous methane, which would have to be in Pluto's atmosphere.

The atmosphere that covers the tiny planet is exceedingly thin compared with Earth's atmosphere. The Arizona team said that the total atmospheric surface pressure on Pluto could be no more than 1/20 of the pressure on Earth, and may be as low as 1/7,000. Some astronomers think the thinness of Pluto's atmosphere may indicate that it is temporary. The methane may exist in appreciable quantities above the planet's surface only when Pluto is in the phase of its orbit that takes it nearest to the Sun. The Sun's heat could then evaporate part of the frost cover, turning it into gaseous methane.

Astronomers Robert S. Harrington and James W. Christy of the United States Naval Observatory in Washington, D.C., who discovered Charon, Pluto's moon, in 1978, reported their latest observations in February 1981. Harrington and Christy found a strict synchronism between the time it takes Pluto to rotate on its axis and the time it takes Charon to orbit around Pluto. One Plutonian rotation, or "day," equals the time it takes Charon to orbit Pluto. If Charon's own rotation is also in synchronism with the time it takes to orbit Pluto, as seems likely, the smallest planetary system is unique. No other system is so coordinated.

Alistair R. Walker of the South African Astronomical Observatory in Sutherland reported in August 1980 that he observed the occultation, or eclipse, of a star by Charon on April 6 that lasted for 50 seconds. Based upon calculations involving this time span and the time it

takes Charon to orbit Pluto, Walker deduced that the moon's diameter must be more than 1,200 kilometers (745 miles). Considering this information together with the observed brightness of the Plutonian system, Walker estimated that Pluto's diameter probably ranges from 2,600 to 4,000 kilometers (1,600 to 2,500 miles), and Charon's diameter may be from 1,200 to 1,800 kilometers (745 to 1,100 miles). The total mass of Pluto and Charon was computed to be about 400 times less than that of Earth.

Halley's Comet is the subject of a new handbook issued on Jan. 15, 1981, by astronomer Donald K. Yeomans of the Jet Propulsion Laboratory (JPL) in Pasadena, Calif. Yeomans provided the most up-to-date opinion on the nature of the comet and what the ground-based observer can expect to see when it approaches the Sun in 1986. The comet reappears every 76 to 79 years.

Based on observations made when the comet last approached the Sun in 1910, scientists believed it consisted of an icy nucleus about 2.5 kilometers (1.5 miles) in diameter that is surrounded by a hazy cloud called a coma, and an immensely long gaseous tail.

According to Yeomans, Halley's Comet is now about 2 billion kilometers (1.2 billion miles) from the Sun, between the orbits of Uranus and Saturn, and is approaching Earth at a rate of about 9 kilometers (5 miles) per second. Astronomers at the Palomar Observatory in California and at Kitt Peak National Observatory in Arizona began trying to sight the comet in 1980.

Kitt Peak observers looked in vain for the comet in November. Their observations were made to a limiting brightness of 24.1 magnitudes. This means that the telescope, operating on a dark night, would be able to detect a golf ball in space at a distance of nearly 8,000 kilometers (5,000 miles). The observers deduced that the comet was probably still too far from the Sun — therefore too cold — to produce its gaseous tail at that time. They also theorized that its nucleus can be no more than 8.5 kilometers (5 miles) in diameter, or they would have seen it.

Even when it appears, the comet will be difficult to observe from the ground, because it will pass on the opposite side

A recent radio photo of Jupiter, the planet that sends out the strongest signals, provides data about Jupiter's magnetism. Radiation "wings" appear on either side of the planet when electrons become trapped in a ring inside Jupiter's asymmetrical magnetic field.

Astronomy

Continued

Photos of Mars by *Viking Orbiter 1* yielded a surprise when a small cloud on one photo, *below,* was found to be in a different position on a photo made just 4.48 seconds later, *below right*. This could mean that the "cloud" is really a column of steam from a geyser or volcano, blown along by winds circulating on Mars. It is the first evidence of continuing activity on the Martian surface.

of the Sun. Three groups — the European Space Agency, Japan, and France in a combined effort with the Soviet Union — announced in 1980 that they would fly missions to view the comet.

More comet tails. Malcolm B. Niedner, Jr., of Systems and Applied Science Corporation in Riverdale, Md., and John C. Brandt of the Goddard Space Flight Center in Greenbelt, Md., reported in May 1980 on how comet tails and their unusual structures may originate. The most impressive feature on Halley's Comet is its ion tail, composed of a hot plasma of atoms that have lost electrons. The tail streams out of the comet away from the Sun for hundreds of millions of kilometers. Comet tails are shaped by magnetic fields of interplanetary space.

Niedner and Brandt examined the photographic records and drawings based on verbal reports of many comets. They found that the most unusual features, such as loops, knots, and spirals, appear just after a relatively stable and well-defined tail becomes disconnected from a comet's head.

Interplanetary gas is pervaded by a magnetic field, which is divided into sectors around the Sun. The field in one sector will point toward the Sun, and away from it in the next sector. Niedner and Brandt believe that comets lose their tails when they pass from one sector to another and experience this reversal of the field. When the head of the comet crosses the opposing magnetic fields, it cancels their effects. Then the pressure of the solar wind is able to detach the tail.

The absence of a stable tail structure immediately behind the comet permits new envelopes of magnetized plasma with opposing magnetic fields to wrap around the comet's head and then collide with one another in the tailless region. The opposing magnetic fields of the colliding plasmas again destroy one another. This leads to the chaotic picture seen by many observers of magnetized loops, knots, and filaments. Later, the material reaches an equilibrium for reasons scientists do not yet understand, and a stable tail structure is once more established — at least until it en-

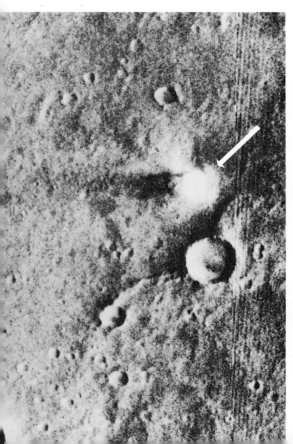
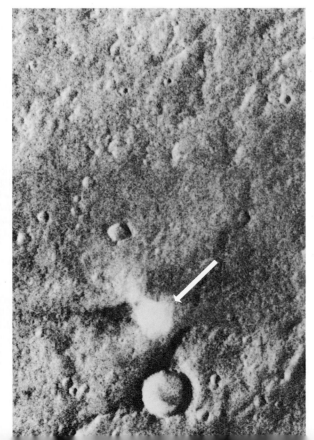

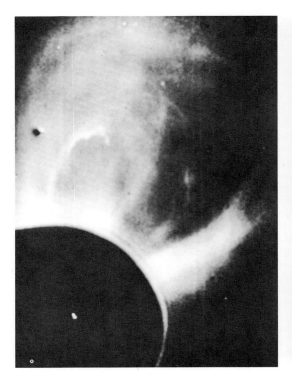

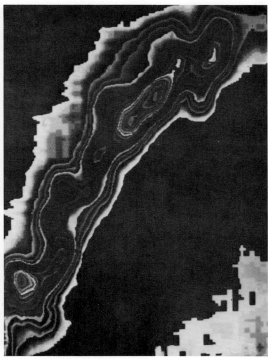

Astronomy

Continued

Coronal transients, *above*, huge spiral streaks of hydrogen ejected from the sun's surface, appear to be cooler than their surroundings in photographs taken with a coronagraph equipped with a special filter, *above right*. Their shape suggests that magnetic fields are wound around them tightly enough to insulate against coronal heat.

counters another reversal of the interplanetary magnetic field.

Martian topography. Planetologists Ladislav E. Roth, George S. Downs, and R. Stephen Saunders of JPL and Gerald Schubert of the University of California, Los Angeles (UCLA), reported in June 1980 that they restudied the topography of the Tharsis region of Mars. Using both ground-based radar data and information from the *Viking* spacecraft, they came up with some new views about the surface of the area. The Tharsis region is dominated by large volcanic mountains, one of which is three times higher than Mount Everest, Earth's largest mountain, and has 10 times the volume of Mauna Kea in Hawaii, Earth's largest volcano.

Earlier *Viking* observations found Tharsis to be a vast domed volcanic plain where the terrain is fractured and crisscrossed with cracks and chasms in some areas, and has no well-defined shape but is chaotic (full of lumps and bumps) in others. The JPL and UCLA scientists used radar data at its highest resolution to show that some Tharsian

features that appear relatively minor in the *Viking* photos are really giant conical volcanic mountains.

Their studies revealed that the fractured terrain, such as is found in the Claritas Fossae area, is high ground rising 1 kilometer (0.6 mile) above the surrounding plains and separated from them by breaks in the surface crust. Some regions of chaotic terrain are as much as 6 kilometers (3.7 miles) below the surrounding area. Much of the bumpy surface is found at the head of massive runoff channels that may have been formed long ago by flowing water.

Earlier, investigators had suggested that such terrain might have been formed by the melting and collapse of a subsurface ice layer, followed by the runoff of a flood of water. However, the new findings seem to indicate that such a cause is unlikely, because the area involved is so huge. The JPL and UCLA scientists believe the bumpy terrain was formed when the Martian surface collapsed after large amounts of molten rock shifted under the planet's crust.　　　[Michael J. S. Belton]

Astronomy

Continued

Stellar Astronomy. The National Aeronautics and Space Administration's (NASA) Solar Maximum Mission (SMM) satellite completed its most significant measurements of the sun in December 1980. Kenneth Frost of Goddard Space Flight Center in Greenbelt, Md., led several teams that observed solar flares, or sudden bursts of radiation from the sun, and erupting prominences, some of the glowing, gaseous structures in the solar atmosphere. The groups obtained data in ultraviolet light, X rays, and gamma rays. These data revealed how flares occur. When magnetic loops, formed from the lines of magnetic force that protrude from the sun, fill with hot plasma, or highly ionized gas, they suddenly explode. This may occur in an isolated loop or when one loop collides with another. The instruments also showed that X-ray emission lines from the loop widen just as a flare begins because of rapid heating, sudden turbulent motions in a loop, or both.

The inconstant sun. Richard Willson of Jet Propulsion Laboratory in Pasadena, Calif., designed an SMM instrument whose precise measurements for the first time revealed definite changes in the solar constant. Astronomers have long tried to detect changes in the solar constant — the total radiation of the sun as received at the earth — because such changes might indicate future consequences for earth's climate.

Willson published measurements in February 1981 that he made in the first 153 days of SMM observations. The data are so precise that a change of a few hundredths of 1 per cent in the sun's light can be readily seen. The largest variations were brightness dips that occurred in early April and late May 1980 as large groups of sunspots, dark, relatively cool areas on the sun's surface, passed near the center of the solar disk. Willson does not yet know if the variations will affect climate.

Rare stars. Joseph P. Cassinelli, John S. Mathis, and Blair D. Savage of the University of Wisconsin in Madison reported in January 1981 that R136a, the central object of the 30 Doradus nebula in the Large Magellanic Cloud,

"One advantage of living near a binary star would be a suntan in half the time."

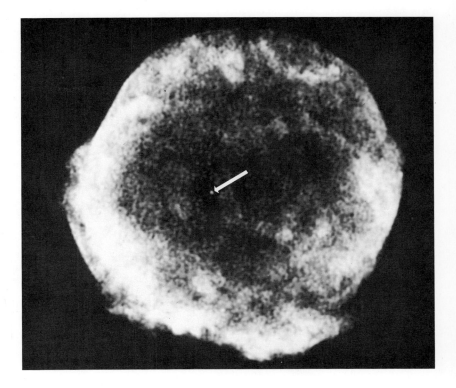

Intense radio signals detected in 1980 at the center of Tycho's supernova, a star seen exploding in 1572, may come from a neutron star that is the object's collapsed core. These observations are the first to tie a supernova of Tycho's type to a neutron star.

Astronomy

Continued

is by far the most massive known star. It is about 100 billion times brighter than the sun, has 2,500 times more mass, 100 times the diameter, and a surface temperature 10 times hotter. The Wisconsin team based their conclusions on information from a spectrometer aboard the International Ultraviolet Explorer satellite.

Bruce Margon of the University of Washington in Seattle; Ronald Downes of the University of California, Los Angeles; and James Gunn of Princeton University in New Jersey reported in January 1981 that they had detected the first close binary star in a globular cluster. Close binaries are pairs of stars so near to each other that mass from one star frequently flows over to the other. Globular clusters typically contain 100,000 to more than 1 million stars, yet no close binary had been found previously in a globular cluster.

Bizarre star SS433 in 1980 occupied much attention for the third year. The object produces two jets of high speed gas that rotate every 164 days, emitting spectral lines that indicate matter from

SS433 is streaming both toward and away from the earth. Robert Hjellming of the National Radio Astronomy Observatory in Green Bank, W. Va., and Kenneth J. Johnston of the Naval Research Laboratory in Washington, D.C., made a series of radio maps of the SS433 region with the Very Large Array near Socorro, N. Mex., and found a curious, corkscrew-shaped pattern centered on SS433.

In December 1980, they reported decoding changes in the pattern, which reveal that SS433 hurls plasma clouds from its rotating jets at irregular intervals. Once a cloud leaves the jets, it sails out into the galaxy along an arching trajectory, like a ball shot from a cannon. Astronomers have never before observed such a phenomenon.

The smoothies. Susan Wilkerson of Kitt Peak National Observatory in Arizona in September 1980 reported on a newly recognized group of spiral galaxies called the smooth-arm, or "smoothy" galaxies, observed with the 306-meter (1,000-foot) Arecibo radio telescope in Puerto Rico. These differ

Astronomy

Continued

from other spiral galaxies in their lack of clumpy regions, the groups of hot young stars enmeshed with glowing hydrogen gas usually found in the spiral arms. Wilkerson showed that the smoothies contain much less hydrogen gas than do other spirals.

Her discovery posed a new problem, because astronomers think that spiral arms result from stars forming while a rotating shock wave travels through a gaseous medium. The smoothies have the stars and arms, but lack the medium. Wilkerson concluded that the smoothies have been stripped of gas by collisions with other galaxies or by passing through the hot intergalactic medium within a cluster of galaxies.

Fuzzy quasar. Six astronomers, led by the wife-and-husband team of Susan Wyckoff of Arizona State University in Tempe and Peter A. Wehinger of the Max Planck Institute for Astronomy in Heidelberg, West Germany, reported in December 1980 that they had detected a faint, apparently nebulous region, or "fuzz," out to a radius of about 150,000 light-years around 3C273, the brightest and one of the closest quasars. (A light-year is the distance light travels in a year at a speed of 299,792 kilometers [186,282 miles] per second).

Astrophysicists have long speculated that quasars, the most intense energy emitters in the universe, are violent disturbances at the center of galaxies. But the galaxies have not been seen because quasars are thousands of times brighter and their glare would obscure any galactic starlight.

The fuzz around 3C273 was first detected on a long-exposure photo taken with the 3.6-meter (141-inch) telescope at the European Southern Observatory at La Silla, Chile. Spectral analyzers on this telescope and on the 3.9-meter (153-inch) Anglo-Australian Telescope in New South Wales, Australia, showed that emission lines of oxygen and neon from the fuzz and the quasar had the same shift of light toward the red end of the spectrum. Astronomers use red shift to measure speed and direction of heavenly objects, so this means both are at the same distance from the earth. Also, the fuzz's color is consistent with what astronomers would expect of stars in a galaxy. So quasars are probably at galaxy centers. [Stephen P. Maran]

High-Energy Astronomy continued to make advances in 1980 and 1981, many of them in the relatively new area of gamma-ray studies. Gamma rays, the most energetic form of electromagnetic radiation, were first detected outside the solar system by *Vela* satellites in 1969. European astronomers have used the *COS-B* satellite, launched in 1975, to survey the sky and search for gamma-ray sources.

As of November 1980, they had catalogued 25 sources. Most of them are within the Milky Way galaxy.

Astronomers do not know exactly what types of cosmic objects produce this energetic radiation. Gamma rays are produced on the earth by nuclear explosions, such as the testing of atomic bombs. Scientists so far have been able to definitely identify gamma-ray sources with only four other known objects in our galaxy. All four emit radio waves. Two are pulsars, or pulsed radio sources, one in the Crab Nebula and the other in the constellation Vela.

A third gamma-ray source was identified with the quasar 3C273. Quasars are the most intense emitters of radio waves, and 3C273 is the brightest quasar. The fourth object identified with gamma rays was an interstellar cloud complex. From the little that is now known, it appears that astronomers may someday discover an entirely new class of galactic objects that emit energy only in gamma rays.

New objects in space. Elihu A. Boldt and Darryl J. Leiter of Goddard Space Flight Center in Greenbelt, Md., reported in April 1981 that data from the first and second High-Energy Astronomy Observatories (HEAO-1 and HEAO-2, the *Einstein* Observatory) suggest that an as-yet unidentified type of extragalactic object may account for the origin of the cosmic X-ray background radiation. This intense radiation pervades all of space.

Boldt and Leiter showed that the energy distribution, or spectrum, of the radiation is similar to what would be expected from a thin, hot gas at a temperature of about 500 million °C. At the same time, I reported on my work at the Smithsonian Astrophysical Observatory (SAO) in Cambridge, Mass. There I analyzed data from the *Einstein* Observatory, which had detected many very faint X-ray sources at a slightly lower energy than that used by Boldt and Leiter. I concluded that the background radiation comes from the total emission of numerous individual sources rather than a gas.

Therefore, Boldt and Leiter proposed that a new class of objects may exist. Perhaps these hypothetical sources, which they called precursor active galaxies, were active long ago, and cannot be detected as individual sources with the instruments we have now. Future, more sensitive X-ray telescopes will determine whether this is correct.

New quasars. Among the other new objects that astronomers have suggested may contribute to the cosmic X-ray background radiation is a new type of quasar reported in the summer of 1981 by John Stocke at the University of Arizona's Steward Observatory. When Stocke and his colleagues were studying optical photographs as part of an effort to match objects detected visually with X-ray sources discovered by the *Einstein* Observatory, they found a type of stellar object with a spectrum similar to that of a quasar, but with very narrow emission lines. Such new objects, which the astronomers called narrow-line quasars, had not been noticed before.

Other astronomers surveying X-ray sources uncovered evidence for the theory that a different mixture of extragalactic objects may have existed in the past. Tommaso Maccacaro of SAO reported in January 1981 that he and his colleagues had discovered more than 100 new X-ray sources from *Einstein* observations. All of these are fainter than the weakest source listed in the catalog of strong X-ray sources seen with HEAO-1 and reported in June 1980 by Giuseppe Piccinotti and his colleagues at Goddard.

Maccacaro compared the types of sources seen in his *Einstein* survey with the Piccinotti catalog and concluded that the sources that appear brightest are mainly nearby clusters of galaxies. Fainter X-ray sources are mainly more distant active galactic nuclei — for example, galactic centers containing radio sources — such as Seyfert galaxies and quasars. In a Seyfert galaxy, radiation comes from energetic processes in a tiny region surrounding a massive compact object — possibly a black hole — instead of from stars.

Since objects far away in space are also further back in time, the astronomers concluded that active galactic nuclei were more common in the past than were clusters of galaxies. This means that there must have been a change in the number or brightness, or both, of different objects at different times in the history of the universe.

Clusters of galaxies. Astrophysicists Riccardo Giacconi, William Forman, and Christine Jones of SAO reported in April 1981 that they looked at the detailed structure of the X-ray-emitting gas in a few nearby clusters of galaxies. These clusters contain hundreds to thousands of galaxies and appear to be filled with hot gas that emits vast amounts of X rays at energies that indicate the gas has temperatures of tens of millions of degrees.

They found that most of this gas is concentrated around individual clumps of galaxies within the cluster and appears to be cooler than the gas that is dispersed more evenly throughout the entire cluster. They interpreted these measurements as evidence that a cluster is not highly evolved, but is still undergoing major changes in structure and is not in equilibrium. By studying many clusters, Jones and Forman showed that most of them are of this unevolved type. Therefore, they concluded that the universe is still in an early phase of its development.

X-ray photos of some clusters show that they have two separate areas emitting strong concentrations of X rays. J. Patrick Henry and his colleagues at SAO reported in February that they examined one of these so-called double-clusters in detail and found that the galaxies within the clusters are grouped in two separate clumps. Furthermore, these two clumps appear to be coming together to form a more condensed cluster. This observation strongly supports a view of cosmology in which galaxies formed first rather than clusters after the big bang, the cosmic explosion that created the universe. In this scheme, galaxies floated randomly through space until gravitational attraction began to pull them together in clusters. See X-RAY EYES ON THE SKIES. [Stephen S. Murray]

225

Astronomy

Continued

Cosmology. Astrophysicists around the world decided in 1980 and 1981 that neutrinos are not what they seemed to be — or not be. Until recently, these minute particles of matter were believed to travel at the speed of light and to have zero mass, so they could pass through the earth as if it were not there. Their only observable characteristics were energy and spin.

According to the big bang theory of cosmology, which says the universe began with the explosion of a primordial fireball, a background of neutrinos should still exist as relics of the early universe. Only a few scientists cared about this, until two groups of physicists announced in 1980 that neutrinos may have a mass of several electron volts or more. At the subatomic level, mass can be expressed in terms of energy. So astrophysicists measure mass in electron volts, which are minute units of energy. The discovery that neutrinos could have mass had a remarkable impact on cosmology because it might answer many questions about the structure and evolution of the universe.

Among the astrophysicists who recently reported on neutrinos are Y. B. Zeldovich and his co-workers at the Institute for Space Science in Moscow, in August 1980; I and J. Richard Bond and George Efstathiou at the University of California, Berkeley, in December 1980; and David N. Schramm of the University of Chicago and Gary Steigman of Bartol Research Foundation in Newark, Del., in January 1981. All of these studies were basically concerned with the vast difference between neutrinos having even a tiny mass and neutrinos having zero mass, and the scientific implications that follow.

Neutrinos without mass could never slow down, but neutrinos with some mass could come to rest and become bound by gravity in such objects as galaxies. Because scientists think that neutrinos outnumber the protons, neutrons, and electrons of ordinary matter by about 10 billion to 1, even a small mass implies that most of the density of the universe would be in the form of these invisible neutrinos.

The amount of visible matter in the universe, in the form of stars and gas, is much less than the amount of mass scientists believe there ought to be, according to theories of gravitational dynamics. The hidden mass that astronomers have theorized would be the predominant form of matter in individual galaxy halos and among the great clusters of galaxies may consist of neutrinos. Neutrinos may even be the missing matter needed to close the universe — that is, to augment the gas throughout space so there would be enough matter to reverse the expansion of the universe and eventually cause it to collapse. See X-RAY EYES ON THE SKIES.

Background radiation variation. The cosmic microwave background radiation — the leftover glow of the fireball from which the universe developed, according to the big bang theory — was discovered in 1965. Ever since then, cosmologists have believed that they should be able to detect a radio signal indicating small temperature variations in the background radiation. The variations should be caused by fluctuations in matter in the distant parts of the universe. Without such fluctuations, galaxies could not have formed. Detecting the radio signal would prove that the early universe contained protogalaxies, masses of gas from which galaxies of stars formed. If there were no gas and therefore no protogalaxies, no such radio signal would be detected.

At the University of California, Berkeley, Michael Wilson and I predicted in January 1981 that such a very weak radio signal should extend over a large portion of the sky — at least 90° — and be detectable and measurable with radio telescopes. Then Stephen P. Boughn, Edward Cheng, and David T. Wilkinson of Princeton University in New Jersey reported in February 1981 that they had found the first strong evidence of such a variation in the cosmic microwave background radiation.

The Princeton group launched a small radio telescope on a balloon that rose above earth's atmosphere in order to make observations without interference from radio signals or other background radiation originating on earth. The scientists concluded that the signal they detected was due to the background radiation. Their experiment showed that regions of the sky separated by 90° differed in temperature by the significant amount of 0.3 per cent.

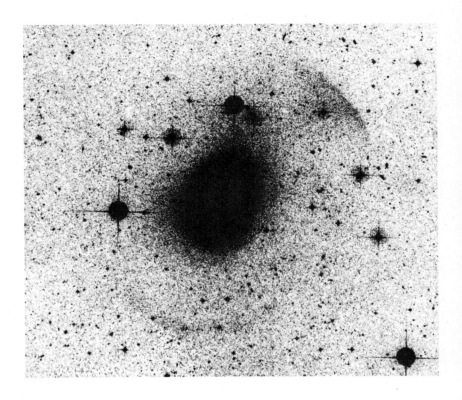

Astronomy

Continued

An elliptical galaxy surrounded by a vast but delicate shell of gas is one of four such objects recently detected with new techniques of enhancing photographs. Finding the objects was a surprise – elliptical galaxies were believed to contain only old stars and no extra gas.

Most remote galaxy. Hyron Spinrad and John Stauffer of the University of California, Berkeley, and Harvey R. Butcher of Kitt Peak National Observatory in Arizona reported in March 1981 that they had detected two galaxies 10 billion light-years away from the earth. That is 2 billion light-years farther than the most distant galaxies known until now.

The farther out astronomers look in space, the further back they see in time. The faint light these astronomers saw and studied left stars in these galaxies 10 billion years ago – about 5½ billion years before the earth was formed. Spinrad and his colleagues expected that such remote galaxies must have formed about halfway between the big bang – which they considered to be about 18 billion years ago – and now. They should therefore look different from closer galaxies, which formed more recently.

This idea was supported by an October 1980 report by Gustavo Bruzual of the University of California, Berkeley; Richard Kron of the University of Chi-

cago; and Beatrice M. Tinsley of Yale University in New Haven, Conn. They reported that younger galaxies should be significantly bluer. The color would arise from more younger, hotter, more massive stars than are present in mature, older galaxies.

But the color of the very distant galaxies observed by Spinrad and his colleagues was not bluer; in fact, it was indistinguishable from that of evolved, older galaxies near earth. This led Spinrad's group to conclude that these remote galaxies, and probably most others as far away, must have formed extremely early in the history of the universe in order for the galactic stars to have had sufficient time to evolve.

In fact, their color was similar to those with an age of 6 billion years. Adding on the 10 billion years it took their light to reach the earth means they must have formed 16 billion years ago. According to Spinrad, this shows that, at least for the large elliptical galaxies, the burst of galaxy formation happened very quickly after the big bang.   [Joseph Silk]

Books of Science

Here are 24 outstanding new science books suitable for the general reader. They have been selected from books published in 1980 and 1981.

Anthropology. *Hands* by John Napier discusses our unique ability to use our hands as powerful tools and precision instruments and as a means of communication and expression. The book also analyzes how hands evolved in human beings. (Pantheon, 1980. 176 pp. illus. $12.95)

Lucy: The Beginnings of Mankind by Donald Johanson and Maitland Edey is an account of Johanson's 1974 discovery of the fossil remains of *Australopithecus afarensis,* the earliest known hominid to walk upright. The book discusses the controversy over the hominid, called Lucy, and other fossil finds. (Simon & Schuster, 1981. 409 pp. illus. $16.95)

Astronomy. *Out of the Darkness: The Planet Pluto* by Clyde W. Tombaugh and Patrick Moore tells how Tombaugh discovered Pluto in 1930 and how astronomer Percival Lowell, who died in 1916, did groundwork for the discovery. The book also discusses the 1978 discovery of Charon, Pluto's moon. (Stackpole, 1980. 221 pp. illus. $14.95)

Voyage to Jupiter by David Morrison and Jane Samz relates discoveries about the planet Jupiter, its moons, and its ring systems, and describes the spacecraft that provided this information. The book is illustrated with photographs of Jupiter and its moons. (National Aeronautics and Space Administration [NASA SP-439], 1980. 199 pp. illus. $7.50)

Biology. *Earthly Pleasures: Tales from a Biologist's Garden* by Roger B. Swain draws on the familiar items in the author's garden and relates them to the larger world of scientific discovery and understanding. The book discusses such topics as the energy content of maple syrup and the difference between plants and animals. (Scribner's, 1981. 198 pp. illus. $10.95)

Splendid Isolation: The Curious History of South American Mammals by George Gaylord Simpson is a study of the evolution of such unusual animals as tree sloths, anteaters, tuco-tucos, and maned wolves. Simpson discusses the importance of the fact that the con-

tinent was an isolated island when the animals' ancestors were developing. (Yale University Press, 1980. 266 pp. illus. $17.50)

The World of the Tent-Makers: A Natural History of the Eastern Tent Caterpillar by V. G. Dethier traces the caterpillars' life cycle through each season. The author explains in detail how caterpillars survive attacks by predators and parasites and extremely hot and cold weather. (University of Massachusetts Press, 1980. 151 pp. illus. $5.95)

Cosmology. *Cosmos* by Carl Sagan is based on the author's popular 13-part television series. The book explores the origins and evolution of the universe, our planetary system, and the role humans play in the universe. It also describes the efforts by a number of scientists to communicate with extraterrestrial beings. (Random House, 1980. 365 pp. illus. $19.95)

Genesis: The Origins of Man and the Universe by John Gribbin systematically outlines what is known about the origins of the cosmos, our galaxy, life, and the earth. The author attempts to provide an overview of the best scientific answers to the question, "Where do we come from?" (Delacorte, 1981. 290 pp. illus. $13.95)

Environment. *The Greenhouse Effect* by Harold W. Bernard, Jr., argues that burning fossil fuels has added large amounts of carbon dioxide to the earth's atmosphere, resulting in a gradual warming. The author presents historical climatic data and forecasts how the warming trend may affect rainfall and sea levels. (Ballinger, 1980. 189 pp. illus. $12.95)

The Wooing of Earth: New Perspectives on Man's Use of Nature by René Dubos reviews how we have shaped our environment and concludes that our actions have not all been destructive. Dubos also speculates on the positive developments that may arise in the future. (Scribner's, 1980. 183 pp. $8.95)

Mathematics. *John Von Neumann and Norbert Wiener: From Mathematics to the Technologies of Life and Death* by Steve J. Heims is a biography of two mathematicians whose lives were greatly affected by their participation in the Manhattan Project, which developed the atomic bomb in the 1940s. Heims also describes their mathematical

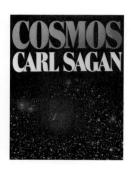

Books of Science

Continued

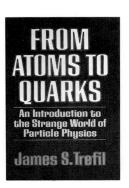

achievements. (MIT Press, 1980. 546 pp. illus. $19.95)

Natural History. *Galapagos: Islands Lost in Time* by Tui de Roy Moore, a native of the Galapagos, captures the islands' extraordinary range of wildlife and physical features in this photo essay. The brief text summarizes the author's own experience with the islands' volcanoes, geology, and wildlife. (Viking, 1980. 71 pp. text, 294 color illus. $25)

Sand Rivers, with text by Peter Matthiessen and color photographs by Hugo van Lawick, is an account of a safari into the Selous Game Reserve in southeastern Tanzania. Matthiessen describes the present state of the reserve and his encounters with its wildlife. (Viking, 1981. 240 pp. illus. $19.95)

Wildlife of the Islands by William H. Amos is a selective survey of plant and animal life on islands in all parts of the world. The author says an island environment is fragile — the species living there are closely related and changes made by humans can seriously disrupt their relationships. (Abrams, 1980. 231 pp. illus. $18.95)

A World Like Our Own: Man and Nature in Madagascar by Allison Jolly tells how the island of Madagascar broke away from the African continent 90 million years ago. As a result of its isolation, about 90 per cent of its species are unique. Jolly describes the biological community from rain forest to deserts. (Yale University Press, 1980. 272 pp. illus. $29.95)

Philosophy of Science. *An Imagined World: A Story of Scientific Discovery* is June Goodfield's record of her observations of a woman biologist and her colleagues over a five-year period as they painstakingly develop and test a new hypothesis. The book describes the excitement of making a discovery as well as the drudgery of cleaning Petri dishes. (Harper & Row, 1981. 240 pp. $12.95)

Mr. Peale's Museum: Charles Willson Peale and the First Popular Museum of Natural Science and Art by Charles C. Sellers is a scholarly account of how Peale, a portrait painter, established an innovative museum of natural history in Philadelphia. The museum was the first to display plants, animals, and other specimens in their natural habitats. (Norton, 1980. 370 pp. illus. $14.95)

The Panda's Thumb: More Reflections in Natural History by Stephen Jay Gould is a collection of essays on how the study of individual organisms helps us understand evolutionary theory. He recounts the scientific evidence for evolution. (Norton, 1980. 343 pp. illus. $12.95)

The Search for Solutions by Horace Freeland Judson is a comprehensive review of how the human mind grasps and solves problems, whether the problem involves scientific theory or household maintenance. The book discusses thought patterns, feedback, and evidence. (Holt, Rinehart & Winston, 1980. 211 pp. illus. $16.95)

Physics. *From Atoms to Quarks: An Introduction to the Strange World of Particle Physics* by James S. Trefil describes the search for the fundamental building blocks of the universe. Trefil explains the work that led to the discovery of atoms, the nucleus, elementary particles, and quarks, and concludes with an overview of future possibilities. (Scribner's, 1980. 225 pp. illus. $12.95)

Hans Bethe: Prophet of Energy by Jeremy Bernstein is drawn from interviews with the Nobel prizewinning physicist. The interviews cover Bethe's childhood in Germany, his emigration to the United States, and his role in the development of the atomic and hydrogen bombs. Bethe's views on the future of nuclear energy are included. (Basic Books, 1980. 212 pp. $12.95)

The Search for Gravity Waves by P. C. W. Davies. Davies explains how the search for gravity waves is being conducted. Few physicists doubt that gravity waves exist, but the waves are so weak that scientists have not yet developed instruments with the extraordinary sensitivity needed to detect them. (Cambridge University Press, 1980. 144 pp. illus. $19.95)

Technology. *Gems Made by Man* by Kurt B. Nassau contains information about synthetic gemstones for the general reader, the gem expert, and also for the technical specialist. Nassau explains how the reader can distinguish man-made stones from natural stones. (Chilton, 1980. 364 pp. illus. $28.50)

[William Goodrich Jones]

Botany

Botanists in 1980 gained further insights into the function of ethylene, a gaseous plant hormone that affects growth. Plant physiologist Raymond M. Wheeler and I at Utah State University in Logan announced in September 1980 that we had determined that the gravitropic response — the tendency of the stem of a plant that has been laid on its side to bend upright within a few hours — depends upon ethylene.

We treated each of four groups of cocklebur plants with a different substance. Two of the substances inhibited ethylene synthesis and two inhibited ethylene action. We matched each of the four groups with control groups that were not treated with chemicals that would affect ethylene, and laid all of the plants on their sides in a darkened room where plants would not bend toward light.

All the treated groups bent upright much more slowly than did the control groups. We obtained the same results in similar experiments with tomato and castor bean plants, and concluded that ethylene is therefore involved in the gravitropic response.

Plant physiologist Mordecai (Mark) J. Jaffe of Wake Forest University in Winston-Salem, N.C., connected ethylene with another phenomenon, thigmomorphogenesis, or response to touch.

Jaffe summarized his work in the spring of 1980, reporting that the most noticeable results of such mechanical stress are retarded stem and leaf growth coupled with thickened stems. Growth is often retarded from 30 to 60 per cent, depending upon the species of plant and the intensity of disturbance. For example, greenhouse-grown tomato plants shaken vigorously for only 10 seconds once each day were less than two-thirds as tall as undisturbed control plants.

Jaffe also found that when rubbed, plants give off increased amounts of ethylene. He rubbed tomato plants, then took stem samples at 30-minute intervals, measuring the ethylene given off by the samples. He also measured the ethylene given off by stem samples from unrubbed control plants. He found that ethylene began to appear about 20 minutes after the plants were rubbed and reached a peak concentration in one to three hours. Jaffe found that plants exposed to appropriate concentrations of ethylene exhibit the same symptoms seen in mechanically stressed plants. He concluded that ethylene is involved in this process.

Desert plants and water. A team of botanists reported in August 1980 that they had found the mechanism that enables a succulent shrub to condense water from unsaturated, but often humid, air over the Atacama Desert in northern Chile, where rainfall rarely occurs. Scientists had previously observed that one of the dominant shrubs found in the Atacama Desert in northern Chile, *Nolana mollis,* is often covered with visible water droplets, while nearby plants of other species are dry.

Harold A. Mooney and S. L. Gulmon of Stanford University, James Ehleringer of the University of Utah in Salt Lake City, and Philip W. Rundel of the University of California, Irvine, located salt-secreting glands on the surface of *Nolana* leaves. They performed two experiments to test whether the salt secreted by the glands was responsible for condensed water on the plants. Crystals of various salts absorb H_2O from humid air.

The researchers soaked blotters in three solutions — a liquid collected from the leaf surfaces, a low concentration sodium chloride (NaCl), or table salt, solution and a high concentration NaCl solution. They suspended the dried blotters in the air overnight and found that the blotter soaked in the plant salts solution had absorbed almost as much water as the blotter treated with the highly concentrated NaCl solution, and significantly more than the blotter treated with the low-concentration NaCl solution. An untreated control blotter absorbed no water.

In the second experiment, the botanists rinsed the leaves of a group of *Nolana* plants with distilled water in the afternoon to remove all natural salts. The following morning, they found that no water had accumulated on the treated plants, but that it had accumulated on the leaves of unrinsed plants that retained their salts.

The next step was to determine how the plant used the water. Water absorbed by such plants would be saturated with salt, and water tends to stay where salt concentrations are high.

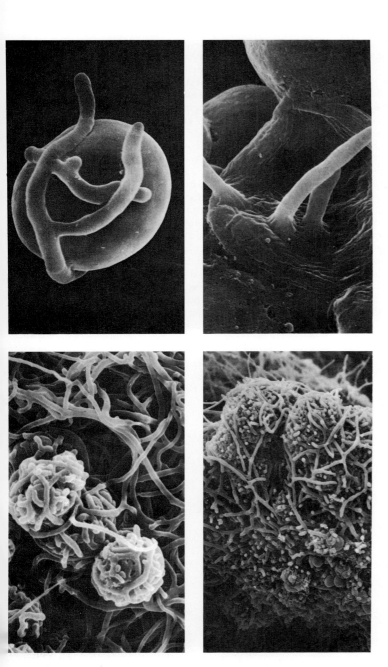

A fungal filament encircles an algal cell, *top left,* breaks through the cell wall, *top right,* and spreads to adjacent cells, *above left* (magnified 450 times) to form a lichen, *above right* (magnified 112 times). The lichen was grown in a laboratory to verify the symbiotic relationship between the alga and fungus comprising it.

This would make it difficult for the plant cells, with their lower salt concentrations, to obtain the water through their cell membranes. The botanists calculated, however, that stored carbohydrates released in respiration would provide enough energy for the plant cells to take up water despite the high salt concentrations.

Solar tracking. Plant physiologists James Ehleringer and Irwin Forseth at the University of Utah reported in December 1980 on their investigation of the solar-tracking ability of plant leaves in desert areas of California and Arizona. In solar tracking, the leaves of many plant species, especially in deserts, move throughout the day so that their surfaces are either perpendicular or parallel to the sun's rays. The perpendicular position exposes the broad leaf surface to the sun, while the parallel position exposes only the edge.

Ehleringer and Forseth found that most of the plant species that tracked the sun with leaves perpendicular to its rays were species that had short growing seasons or that must complete a life cycle within a few weeks. Such plants must absorb a maximum amount of light. Leaves that turn to remain perpendicular to the sun's rays may absorb anywhere from 38 to 167 per cent more light energy than do fixed leaves.

As long as the soil has enough moisture, such plants grow more rapidly. However, this exposure captures more heat as well as more sunlight, so the plants lose more water through their leaves as they heat up. When the soil is dry, it is to the plant's advantage to have its leaf surfaces parallel rather than perpendicular to the sun's rays.

Ehleringer and Forseth observed that some species with compound leaves folded their leaves along the midrib when they had completed most of their growth and no longer needed maximum light. This put the leaves in a position parallel to the sun's rays, cutting down the amount of light absorbed and, as a result, reducing water loss.

Strains of some agricultural plants exhibit solar tracking. Ehleringer and Forseth suggest that selective breeding for this trait may result in crops that produce higher yields in short growing seasons and survive brief periods of drought. [Frank B. Salisbury]

Chemistry

Researchers at Bell Telephone Laboratories in Murray Hill, N.J., announced in February 1981 that they had built a liquid junction solar cell that converts 11.5 per cent of the sunlight that strikes it into electricity. This type of cell contains a liquid sealed between two thin, rectangular electrodes, or positive and negative electrical terminals.

When light strikes the cell, electrons flow through the liquid from one electrode to the other, creating an electrical current. The liquid junction provides much better electrical contact between electrodes than do the solid-state solar cells now in commercial use.

In creating the new solar cell, the Bell chemists Adam Heller, Barry Miller, and materials scientist Ferdinand A. Thiel made a cathode, or negative electrode, of a crystal of indium phosphide, a semiconducting inorganic compound. Semiconductors are materials that are excellent conductors of electricity at high temperatures but are poor conductors or insulators at low temperatures. The anode, or positive electrode, is carbon.

The cathode in the new solar cell is in contact with a liquid made up of hydrochloric acid and vanadium ions. When sunlight strikes the indium phosphide crystal cathode, electrons flow to its surface, where vanadium ions in the liquid pick up one electron each. The ions then deliver the absorbed electrons to the anode, completing the electrical circuit. When a vanadium ion gives up its electron, it is ready to function again as an electron carrier.

Older types of liquid junction solar cells use anodes of materials such as silicon as the light-sensitive electrode. Those cells fail after a few days, however, because sunlight causes the anodes to react chemically with the liquids, destroying the anodes.

The Bell solar cell operated near its maximum output of 0.5 volt under laboratory lights for a period equivalent to two months of sunlight. Heller believes that the continual flow of electrons from the inside of the crystal to its surface protects the crystal from corrosion by preventing the surface from losing its own electrons.

An aluminum-alloy plate reacts with air and tap water pumped through hoses to generate electrical energy in an experimental power cell. It was developed as an alternative automotive fuel source at Lawrence Livermore National Laboratory in California.

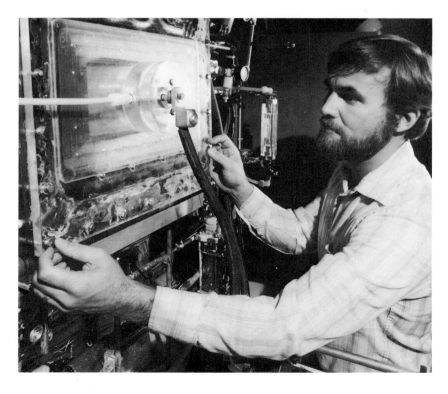

"Congratulations! You've just created life in a test tube."

Chemistry

Continued

The cell's efficiency and life are outstanding, but the cost of the indium phosphide electrode makes the cell too expensive for practical applications. The Bell researchers are trying to develop new and less expensive semiconductor electrodes that are as effective as the crystal.

Solar splitting of water. Chemist Michael Grätzel and colleagues at the Swiss Federal Polytechnic Institute in Lausanne reported in January 1981 that they have developed a system that produces oxygen and hydrogen from water and sunlight. Research groups are trying to harness the sun's energy to split water into oxygen and hydrogen, a potential future fuel.

The new system uses a special semiconductor catalyst composed of ruthenium dioxide and platinum dispersed on tiny spheres of titanium dioxide. The catalyst is sensitized by an organic compound known as *tris*-(bipyridine)ruthenium(II) di-cation. Catalysts are chemicals that speed up chemical reactions while themselves remaining essentially unchanged. A sensitizer begins a reaction. See CHEMISTRY'S SPEEDY SERVANTS.

The chemists shone artificial light or sunlight on a flask of water containing the catalyst and sensitizer. This caused a small stream of oxygen and hydrogen bubbles to form. In one experiment, 25 milliliters (slightly less than 1 ounce) of water produced 1.5 milliliters of hydrogen gas per hour for two days.

The Swiss chemists think that the catalyst first draws the sensitizer to its surface and holds it there. Then light strikes the sensitizer, contributing energy to its electrons. Some of the electrons absorb so much energy that they leave the sensitizer and flow directly into the catalyst. These electrons move through the inside of the catalyst until they reach the platinum particles on the catalyst's titanium dioxide surface. Water molecules then pick up electrons from this surface. These extra electrons energize chemical bonds that join the water's hydrogen (H) and oxygen (O) atoms, so the water molecules break apart and recombine into hydrogen gas (H_2) and hydroxide ions (OH^-).

Meanwhile, the ruthenium dioxide on the titanium dioxide catalyst's surface removes electrons from water molecules, which in this reaction break apart to form oxygen gas (O_2) and hydrogen ions (H^+). Finally, the electrons from the ruthenium dioxide flow back to the sensitizer to convert it to its original form. The hydrogen ions combine rapidly with hydroxide to form water, and the process begins again.

This system is still in the experimental stage, but it may serve as the basis for the future production of hydrogen fuel from water. The gaseous oxygen and hydrogen, which are potentially explosive together, would have to be separated. One method of separation might be diffusion through a semipermeable membrane that would allow the smaller and lighter hydrogen molecules to pass through, but would block the heavier oxygen molecules. Scientists might also separate the gases by lowering the temperature. The oxygen molecules would first form a liquid that would run off into a tank. The hydrogen would condense at a lower temperature and be pumped into metal bottles for storage under pressure.

Optically active epoxides. In January 1981, chemists at Stanford University in California reported that they had used a new method of making optically active epoxide molecules to produce optically active compounds identical to natural substances. K. Barry Sharpless, Tsutomu Katsuki, and Bryant E. Rossiter synthesized the gypsy moth pheromone, or sex attractant; two antibiotics; and a biochemical suspected of causing inflammation after an injury or allergic reaction. An optically active molecule is one of two molecules that are identical in all respects except that they are mirror images of one another. In this way they differ much as your left hand does from your right. Ordinary laboratory reactions produce both optically active forms of a molecule in equal amounts, but only one form is usually found in nature. The opposite form is usually ineffective.

The Stanford chemists started with a molecule that contained a carbon-carbon double bond—two carbon atoms sharing four electrons. They then added an oxygen atom to one side of the double bond, converting it to a single bond and forming a triangular ring called an epoxide that contained two carbon atoms and one oxygen.

Sharpless and his colleagues selected allyl alcohols to provide the carbon-carbon double bond. The oxygen atoms came from *tertiary*-butyl hydroperoxide. The resulting epoxide of allyl alcohol contains 95 to 99 per cent of one optically active form.

The Stanford researchers used their epoxides to form key chemicals in the synthesis of the antibiotics erythromycin and methmycin and the inflammatory substance leukotriene C-1. The reaction also seems to provide the best and cheapest way to prepare the female gypsy moth pheromone, which can be used for pest control. The synthetic attractant will be used to control gypsy moth infestations by trapping males. Gypsy moths cause millions of dollars in damage to hardwood trees yearly.

Anticancer chemicals. In December 1980, chemists Paul A. Grieco, Sergio Ferrino, and Giovanni Vidari of Indiana University in Bloomington synthesized quassin, a natural chemical that may be related to drugs that are used to treat leukemia. Quassin is made up of carbon, hydrogen, and oxygen atoms. Its structure consists of four rings containing six carbon atoms and seven optically active carbon atoms.

The Indiana chemists synthesized quassin in 16 reactions, some of which involved complex chemical processes. For example, in one of the last steps, the chemists used sodium methoxide and methyl iodide in a mixture of the two solvents dimethyl sulfoxide and methanol to bring about four reactions; freeing a hydrogen atom from a bond with an oxygen atom, changing a carbon atom from one optically active form to another, and adding two methyl groups (one carbon atom bonded to three hydrogen atoms) to the molecule that they were building.

Quassin does not work against cancer, but researchers can now use steps similar to the Indiana chemists' reactions to tailor-make related natural compounds that appear to be effective against leukemia. One such relative is bruceantin, a substance isolated from an Ethiopian tree, which doctors are testing on leukemia patients. Its structure differs from quassin's only by an

Chemistry
Continued

A carpenter saws an experimental woodlike material made out of recycled polyester soft-drink bottles.

additional five-membered ring that contains oxygen. See PHARMACIES IN THE JUNGLE.

Twelve-sided molecule. In February 1981, chemist Leo A. Paquette and his colleagues at Ohio State University in Columbus synthesized a pentagonal dodecahedron, an almost spherical 12-sided molecule with each side composed of a cyclopentane ring – five carbon molecules arranged in a regular pentagon. The molecule contains only hydrogen atoms attached to carbon atoms. However, Paquette and his colleagues were unable to build the molecule without two methyl groups attached opposite each other on the outside of the molecule. The methyl groups look like a knitting needle stuck through a ball of yarn.

The researchers begin their synthesis with the easily made cyclopentadiene anion, a charged molecule that has five carbon atoms grouped in a regular pentagon. They then needed 20 successive reactions to obtain colorless crystals of the dodecahedron.

The inside of the molecule measures only 0.9 angstrom unit in diameter. (One angstrom unit equals one ten-millionth of a millimeter.) The molecule is too small to enclose any but the smallest ions, but the researchers are already thinking of ways to put an ion inside it. Medical scientists use similar closed molecules to carry ions for treating body cells. Such molecules do not dissolve in blood, so they keep the ions trapped as they flow through the bloodstream. But the molecules do break up in body cells, releasing the ions.

Superoxide ion. Chemists Donald T. Sawyer and Julian L. Roberts of the University of California, Riverside, reported in February 1981 that superoxide ion, a form of oxygen that has one extra electron, can remove tightly held chlorine atoms from toxic organic compounds and convert them into nonpoisonous chemicals. Superoxide ions are formed by passing an electrical current through an organic solvent containing dissolved oxygen.

The ion reacts with organic chlorine compounds, such as carbon tetrachloride, which is made up of four chlorine atoms attached to one carbon atom. Three superoxide ions replace the chlorine atoms in a series of steps, forming a carbonate ion. Carbonate is a harmless component of such products as baking soda and carbonated water.

Scientists hope to use the reaction to convert toxic compounds that often become chemical waste products – such as carbon tetrachloride, chloroform, and dichlorodiphenyl-trichloroethane (DDT) – into chemical substances that do not threaten the environment.

Strong hydrogen bonds. Several types of bonds join atoms together to form molecules. One of the weakest bonds is so-called hydrogen bonding, the result of an attraction between a hydrogen (H) atom in one molecule and some other atom of another molecule. Hydrogen atoms that form this weak bond most commonly are joined to nitrogen (N) or oxygen atoms in a molecule. For example, hydrogen bonds between NH groups and oxygen atoms help hold together the double helix of deoxyribonucleic acid (DNA), a molecule that contains genetic information in living cells.

Most hydrogen bonds are only about 10 per cent as strong as ordinary chemical bonds. But chemists John Emsley, Deborah J. Jones, Richard E. Overill, and Roland A. Wassilove of the University of London in England and John M. Miller of Brock University in St. Catherines, Canada, in January 1981 reported finding a hydrogen bond that was 50 per cent stronger than an ordinary hydrogen bond. This was the strongest such bond ever found between hydrogen and an organic molecule. Only a hydrogen bond between hydrofluoric acid (HF) and a fluoride ion is stronger.

The hydrogen bond that the chemists discovered forms when a fluoride ion dissolves in a liquid amide, which has an NH_2 group. This bond may have significance for other areas of chemistry and biochemistry. Hydrogen usually forms only one bond, sharing a pair of electrons with the atom to which it is bound. But the hydrogen in the bond that the researchers measured appears to be bonding strongly to two other atoms. Introducing fluoride ions into an organism that contains oxygen atoms may cause NH to form a hydrogen bond with a fluoride atom rather than an oxygen, thus damaging the organism. [Lawrence P. Verbit]

Deaths of Scientists

Notable scientists and engineers who died between June 1, 1980, and June 1, 1981, are listed below. An asterisk (*) indicates that a biography appears in *The World Book Encyclopedia.*

Andervont, Howard B. (1899-March 11, 1981), virologist and cancer researcher who directed early studies linking cancer and filterable viruses.

Andrews, Gould A. (1918-July 1, 1980), physician who introduced the technique of injecting radioisotopes to treat cancer patients.

Ashbrook, Joseph (1918-Aug. 4, 1980), astronomer who was editor of *Sky & Telescope* magazine from 1964 to 1980. He discovered Ashbrook-Jackson, a comet, and 2157-Ashbrook, an asteroid.

Bateson, Gregory (1904-July 4, 1980), British-born anthropologist and psychologist known for his studies of primitive cultures with anthropologist Margaret Mead, his first wife.

Converse, John M. (1909-Jan. 31, 1981), plastic surgeon who developed many techniques including cranial-facial restructure. He was founder-director of New York University's Institute of Reconstructive Plastic Surgery.

Delbrück, Max (1906-March 9, 1981), German-born molecular geneticist who shared the Nobel prize for physiology or medicine with Salvador Luria of Massachusetts Institute of Technology and Alfred Hershey of the Carnegie Institution of Washington for his work with bacteriophages, viruses that attack bacteria.

Denny-Brown, Derek E. (1901-April 20, 1981), New Zealand-born neurologist who conducted early research on degenerative nervous disorders. He introduced the idea that an insufficient supply of blood to the brain could cause a stroke. He was director of Harvard Neurological Unit at Boston City Hospital from 1941 to 1967.

Dornberger, Walter (1895-reported July 2, 1980), German-born aeronautical engineer and physicist who headed Nazi Germany's V-2 rocket project during World War II. He later worked in the United States missile industry.

Douglas, Donald W., Jr. (1892-Feb. 1, 1981), aeronautical engineer and founder of Douglas Aircraft Company. His development of the twin-engine DC-3 in 1936 and the introduction of the DC-8 in 1959 brought mass airline travel to the world.

Fahey, Joseph J. (1902-June 29, 1980), geochemist who developed methods for detecting trace amounts of mercury in the environment and devised a technique for detecting fluorine in rocks and water.

Farrand, Clair L. (1895-Jan. 6, 1981), wireless reporter who invented the radio loudspeaker. He later worked with Warner Brothers in developing both sound and color for motion-picture photography.

Goubau, Georg (1913?-Oct. 17, 1980), German-born engineer who pioneered in microwave circuits. He invented a transmission system in the 1940s that enabled a single strand of wire to carry large volumes of messages to isolated areas otherwise reached only by coaxial cable.

Haggerty, Patrick E. (1914-Oct. 1, 1980), electronics engineer and a leader in the computer industry. He served as chairman of Texas Instruments Company from 1966 to 1976.

Halberstam, Michael J. (1932-Dec. 5, 1980), cardiologist and editor of *Modern Medicine* magazine.

Jones, Henry A. (1889-Feb. 24, 1981), geneticist who developed a breeding method in 1925 that made the production of hybrid onions commercially feasible.

Kanner, Leo (1894-April 3, 1981), Austrian-born child psychiatrist who first identified early infantile autism. His popular book *In Defense of Mothers* advocated a common-sense approach to raising children.

Keeton, William T. (1933-Aug. 17, 1980), biologist whose studies showed that birds use the earth's magnetic field as a navigational aid.

Kendrick, Pearl L. (1890-Oct. 8, 1980), microbiologist who helped develop a whooping cough vaccine.

Kuffler, Stephen W. (1913-Oct. 10, 1980), Hungarian-born neurobiologist noted for his work on neuromuscular synaptic transmission. He received the Wakeman Award in 1976 for his contributions to the treatment of paraplegia.

Lancefield, Rebecca C. (1895-March 3, 1981), bacteriologist who developed the Lancefield classification system of streptococcal bacteria in use throughout the world. Her research made

Max Delbrück

Walter Dornberger

Willard F. Libby

Deaths of Scientists

Continued

Henrietta H. Swope

Harold C. Urey

John H. Van Vleck

it possible to do the epidemiological studies that determined the patterns of streptococcal infection.

Leontovich, Mikhail A. (1903-April 1, 1981), leading Russian nuclear physicist. He was head of theoretical research on controlled nuclear fusion and plasma physics at the Soviet Academy of Sciences Institute of Atomic Energy since 1951.

***Libby, Willard F.** (1908-Sept. 8, 1980), chemist who won the 1960 Nobel prize for chemistry for his work on radiocarbon dating. His laboratory research during World War II helped create the gaseous diffusion process for the separation of the isotopes of uranium — a fundamental step in the development of the atomic bomb.

Martin, Sir James (1893-Jan. 5, 1981), British engineer who invented the Martin-Baker rocket ejection seat in 1944.

Matthias, Bernd T. (1918-Oct. 27, 1980), German-born physicist credited with the discovery of many chemical elements and compounds with superconducting properties.

McDonnell, James S. (1899-Aug. 22, 1980), aeronautical engineer, chairman of the McDonnell Douglas Corporation since 1972 and a pioneer in the development of spacecraft.

Northrop, John K. (1895-Feb. 18, 1981), aeronautical engineer who founded the Northrop Corporation. His pioneering designs included the original Lockheed Vega and the World War II P-61 night fighter known as the Black Widow.

Peshkin, M. Murray (1892-Aug. 17, 1980), pediatric allergist, a leader in the diagnosis and treatment of childhood allergies with an underlying emotional cause.

***Piaget, Jean** (1896-Sept. 17, 1980), Swiss psychologist, noted for his study of human intelligence and the thought processes of children. He believed that children learn by passing through a series of distinct intellectual stages and that each child is a significant agent in the construction of his own reality.

Price, Dorothy (1899-Nov. 17, 1980), zoologist who helped develop the Moore-Price law dealing with the reciprocal relationship between hormone production by the gonads and the anterior pituitary gland.

Stern, Elizabeth (1916-Aug. 9, 1980), Canadian-born pathologist who discovered that the prolonged use of birth control pills might cause cervical cancer. In 1963, she published the first case report linking a specific virus to a specific cancer — herpes simplex virus to cervical cancer.

Swope, Henrietta H. (1902-Nov. 24, 1980), astronomer whose work on variable stars helped provide a yardstick for measuring distances to extremely distant stars and galaxies.

***Urey, Harold C.** (1893-Jan. 5, 1981), winner of the 1934 Nobel prize for chemistry for his discovery of heavy hydrogen (deuterium), which opened the door to the development of the hydrogen bomb. He was a lifelong critic of military force, stating that "atomic bombs are evil and that they cannot be used to maintain peace."

Van Vleck, John H. (1899-Oct. 27, 1980), physicist who won the 1977 Nobel prize for physics for his work in the 1930s describing the magnetic properties of solids. His major work, *The Theory of Electrical Magnetic Susceptibility,* (1932) is still a widely used source.

Wangensteen, Owen (1898-Jan. 13, 1981), a surgeon who helped develop open-heart surgery techniques, particularly the "Wangensteen suction approach," now a standard procedure in preventing intestinal blockage after abdominal surgery.

Welsch, Exie E. (1908?-Oct. 28, 1980), child psychiatrist who advocated a broader approach to mental illness, emphasizing neurological, physiological, and environmental aspects. She was the first woman to be elected president of the American Orthopsychiatric Association in 1956.

Weltfish, Gene (1902-Aug. 2, 1980), anthropologist noted for her studies of Indian tribes in the American West. Her published work includes "The Races of Mankind," a pamphlet written during World War II to dispel Nazi theories of racial superiority.

Young, William G. (1902-July 5, 1980), chemist who helped establish the University of California, Los Angeles, as an international center in physical organic chemistry. He was noted for his work on displacement reactions of allylic compounds.   [Irene B. Keller]

Drugs

The results of a successful large-scale trial of a drug for preventing heart attacks in people who have already suffered one heart attack were reported in April 1981. The Norwegian Multicenter Study Group, composed of 20 clinical centers throughout Norway, tested timolol in a study coordinated by medical researcher Terje Pedersen of the University of Bergen. Timolol is one of a group of drugs called the beta adrenergic blocking drugs, or beta-blockers. Beta-blockers prevent adrenalin from acting on the heart. This results in a slower heart rate and, often, a reduction in cardiac arrhythmias, or abnormal heart rhythms.

The researchers studied 1,884 patients who met the research group's criteria for having had a previous heart attack. These were divided into low-, medium-, and high-risk groups. The patients in each group were randomly assigned to take timolol or a *placebo* (an inert substance) in a double-blind study — neither the patients nor the doctors knew which patients were receiving the drug.

Researchers studied the patients for periods ranging from 12 to 33 months. The average study period was 17 months. Slightly more than 20 per cent of the control patients given the placebo but less than 14.4 per cent of those who took timolol had second heart attacks, a reduction of 28.4 per cent for the timolol users. There were 152 deaths in the 939-patient placebo group and 98 deaths in the 945-patient timolol group. The sudden-death rate from all causes was a significant 44.6 per cent lower for the timolol patients.

Calcium-blockers. The effects of calcium-blockers, another group of blocking drugs, on forms of angina pectoris were described by researchers at the University of Texas Health Science Center in Dallas in March 1981. Angina is chest pain caused by spasms of blood vessels leading to the heart.

Calcium-blockers have been used outside the United States for more than 10 years. Recently, trials of the drugs have been started in the United States. The drugs relax and dilate the blood vessels throughout the body. More im-

Sickled red blood cells, *below,* formed when the normally liquid cell hemoglobin gels in victims of sickle cell anemia, are restored to normal shape, *below right,* after treatment with phenylalanine benzyl ester, a new drug.

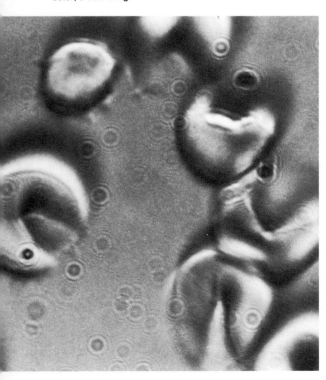
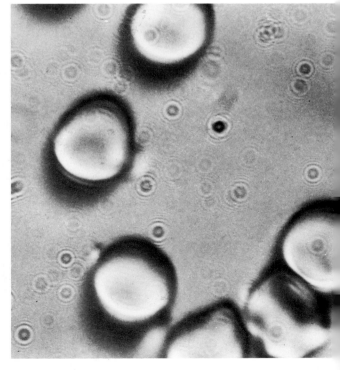

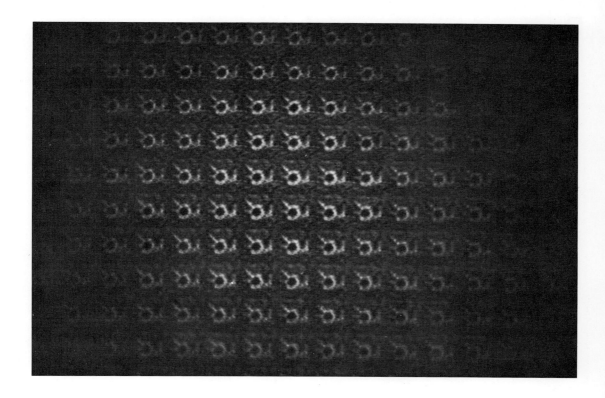

Drugs

Continued

The hormone vasopressin, used to raise blood pressure, reveals its individual molecules, magnified 3.7 million times in this electron micrograph. Each molecule is about 1.7 nanometers (billionths of a meter) in diameter, and is composed of a ring of six amino acids and a hooked tail of three amino acids.

portantly, they affect the action of calcium, which is involved in triggering the heart muscle's pumping action.

Internist Stacy M. Johnson and associates at the University of Texas Health Science Center ran a double-blind random test of verapamil, a calcium-blocker, on a group of patients suffering from Prinzmetal's variant angina, which strikes while the patient is resting. The nine-month test showed significant improvement in patients treated with verapamil. They experienced chest pain about 2 to 5 times per week, compared with control-group patients who suffered 12 to 26 pains per week. The researchers also determined that the drug had no serious side effects.

High-pressure drug. Captopril, a new drug for treating severe hypertension, or high blood pressure, was approved by the FDA in April 1981. The drug is a result of more than 20 years of research on the causes and effects of hypertension by physician John H. Laragh and his colleagues at New York Hospital-Cornell Medical Center in New York City.

Many patients suffering from hypertension have high levels of renin, a hormone formed in the kidney and released into the blood. There, renin converts angiotensin 1, a blood protein, to another form, angiotensin 2. Angiotensin 2 constricts veins and arteries and promotes salt and water retention, both of which increase blood pressure.

Captopril blocks the manufacture of angiotensin 2 and thus prevents the renin from raising blood pressure. The new drug should help many of the 15 to 20 per cent of U.S. adults with some form of high blood pressure, the most important risk factor linked to heart and kidney disease and stroke.

Adverse reactions. Some patients taking the drug hydralazine for high blood pressure tend to develop lupus erythematosus, an arthritislike disease. Risk factors that might lead to this reaction were identified in a May 1980 study by medical researchers at The Royal Post Graduate Medical School in London and at other institutions.

Usually, studies of adverse drug reactions simply report the total number

Drugs
Continued

of persons taking the drug in a clinical test and the number of these who suffered adverse reactions. From this, scientists can calculate the frequency of adverse reactions for a drug, but they learn nothing about why some people react adversely. The new work corrects this in the case of hydralazine.

The group studied 26 patients who had developed lupus after taking hydralazine and compared them with control patients who had not developed lupus. All but one of the lupus victims metabolized hydralazine slowly. Slightly more than half the patients in the control group metabolized the drug slowly. In addition, 73 per cent of the lupus cases had a specific genetic trait called HLA-DR 4, found in the white blood cells, while less than 35 per cent of the controls showed this trait. Finally, most of the patients who suffered this adverse reaction to hydralazine were women. In fact, every female patient studied who was treated with this drug, was a slow metabolizer, and had the genetic trait HLA-DR 4 developed lupus erythematosus.

Frugal facial. A comparative study of several acne treatments revealed in 1980 that the cheapest treatment tested was as effective as the most expensive. Dermatology researchers Leonard J. Swinger and Thalia A. Swinger of the University of Utah in Salt Lake City and Michael R. Britt of the Utah Professional Standards Review Organization evaluated 118 patients who finished a 16-week course of one of the following three treatments: scrubbing the skin twice daily with a soap containing sulfur and salicylic acid and taking the antibiotic tetracycline internally twice a day; applying tretinoin cream to the skin nightly, washing twice daily with mild soap, and taking tetracycline internally; and using only surface ointments, such as tretinoin and an emollient cream nightly, and applying benzoyl peroxide gel several times a day to new acne pimples.

The investigators found that the third method of treatment, with surface ointments only, was as effective as the others. It was also the least expensive treatment.   [Marcus M. Reidenberg]

Ecology

Concern over the environmental impact of various human activities prompted an increased number of field studies and experiments in applied ecology during 1980 and 1981.

Reclaiming land after surface mining was the subject of a study published in June 1980 by ecologists Warren H. Tracey and Beverley L. Glossop of Alcoa Aluminum Company of Australia. Tracey and Glossop reported on three different techniques used for replacing topsoil to rehabilitate land where miners have taken out bauxite, aluminum ore, in the eucalyptus forest region of southwestern Australia.

Rehabilitation is defined as establishing the type of plants that will best contribute to a particular long-range use of the land. Such lands might be designated to store water supplies, produce wood, or be set aside for other purposes such as recreation, conservation, scientific study, and education.

The Australian ecologists studied three areas where different techniques had been used for replacing topsoil that had been removed by surface mining.

In one mined area the soil was removed, then stockpiled for two years before it was respread. In the second area, the topsoil was replaced immediately after mining was completed. In the third, the top 5 centimeters (2 inches) of soil was scraped off and held aside. When the mining was completed, the subsoil was replaced, and the topsoil immediately returned as the top layer.

Four years after the soil was replaced, Tracey and Glossop analyzed the vegetation that had grown up in each area. They noted numbers of tree seedlings, the diversity of species, and the amount of territory covered by vegetation in each mined area and in an unmined forest. To do this, they marked off test plots in each of the four areas. They recorded the number of plants under 2 meters (6.6 feet) and the total number of plant species.

In the area in which the top 5 centimeters of soil had been returned, they found that the new plants covered a wider area. There were also more plant species and a greater diversity of plant species than in the other two mined

Ecology

Continued

A scientist vacuums a banana leaf to collect insects in an ecological study of the Puerto Rico tropical rain forest.

areas. In fact, this area was covered by almost 50 per cent as many live plants as the natural forest.

They attributed the abundant plant growth in this area to the fact that seeds falling from plants naturally land in the upper 2 centimeters (0.8 inch) of soil. They remained approximately at this depth when the top 5 centimeters of the soil were respread. In the other techniques, however, the layers of soil removed in mining were mixed together when they were stored and respread, burying seeds at depths from which they cannot grow. Tracey and Glossop's study pointed out the importance of developing reclamation techniques that restore the most important characteristics of the native ecosystem—in this case, respreading the layer of soil in which seeds are normally found on top of the subsoil.

Broken-down beaches. Ecologists Paul E. Hosier and Thomas E. Eaton of the University of North Carolina at Wilmington reported in spring 1980 on the effects of motorcycles, dune buggies, and other off-road vehicles

(ORVs) on barrier beaches on Cape Fear, an area representative of the low, narrow coastal barrier island system of southwestern North Carolina. They studied Fort Fisher Beach, which is readily accessible and widely used by motor vehicles, and Bald Head Beach, which is undeveloped and inaccessible.

At each site, the ecologists marked off four transects—long, narrow strips of land—perpendicular to the beach. They subdivided each transect into grassland, dune, and marsh areas—based on the subdivision's elevation and its plant species. They analyzed the number of plant species, the diversity—or degree of variation—among those species, and the percentage of each area covered by plants. They also analyzed the composition of beach soils and how tightly the soils were compacted.

The ecologists found that there were fewer and less diverse plant species on the Fort Fisher Beach than on Bald Head Beach. Marshland vegetation covered a 45 per cent greater area on Bald Head Beach than on Fort Fisher

Ecology

Beach; grasslands covered 28 per cent more territory; and dunes covered a 429 per cent greater area.

Hosier and Eaton found an even more pronounced difference in the beach soils. At Bald Head Beach, sands and shell deposits that were continually washed over by water formed a hard covering on the dunes. There was little loose sand, and most of it had formed into low dunes. Fort Fisher Beach had a greater volume of blowing sand and a larger accumulation of loose sand, forming higher dunes.

They attributed the increased volume of loose sand to the constant churning of ORV wheels. The combination of less vegetation and more loose sand makes Fort Fisher Beach more vulnerable to the effects of wind, which can cause blowouts — large holes — in the dunes. Because there is little vegetation to slow down the speed of waves hitting the shore, the waves wash farther up on the beach and wash away more sand. On the basis of these studies, Hosier and Eaton projected that the continued heavy use óf ORVs may greatly erode these coastal islands.

The otter's impact. Ecologist David O. Duggins of the University of Washington in Seattle reported in June 1980 on the impact of sea otters on sea urchins and kelp beds in the vicinity of Torch Bay and Surge Bay, Alaska. Sea otters feed on sea urchins, which feed on kelp. After near-extinction in the 1800s and 1900s, protection and relocation programs have re-established otter populations along much of their ancestral range in Alaska.

In the Torch Bay area, Duggins donned scuba gear and marked off a series of plots perpendicular to the shoreline and extending to points where the sea was 20 meters (50 feet) deep. He counted the number of sea urchins in each plot and computed the density of their populations. He then took kelp samples in each area and calculated the average plant size of each species of kelp and its proportion of the total amount of kelp in the plot.

To simulate the effects of sea otters feeding upon sea urchins in Torch Bay, he removed urchins from experimental plots and used adjacent plots, in which sea urchins lived, as controls. Duggins analyzed the makeup of both kelp and sea urchin populations twice each month for two years.

He found that within a year after he had removed the sea urchins, there was more kelp and a greater diversity of kelp species in the experimental plots than in the control plots. In the second year, however, there was less diversity of species in the experimental plots because, although the total kelp population was larger, a single kelp species became dominant.

On the basis of these experiments, Duggins concluded that the further reintroduction to the Alaskan coastlines of the sea otters who prey upon sea urchins would reduce the sea urchin population and, as a result, would produce a massive increase in the growth of kelp.

Duggins' Torch Bay experiments duplicated the natural situation in Surge Bay. The area became so congested with kelp several years after otters were reintroduced in 1965 that some fishing boats were unable to move through the beds. These studies suggested that the otter population should be held down considerably to avoid a kelp build-up that may threaten marine commerce in the future.

Flooded forests. A team of ecologists from the U.S. Forest Service and Colorado, Mississippi, and South Carolina state forest experiment stations, Clemson University in South Carolina, and the University of Georgia in Athens in December 1980 reported on the relationship of floodwater depth to the death of tree species that predominate in a swamp forest. The trees included Carolina ash, pumpkin ash, bald cypress, red maple, swamp tupelo, cabbage palm, button bush, and several species of oak and elm.

The ecologists conducted their study on Lake Ocklawaha, an artificial lake that forms part of the north and west boundary of the Ocala National Forest in north-central Florida. The 5,265-hectare (13,126-acre) lake was constructed as part of the Cross Florida Barge Canal. Work on the canal was halted in 1971, when it was about one-third complete, to permit an assessment of the changes this project caused on the region's environment. For example, the creation of the lake covered 1,620 hectares (4,500 acres) of hard-

Ecologists measure the volume of water crossing a V-shaped dam that collects rain falling on one side of a ridge during watershed studies of a forested area near Oak Ridge National Laboratory in Tennessee.

Ecology

Continued

wood swamp forest with floodwaters up to 3 meters (10 feet) deep.

The ecologists divided the flooded forest into six areas and established two control areas outside the reservoir. They collected data from all eight areas during the growing seasons three, four, six, and seven years after the forest had been flooded. Each time they identified all plant species; measured the diameter at about 1.2 meters (4 feet) of all trees living and dead; and estimated the amount of stress the trees had been subjected to by noting their color, leafiness, and general health.

They also examined root systems for signs of stress. They knew that healthy root systems send out small roots less than 2.5 millimeters (0.1 inch) in diameter. The absence of these small roots indicates that a root system is dead or dying. They subdivided each area into smaller plots and examined roots in each plot. If the ecologists found that a tree had even one large living root that was sending out small roots, they classified the tree as viable, or capable of staying alive.

The ecologists found that three years after flooding, tree death was closely related to the species of tree and the depth of the water around it. Some species, such as bald cypress, swamp tupelo, and cabbage palm, were better able to withstand prolonged flooding than other species, such as ash, maple and oak.

However, all trees had died in areas where the water was deeper than 1.3 meters (4.7 feet). Fewer trees died in areas where the floodwaters were below 1 meter (3.3 feet). At 0.8 meter (2.5 feet), for example, 41 per cent of all trees in a plot were dead; at 0.7 meter (2.3 feet), 17 per cent were dead. At 0.2 meter (0.7 feet), 2 per cent were dead, and this was the same percentage of dead trees as in the unflooded control areas. Studies at the end of growing seasons four, six, and seven years after the flooding showed that only the most adaptable species remained in depths up to 0.6 meter (2 feet). These trees were dying at a rate that had slowed to only slightly higher than the natural mortality rate. [Stanley I. Auerbach]

243

Electronics

Physicists Richard E. Howard, Evelyn L. Hu, and Lawrence D. Jackel of Bell Telephone Laboratories in Holmdel, N.J., built the world's smallest and fastest Josephson junction devices in April 1981. These devices are microscopic electrical circuits that operate at temperatures near absolute zero ($-273.15°C$ or $-459.67°F$.), switching an electrical signal more rapidly than any other kind of circuit.

The smaller the junction, the faster it switches. The Bell device, a square that measures 1,000 angstrom units on a side, is about 20 per cent as large as any previous Josephson junction device. (One angstrom unit equals 1 ten-millionth of a millimeter.) This is so small that the device will switch in about one-trillionth of a second, making it about 10 times faster than any previous Josephson junction. In computers, the junction may cut gate delays — the time that an electrical signal takes to go through a component or a group of components that performs a logic function — to about 10-trillionths of a second. This is 0.1 per cent as long as gate delays in present computers.

Bell Labs' junction consists of a layer of lead-indium metal on a silicon chip. On top of the lead-indium is a thin insulating layer of oxide and on top of that is a lead stripe. The Josephson effect, the rapid flow of current through a thin insulator, takes place in the oxide layer.

To make the junction, the team first coated the silicon with two layers of a material called resist. They bombarded the resist with a beam of electrons, drawing a narrow line across the resist, except for a gap in the center.

Next, the scientists used chemicals to dissolve the resist that the electrons had struck. This dug a trough in both layers, exposing silicon, except for a narrow strip that remained at the gap. Another chemical treatment removed the strip's lower layer, so the strip spanned the exposed silicon like a bridge over a river.

Howard and his colleagues then directed a beam of vaporized lead-indium at the silicon at an angle to the resist. This can be pictured as beams of light from the morning sun striking a bridge across an east-west river. The beam did not penetrate the resist, so

An electronic pay telephone in Great Britain displays the amount of unused money left on deposit as the user talks, then gives change when she hangs up

when the resist "cast its shadow westward" in the trough, the lead-indium was deposited throughout the trough, except in the shadow area.

The scientists then exposed the lead-indium to oxygen to oxidize its surface and deposited the lead from the "west." The strip "cast its shadow eastward" beyond the first shadow and the lead filled in the trough except for the area shielded by the strip.

The two deposits overlapped in a large area at each end of the trough and a small area at its center, underneath the strip. Finally, the scientists dissolved all of the remaining resist, including the strip. The small overlap area was the junction.

System on a chip. Researchers at International Business Machines Corporation's (IBM) Data Systems Division in East Fishkill, N.Y., announced in October 1980 that they had reduced the central processing unit that performs the arithmetic and logic functions for the company's System/370 computer to a single square silicon chip 7 millimeters (0.276 inch) on a side. IBM conducted this experiment to test its computer-aided design (CAD) program in designing very-large-scale integration (VLSI) circuits. The CAD program lays out, plots, and checks the patterns of components and connectors that are built into a chip. A VLSI circuit has tens of thousands of three-layered devices called bipolar junction transistors on a single chip.

IBM researchers had to decide where to place nearly 5,000 gates on the chip and how to connect them. The gates comprise over 45,000 transistors and resistors, making the chip the most complex integrated circuit made of junction transistors to date.

Consumer electronics. Ise Electronics Corporation of Japan announced in April 1981 that they have developed a square vacuum-fluorescent (VF) tube that displays TV pictures on a flat panel. One of the most active areas in consumer-electronics research is flat displays for future TV sets. Several technologies are being evaluated, all aimed at replacing the power-hungry, space-consuming cathode-ray tube (CRT), the heart of today's TV set.

VF technology is seen most often today in the blue-green digits of clock

Drawing by H. Martin; © 1981 The New Yorker Magazine, Inc.

"He's an absolute treasure. We got him for four thousand eight hundred and ninety dollars at Radio Shack, batteries not included."

Electronics

Continued

radios and cash registers. Like CRTs, VF displays rely on generating free electrons by heating metal filaments — thin wires — then shooting these electrons at phosphors, substances that give off light when struck in this way.

Patterns of such light on phosphors at the front of a CRT build up the TV image. The filament of an ordinary CRT is in the back of the tube, but the thinner VF tube has filaments along one edge of the screen and a network of wires behind the screen. The filament emits electrons that travel slightly behind the screen toward the opposite edge until electrical charges in the wires force them down to the screen, where they strike the phosphors.

Both CRTs and VF tubes display their pictures in pieces called pixels, or picture elements. The more pixels, the greater the detail. Researchers are trying to build VF screens that have enough pixels to match the detail of CRT pictures, which have several hundred thousand pixels.

Ise's VF display is 7.6 centimeters (3 inches) on a side and has 16,000 pixels.

Ise claims that this type of display soon will be competitive with CRTs. But VF displays are only in black and white.

More promising technology for flat screens involves liquid-crystal displays (LCDs), the type used in most digital watches showing black digits on a gray background. LCDs in these devices change from transparent to opaque in the presence of an electrical field, creating the numerals. An LCD TV screen works in the same way.

LCD researchers were working during the year on nagging picture problems. LCD pictures do not have as much detail as CRT pictures, and they respond to picture signals so slowly that fast-moving images smear. Moreover, LCDs can produce only black-and-white images now.

The most practical replacement for ordinary CRTs might be a flat CRT under development at Sinclair Research Limited in Cambridge, England. An ordinary CRT's electron gun is perpendicular to the screen, while the flat CRT's gun is mounted to one side of the screen and parallel to it. The

245

Electronics

beam from the flat CRT gun strikes the screen at a low angle, creating an elliptical spot 1.5 times as wide as it is tall. However, the flat CRT's electron beam does not spread out as much as an ordinary CRT beam, so the elliptical spot is brighter than a spot on a conventional CRT. Sinclair researchers say that the elliptical effect is offset by the flat CRT's brightness, so the spot does not need to be as large. Therefore its shape would not be so noticeable.

Solar power. In October 1980, Texas Instruments, Incorporated (TI), of Dallas announced a solar cell that converts about 13 per cent of the sunlight reaching it into electricity, a competitive figure by today's standards. Ordinary solar cells use the sun's energy to transport electrons from one area of the cell, called an electrode, to another. Electrons are negatively charged, so the electrode that receives electrons becomes negative and the electrode that loses them becomes positive. Connecting the electrodes with a wire causes a small, but usable, electrical current to flow through the wire from one electrode to the other. An interconnected array of many such cells will deliver useful amounts of electricity.

Improvements in solar-cell materials and manufacturing techniques have brought solar energy closer as a practical, economical source of energy. Even so, solar cells operate only when the sun is shining. In order to make solar power available at other times, cells must generate more power than is consumed when the sun is shining, and some other apparatus must store the extra power. But storing that energy for a rainy day remains a sticky problem. Solar cells require large numbers of expensive, bulky batteries that are difficult to maintain.

But the TI device also stores energy. The cell's ability both to convert and store energy makes it the most promising of all solar devices to date.

The cell contains two types of silicon spheres about as big as buckshot. These spheres are embedded in two separate areas of a glass plate. Only the tops of the spheres stick out above the plate. A conductive backing layer

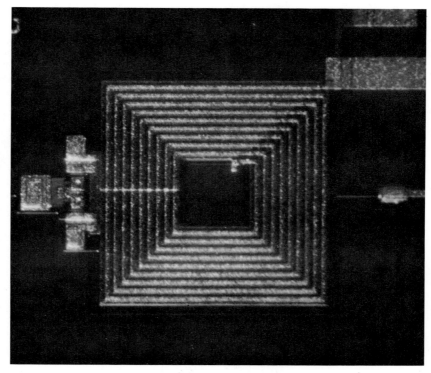

A new experimental Superconducting Quantum Interference Device (SQUID) coupled to a square electrical coil promises a 100-fold improvement in measuring minute changes in magnetic field strength. SQUIDs have a wide range of use, from searching for geothermal energy to measuring brain waves. Coil width is about 175 micrometers (0.007 inch).

Electronics

Continued

A new electronic telephone directory displays the complete name and number of the person being called and places the call as soon as the caller types enough of the name to trigger its computer memory. It stores up to 340 names and numbers.

under the glass plate touches the bottoms of the spheres. TI has been experimenting with small plates in the laboratory, but sheets as large as 1.2 meters by 2.4 meters (4 by 8 feet) may be practical for home use.

The plate is laid on the bottom of a square tank containing a solution of hydrogen bromide so that the tops of the spheres and the glass plate—but not the conductive backing—contact the solution. A vertical glass panel divides the tank into two compartments. The edge of the panel sits across the plate at the dividing point between the two kinds of embedded spheres. This panel prevents fluid that reacts with one type of sphere from coming in contact with spheres of the other type.

When the tank is exposed to the sun, sunlight strikes both types of spheres. Solar energy transports electrons from the backing layer through one type of sphere to the solution, where the electrons convert hydrogen bromide to hydrogen gas. Solar energy hitting the other type of sphere collects electrons from the solution by converting hydro-

gen bromide to liquid bromine, then transports these electrons through the spheres to the backing plate.

The backing plate allows an electrical current to flow between the two areas of the plate, so spheres that gain electrons from the solution can contribute electrons to spheres that lose them.

Maintaining electron balance allows the reaction to proceed efficiently, but electrical energy cannot be obtained directly from the TI solar cell. Rather, the energy is obtained from the liquid bromine and hydrogen gas, which are easily collected and stored separately in tanks. These substances provide useful energy when they combine in a device called a fuel cell. The chemical reaction generates electricity and produces hydrogen bromide, which is used again in the solar collector.

In addition, the sunlight warms hydrogen bromide, so the cell converts sunlight to both electrical and thermal energy. A consumer could run water pipes through the tank, allowing this thermal energy to heat the household water.   [Raymond P. Capece]

Energy

Using a computed tomography (CT) X-ray scanner, one of medicine's most advanced diagnostic tools, a General Electric Company research team headed by Donald H. Maylotte reported in March 1981 that they had looked inside a piece of coal while it was burning and giving off gas.

Maylotte and his associates used a small high-temperature furnace designed to fit inside the CT scanner just as a human patient does. Maylotte reported that the CT images clearly showed how coal expands and "melts" as it is heated, going from a relatively dense solid at room temperature to a frothy-looking foam when it reaches about 398°C (750°F.).

Coal is a complex compound of carbon, hydrogen, oxygen, and a variety of minerals and organic materials. It tends to decompose at high temperatures. As its chemical bonds weaken, the coal "cracks," or releases hydrogen, hydrogen sulfide, methane, and other hydrocarbon gases.

Using special heat-sensitive electrodes inside the small furnace, the scientists measured temperatures in and around the burning coal. They also piped combustion gases from the furnace to a mass spectrometer, an instrument that analyzes and measures various components of the gas. The CT research will give scientists a better look at the processes involved in coal combustion. This should help them design improved techniques for gasifying and liquefying coal.

Clean burns. The first experimental test burn of shale oil in a gas turbine generator to produce electricity was conducted in August 1980 at the Long Island Lighting Company's Barrett Power Station in New York. During the 23-hour experiment, the power station burned 126,600 liters (32,000 gallons) of shale oil to generate 305 megawatt hours of electricity.

The test showed that shale oil has potential for use in utility power plants. Operating temperatures for the turbine using shale oil were in the normal range, and the plant equipment exposed to the flame and combustion products appeared clean. The combustion products were higher in nitrogen oxides than those obtained from conventional fuels, but the concentration could be reduced to levels acceptable by the U.S. Environmental Protection Agency (EPA) by mixing water with the shale oil before burning.

In another energy first, electricity was produced from hot, dry rock in June 1980 at the Department of Energy's (DOE) Hot Dry Rock Geothermal Energy Site in Fenton Hill, N. Mex. The heat from naturally hot granite 3.2 kilometers (2 miles) below the surface was tapped to produce 60 kilowatts of electricity. In this method of harnessing geothermal energy, two holes were drilled in hot, dry rock deep within the earth. Water was forced into one hole under enough pressure to cause the rock between the two holes to crack, creating a reservoir for heated water.

Fresh water was then pumped through the first hole down to the rocky reservoir. The water passed through the cracks, where it was heated to temperatures well above the boiling point and then brought to the surface through the second hole under enough pressure to keep it from turning to steam until it is ready to use to turn turbines to produce electricity or for industrial processes. Once the heat energy is extracted, it is pumped back underground to be reheated.

Fill 'er up with aluminum. A promising fuel cell for electric cars that uses aluminum, air, and tap water was announced in October 1981 by research chemist John F. Cooper at the Lawrence Livermore National Laboratory in California. Two major requirements for batteries that power electric vehicles are high-energy storage per kilogram of battery weight and short recharging time. Cooper used a lightweight aluminum alloy plate both as fuel and as the negative electrical terminal in the fuel cell. Air and water pumped through the cell react with the aluminum to produce electricity. Hydragillite, a byproduct formed during the reaction, can be recycled into aluminum.

Cooper is developing the fuel cell as a rapidly refuelable power supply for electric vehicles. His experiments showed that a battery of 60 cells that weighs about 453 kilograms (1,000 pounds) could power a five-passenger vehicle for up to 480 kilometers (300 miles) at a speed of 89 kilometers (55 miles) per hour without stopping for

Super Bikes

Strange configurations aimed at improving speed and rider efficiency are characteristic of new human-powered vehicles. Low-slung, streamlined Vector 4, *below left,* is the fastest one-person superbike. Redshift 3, *bottom right,* is a racing model. Equally innovative are road racers, *below right,* and a three-person vehicle, *bottom left,* that make up in advanced aerodynamic design what they lack in flashy style.

How would you like to ride your bike at 80 kilometers per hour (kph), or 50 miles per hour (mph) — not in the Tour de France bike race, but to get to school or to work or just for fun? New designs based on aerodynamic principles herald an era when pedalers who now average cruising speeds of 16 kph (10 mph) will be able to go five times faster without exerting any more effort. The new designs take into account that riders of standard bicycles use one-third of their energy just pushing air aside.

The rider is still the sole source of energy for the new human-powered vehicles (HPVs), as the superbikes are called. But these HPVs perform differently, and they look different. The inventors who created superbikes developed mechanical techniques for applying pedal power more efficiently and sleek designs for cutting wind resistance. To do this, they lowered both the bike and the biker.

They put the pedal pusher in an almost prone position to improve leg leverage. A biker can generate more force by pushing outward than by pushing downward. The superbikes were given plastic shells that keep handle bars and parts of the rider's body from sticking out. This reduces drag by as much as 50 per cent.

The superbike's speed potential was proved dramatically at the first European competition for HPVs, held in Brighton, England, on Sept. 6, 1980. The Vector Tandem, a two-person bike designed by California aerospace scientist Al Voigt and three colleagues, covered a 200-meter (220-yard) course in 9.43 seconds — a speed of 77.6 kph (47 mph). Earlier in 1980, the bike set a record of 101.25 kph (62.93 mph).

United States bicycle manufacturers have been watching the development of HPVs with keen interest. By the end of the 1980s, HPV prototypes that now cost as much as $5,000 may evolve into mass-produced, cheap transportation.

Because they are so fast and so low-slung, superbikes in general use would require their own traffic lanes. Superbikes may soon give us a cleaner, quieter, more fuel-efficient, and enjoyable way to travel.   [Barney Cohen]

The *Solar Challenger, top,* designed by aeronautical engineer Paul MacCready and powered by the sun, made a test flight in December 1980. The wings and tail contain about 1,500 photovoltaic cells. The first solar-powered motorboat, *above,* carries six solar collecting panels on its surrey top.

refueling. To refuel the cell, the driver removes the hydragillite and adds fresh tap water. The aluminum alloy plates would have to be changed every 1,600 to 4,800 kilometers (1,000 to 3,000 miles) depending upon the thickness of the plates. Changing the plates would take no longer than 30 minutes.

The aluminum in the fuel cell yields about six times the energy content of an equal volume of gasoline. Also, the fuel cell produces almost 15 times the energy of lead-acid batteries of equal weight. A prototype vehicle powered by the aluminum-air battery is scheduled to be produced by 1989.

Better gasohol production. Engineers at Colorado State University in Fort Collins during 1980 and 1981 were studying ways of using geothermal energy and debris left over from tree-cutting and crop-harvesting to make alcohol for gasohol. They hoped to avoid the two major drawbacks in the production of gasohol — using corn that could serve as food and burning large amounts of fossil fuel.

The project scientists, under the direction of engineer Vincent Murphy, developed one process that converts wheat straw to alcohol. The cellulose in wood or straw is composed of glucose, a sugar that can be fermented into alcohol. The researchers separated out the cellulose, and cooked it with enzymes to convert it to glucose. The glucose was then fermented and distilled.

The Colorado State engineers demonstrated the process at the DOE Raft River Geothermal Site at Malta, Ida., in October 1980. To conserve energy in processing the cellulose, the researchers used naturally hot water from a geothermal well. However, they had to heat the water further before using it in the process. The researchers produced 180-proof ethanol alcohol at the rate of 0.9 liter (1 quart) of ethanol per 4.5 kilograms (10 pounds) of wheat straw, or about 3.8 liters (1 gallon) of alcohol from each bale of straw.

Harvesting leaves behind about 71 million metric tons (78 million short tons) of crop residues from nine major crops each year in the United States. The researchers believe that these residues could produce as much as 11 billion liters (3 billion gallons) of alcohol, or about 3 per cent of the equivalent of

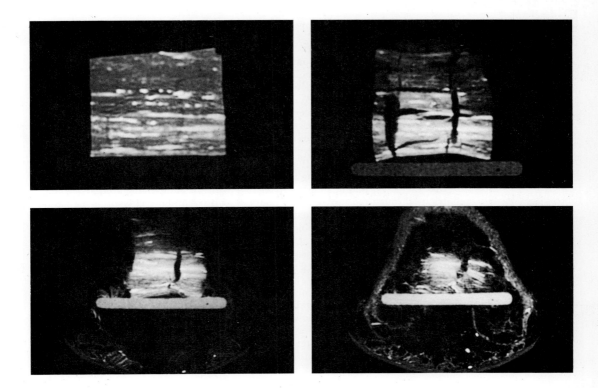

Energy

Continued

Images made by a medical scanner reveal that as coal burns, *clockwise from top left,* it expands and melts into a form of foam as it is heated to 398°C (750°F.). This fact may be helpful in the design of improved coal gasification and similar techniques.

the gasoline consumed in the United States, without affecting the nation's food supply.

Sun-powered flight. In July 1980, Janice Brown, a teacher and commercial pilot, flew the first solar-powered aircraft, the *Gossamer Penguin,* about 3.2 kilometers (2 miles) at an altitude of 4.6 meters (15 feet). Brown flew a second solar plane, the *Solar Challenger* for 22 minutes in December 1980. This time, the aircraft traveled about 9.6 kilometers (6 miles) and reached an altitude of 152 meters (500 feet). Both solar craft were designed by aeronautical engineer Paul MacCready of Aerovironment Incorporated in Pasadena, Calif. He had earlier won fame, plus prize money, with his human-powered *Gossamer Condor,* which made aviation history in 1977, and the *Gossamer Albatross,* a human-powered plane that flew across the English Channel in 1979. (See FLIGHT OF THE GOSSAMER CONDOR, *Science Year,* 1979.)

The solar aircraft, the *Gossamer Penguin* and the *Solar Challenger,* get their energy from photovoltaic cells that convert sunlight into electricity. The electricity powers a motor that drives a propeller.

The *Gossamer Penguin* has a wingspan of 22 meters (72 feet) and two panels carrying 2,800 solar cells mounted atop the vehicle. Some 16,000 photovoltaic cells are mounted on the wing and horizontal stabilizer of the *Solar Challenger.*

MacCready planned to have the *Solar Challenger* fly from Paris to London in mid-1981. He said the flight was planned so that the rising sun would be behind the aircraft. In that way, the craft's solar cells could convert more solar energy to electricity.

Pioneer plant. The Southern California Edison Company announced in 1981 that construction of Solar One, the first central solar-electrical power plant in the United States, would be completed in December. Solar One, at Daggett, Calif., is expected to produce 10 megawatts of electrical power during peak daylight hours. A field of 1,818 sun-tracking mirrors, covering about 40 hectares (100 acres), reflects the sun's energy to a central tower 91 meters (300 feet) high.

Each of the glass mirrors has a surface area of about 39 square meters (430 square feet). A computer directs the mirrors to turn throughout the day, so that they receive the maximum amount of solar rays. A boiler on top of the tower produces steam as hot as 509°C (950°F.), which drives a conventional electrical turbine generator on the ground. The plant will also store heat energy collected during the day so that the power plant can generate electricity through the early evening hours, after the sun has set. Scientists will study the results to determine whether a large-scale solar-electric power plant of this type is technically feasible and whether it may have any effect on the environment.

Solar irrigation. The University of Arizona's solar-electric irrigation facility near Coolidge, Ariz., powers three 50-kilowatt pumps that bring up 5,300 liters (1,400 gallons) of water per minute. The system could also provide about 70 per cent of the electricity

needs for 100 homes. Its conversion efficiency is 45 per cent.

Energy-efficient house. The DOE's Brookhaven National Laboratory on Long Island, N. Y., built Brookhaven House to demonstrate solar efficiency in the harsh climate of the northeastern United States. Brookhaven House, opened in December 1980, was heated with 185 liters (49 gallons) of oil during December 1980, compared with the estimated 1,285 liters (340 gallons) needed to heat a similar Long Island house with the same living area.

Brookhaven House is a three-bedroom, two-story house with 165 square meters (1,800 square feet) of living space. The main living areas are placed on the south side for maximum exposure to sunlight. The house's well-insulated and tightly constructed shell retains a great deal of heat. All windows are triple-glazed. Part of the walls are enclosed by a greenhouse that traps the sun's heat, which is then absorbed by interior brick walls. This solar heat energy is stored by the walls to heat the house at night. [Marian Visich, Jr.]

Environment

The availability of a safe and adequate supply of drinking water became a major area of environmental concern in the United States in 1980 and 1981. Studies revealed that a significant portion of the nation's ground water, the water found below the earth's surface, has been contaminated.

Incidences of pollution. The Environmental Protection Agency (EPA) in November 1980 published a list of common practices that contribute to ground-water pollution. The list included the heavy use of pesticides and fertilizers, disposal of mining wastes, and the extensive use of salts to melt ice on highways in the Northern states. At the top of the list, however, was the disposal of industrial chemicals near drinking-water supplies. This practice causes the build-up of chemicals that are known or suspected toxins.

Ground water, the largest source of drinking water in the United States, is 50 times as plentiful as surface water. Because it is stored underground, it evaporates more slowly than surface water and is less likely to be depleted

by short-term droughts. Many substances, such as biodegradable organic compounds, are removed from the water by soil bacteria, absorption, and chemical processes as rain water seeps through the soil, so ground water can usually be consumed untreated. Therefore, it had been thought to be better protected from contamination than surface water.

In another study pointing to the pollution of ground water, the Council on Environmental Quality (CEQ) reported in January 1981 that 33 toxic organic compounds, such as the industrial solvent trichloroethylene, are commonly found in drinking-water wells in virtually all of the states east of the Mississippi River. For example, more than one-third of the communities in Massachusetts have been affected. In Bedford, Mass., 80 per cent of the contaminated drinking water contains up to 2,100 parts per billion (ppb) of dioxane that, at higher concentrations, can be toxic to humans, and 500 ppb of trichloroethylene, which is known to cause cancer in animals.

"Don't you love being miles from anywhere, all cozy by the fire, listening to the gentle pitter-patter of sulfuric acid on the cabin roof?"

Environment

Continued

In New York state, 23 community wells in Nassau County and 13 in Suffolk County were closed, cutting down the drinking-water supplies for more than 2 million persons. More than 600 wells in the New York City metropolitan area have been closed since 1978 because of chemical contamination.

Ground-water contamination is a particular concern because pollution persists much longer in ground water than in surface waters. Because ground water typically moves less than 10 meters (30 feet) per year, and bacteria in the rocks and soils through which it filters do not remove carbon-based chemical contaminants, ground-water pollution can persist for hundreds of years. These chemicals are also difficult to remove from water.

Health concerns and water. In January 1981, CEQ studies revealed that chemicals found in low concentrations in ground water can cause cancer in animals. Although the concentrations of synthetic carbon-based chemicals in ground water are often greater than those in contaminated surface water,

the concentrations are still too low to enable scientists to make accurate connections between ground-water pollution and known human health problems. However, information from CEQ studies of workers exposed to higher concentrations of these chemicals indicate that 11 of the 33 pollutants most commonly found in ground water can cause central nervous system disorders and lead to infertility and miscarriages.

In the CEQ studies, 14 of the 33 compounds were tested in mice, rats, and other rodents. By May 1981, 11 compounds had been found to cause cancer in at least one of those species. Animal tests are used to determine the effects of toxic chemicals, because the effects of low concentrations of such chemicals on humans can only be studied when populations in the tens of thousands have been exposed to the chemicals for long periods of time. Moreover, high concentrations of toxic chemicals should not be deliberately tested on humans.

Another connection between some chemicals found in drinking water and

Environment

Continued

cancer appeared in a report released in December 1980 by mathematical statisticians Kenny S. Crump and Harry A. Guess of Science Research Services in Ruston, La. They reviewed data compiled in Illinois, Louisiana, New York, North Carolina, and Wisconsin, and noted a 1.1 to 1.9 times greater frequency of deaths from rectal cancer and similar increases in colon and bladder cancers among people who drank chlorinated water than among those who drank unchlorinated water. Chlorine combines with other elements in water to form organic compounds related to many of the 33 contaminants found in ground-water supplies.

Hazardous waste control. Shortly before adjourning in December, the Congress of the United States passed the Comprehensive Environmental Response Compensation and Liability Act of 1980, usually called the Superfund. The bill appropriated $1.6 billion to clean up hazardous-waste-disposal sites and chemical spills. The measure did not provide payments for health damages resulting from hazardous

waste pollution. A tax on crude oil, petroleum products, and certain chemicals will be used to raise 87.5 per cent of the fund and the remainder will come from general federal funds.

The EPA adopted regulations on May 5, 1980, that implemented the hazardous-waste-management provisions of the Resource Conservation and Recovery Act (RCRA) of 1976. The regulations are intended to prevent any future contamination of ground water from toxic-waste disposal. They also require all individuals and corporations that produce potentially hazardous wastes to obtain disposal permits.

However, Vice-President George H. W. Bush, in his role as head of the President's Task Force on Regulatory Relief, announced on March 25, 1981, that a number of environmental regulations and rules would be subjected to cost-benefit analysis. Therefore, enforcement of some provisions of the RCRA might be postponed indefinitely. Other proposed environmental regulations were withdrawn by the EPA on March 19, 1981, including one that

Researchers from the United States Department of Energy launch a balloon that carries instruments to measure the content of the air in southeast Washington state as part of a study of air pollution in mountainous regions of the nation.

Environment

Continued

controlled organic contaminants in drinking water.

President Ronald Reagan, in his effort to reduce federal involvement in environmental quality control, also proposed during the year to cancel a $1.7-billion appropriation for the construction of sewage-treatment plants; to eliminate federal funding for state programs to protect the environment of coastal areas; and to reduce CEQ funds by 72 per cent. Acting CEQ Chairman Malcolm F. Baldwin stated that this reduction will hinder the council's ability to make reports and oversee the National Environmental Policy Act.

Soil depletion. "Global Future: Time to Act," issued by the CEQ in January 1981, emphasized the critical need to protect and manage agricultural lands so that they can produce food for the increased world population expected by the year 2000. The report stated that the United States is losing 400,000 hectares (1 million acres) of prime agricultural land each year to commercial development and the same amount to soil breakdown, erosion, and salt accu-

mulation. Soil depletion losses of the richest U.S. farmlands, in Iowa and Illinois, average 3.6 to 7.2 metric tons per hectare (10 to 20 short tons per acre) of topsoil each year — two to four times as much as can be lost without reducing productivity, according to the U.S. Soil Conservation Service.

Many farmers, faced with decreased crop yields due to soil loss, compensate by using more chemical fertilizers and pesticides. These chemicals carried away in runoff water pollute both surface and ground-water sources. Proposals by energy experts to use stalks, leaves, hulls, and other parts of crop plants that are not harvested for producing ethyl alcohol for the fuel gasohol may lead to further soil loss because these leftovers are usually plowed under to rebuild the soil. A study released in 1980 by the U.S. Department of Agriculture called the use of organic techniques such as crop rotation and contour plowing the "best management practice for controlling soil erosion, minimizing water pollution, and conserving energy." [Harold R. Ward]

Genetics

A needle is used to inject DNA from a virus into a mouse embryo cell held by a pipette, (magnified 300 times), in the first successful transplant of genetic material from a different form of life into an animal embryo. Scientists at Yale University performed the gene transplant in September 1980.

Molecular biologists Karl Illmensee of the University of Geneva in Switzerland and Peter C. Hoppe of Jackson Laboratory in Bar Harbor, Me., announced in January 1981 that they had transplanted the nucleus of a cell from one mouse into an egg produced by another mouse. This was the first successful nuclear transplant involving cells of a warm-blooded animal. Genes in the transplanted nucleus directed the egg's development and so produced the first clones, or genetically identical copies, of a mouse embryo.

Illmensee and Hoppe obtained the nuclei from mouse embryos in an early stage of development called the blastocyst. At this stage, the embryo consists of several thousand cells arranged in a hollow ball. On the inner surface of the ball is the region of the blastocyst that develops into the mouse embryo, a small clump of cells called the inner cell mass (ICM). The remainder of the blastocyst consists of trophectoderm (TE) cells, which eventually form the membranes that cover the embryo during its development.

Illmensee and Hoppe extracted blastocysts from females of a gray-coated mouse strain that had been mated with males of the same strain. They then removed fertilized eggs from females of a black-coated strain. They carried out the next steps of the transplant under a microscope equipped with a device for holding and controlling a hollow glass needle. The tip of this needle has a diameter so small that almost 500 could fit on any period on this page.

Scientists first pierced a cell from the ICM of the blastocyst with the needle and gently sucked the cell's nucleus into the hollow tip. They then injected the nucleus into a fertilized egg of the black-coated strain. Only fertilized eggs will divide to form an embryo.

At this early stage of fertilization, the egg actually had three nuclei — the transplant and two from the original egg. One of the two original nuclei was from the sperm, the other was from the egg itself. Ordinarily, these nuclei would fuse to create a fertilized egg with one nucleus. But the scientists removed both of these nuclei by sucking

Genetics

Continued

Making Mouse Multiples
An embryo is removed from a gray female mouse that has mated with a male of the same strain. The nucleus of a cell from the embryo's inner cell mass is added to a fertilized egg taken from a black mouse. The original sperm and egg nuclei are removed. The egg containing only the transplanted nucleus divides to form an embryo, which is implanted in the uterus of a white foster mother. The procedure, repeated in many eggs, produced three gray mice, each a genetic carbon copy of the original embryo.

them into the tip of the needle, leaving only the single nucleus from the blastocyst cell of the gray-coated mouse strain. They repeated this process several times with different eggs.

After each transplant, Illmensee and Hoppe placed the egg cell in a rich broth of nutrients for four or five days. Most cells died at this stage. Of 363 eggs transplanted with ICM nuclei, only 48 lived. But these survivors began to divide just like normal fertilized eggs, and they soon developed into normal blastocysts.

The researchers injected 16 of these transplant blastocysts into the uteruses of female white mice that had been treated with female hormones to prepare them for pregnancy. They also injected 44 normal blastocysts from white mice into the same females as a control. In approximately three weeks, the babies were born. Thirty-two of the babies were white, and the researchers concluded that they developed from the 44 normal blastocysts. But three of the newborn — two females and one male — were gray. Illmensee and Hoppe con-

cluded that the gray mice developed from the transplants of ICM nuclei from the original gray-coated strain.

The success of nuclear transplantation in mice is important because it shows that ICM nuclei can be substituted for the egg nucleus. However, the success rate is not high — only about 1 in 50 nuclear transplants results in a baby mouse. Illmensee and Hoppe believe that most of the unsuccessful cells die from damage caused by the needle.

One of the three newborn gray mice, a female, died of unknown causes. The other two survived and were mated with each other and with normal gray mice. As of January 1981, the transplant mice had 113 offspring, all normal with the expected gray coats.

Illmensee and Hoppe also tried to transplant nuclei from the surrounding TE cells of the blastocyst, but all 179 eggs transplanted with TE nuclei either died or developed abnormally. Evidently, TE nuclei have undergone changes that prevent them from substituting for an egg nucleus that will develop into an embryo.

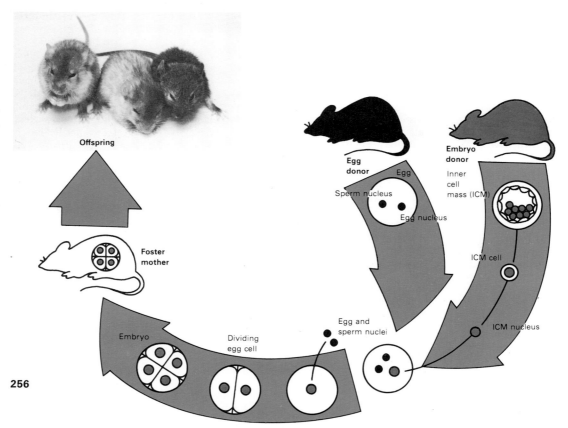

Offspring

Foster mother

Embryo

Dividing egg cell

Egg and sperm nuclei

Egg donor

Egg

Sperm nucleus

Egg nucleus

Embryo donor

Inner cell mass (ICM)

ICM cell

ICM nucleus

v. harris

Genetics

Continued

Mitochondrial DNA sequenced. In April 1981, biochemist Frederick Sanger of the Medical Research Council Laboratory of Molecular Biology in Cambridge, England, and 13 colleagues published the complete nucleotide sequence of the genetic material in human mitochondria. The mitochondria, known as the powerhouses of the cell, are minute structures outside the cell nucleus. They play a key role in converting the food we eat into energy.

Although most of the genes of the cell are located on strands of deoxyribonucleic acid (DNA) in the nucleus, the mitochondria also contain DNA that comprises their genes. All DNA is composed of nucleotides, small chemical units linked end to end, and the order in which the nucleotides appear determines the genes' functions. Human mitochondrial DNA, with 16,569 nucleotides comprising 37 genes, is the longest DNA molecule yet sequenced.

To determine the gene sequences, Sanger and his colleagues used the technique for which Sanger was awarded a share of the Nobel prize for chemistry in 1980 (see Science AWARDS). They extracted human mitochondrial DNA and used it as a pattern upon which they synthesized DNA fragments from laboratory chemicals, including radioactive nucleotides. The scientists then analyzed the positions of the radioactive nucleotides in the synthetic fragments to determine the sequence of nucleotides in mitochondrial DNA.

The sequence of nucleotides revealed several unusual characteristics. The mitochondrial genetic code differs from the nuclear genetic code. In many cases, the same sequence of DNA that codes for a specific amino acid in the nucleus codes for another amino acid in the mitochondria. Proteins are made up of amino acids.

In the nucleus, long sequences of DNA appear to have no coding function. But almost all the mitochondrial DNA coded for specific proteins. In this respect, the mitochondrial DNA differed not only from nuclear DNA, but also from previously sequenced mitochondrial DNA in yeast and other organisms. [Daniel L. Hartl]

Geochemistry. During 1980 and 1981, geochemists and other earth scientists made significant progress toward understanding the earliest history of the earth, including how and when the first continents formed.

New measurements of the isotopes of lead in volcanic rocks from oceanic islands, from large complex bodies of igneous rocks on continents, and from the most ancient lead ores — found in Canada — are telling the same story. A large region deep in the mantle — the thick layer of hot rock between the crust and the core — has been repeatedly tapped throughout the history of the earth to produce the rocks on the earth's surface. Unlike those parts of the mantle that participate in the cycle of upwelling and subduction of the rocks that make up the ocean basins, these regions are a reservoir of pristine material. They have not experienced the complex geochemical activity, heat, pressure, and weathering that has produced the great variety of types of rocks and materials formed at or near the earth's surface.

The new measurements also demonstrate that the liquid iron core separated from the silicate rocks that make up the mantle and the rest of the earth soon after the earth formed.

Identifying the source. Geochemists Gerard Manhes, Claude Allegre, Bernard Dupré, and Bruno Hamelin of the University of Paris reported in May 1980 that they had used isotopes of elements, especially neodymium, to identify the source of two large bodies of igneous rocks, one in Greenland and one on the Kola Peninsula in Russia, that apparently remained unchanged from their original composition. These two selected bodies of rocks are of different ages — 3.6 billion and 2.6 billion years, respectively. Yet their lead isotope measurements show that they must have come from the same isolated region of the mantle.

Isotopes of uranium are radioactive and disintegrate at a known rate into isotopes of lead. The quantity of lead isotopes that have accumulated in an area permits us to calculate the time that has elapsed since the ratio of uranium to lead — 1 to 10 — was established in the earth. Thus we can estimate when this reservoir was created.

Calculations show that this ratio was established around the time the earth formed — 4.5 billion years ago. When the earth began to form, the ratio was much lower — about 1 to 100. The most likely cause of this increase in the ratio of uranium to lead as the earth was forming was the melting of iron and its sinking to the center of the earth to form the core. The chemical properties of lead are such that much of it would sink along with the iron. Uranium would be left behind, increasing the ratio of uranium to lead in the mantle.

Other new data from geographic formations of very different kinds are confirming the work by Manhes and his colleagues. Geochemist Clement Chase of the University of Minnesota, for example, studied lead isotope data from volcanic rocks on oceanic islands still being formed by volcanos, such as the Hawaiian and Canary Islands. Chase finds that these rocks came from regions with a more complex geochemical history than a deep mantle reservoir and are up to 2.6 billion years old. However, the source regions separated from a reservoir of the same age, 2.6-billion-years, and with the same 1 to 10 ratio of uranium to lead, as that identified by the French workers. In addition, Fouad Tera of the Carnegie Institution of Washington finds that 2.6-billion-year-old lead ores in Canada were derived from a source with these same isotope ratios.

These results answer some questions, but they also raise some new ones, particularly about the formation of the earth's core. On the one hand, evidence that the core formed early in the earth's history fits in very well with the conclusion I came to in 1981: While it was forming, the earth was hot and both its metallic iron and some of its rocky silicates were molten. Under these circumstances, the liquid iron would be expected to have separated out continuously throughout the approximately 50 million years that it took the earth to form.

On the other hand, the conclusion that the earth was formed at a high temperature and that some of its interior became molten immediately runs contrary to some long-held geochemical opinions. Over the years, many geochemists have argued that the chemical

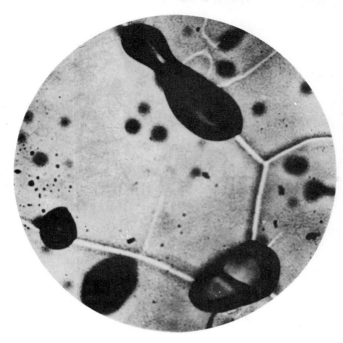

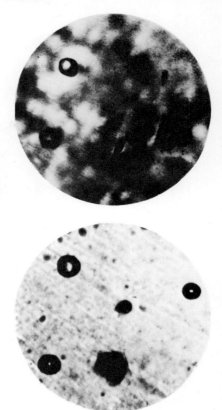

Bubbles of an ancient atmosphere were trapped in Antarctic ice. The varying depths from which the samples were taken account for the different sizes of the bubbles and represent different epochs. (Magnification about 250 times.)

Geoscience

Continued

separations that produced the continents would have taken place much faster than they did in a hot, molten, primitive earth. This means the continents would all be very old — more or less the same age as the earth itself.

Previous data, plus new evidence published in 1981, shows that the continents formed quite slowly at first, and did not reach their peak until 2 billion years after the earth was formed. They are still forming, of course, but at a much slower speed. Recent evidence of this includes results of neodymium and strontium isotope studies reported in August 1980 by geochemist Donald J. DePaolo of the University of California, Los Angeles (UCLA). He showed that continental crust was formed from the deep mantle reservoir during episodes that occurred about 2.6 billion and 1.7 billion years ago.

Geochemists Paul N. Taylor, Stephen Moorbath, Roy Goodwin, and Anne C. Petrykowski of Oxford University in England are studying the most ancient continental rocks known, the 3.7- to 3.8-billion-year-old, as well as

2.9-billion-year-old rocks in Greenland. They find that, for the most part, these rocks are not the results of older reprocessed continental crust, but formed from material fresh from the mantle. All of this evidence makes it clear that the average age of the continents is about half the age of the earth.

How could a largely molten earth avoid producing continental material immediately? The answer may be in the transport of initial interior heat to the surface. Geochemists David Stevenson and Gerald Schubert of UCLA have made calculations using the property that even solid rocks can slowly "flow" and thus transport heat by convection. At the surface, the heat escapes by radiation. The UCLA scientists have also calculated that it is likely that melting probably did not take place at depths of less than 100 kilometers (62 miles) beneath the surface.

This method of moving heat to the surface of the earth without melting the whole earth cannot entirely explain the relative youth of the continents. Geochemists used to think that whole-earth

Geologists
Don't Get
the Drift

The geologists who formed the International Stop Continental Drift Society had the best of intentions. They wanted the continents to stop moving, the sea floor to stop spreading, and such inconveniences as major earthquakes and volcanic eruptions to cease immediately. Although they have worked hard on these goals since 1976, they were ready to admit defeat by 1981. Geologist John C. Holden, a consultant living in Washington state and the society's president, confesses, "So far, our demands have not been satisfactorily met."

Of course, Holden is joking about stopping all earth movements. But he is bothered by the way most scientists uncritically accept the plate tectonics theory. The theory proposes that the earth's surface is composed of about 20 giant plates that move in relation to one another at a rate of 1.3 to 10 centimeters (0.5 to 4 inches) a year. The plates form mountain ranges when they collide head-on, cause earthquakes when they slide past one another, and create volcanoes when one plate is forced down beneath another.

During the past 20 years, nearly all geologists have based their work on the theory. Holden says he, too, accepts plate tectonics, but he thinks that geologists have been so eager to embrace the concept that they have closed their minds to other theories about the earth.

Holden began his campaign by offering bumper stickers with the society's motto, "Eschew Sea-Floor Spreading," and a newsletter that, "like most natural disasters, will appear at unscheduled times." The society charges a modest $5 in annual dues.

It listed 300 members around the world in 1981, most of them scientists who enjoy kidding the geological establishment in poems, cartoons, and comic parodies of research papers published in the newsletter. A report from the so-called Institute of Geotectonic Redundancies dealt with the most serious question unanswered by plate tectonic theory: What makes the continents move? "After several days of deep meditation and prayer," the researchers concluded that the plates move because God propels them with "a giant

Dutch geologists drive a giant screw into the ground at Leiden, The Netherlands, in an attempt to stop the Eurasian tectonic plate from moving. The scientists are members of the International Stop Continental Drift Society whose purpose is to put some stability in the earth's crust.

celestial broom." This was called the Holy Housecleaning Model.

Members of The Netherlands chapter took stronger action. They sank a giant screw 1 meter (3 feet) into the ground outside the Geology Department at State University of Leiden, and proclaimed that this would prevent the Eurasian Plate from drifting. But this bold gesture led to controversy; some members argued that the screw should have been threaded counter-clockwise to withstand the earth's rotation.

Two years later, The Netherlands' government transferred the Leiden Geology Department to Utrecht, about 50 kilometers (31 miles) away, and the geologists announced, "It is our sad duty to report that the Leiden screw did not secure the Eurasian Plate." They reasoned that since their department moved 50 kilometers in the two years after they bolted the plate, this must mean that Europe was drifting 25 kilometers (15.5 miles) per year.

Some of the society's geologists really do not accept the plate tectonics theory, and they submit serious reports to the newsletter's Continental Drift Hit List section that cast doubt on the main points of plate tectonic theory. For example, one Hit List article reported that plant and animal species in India were similar to those in China about 250 million years ago, raising questions about whether the two land masses were separated by an ocean.

Members have also written about the discovery of fossil crab-like creatures called trilobites mixed with rocks on the Atlantic Ocean floor. According to plate tectonics theory, the rocks in that area came to the surface of the earth less than 50 million years ago. But trilobites became extinct about 225 million years ago. So how did the fossils get there?

Geologist S. Robert Dietz of Arizona State University in Tempe, a prominent authority on plate tectonics who coined the term "sea-floor spreading," belongs to the society and says that many of his peers enjoy the newsletter. "There's no reason to doubt seriously the basic premises of plate tectonics," he says. "But it's become such a dogma now that people are very much in favor of some criticism of it. And we need a little humor." [John Tierney]

melting would have very quickly produced light rocks similar to granite, a dominant component of the silicate continental crusts. Because granite is relatively light, these rocks have not returned to the mantle and, except for erosion, have remained unchanged for billions of years. Dense rocks, such as the basalts, which are predominant in the ocean basins, sink back into the mantle in so-called subduction zones that are beneath the great trenches in the sea floor.

Earth scientists are taking another look at the processes by which granite rock is formed and the nature of the primitive earth and find that they seem to imply that the formation of granites requires a lot more than melting rocks of composition similar to that of the earth — primarily silicon and oxygen.

Geochemist Kent C. Condie of the New Mexico Institute of Mining and Technology, for example, reasoned that for the first 500 million years of the earth's history, only basaltic rocks were formed at the surface, and that these resembled the rocks of the mantle more than the basalts produced on the sea floor do today. These basalts were quite ineffectual in producing granitic crusts, both because of their composition and because the rapid heat transfer in the early earth caused them to be rapidly swept back into the mantle. Condie argues that not until about 4 billion years ago did these processes slow down sufficiently to permit the melted rocks to separate.

In another 1981 study, Robert C. Newton and Joseph V. Smith of the University of Chicago and Brian F. Windley of the University of Leicester in England explained how these earliest granitic continental nuclei may have achieved the chemical and physical stability necessary for them to survive for billions of years. According to these scientists, carbon dioxide in the mantle flushed radioactive elements up toward the surface of these ancient continents soon after they were formed. This kept the lower portion of the continent from melting from the heat produced by the radioactive elements. This process could have provided relatively cool and strong, low-density "roots" that supported the rocks of the upper portion of the crust. [George W. Wetherill]

Geoscience

Continued

Geophysics. A team of astronomers and geophysicists led by scientists at the Massachusetts Institute of Technology (M.I.T.) in Cambridge reported in March 1981 that they have devised the first system for actually measuring continental drift, a key component of the theory of plate tectonics. According to this theory, the earth's surface consists of some 20 gigantic plates that move relative to one another at speeds of from 0.5 centimeter (0.2 inch) to 13 centimeters (5 inches) per year, carrying continents with them.

The M.I.T.-led consortium of scientists used a radio-telescope technique called Very Long Baseline Interferometry (VLBI) to make their measurements. Each VLBI station consists of a number of radio telescopes spread out over a distance of several kilometers to receive signals from distant stars that emit radio waves. The scientists used VLBI telescopes in Onsala, Sweden; Westford, Mass.; Green Bank, W. Va.; and Owens Valley, California.

The VLBIs monitored radio sources in the northern sky and recorded their signals on high-speed computer tapes, which were synchronized by extremely accurate hydrogen-maser clocks. The tapes from each VLBI were then processed by computer to determine the minute differences in time when radio signals from several stars were received at each station. The scientists then used those time differences in a complex mathematical formula to calculate the precise distances between VLBI stations, with an error margin of only 5 centimeters (2 inches).

They determined that the absolute distances from the Onsala radio telescopes to those in Westford is 5,599.71 kilometers (3,478.08 miles); to those in Green Bank, 6,319.32 kilometers (3,925.04 miles); and to those in Owens Valley, 7,914.13 kilometers (4,915.61 miles). The Swedish antenna is on the Eurasian Plate, and the Westford, Green Bank, and Owens Valley antennas are on the North American Plate.

Geophysicists calculate that the distance between the European and North American continents is increasing at the rate of 1.7 centimeters (0.7 inch)

Sand tubes, *below,* create a fantasy landscape on the shore of Mono Lake, California. Each hollow tube, *below right,* was formed where calcium-rich spring water bubbled into the alkaline lake, leaving calcium carbonate deposits. Wind erosion exposed them after the water level dropped.

Geoscience

Continued

per year. Therefore, in only three to five years the M.I.T.-led scientists will be able to detect plate motion with the VLBI system.

How diamonds form. S. Thomas Crough and a team of geoscientists at Princeton University in September 1980 presented a theory that clarifies the relationship between the origin of kimberlites, rocks containing diamonds, and plate tectonic theory. Diamonds, which form when carbon is subjected to intense pressure deep within the earth, are often found in rock formations called kimberlite pipes. Scientists believe these are a special kind of volcanic vent through which diamonds were blasted by the action of volcanic gas from depths of at least 150 kilometers (93 miles). The central point of the Princeton scientists' theory is that the diamond-bearing kimberlites formed when continental areas were over so-called hot spots, or plumes of molten rock, in the earth's mantle, the layer of rock under the earth's crust. For reasons scientists do not yet understand, these hot spots form in the mantle and find pathways through the plate to the surface.

Scientists are fairly certain about the effects of hot spots beneath the ocean floor. These heat sources, which appear to be active from periods of 5 million to 80 million years, give rise to volcanic mountains, and many of their peaks form strings of islands. The best known of the volcanic features produced by hot spots are the Hawaiian Islands, which extend from the main island of Hawaii some 3,200 kilometers (2,000 miles) westward to Midway Island and then northward to the Emperor Seamounts, a line of underwater mountains. Scientists believe this string of volcanoes resulted from the Pacific Plate moving eastward then southward at 6 to 8 centimeters (2 to 3 inches) per year for 80 million years.

Crough and his colleagues assume that a series of volcanic features also formed on continental areas as they moved over these hot spots. They believe that millions of years ago these hot spots were responsible for producing diamond-bearing kimberlites, such as the ones in southwest Africa and South America. The scientists looked for evidence of ancient plumes in areas that now contain kimberlites. For example, they found that Tristan da Cunha, a volcanic island over a hot spot in the South Atlantic Ocean some 1,800 kilometers (1,100 miles) due east of the Cape of Good Hope, was located on the edge of southwest Africa before South America drifted away.

The Princeton scientists also reported evidence linking a former hot spot in what is now the mid-Atlantic Ocean to the diamond deposits in the heart of South America. They believe that 90-million-year-old volcanic rock found on the ocean floor some 1,200 kilometers (750 miles) east of Rio de Janeiro was produced by the same hot spot responsible for 120-million-year-old volcanic rock near the Brazil-Bolivia border. The scientists believe that diamond-bearing kimberlite might also be found there. The volcanic deposits were forced up as the South American continent passed over this hot spot 120 million years ago. This new hypothesis provides a possible framework for understanding how Brazil's diamond deposits are distributed.

The Princeton group also speculates that alkaline rocks — similar in chemistry to kimberlites, but in which diamonds have not yet been discovered — were produced by a plume under northern Ontario some 160 million years ago. Then, 120 million to 100 million years ago, as the North American Plate moved westward, this hot spot found pathways through the crust at what is now the New York-Quebec border and injected molten rock at various points along the Appalachian mountain chain. The scientists propose that as the continent drifted farther westward, the hot spot appeared offshore and created the string of seamounts east of Massachusetts known as the New England Seamounts. They believe that the hot spot is now located beneath the great Meteor Seamount west of the Canary Islands.

Many of the rocks that Crough's team proposes are related to the migration of continents over hot spots must be tested to determine their chemistry and age. If these tests uphold the hypothesis, the Princeton scientists will have created a valuable theory for economic geologists to use in their search for diamonds.   [Thomas J. Ahrens]

Geoscience

Continued

Paleontology. Fossil reptiles that were a last meal for two of their larger reptile relatives apparently belong to a previously unknown species, according to a December 1980 report by paleontologist Sankar Chatterjee, now of Texas Tech University in Lubbock.

About 180 million years ago, on a riverbank in India, two hungry phytosaur reptiles that resembled today's crocodiles each grabbed a small eosuchian reptile and swallowed it whole. But before they could digest the smaller reptiles, the phytosaurs died and were quickly buried side by side, perhaps by a flood. Chatterjee, who discovered the phytosaur skeletons and the bones of their last meal in the late 1960s, reported that the prey were each about 1.3 meters (4 feet) long and had not been described before.

The predators, *Parasuchus hislopi,* belong to the suborder Phytosauridae, an extinct group of large reptiles. Although still immature, they were 2.2 meters (7.5 feet) long. They swallowed their prey whole, just as crocodiles do today. Chatterjee named the smaller reptiles *Malerisaurus robinsonae,* for the Maleri formation — the area in India where they were found — and for Pamela Robinson — a paleontologist who has worked in India for years.

The newly identified reptile belongs to the order Eosuchia, which may have included the ancestors of modern lizards. Chatterjee said that *Malerisaurus* walked on its hind legs and may have been able to climb trees.

The oldest whale? A complete fossil whale skull — perhaps the oldest intact skull yet found — was discovered by Louisiana State University geologists on July 31, 1980. The skull, 1.3 meters (4 feet) long, was found on the banks of the Red River at Montgomery Landing, La. Judith Schiebout and William van den Bold, who made the discovery, estimated that the skull is 45 million years old.

The fossil whale, *Basilosaurus cetoides,* belongs to the most primitive group of whales, the Archaeoceti, which lived 30 million to 45 million years ago. Some grew to be 27 meters (90 feet) long. All species of living

The intact fossil skull of a whale that lived about 45 million years ago was found at Montgomery Landing, La.

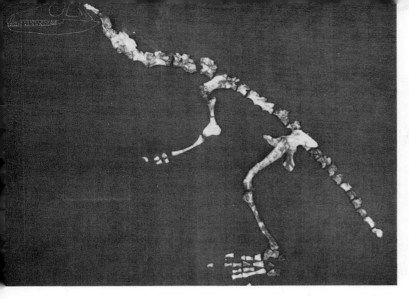

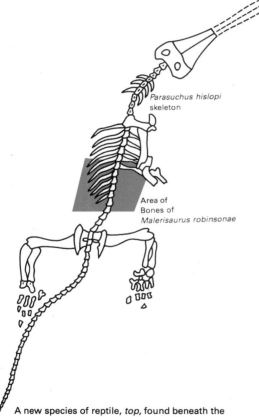

Parasuchus hislopi
skeleton

Area of
Bones of
Malerisaurus robinsonae

A new species of reptile, *top,* found beneath the ribcage of a larger reptile, *above,* was apparently the last supper of the bigger beast. The fossils, dated at 180 million years, were found in India.

whales probably evolved from this group. Archaeoceti whales ate fish, as do many present-day toothed whales.

Along with the whale skull, the scientists found teeth, ribs, a dozen vertebrae, and a humerus bone.

Big bird. Argentine paleontologists announced in September 1980 that they had discovered fossils of the world's largest flying bird. Eduardo P. Tonni and Rosendo Pascual of La Plata Museum in Argentina named the bird *Argentavis magnificens.* They said that it lived 5 million to 8 million years ago and was related to present-day condors. It stood about 1.8 meters (6 feet) tall and had a wingspan of 7.5 meters (25 feet). *A. magnificens* is a member of the Teratorn family of extinct birds.

Tonni and Pascual, after finding a number of fossil bone fragments in central Argentina, determined that they belonged to a single bird. They consulted with Teratorn experts at the Natural History Museum of Los Angeles County, California, to make a reconstruction of *A. magnificens,* which went on display in 1980.

Evolution in a clam shell. Two Harvard University paleontologists came up with a new explanation of why there are so few brachiopods and so many clams in the world today, and what this might mean in terms of evolutionary theory. Stephen Jay Gould and C. Bradford Calloway in December reported on their study of how the number of species of brachiopods and species of clams have varied during the last 600 million years.

A brachiopod is similar to a clam. Both have two rounded valves, live on the ocean bottom, and eat by filtering tiny organisms out of seawater. Brachiopods were plentiful and clams were rare for about 400 million years, throughout the Paleozoic Era. Then, starting at the end of the Permian Period about 225 million years ago, clams increased dramatically while brachiopod numbers and species dwindled. Today, brachiopods are rare.

Most paleontologists and biologists believed that clams gradually replaced brachiopods through competition. This would mean that clams are genetically superior to brachiopods in their ability to survive. But when Gould and Calloway looked closely at the record, they

Geoscience

Continued

A lizard enclosed in amber is the oldest and only complete fossil of its genus, which has a sparse fossil record. Found in the Dominican Republic, the lizard may be 40 million years old.

found that clams did well when brachiopods were also doing well, and vice versa. The reversal in their fortunes was not gradual but was due to one dramatic event—a mass extinction in the Permian Period, when about 90 per cent of all species died out. Many more brachiopod species died off than clam species, and the clams have stayed ahead. So Gould and Calloway argue that the record does not support the idea that clams are better adapted in general than brachiopods. It only shows that clams were better able to survive a major catastrophe.

This raises another question for scientists to ponder: Why did the brachiopods lack the flexibility to survive the upheaval at the end of the Permian Period? Gould and Calloway contend that scientists cannot generalize about the course of evolution over millions of years from studying only the gradual changes that occur from day to day within a community. The evolutionary pattern for brachiopods and clams was not set by small gradual changes during periods of calm on earth, but by

these species' different responses to unique and dramatic events, such as mass extinctions.

Extinct reptile. Paleontologists R. E. Molnar of Queensland Museum and R. A. Thulborn of the University of Queensland, Australia, reported in November 1980 that they had found three fossil bones of a pterosaur in a limestone bed in west Queensland. This was the first time the remains of this extinct flying reptile have been found in Australia. The researchers estimate that the pterosaur they found had a wingspan of about 2 meters (6.6 feet).

Pterosaurs died off during the Cretaceous Period about 65 million years ago, when about 70 per cent of all species perished in a mass extinction. Scientists are debating what caused the extinctions. See END OF AN ERA.

Paleontologists had previously found the remains of only a few pterosaurs in the Southern Hemisphere and none as far south as Queensland. This discovery may mean that pterosaurs were more widely distributed than scientists had thought.   [Ida Thompson]

Immunology

Immunologists in 1980 published reports that are helping to clear up the question of how the limited amount of genetic information in the human body can code for the vast numbers of different antibodies it produces. Antibodies are molecules made by white blood cells called B-lymphocytes. Each antibody reacts specifically with one particular antigen, or molecule that identifies a substance as foreign and thus provokes the immune system to action.

Three research groups—at California Institute of Technology (Caltech) in Pasadena, Basel Institute for Immunology in Switzerland, and Royal Melbourne Hospital in Australia—found different steps in the antibody-assembling process that are responsible for producing thousands of different antibody types.

Antibody molecules are shaped like lobsters. The lobster "body" is formed from two chains of molecules called heavy chains that also form the outside of two "claws." The inside half of each claw is formed by a smaller molecular chain called a light chain. The B-

lymphocyte produces the heavy chain and light chain separately, and these combine after they are completely formed. Each chain is further divided into distinct areas with different functions—a variable (V) region at the tip of the claw, which is responsible for attaching to the antigens; and a constant (C) region, which calls other parts of the immune system to eliminate an attached antigen.

There are five classes of antibody molecules. Each B-lymphocyte produces two classes of antibody molecule. The first class produced remains attached to the cell membrane but, as the B-lymphocyte matures, it produces other classes of antibodies, which it releases into the bloodstream.

Each class has a different function and a different heavy chain. These heavy chain differences are due to differences in the C region structure. There are also two types of light chains, and distinct sequences of deoxyribonucleic acid (DNA) code for the production of both of these, as well as for the five types of heavy chains.

Immunology

Continued

The DNA sequences that code for these chains are arranged in series on chromosomes, rodlike structures in the cell, and are termed *germline* genes. A large number of V genes in the germline contributes to the variety of antibody molecules.

To make an antibody molecule, the DNA that contains the blueprints for the molecule must be transcribed by other molecules called messenger RNA (mRNA). Special molecules in the cell read the instructions in the mRNA to produce the antibody specified by the germline genes. The blueprint for antibody synthesis must be read in the proper order so that the right V gene combines with a particular C segment to produce an antibody molecule that will attach to a specific part of an antigen called an antigenic determinant.

The J gene. Early in 1980, microbiologist Leroy Hood and his associates at Caltech reported that the DNA sequences for the V and C sequences are brought together by a complex process involving genes called "joining" or J sequences. Hood's group found that the germline gene must be copied in a particular order — V-J-C — to produce a light chain. Only one each of the V, J, and C genes is needed to produce a single light chain. Since there are about 10,000 types of the genes, a large number of combinations is possible.

In the spring of 1980, Hood's team discovered that V genes were separated from the J gene and the C gene by a DNA segment with no known purpose called an intervening sequence. To produce either a light or a heavy chain molecule, the mRNA copies the entire stretch of DNA containing V-J-C gene sequences, any intervening sequences separating them are cut out, and the V-J-C sequences in the mRNA are spliced together in the proper order.

Microbiologists O. Bernard and W. M. Gough of Royal Melbourne Hospital discovered that the J gene and the DNA sequences surrounding it are a source of great antibody variety. They reported in June 1980 that stretches of DNA in the gene are often deleted or changed during transcription. They had found in earlier work that mutations in the intervening sequences flanking the J gene also produced variations in the light chain.

J genes are also present in the germline genes for heavy chains, along with five classes of C genes and 10 different diversity (D) genes. Scientists think that D genes may be located between V and J genes.

Cutting and splicing. Molecular biologists Hitoshi Sankano, Richard Maki, Yoshikazu Kurosawa, William Roeder, and Susumu Tonegawa at Basel Institute for Immunology in Switzerland reported in August 1980 that at least two types of cutting and splicing operations are necessary to assemble a complete antibody heavy chain gene. The first occurs when the V and D genes have been joined, and the J gene is added on; the second, when the C gene is added. The first process takes place before, and the second after, the antibody molecules have begun to appear on the surface of the B-lymphocyte.

Because there are a large number of different V, D, and J region genes as well as five different C gene sequences, these two operations allow the cell to make a very large number of V, D, J, and C combinations.

These findings also help explain how individual B-lymphocytes produce different forms of one specific antibody. When B-lymphocytes are first stimulated by an antigen to produce specific antibodies, they produce only the first class of heavy chain with a particular C region. These chains never leave the B-lymphocyte. As the B-lymphocyte matures, it switches from making the first class of heavy chain, and begins to produce another class of heavy chain, and thus, antibodies that are released from the cell to circulate through the bloodstream.

Although the C portion of the heavy chain is different on these second-generation antibody molecules, they are spliced to the same V, J, and D regions as the first. Thus, a single J and D combination can appear spliced to different C regions, but since the V-J-D area determines which antigen the antibody will attach to, each antibody molecule produced by a particular B-lymphocyte will attach to the same antigen. Thus, one B-lymphocyte can use a limited amount of genetic information to produce two classes of antibodies, both fitting the same antigenic determinant.   [Ralph Snyderman]

Medicine

Dentistry. Dental researchers Guillermo Millicovsky and Malcolm C. Johnston of the University of North Carolina in Chapel Hill described in May 1981 how the commonly prescribed anticonvulsive drug phenytoin (Dilantin) may contribute to cleft palate and cleft lip. They also found a way to reduce these drug-caused birth defects.

Cleft lip and cleft palate are among the most common human birth defects, occurring about once in every 1,000 births. Because of faulty development and maturation, the two halves of the embryo's palate, or roof of the mouth, fail to unite. This produces an opening between the mouth and the nasal cavity that interferes with eating, drinking, and speech. Researchers reported in 1968 that some human birth defects, including cleft lip and palate, were associated with the use during pregnancy of phenytoin, which is used to treat convulsive disorders such as epilepsy.

Phenytoin depresses heartbeat and breathing rate in pregnant mice, thus cutting down the amount of oxygen delivered to the mother's tissues. The North Carolina researchers reasoned that the drug's ability to cause birth defects might be related to this lack of oxygen. To test this theory, they injected pregnant mice with phenytoin on the 10th day of pregnancy and then placed them in a chamber filled with an oxygen-enriched atmosphere for 18 hours. Pregnant mice in a control group were also injected with phenytoin but were exposed only to room air.

The pregnancies were terminated on the 17th day of gestation and the fetuses were examined. The researchers found cleft lip or palate in 84 per cent of the fetuses from the control group but in only 25 per cent from the oxygen-treated group. Their findings indicate that giving oxygen to pregnant women who must take phenytoin can protect against these birth defects.

The researchers also concluded that the lack of oxygen rather than the phenytoin acting on the fetus may have caused the malformations. A drug may not have to reach the embryo to harm the fetus. It may do so by affecting the mother. [Paul Goldhaber]

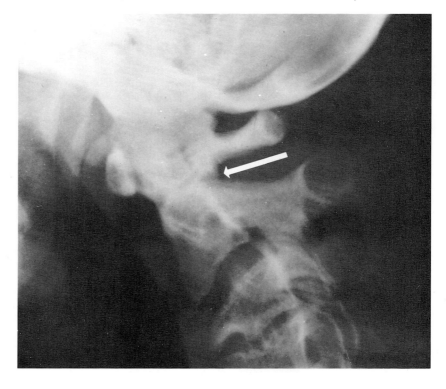

Fused neck vertebrae and decreased space between vertebrae were caused by osteomyelitis, a bone infection that arose after a tooth extraction. Such infections are rare, but severe neck pain after an extraction should receive prompt attention.

Medicine

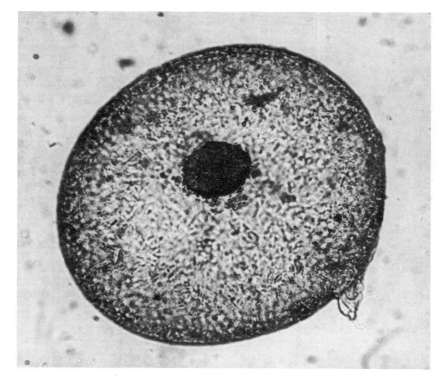

Continued

Internal Medicine. An innovative experiment reported in March 1981 by internist William P. Peters and his colleagues at Harvard Medical School cast new light on how the body regulates blood pressure, and also offered promise that a new treatment may help some patients with septic shock. Life-threatening septic shock often results from sepsis, bacterial infection in the bloodstream.

Sepsis is not uncommon, particularly in patients who have severe diseases or whose immune system has been weakened by anticancer therapy. One aspect of sepsis that has proved very difficult to treat is hypotension (low blood pressure), which can cause septic shock.

Opiate drugs, such as morphine, can lower blood pressure when injected intravenously. Beta endorphin, a natural opiate produced by the pituitary gland, can also lower blood pressure.

The Harvard group noted that stress can cause the pituitary gland to secrete both beta endorphin and adrenocorticotropic hormone (ACTH), which can raise blood pressure by stimulating the adrenal gland. They concluded that they could remove the cause of hypotension — beta endorphin — and raise the blood pressure of septic shock patients by administering naloxone, a drug that blocks the action of opiates.

The scientists injected naloxone into 13 patients suffering from septic shock. They found that blood pressure rose promptly and sharply in eight of nine patients who were not being treated with cortical steroids, drugs related to ACTH. In four patients receiving steroids, there was no rise in blood pressure. This agrees with a previous finding that steroids inhibit the release of both beta endorphin and ACTH.

The rise in blood pressure tended to be short-lived, and most of the tested patients ultimately died of septic shock despite the temporary improvement. But the scientists believe these preliminary results justify further examination of this potentially revolutionary treatment for septic shock.

Pancreatic cells and diabetes. Medical researchers Franklin Lim of the Medical College of Virginia in Rich-

A dark mass of rat pancreas cells is encased in a capsule with a protective membrane that was injected into a diabetic rat. The membrane protects the cells from attack by the rat's immune system while the cells, reacting to blood-sugar levels, make insulin to control the animal's diabetes.

" I stopped taking the medicine because I prefer the original disease to the side effects."

Medicine

Continued

mond and Anthony M. Sun of the Connaught Research Institute, Willowdale, Canada, reported in November 1980 on a series of experiments in which insulin-producing pancreatic cells were injected into the abdominal cavity of diabetic rats. The technique may be a significant advance in helping diabetics to maintain proper insulin levels.

Maintaining normal or near-normal blood-sugar levels throughout the day may help control many of the complications of diabetes. Unfortunately, a single dose, or even several daily doses, of insulin cannot maintain normal blood sugar because people's level of physical activity constantly varies, as does the absorption of food by their bodies.

In their experiments, Lim and Sun removed pancreatic cells from rats and combined them into small droplets that were then enclosed in tiny protective capsules made from polysaccharides, a kind of carbohydrate. The pancreatic cells inside the microcapsules, which are small enough to pass through a standard-sized hypodermic needle, respond to increasing levels of glucose by

producing increased insulin. The capsules' polysaccharide membranes keep out large immune molecules that would destroy the cells, but allow small molecules, such as glucose and insulin, to move in and out of the capsule.

After the droplets were injected into a diabetic rat's peritoneum, the membrane that lines the abdominal wall, the rat's blood-sugar levels were normal for about three weeks. Other droplets not protected by capsules survived only a few days before the rat's immune system destroyed them.

Scientists will continue their studies to determine which area of the body is best for injection. More importantly, they must determine whether the technique can be applied to humans.

Cold in the old. A research team in the Department of Geriatric Medicine at the London School of Medicine's University College reported experimental data in January 1981 that help to explain why many elderly persons suffer hypothermia, or reduced body temperature. Hypothermia slows metabolism and can endanger life.

Medicine

Continued

Elderly persons cannot detect changes in temperature as well as they once could and are therefore less likely to protect themselves from the cold. The British physicians studied two groups — 17 old men and 13 young men — to determine whether men 70 to 80 years old could sense heat and cold as well as men 18 to 39 years old. The two groups lived at home, were healthy, and were similar in size and weight.

In the experiment, each subject was placed in a cold, isolated room. During a stay of three hours he could alter the room temperature to suit his own desires by manipulating an unmarked thermostat dial. The participants wore ordinary clothing and recorded their comfort or discomfort regularly.

Both young and old indicated that they preferred a temperature of 21.1° C (70°F.). Younger subjects were able to regulate their environment even with an unmarked thermostat so that the room temperature came quite close to this ideal because they detected discomfort after only modest temperature swings. By contrast, the older men were less sensitive to discomfort and had more trouble maintaining the temperature they preferred. They tended to overshoot their thermostat adjustments and temperature swings were much greater before they were noticed.

These results suggest that the elderly cannot sense temperature changes as quickly as young people, so they cannot respond as promptly to these changes even though they have the same innate desire for a comfortable heat level.

New bone. A new method for producing bone in living human subjects was described by surgeon M. Judah Folkman and his colleagues at Harvard Medical School in May 1981.

Many victims of bone-destroying accidents and persons with certain congenital defects are treated with bone grafts. Surgeons insert the grafts to serve as a framework onto which new bone cells, migrating from nearby bone tissue, can reconstruct bone.

The two bone-grafting techniques currently available have serious limitations. One method involves the use of cadaver bone. But cadaver-bone grafts

Dark areas in an X-ray scan of a patient's liver, *below left,* are tumor cells before a new treatment. The cancerous area has dramatically diminished, *below right,* after therapy with radioactive iodine carried to cancer sites by molecules that seek out a protein found in the cancer cells.

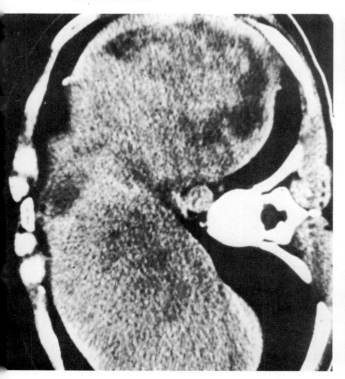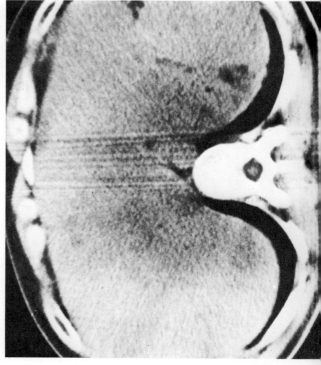

Dances of Danger

Every so often, a new disease pops up in the press to terrify the public. In recent years, Lassa fever has come out of Africa, and Legionnaires' disease out of Philadelphia. Toxic shock syndrome made headlines in 1980 (see PUBLIC HEALTH). Fears of new occupational disorders appear, such as the recent flurry about the possible hazards of office Video Display Terminals.

Over the last several years, the prestigious *New England Journal of Medicine* (*NEJM*), a sober giant among medical journals in the United States, has published a string of reports by U.S. doctors about new ailments that have struck Americans at play. The doctors reported that jogging, cycling and roller-skating have produced new recreational disorders to join such old favorites as tennis elbow and golfer's knee.

Even dancing now has its hazards. Dancing would seem to be the most innocent of occupations, if only because when you are dancing, you cannot easily be doing anything else. For example, gossip, libel, and slander are denied to dancers by popular music that drowns out conversation.

"Disco felon," the first of these dance-hall disorders, was reported to *NEJM* by Frederick W. Walker and other doctors at Johns Hopkins Hospital in Baltimore in July 1979. "A 17-year-old girl came to the emergency room complaining of an infected finger," they wrote. "Physical examination showed . . . a classic felon [a painful inflammation of the finger, usually near the fingernail] of the left middle finger. . . . the patient had noticed a small crack on her finger. . . . She thought that the crack might have resulted from snapping her fingers while she was disco dancing. . . "

The doctors treated the girl by draining and bandaging the inflammation. She recovered, but Walker and his associates sounded a dire warning to other disco dancers and their doctors. "Disco dancing may eventually be shown to damage a variety of body systems: namely visual, auditory, orthopedic, and nutritional. [Nutritional] damage might result from self-imposed starvation in an attempt . . . to wear the latest outfits."

Another medical problem surfaced in December 1980, when the *NEJM* published a letter from Robert F. Caspari, a doctor with the Harvard Medical Plan in Wellesley, Mass. Caspari wrote, "A healthy 20-year-old man was seen because of redness in both eyes that had persisted for four days. Examination revealed bilateral subconjunctival hemorrhages without any other findings. After close questioning, the patient disclosed that on the night before the appearance of the redness, he had been vigorously involved in a dance called the 'pogo' which is performed to 'new wave' music. . . . This dance requires repeated bouncing movements for long periods of time.

"Certainly red eyes the morning after are nothing new, but subconjunctival hemorrhage should now be added to the list of probable causes." The red-eyed young man recovered and the disease became known as "punk eye."

A new peril was added to disco felon and punk eye in February 1981, when Robert D. Powers and other doctors at St. Paul-Ramsey Medical Center in St. Paul, Minn., described "urban-cowboy rhabdomyolosis" to horrified readers of *NEJM*. "A previously healthy 20-year-old man presented to the emergency room and reported severe cramps in his thighs . . . and passage of dark red urine on the day he was seen. He had ridden a mechanical bull several times two days previously, with an estimated total riding time of about 90 seconds. . . . The patient was treated conservatively with analgesics, rest, and oral hydration. . . . We wish to alert our colleagues to . . . urban-cowboy rhabdomyolosis [muscle strain] as a consequence of . . . the growing sport of mechanical-bull riding."

The patient recovered. Experts consider his ailment a dance-hall disorder. Mechanical-bull riding is not, strictly speaking, dancing but it usually takes place in dance halls as do other new recreational ills that continue to appear in *NEJM*. The latest are "space-invader's wrist," blamed on the chronic and uncontrollable playing of video games, and "slot-machine tendonitis," an ailment confined mostly to Nevada.

It is not clear whether the new ailments represent a serious public health menace, an overdose of doctoral whimsy, or merely the end of civilization as we know it.   [Edward G. Nash]

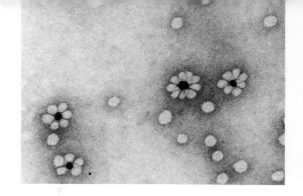

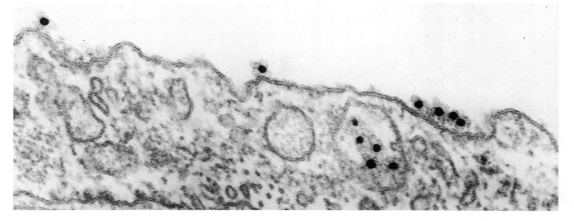

Looking like flower petals when viewed in the electron microscope, fat molecules bind to dark gold particles, *right* (magnified 250,000 times), in a technique that uses gold as a marker to follow the interactions of fat with human cells. The gold-bound fat attaches to receptor sites on the cell membrane, *below* (magnified 160,000 times), and is taken into the cell where it is broken down, in part, into cholesterol.

Medicine

Continued

do not stimulate very high yields of new bone tissue. In the other technique, bone is transferred from one part of the patient's body to another. This produces more new bone tissue than cadaver bone does, but it involves two operations — one to extract bone and another to reimplant it — and greater risk of complications such as infection.

In the new process, doctors use cadaver bone from which the minerals have been removed by adding hydrochloric acid. Normal mineralized bone is often unsuitable for transplantation because it attracts immune-system cells that break it down before new bone tissue has a chance to develop.

The bone, now free of calcium, phosphorus, and magnesium, is sterilized and frozen, and can be stored as a powder until needed. It is then transformed into a paste by adding water. In this form, it can be readily molded to fit the area of the graft. Once in place, the demineralized bone stimulates the body's fibroblasts, or connective-tissue cells, to convert to chondroblasts, which produce cartilage and new bone.

Doctors have used this new technique successfully in 55 bone operations on 44 subjects from 1 to 60 years old. Most of the operations were performed to repair birth defects such as cleft palate.

Hodgkins' disease. Evidence that Hodgkins' disease, a cancer of the lymph system, is transmitted by a virus was reported by epidemiologists Nancy Gutensohn and Philip Cole of Harvard School of Public Health in January 1981. The symptoms of Hodgkins' disease include enlarged lymph glands and giant cells known as Reed-Sternberg cells. Since English physician Thomas Hodgkins first described it in 1832, the disease has fascinated physicians because it has varied forms and can often be treated successfully.

More recently, bits of evidence have suggested that an infection may cause the disease. For example, many cases of the disease are sometimes found in the same geographic area, and several cases may occur in the same household. These facts suggest an infectious cause, but solid data obtained through the

Medicine

Continued

study of a large population has only now become available.

The Harvard researchers studied cases of Hodgkins' disease that had been diagnosed in the Boston-Worcester region of Massachusetts between July 1973 and Dec. 31, 1977. The disease occurs in a double pattern; there is an early — and larger — peak in the number of cases among persons between 15 and 30 years of age and another peak after age 50. The present study involved 262 Hodgkins' patients between the ages of 15 and 34. Two healthy persons of the same age and sex were chosen as controls for each case.

The investigators had theorized that Hodgkins' disease might be produced by a process similar to that which causes polio. Before polio vaccine was commonly used, this paralytic condition resulted from a rare response to a very common viral infection. The older the individual was when first exposed to the virus, the more likely he or she was to develop paralysis. Young members of small or wealthy families — whose status led to some social isolation —

were often unexposed to the infection. Thus, paralytic polio more often struck the affluent and the only child.

The Massachusetts study revealed a similar pattern for Hodgkins' disease. The number of cases was low in large families, particularly among younger children. More affluent youngsters, and those with fewer playmates, were at higher risk. Many victims of Hodgkins' disease also had earlier bouts of infectious mononucleosis, caused by the Epstein-Barr virus.

However, this second finding does not prove that the Epstein-Barr virus also causes Hodgkins' disease. No such virus has ever been found in Hodgkins' patients. Moreover, many victims of Hodgkins' disease have no history of infectious mononucleosis. Perhaps the Epstein-Barr virus and the supposed Hodgkins virus merely share an infectious pattern.

If researchers can find a virus that causes Hodgkins' disease, they may be able to make a vaccine. This might be the first specific preventive for a human cancer.   [Michael H. Alderman]

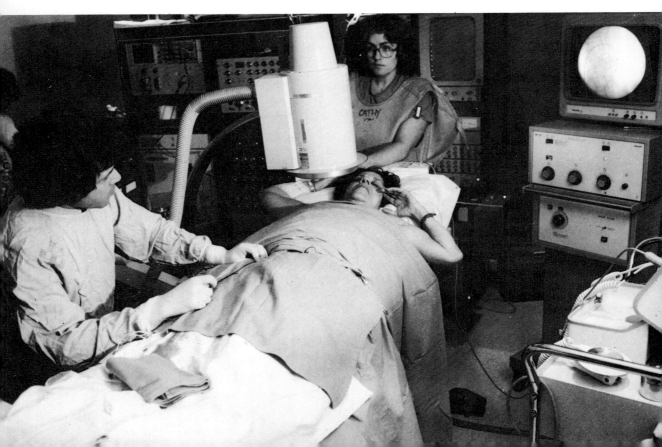

A surgeon guides an electronic probe through a patient's heart, while observing the heart on the screen of a monitoring device. This procedure "maps" the heart and pinpoints weak or damaged areas that may produce ventricular tachycardia, an often deadly form of heart attack.

Medicine

Continued

Surgery. Two new treatments for scoliosis, or curvature of the spine, were being tested in 1980 and 1981. This bone affliction strikes its victims — especially girls — as they approach puberty. Scoliosis can vary in severity from an almost imperceptible curvature to a marked abnormality that results in the so-called hunchback.

Traditional treatment has included the use of a brace for mild cases and surgical implantation of a metal rod along the spine for more severe curvatures. Many young people have to wear braces for years until the bone structure stabilizes. Both methods are difficult for the patient. The brace is cumbersome and limits the patient's activities. Surgery is effective, but implanting a metal rod along the spine is a major procedure and cannot be done without some risk.

Both of the new treatments use electrical stimulation to correct the curvature. Orthopedic surgeon Wallace Bobechko, chief of orthopedic surgery at the Hospital for Sick Children in Toronto, Canada, surgically implants electrodes under the skin. In the other system, developed by orthopedic surgeon John C. Brown at Rancho Los Amigos Hospital in Los Angeles, the electrodes are positioned on the surface of the skin. Both methods stimulate the deep back muscles that help support the spine and hold it upright during adolescent development.

Bobechko's implanted electrodes deliver electrical energy to the deep muscles of the back at night for eight-hour periods, but the treatment does not affect normal sleep. The implanted electrodes are disconnected from the power source during the day so the patient can live a normal life.

In the system using electrodes on the skin surface, the electrodes are removed during the day and the parents can apply them at the appropriate place on their child's back at bedtime. The current is turned on every night for about eight hours.

Preliminary tests on these methods have been highly successful. These represent a significant advance in the treatment of scoliosis. The long-term effects, however, remain to be seen. Spinal corrections made by electrical stimulation may not hold when treatment is stopped. But most orthopedists believe that if the treatment is continued until the young person's skeleton has matured, it will remain stable.

New colitis surgery. Pediatric surgeon Robert L. Telander and internist Jean F. Perrault of the Mayo Clinic in Rochester, Minn., described a new technique in January 1981 called the ileal endorectal pull-through, designed for patients with ulcerative colitis.

Ulcerative colitis and granulomatous colitis affect many children and young adults. Treatment sometimes involves removing the large intestine, including the rectum. Thus, normal bowel function without the rectum and its sphincters, the circular muscles that can be opened and closed at will, is no longer possible. Surgeons must then fashion an ileostomy. They open the intestine and attach a baglike device with an opening on the abdomen to collect intestinal waste. While the patient can live an almost normal life, this procedure presents social problems.

In the new operation, the surgeon removes the colon but leaves the rectum in place. Then the lining is separated from the rectum's muscular wall. This procedure effectively removes the diseased tissue, since ulcerative colitis primarily affects the intestine's lining rather than the wall. Leaving the rectal wall in place makes it possible to preserve the sphincter muscles around the rectal outlet so the patient can retain bowel control.

Finally, the surgeon pulls the small intestine down into the pelvis and passes it through the rectal stump. The small intestine is then sutured to the lining of the anus. One problem with this operation is the high incidence of complications, mainly from infection, during recovery. A temporary ileostomy is usually necessary, but this can be closed later. So far, the procedure has preserved bowel control in 11 of 12 children on whom the operation has been performed.

Steadying the beat. An implanted device that automatically stops the heart muscle helps control potentially fatal heartbeat irregularities, according to an August 1980 report by heart specialist M. Mirowski and 10 co-workers at Sinai Hospital in Baltimore. The team has successfully implanted the in-

Medicine

strument, called a defibrillator, in three patients.

Normally, electrical impulses travel over conducting nerve fibers in the heart, causing coordinated contraction of the heart muscle, or regular heartbeats. This natural system is sometimes disturbed, and irregular beats occur. These irregular rhythms can range from occasional premature or extra beats, which do not seem to be dangerous, to severely irregular heartbeats, which are often fatal.

Clinicians have long used a defibrillator to reverse such arrhythmias. This instrument delivers a controlled electric shock to the heart, stopping all electrical activity and thus halting abnormal electrical conduction. This enables the heart to restart itself with a normal rhythm. But the system is available only in hospitals and depends on the immediate recognition of the abnormal rhythm and prompt action by the medical staff in applying the defibrillating electrodes to the patient's chest. Physicians have been frustrated by their inability to deal with such

"electrical deaths" that occur after patients leave the hospital. In most cases, the heart muscle still has adequate pumping strength and would function if only the abnormal rhythm could be corrected in time.

The automatic defibrillator is encased in titanium and weighs 250 grams (9 ounces). It is powered by lithium batteries that can monitor heartbeat for three years or deliver about 100 defibrillating shocks. The device is implanted surgically and requires two electrodes. One is placed inside the heart to monitor the heart rate. This electrode can detect a serious arrhythmia and automatically activate the defibrillator. The second electrode is attached to the top outside surface of the heart so that the current will travel across the heart muscle between the electrodes. Wires from the electrodes go to the defibrillator which is implanted under the skin of the abdomen.

Next of skin. Human skin grown in the laboratory may someday be used to replace skin lost by burn and wound victims, if clinical trials reported in

A polyurethane artificial heart, developed by surgeons at the University of Utah, has been tested successfully in animals. The two-chambered pump device is driven by a compressed-air turbine.

Medicine

Continued

September 1980 prove successful. Biochemists Eugene Bell and Howard Green of Massachusetts Institute of Technology in Cambridge used two different methods to culture and grow "test-tube" skin.

For many years, the only option in treating patients with severe burns was to use their own skin, taken in thin sheets from unburned parts of the body. However, harvesting it creates a new wound, causing loss of blood and fluid and the danger of infection.

In the past, surgeons have tried to cover burns with skin taken from relatives, cadavers, and animals. But the patient's immune system rejected such foreign grafts in a matter of a few weeks. Researchers have developed a wide variety of artificial skins, but these could not block bacteria from entering the body as well as human skin does.

When their methods are perfected, both Bell and Green will use the patients' own skin so there will be no concern about rejection. Bell, who has worked only with animal skin so far, takes 1-centimeter (0.1-inch) squares of skin and grows them in a nutrient medium. As the skin cells multiply, his test samples have grown into 100-centimeter (15-inch) squares in as little as three weeks.

By growing the samples on forms, he can also mold the skin into shapes. This would allow a skin transplant to be grown to cover specific curved body areas. Bell has successfully cultured animal skin almost identical to the original skin, except that it lacks oil and sweat glands and hair follicles, and transplanted the grafts on test animals.

Green has already started work with human skin cells. He places cells from human skin in an enriched medium in cell-culture dishes. There the cells divide rapidly to form a single layer of skin. By dividing the cultured skin into separate lots, he can grow up to 0.6 square meter (6.5 square feet) of skin from a small culture in two weeks.

These techniques might be applied to other organs or tissues. Vein and artery grafts might be grown around a tube rather than on a flat surface, for example.   [Frank E. Gump]

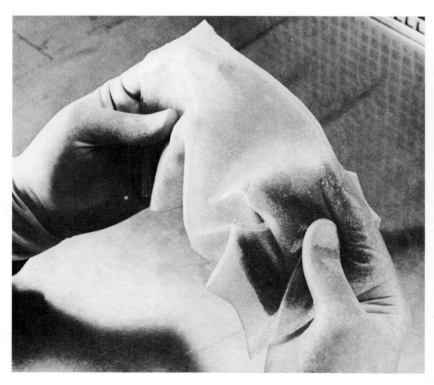

Artificial skin, made of silicone bonded to a polymer material, has been used successfully to cover burn areas and prevent fluid loss and infection while the burn victim's own skin grows back over the wound.

Meteorology

Meteorologists during 1980 and 1981 continued their intensive study of the possible effects on the climate of the rising carbon dioxide (CO_2) level in the earth's atmosphere. Carbon dioxide comprises a small but vital part of the earth's atmosphere — about 0.035 per cent. It helps to maintain the earth's temperature by trapping heat. Sunlight passes through the atmosphere to warm the earth. But the earth also radiates heat back into space. CO_2 absorbs some of this heat and reflects some of it back to the surface — a process called the greenhouse effect.

Scientists have been concerned for some time that the CO_2 level is rising, due to the burning of fossil fuels and various other causes, and that such a rise may change the earth's climate. They fear that by the year 2025, the atmospheric CO_2 content will be double the 290 parts per million that it was in about 1860, before the Industrial Age added so much CO_2 to the earth's atmosphere. This doubling of CO_2 levels could raise the average surface temperature by 2° to 3°C. This could cause a rise in sea levels because of melting polar ice caps, and turn fertile farmlands into hot, barren deserts.

Meteorologists Richard T. Wetherald and Syukuro Manabe of the National Oceanic and Atmospheric Administration's (NOAA) Geophysical Fluid Dynamics Laboratory at Princeton University in New Jersey reported in February 1981 on an extension of their earlier work that involved making models of the climate. They used a general circulation model, a computer program that simulates in detail the three-dimensional behavior of the earth's atmosphere as it changes over time. Scientists study such hypothetical climate situations to understand the real world better.

The researchers constructed an atmospheric model representing three layers in the stratosphere, the region of the atmosphere from 16 to 32 kilometers (10 to 20 miles) above the earth and six layers in the troposphere — the region of the atmosphere between the earth and the stratosphere. The world simulated by the program also included a shallow mixed layer of ocean water — about the top 50 meters (164 feet) of water — and seasonal variations in the amount of sunshine reaching the top of earth's atmosphere.

Wetherald and Manabe found that including the seasonal variations in sunshine in the computer program resulted in about 25 per cent less annual average warming with increased CO_2 levels than was found without considering them. They concluded that this was due to the cooling effects of water vapor, surface snow, and ocean ice on the surface temperature. The effects of these factors were not estimated correctly in models that did not include the seasonal variations in sunshine.

Atmospheric scientist Barry Hunt of the Australian Numerical Meteorology Research Centre in Melbourne reported in February 1981 on the relationship of temperature and clouds to the CO_2 problem. He used a device that simulated the effects of radiation, vertical atmospheric turbulence, and cloudiness on the exchange of heat between the atmosphere and the ocean. Hunt reported that a 10 per cent increase in either the amount or the brightness of low clouds was enough to reflect heat and thus offset the surface warming that would otherwise be caused by doubling the atmospheric CO_2. Hunt also found that the temperature of the sea surface and the layer of water just below it was sensitive to wind changes over the ocean.

Clouds and surface winds were among the more difficult elements to simulate in climate models. This made Hunt wonder if it was realistic to predict that doubled CO_2 would result in an average warming of 2°C to 3°C, as simulations had shown.

Variations in planetary waves. For many years, meteorologists have suspected that there are recurrent weekly or monthly patterns in the large-scale circulation of air around the earth. Understanding these variations could lead to more accurate weather forecasts. Research meteorologists John M. Wallace and David Gutzler of the University of Washington in Seattle reported new support for this view in December 1980. They studied data on atmospheric pressure at sea level and in the mid-atmosphere over mid and high latitudes in the Northern Hemisphere for the winters between 1963 and 1977. Warm air circulates around low-

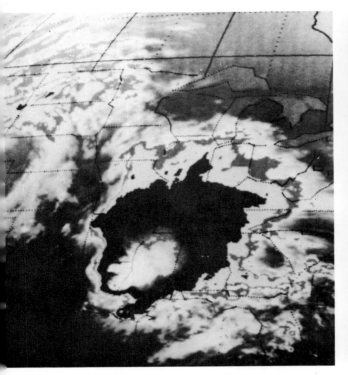 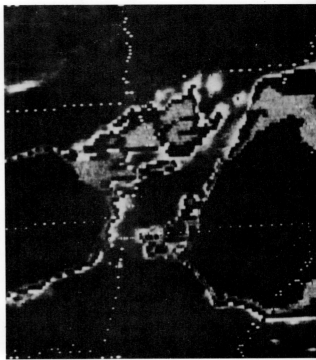

Meteorology

Continued

A new class of storm system that produces thunderstorms in the Midwest is seen in infrared photos, *above,* taken by weather satellites. The vast system covers several states. Two thunderstorms are apparent in the enlarged photo of part of the system, *above right.* Once thought to be small, isolated disturbances, thunderstorms are now considered part of large and probably predictable weather patterns.

pressure areas, or cyclones, bringing storms. Heavier, cold air flows away from high-pressure areas, or anticyclones, bringing clear weather.

Wallace and Gutzler found that there were definite correlations between atmospheric pressure in many widely separated regions from about 40° north latitude to the North Pole. For example, they found that as the Icelandic low-pressure area, a permanent feature near 65° north latitude, grows stronger, the sea-level pressure falls in a broad area near 40° north latitude extending from the East Coast of the United States to the Mediterranean Sea. The reverse is also true. The researchers judged such teleconnections, or relationships at a distance, to be evidence of long-term variations in planetary waves, the long-wavelength air currents that meander around the earth's North Pole. These influence the shorter waves, the air currents and cyclones and anticyclones, that form and move in middle latitudes.

In a related study, Wallace and John Horel, also of the University of Wash-

ington, reported in December 1980 that there are particularly strong teleconnections in the seasonal changes in water temperature, sea-level pressure, and wind circulation between the equatorial Pacific Ocean and higher latitudes. The scientists used data gathered from 1951 to 1978 at weather stations near the equator in the Central Pacific. It confirmed the results of an earlier study by Jacob Bjerknes of the University of California, Los Angeles, showing that sea-surface temperature tends to rise with increased rainfall. Wallace and Horel then showed that changes in the average temperature of the troposphere occur at the same time as seasonal changes in the sea-surface temperature at the equator, not only in the Pacific but all around the earth.

Most importantly, the researchers found well-defined teleconnection patterns between these changes and abnormal winter weather in higher latitudes. They reported that above-normal sea-surface temperatures in the central equatorial Pacific tend to be accompanied by below-normal pres-

A new launcher developed at the National Center for Atmospheric Studies sends out meteorological balloons easily even on stormy days. The tube's fabric cover rotates open to permit a balloon to emerge as it is filling with helium.

Meteorology

Continued

sure over the North Pacific and the Southeastern United States and above-normal pressure over western Canada.

These features closely resemble results found in recent model studies on effects of planetary waves traveling around the earth, reported in September 1980 by theoretician Brian Hoskins of the University of Reading in Great Britain. If other studies confirm this resemblance between observed and modeled seasonal changes, then weather forecasters may be able to predict whether a winter season will be colder, wetter, or longer than usual in North America and Western Europe.

The 1980 heat wave and drought that plagued much of the Eastern United States was the result of what meteorologists call a *block,* a temporary interruption of the normal west-to-east progression of weather systems in the Central United States, by a pattern of nearly stationary highs and lows. This situation can lead to prolonged periods of unusual weather conditions. Unusually high pressure remained over the eastern Pacific Ocean throughout July

and August, and similar blocking ridges were found over eastern Canada, Scandinavia, and eastern Siberia.

As a result, high temperatures during July and August set all-time records in the Eastern United States, with temperatures over 38°C (100°F.) reported almost every day east of the Continental Divide. The precipitation in August was less than 50 per cent of normal over much of the South-Central and Southeastern portions of the country, resulting in widespread crop and livestock losses. Such extreme weather underscored the need to develop accurate long-range forecasts.

Mount Saint Helens in the state of Washington erupted on May 18, 1980, and meteorologists expected that the event would give them a unique opportunity to observe how great quantities of tiny particles in the air would affect the weather. However, they did not learn a great deal, perhaps because not enough smaller particles of ash and other matter were propelled into the stratosphere. See FIREWORKS MOUNTAIN.   [W. Lawrence Gates]

Molecular Biology

Scientists took great strides in 1980 and 1981 toward producing larger quantities of interferon, a protein produced by the body in response to an invasion by a virus. Interferon has been at least partially effective in protecting humans and other animals from viral infection in clinical trials, and preliminary studies suggest that it might even be effective in treating some types of cancer. See THE ELUSIVE PROMISE OF INTERFERON, *Science Year,* 1980.

There are three types of interferon, each named for the type of cell from which it originates. Leucocyte interferon is made by leucocytes, or white blood cells; fibroblast interferon is made by the fibroblasts, cells that compose connective tissue; and immune interferon is made by cells produced by the immune system.

Interferon is scarce and this has been a major obstacle in studying its effects. It is produced only in extremely small quantities by animal cells and is very difficult to purify.

However, molecular biologist Tada Taniguchi of the Japanese Cancer Institute in Kyoto in July 1980 reported that he had used bacteria to make clones, or identical copies, of the gene for human fibroblast interferon. Genes are segments of deoxyribonucleic acid (DNA) that carry instructions for making proteins. These instructions are copied into another molecule, messenger RNA (mRNA) in a process called transcription. A ribosome—a small structure outside the cell nucleus—reads the mRNA's instructions and assembles the protein accordingly.

Taniguchi began the process of making gene clones by treating fibroblasts growing in culture with genetic material from a virus. This made the fibroblasts produce interferon. He then ground up the cells and separated the mRNA that was attached to the ribosomes. He knew that some of this mRNA carried the blueprint for manufacturing interferon. Next, he separated the mRNA into segments by size and injected each fraction into frog eggs. There the frog-egg ribosomes assembled the proteins each mRNA segment called for.

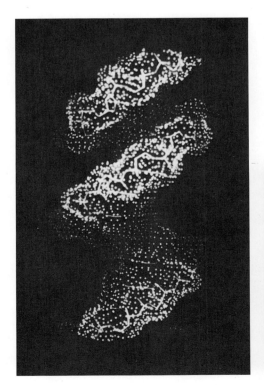

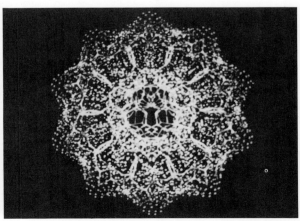

A three-dimensional computer image of a DNA molecule can be viewed from the side, *left,* or the top, *below.* The technique, developed at the University of California, San Francisco, provides a variety of previously unseen views of molecular structures.

Genes
by Machine

The introduction of machines that make genes – those marvelous twisted strands of deoxyribonucleic acid (DNA) that determine how all plants and animals look and function – caused a flurry of excitement in the United States bioengineering community in 1981. Automated DNA synthesizers, as the devices are called, have the potential to greatly accelerate the process of making genetic material for research. They may also manufacture genes to produce such medically valuable proteins as insulin to treat diabetes, interferon to combat viruses, and somatotropin to increase the growth of underdeveloped children.

The DNA molecule is constructed like a spiral staircase with rungs of complex sugar molecules joined to sides of four types of base molecules – adenine, thymine, guanine, and cytosine. These bases serve as a four-letter alphabet that spells out the instructions the cell needs to manufacture proteins. The order of the bases in a DNA strand determines the content of the genetic information carried. This information is coded in a series of three-base "words," each directing a cell to make a particular amino acid. The amino acids are assembled into proteins.

To make genes manually, scientists first isolate the gene for the desired protein. Once they identify its particular sequence of bases, they make duplicates of a fragment of it by constructing a single chain of base chemicals.

The first fragment, usually 12 base pairs long, is added to a mixture of strands of natural DNA in a chemical that forces the DNA strands to separate slightly. The man-made fragment pairs with a complementary fragment in a longer strand of natural DNA, identifying that strand as the desired gene. The entire gene is fished from this genetic soup and spliced into the DNA of the bacterium *Escherichia coli*. These bacteria reproduce or double their numbers every 15 or 20 minutes, thus making many copies of the gene in a short time. *E. coli* then begin to produce the insulin or other proteins for which the inserted gene codes.

Because it is easier to put a gene fragment together from a known sequence of bases than to isolate the natural gene, scientists and pharmaceutical companies make up gene fragments to order. However, manufacturing a gene fragment of only 12 base pairs manually in the laboratory can take up to six months, and commercially synthesized fragments are expensive.

The gene machines have supposedly removed both of these obstacles. Vega Biochemicals of Tucson, Ariz., introduced the first gene machine priced at $49,500 in December 1980, and Bio Logicals of Toronto, Canada, announced a second type priced at $19,000 in January 1981. Other firms in the United States, Denmark, and Great Britain currently have synthesizers under development.

Each synthesizer comes equipped with four columns, each containing a different base. Valves connect a column to vessels holding the other bases and the chemicals needed to hook them to the starter base. The computer is programmed to open the valves in the vessels in a prearranged order to produce the sequence of three bases for a particular amino acid.

Bio Logicals claims that its machine will add one base to a gene sequence every 30 minutes. Vega's synthesizer takes three hours. The complete process necessary to make a 20-base segment, however, takes from 20 to 60 hours. One of the first gene-machine customers, biochemist David Bishop of the University of Alabama School of Medicine in Birmingham, claims that his machine can produce the gene fragments needed for 100,000 experiments for only $400, compared with $6,400 for commercially prepared DNA.

As with any new and complex device, problems exist. Experts say that both the mechanical parts and sophisticated computer programs needed to run the machines still need to be refined. Josef Jiricny of the Imperial Cancer Research Fund in England claims that the machine has a higher rate of error than the test tube.

Once operating problems are solved, the gene machines should enable genetic engineers to move ahead much more rapidly with the work at hand – unraveling nature's multitude of genetic codes, synthesizing valuable quantities of rare human proteins, and perhaps even creating genes to repair birth defects.　　　　[William J. Cromie]

Molecular
Biology
Continued

Taniguchi analyzed the protein produced by each egg in a virus culture for its ability to protect animal cells from infection. He collected all the active mRNA fractions to create DNA. For this he used reverse transcriptase, an enzyme that causes mRNA to make copies of the RNA called cDNA.

Taniguchi next spliced this cDNA into the DNA of the bacterium *Escherichia coli*. To do this, he removed the small circle of bacterial genetic material known as a plasmid. Then he used restriction enzymes, which act as biochemical scissors, to cut a small segment from the plasmid and he inserted the cDNA in its place.

Taniguchi did not know which genes coded for interferon, so he transplanted all cDNA segments into various bacteria. Each of the bacteria reproduced to form a colony of thousands of bacteria. He knew that only 1 in 5,000 bacterial colonies bearing the cDNA actually contained interferon cDNA. To sort out the interferon-producing colonies, he added RNA containing the gene for interferon and, as a control, RNA from cells not exposed to a virus. Bacteria containing interferon cDNA absorb interferon RNA. So he knew that the colonies that absorbed considerably more RNA from the cells exposed to a virus than from the unexposed cells were likely to contain the interferon gene. He was then able to separate a small number of bacterial colonies containing the interferon gene from thousands of *E. coli* colonies.

Other research groups used similar procedures to clone interferon. A group at the Basel Institute for Immunology in Switzerland in October 1980 reported that they had cloned a gene for human leucocyte interferon and, more importantly, that bacterial cells containing the cloned gene had produced minute amounts of interferon. In October 1980, a team at Genentech, Incorporated, in San Francisco announced that they had cloned a leucocyte interferon gene and had subsequently attached to it bacterial controls — segments of DNA that turn on the process of transcription. This caused the gene to code for the production of large amounts of interferon. A group led by biochemist Mark Ptashne at Harvard University in Cambridge,

Mass., announced in July 1980 that they had attached similar bacterial "start" signals to the fibroblast interferon gene.

Finding start signals. Molecular biologists in 1980 and 1981 developed new techniques to locate promoter sequences — DNA sequences that direct an enzyme, RNA polymerase, to transcribe the information on genes to produce proteins. The process of transcription involves three types of RNA — mRNA, which copies the information from the DNA molecule coding the cell's proteins; tRNA, which brings the amino acids, the molecules that comprise proteins, to the ribosome; and rRNA, which helps to assemble the protein from the amino acids. In *E. coli* and all other bacteria studied thus far, which have no cell nuclei, there is only one basic type of RNA polymerase, the enzyme that synthesizes all three types of RNA — mRNA, tRNA, and rRNA.

The RNA polymerase turns on the transcription process after it comes in contact with a set of promoter sequences which, though not identical, are generally easily recognized. They all have the same sequences of molecules located "upstream" on the DNA molecule from the starting point of the messages. (In locating molecules in a DNA strand, scientists use the term *upstream* to refer to all DNA beyond the start point.) Mutations can keep promoters from functioning by changing their molecular sequences so that the RNA polymerase does not recognize them. Scientists have determined the DNA sequence of many promoters cloned on a plasmid and have found mutations in certain regions. If the mutations occur in a promoter region, the gene will not produce a protein. By comparing mutations in several plasmids and the plasmids' ability to produce proteins, researchers can determine where bacterial promoters begin and end.

Scientists have had more difficulty in locating promoters in eucaryotes, organisms that have cells with nuclei, because they have three types of RNA polymerase — forms I, II, and III. These direct the synthesis of rRNA, mRNA, tRNA, and 5sRNA — another ribosomal RNA — respectively. Scientists have been able to clone and determine the molecular sequence of various

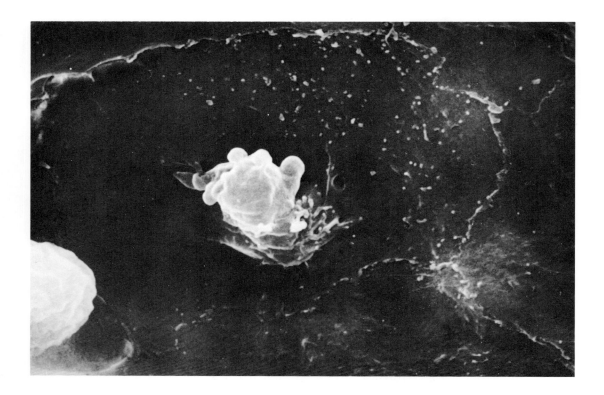

Molecular Biology

Continued

A leukemia cell in a rat (magnified 3,400 times) emerges through a cell in the lining of a tiny vein. It indicates that tumor cells invade the bloodstream by creating pores in the cells rather than by passing through existing spaces between the cells in vessel walls.

genes that attract different forms of RNA polymerase. But, in comparing a number of gene sequences, researchers have found that the molecular sequences in the genes' "start" regions varied with each gene, so they could not find a common promoter region. However, there is one similarity – the Goldberg-Hogness box, a molecular sequence found roughly 20 molecules "upstream" from the point where mRNAs begin to copy the gene.

To overcome the difficulty of finding promoter mutations and thus determining what bases enable the promoters to function, scientists have tried forcing mutations in the laboratory. To do this, they first clone the gene by splicing it into a bacterial plasmid and allowing the bacterium to reproduce. Each new bacterium will carry the gene. They then remove a series of molecules around the gene.

As they remove each segment, they analyze its molecular sequence. Then they return stripped-down genes to a suitable eucaryotic cell to see if the promoter still works. If it does, the

appropriate RNA molecule will transcribe the gene, and they will know that the molecules were not part of the promoter. They continue to remove molecules until the cell stops transcribing the gene. At that point they have found one boundary of the promoter. They repeat this process, making a series of deletions from the other end of the DNA molecule to find the other boundary of the promoter.

A group of molecular biologists at the Carnegie Institution of Washington, D.C., first reported on this technique in the spring of 1980. They made a series of deletions starting from points near the "downstream" or "upstream" ends of a cloned copy of a gene transcribed by one type of tRNA. They recorded the DNA sequence of each section deleted and cloned the remaining genetic material. They then tested each clone for a functioning promoter by injecting it into a frog egg. They found that the segment containing the promoter of the tRNA gene was located in the middle of the gene and not at the upstream end.

Molecular Biology

Continued

In the last year, several groups have analyzed other genes coding for mRNAs. Their findings indicate that, like bacterial promoters, the promoters recognized by RNA polymerase II, which makes mRNA, lie upstream on the eucaryotic genes.

Pierre Chambon of the French National Center for Scientific Research in Paris in March 1981 reported that, when his group of researchers made deletions by approaching a gene from the downstream side, they began to destroy promoter activity when they reached a point some 200 molecules from the beginning of the gene. The exact distance varies from gene to gene and from species to species.

Protein revelations. Two groups of researchers in April 1980 reported the structures of two proteins that react with DNA — the cro repressor of the lambda virus and the catabolite gene-activating protein (CAP) found in *E. coli*. Cro, as a repressor, stops RNA transcription, and CAP, as an activator, starts RNA transcription. In transcription, the double-stranded DNA molecule is unzipped by enzymes to allow the mRNA molecule to copy the strand carrying the information.

Individually, the reports provided the first three-dimensional models of these proteins as well as information on how they might interact with DNA. Together, they cast light on a unique property of DNA discovered in 1979 — its ability to take on different configurations. The original DNA model, now known as B-DNA, is a double helix, or spiral staircase that twists to the right. Scientists have proposed two other models — Z-DNA and left-handed B-DNA — that twist to the left.

Molecular biologists W. F. Anderson, B. W. Matthews, and D. H. Ohlendorf of the University of Oregon in Eugene and Yoshi Takeda of the University of Maryland in Catonsville used X-ray crystallography to determine the cro structure. They projected X rays through a crystal form of the protein. The X rays strike atoms in the crystal and are diffracted onto a film, producing a pattern that indicates the positions of the atoms. These positions are then analyzed mathematically to provide the information necessary to construct a three-dimensional model.

Anderson's team reported that the cro exists as a dimer — a molecule composed of two identical molecular units. They compared the model of the cro molecule to various models of DNA, looking for points at which the cro might attach to the DNA molecule to stop transcription. They found that helices, or spiral forms, protruding from each unit of the dimer, wrapped around a certain section of the B-DNA molecule, locking perfectly into the molecule at that point. Moreover, by attaching at these specific points, the cro protein prevents chemical reactions necessary to transcribe DNA.

Molecular biologists David B. McKay and Thomas A. Steitz of Yale University in New Haven, Conn., also used X-ray crystallography to determine the structure of CAP. CAP combines with a small molecule, cyclic adenosine monophosphate (cAMP), and attaches to certain areas of the DNA molecule to start transcription.

McKay and Steitz made a three-dimensional model of the CAP-cAMP complex, showing the molecule as a dimer. Each of its two units are composed of two other sections hinged together biochemically. In one unit the hinge is open, in the other it is closed. As in the cro molecule, helices protrude from both units.

The researchers tried to fit their model to various DNA models to determine where and how it attached. But, even using the hinges to change the angles of the sections within each unit of the model, they were unable to attach the helices to any points along the B-DNA or Z-DNA models. However, when they matched the CAP-cAMP model to a model of left-handed B-DNA, they found that, along a certain region, the helices locked in.

Because earlier research has indicated that B-DNA originates as a right-handed rather than a left-handed molecule, McKay and Steitz postulated that the section of the DNA molecule to which the complex attaches changes from right-handed to left-handed when CAP combines with it.

Both teams of researchers are engaged in further reseach to determine if their assumptions about the manner in which each protein attaches to DNA are correct.   [Thomas M. Roberts]

Neuroscience

The brain's map of the body can change, according to neuroscientists Michael M. Merzenich, Randall J. Nelson, Jon H. Kaas, and their colleagues at the University of California, San Francisco, and Vanderbilt University, Nashville, Tenn., in a November 1980 report. When nerves connecting a part of the hand to the brain were severed in squirrel and owl monkeys, nerve fibers from nearby parts of the hand established connections with the affected brain areas.

The surface of the body is "mapped" on the cortex — the outer layer of the brain — in a highly detailed but disproportionate way. The amount of the cortex that is devoted to a particular part of the body reflects that part's relative importance in providing information about the outside world to the brain. The hand, for example, has much more representation in the cortex than does the back.

In a series of studies, the California researchers examined the areas of the monkey cortex devoted to the hand by recording the electrical responses from microelectrodes inserted, under anesthesia, into different parts of the cortex. Lightly stimulating different parts of the hand produced these responses, which formed a pattern, or map, of the brain areas devoted to the hand. When the scientists cut the median nerve, one of the three nerves in the hand that send sensory information to the brain, they found, as expected, that stimulating the median nerve areas of the hand no longer produced responses in the appropriate cortical areas.

However, these areas of the brain soon began to respond again, but to stimulation from other parts of the hand. The brain's map of the hand had changed as other parts of the hand sent their impulses to the disconnected cortical area. This new understanding of how the brain processes sensation may prove important in treating human patients with nerve damage.

Leech links. Neuroscientists Birgit Zipser and Ronald McKay of Cold Spring Harbor Laboratory in New York reported in February 1981 that they have distinguished specific sets of

Small holes in nerve cell endings open, expand, and disappear, as nerves release a neurotransmitter, or chemical message carrier, to relay an impulse to another nerve.

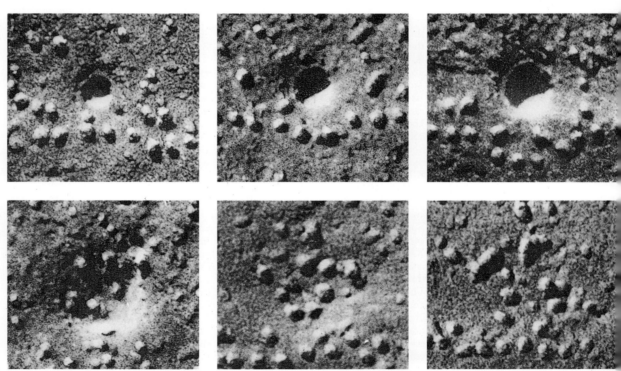

"It's finally happening, Helen. The hemispheres of my brain are drifting apart."

Neuroscience

Continued

nerve cells in the leech that are involved in particular kinds of sensory and motor function. They used a new technique that involves developing monoclonal antibodies to this animal's entire nervous system. See USING CANCER TO FIGHT DISEASE.

The leech's nervous system is made up of a chain of 34 similar — some identical — bundles called ganglia, each containing about 400 nerve cells. Some types of nerve cells are involved in the same motor or sensory functions, no matter which ganglion they are in.

To identify the various types of nerve cells, the scientists made monoclonal antibodies, which react only to specific molecules on a cell. They fused white blood cells, each bearing a specific antibody, with cancerous cells that reproduce rapidly. These hybrid cells made clones, or multiple copies, of themselves. The investigators tested more than 400 cell lines and found 41 antibodies that reacted to particular sets of nerve cells and connecting fibers in the various ganglia. For example, one antibody tagged four of the cells that process pain in each ganglion, thus tracing a pain network. Another bound to various cells in different ganglia known to be involved in the reproductive system.

Some cells previously identified as part of the pressure-sensing process reacted to several different antibodies. This suggested the existence of complex chemical circuits, similar to electrical circuits, that bring different nerve cells together in varying patterns as the animal interacts with its environment. The use of monoclonal antibodies gives neuroscientists a new way to study the cellular basis of nerve development and interaction and the infinitely more complex — and less well known — molecular basis as well.

Short-wave reading. Neuroscientists E. Roy John, Hansook Ahn, and their associates at New York University Medical Center's Brain Research Laboratories in New York City have increased the usefulness of measuring brain waves. They reported in December 1980 on their efforts to simplify the interpretation of electroencephalograph (EEG) recordings and thereby make

Neuroscience

them more useful in diagnosing possible brain damage.

Using computer-processed data from EEG records of hundreds of children of different ages in the United States and Sweden – all measured in the same way – the New York researchers derived mathematical equations that provide reliable standards of normal EEG patterns for children from 6 to 16 years old. The measurements appeared to be independent of cultural or ethnic background. Researchers found no differences among test groups of urban, suburban, rural, middle-class, working-class, black, white, male, and female children.

This rapid computerized diagnostic system compares a 60-second EEG sample from a patient with the previously established norm. It thus provides an objective, simple, and inexpensive way to screen for brain damage in children who, because of behavior or learning problems, are suspected of having such damage.

Nose for nostalgia. Treatment with arginine vasopressin, a peptide or small protein that is synthesized naturally in the brain, can improve human memory, according to a February 1981 report by neuroscientists Herbert Weingartner, Philip Gold, and their colleagues at the National Institute of Mental Health in Bethesda, Md. In a series of experiments with small groups of volunteers, the investigators found significant improvements in scores on standard tests of learning, retention, and recall in six normal subjects who received the vasopressin in a nasal spray compared with a similar number treated with a placebo, a dummy spray. Similar improvements were found in a group of six depressed patients. Preliminary trials of the treatment with senile patients suffering from memory problems were also promising.

Scientists do not know how vasopressin affects memory, but continuing research on this and similar natural substances may help answer fundamental questions about the mechanisms of memory and learning, and may produce a therapy for treating learning defects, as well.   [George Adelman]

Nutrition

The widely held belief that coronary disease is related to cholesterol and fats in the diet received a statistical boost when the results of a 20-year study were reported in January 1981. Preventive medicine specialist Richard B. Shekelle and his associates at Rush-Presbyterian-St. Luke's Medical Center in Chicago and other research centers analyzed the causes of death among men whose diet, health, and life style were first evaluated in 1957.

The researchers studied 1,900 male employees of the Western Electric Company in Chicago who were 40 to 50 years old when the study started. During the first two years of the study, they gathered information on the workers' intake of calories, cholesterol, saturated and unsaturated fats, and other elements of diet. They also noted body weight, levels of cholesterol in the blood, smoking habits, alcohol consumption, and other health variables. In the 1981 report, the researchers compared these data with the causes of death of the 453 workers who died between 1958 and 1978.

The researchers reported that the amount of cholesterol in the diet was positively related to the level of cholesterol in the blood during the 1957-1958 period. The risk of death from coronary heart disease increased as dietary cholesterol went up. But the more polyunsaturated fats in a worker's diet, the less risk there was of coronary heart disease. The amount of saturated fats in the diet was not significantly related to death from heart disease.

Wait before weaning. Babies can be breast-fed exclusively for at least six months after birth without adversely affecting rates of growth and weight gain, according to a 1980 study of 96 infants in the Washington, D.C.-Baltimore area. Nutritionists Chung Hae Ahn and William C. MacLean, Jr., of Johns Hopkins University Medical School in Baltimore found that these exclusively breast-fed infants grew at rates comparable to the standards established by the National Center for Health Statistics (NCHS).

For generations, there have been disputes regarding how long an infant

Fewer Pumps for the Portly?

Are fat people fat because they eat too much? Or are they at the mercy of some quirk of metabolism, the body's process for converting food into energy? In most cases, we have no definitive answer, but researchers are increasingly considering the possibility that metabolism makes some people more likely to become fat.

Obesity may be viewed as a disorder in the body's energy balance. Consider a body equation with energy intake — food — on one side, and energy expenditure on the other. When the two are equal, body weight does not change. But when energy intake exceeds energy expenditure, net energy gain occurs, and the body stores the excess energy as fat — the one tissue in the body that is specialized for that purpose. Excessive fat storage may result from excessive energy intake, low energy expenditure, or a combination of the two.

For years, most researchers tried to understand why obese individuals took in too many calories, concentrating on the factors that control appetite and food intake. Now some are looking at the equally important other side of the equation, the role of energy expenditure in determining how much energy is stored as fat.

Recently, some investigators, including myself and others at Harvard-Thorndike Laboratory in Boston's Beth Israel Hospital, studied possible biochemical differences between overweight and thin individuals that might unbalance the energy-expenditure side of the equation. We were particularly interested in a group of obese individuals whose food intake did not seem excessive. One interesting difference we found involves the function of a very important enzyme called sodium-potassium-ATPase that is found in nearly all cells.

Sodium-potassium-ATPase which is known as the sodium-potassium pump, splits adenosine-triphosphatase (ATP), the cell's main energy supply molecule, and releases the energy it contains. Some of this released energy is dissipated as heat, but most is used to pump electrically charged atoms from one side of the cell membrane to the other. For each molecule of ATP that is broken down, three molecules of sodium are pumped from the inside of the cell to the outside of the cell, and two molecules of potassium are pumped from the outside of the cell to the inside of the cell.

The body uses a certain amount of energy just to maintain itself. A substantial part of that energy is consumed by the sodium-potassium pump. The pump's numerous functions include maintaining high potassium and low sodium levels in the cell and transporting many other small molecules in and out of the cell. The pump also plays an important role in producing heat in warm-blooded animals.

To test the theory that some individuals are overweight because they expend energy poorly, thus altering their energy equation despite normal energy intake, we began to explore the sodium-potassium pump as the possible site of a biochemical abnormality related to obesity.

Researcher Mario DeLuise measured the levels and activity of the sodium-potassium-ATPase enzyme in red blood cells. He found that a test group of obese people had fewer of these molecules in their red blood cell membranes, and also had lower potassium-pumping activity in their red cells when compared to a control group of thin people. There was a very significant average difference between the enzyme levels in the obese and thin groups. Individual levels often overlapped between these two groups, so enzyme levels cannot predict obesity absolutely. But in general, the more obese the individual, the lower were the levels of the enzyme.

In addition, we noted that major weight reduction by dieting did not increase the enzyme level. This may indicate that the enzyme defect is a primary biochemical defect that results in obesity and not simply a consequence of obesity or over-eating.

We hope to study other types of cells and determine whether different groups of obese people have the same defect. We must also learn the underlying cause of the altered enzyme level in obese persons. Many experiments will be needed before we know whether inadequate sodium-potassium-ATPase, the sodium-potassium pump, is really a cause—or merely just one consequence —of obesity.   [Jeffrey S. Flier]

should be fed only breast milk. In the late 1950s and 1960s, pediatricians advised mothers to give their babies strained foods at 2 to 6 weeks. They cited studies of exclusively breast-fed infants in impoverished countries that seemed to indicate supplemental food was necessary by the age of 6 months to prevent a slowing of growth.

However, the infants studied by Ahn and MacLean remained above average in growth through the sixth month. Those infants who were breast-fed exclusively through the ninth or 10th month grew more rapidly than 25 per cent of all infants as measured against NCHS figures. The findings give scientific support to the practice of exclusive breast-feeding for six months, which is now commonly done in the United States. The researchers suggested that weaning should be delayed for the first year in developing countries because the foods usually used in weaning in those areas are associated with a decrease in nutrient intake and an increase in illness from diarrheal disease.

Double portions. The first evidence that genes might regulate the amounts of various nutrients different people prefer in their diets came from studies of 13 sets of *monozygotic* (one-egg, or identical) twins and 10 sets of *dizygotic* (two-egg, or fraternal) twins by J. Wade, J. Milner, and M. Krondl of the Department of Nutrition and Food Science, University of Toronto, Canada. They reported in February 1981 that genes strongly influence the percentage of calories consumed as proteins and carbohydrates and the total amount of carbohydrates in the daily diet.

The researchers collected food records for three days from 23 pairs of female Caucasian twins, who ranged in age from 19 to 58 years old. Each set of twins had lived in the same household as children but are now living in separate households as adults. The patterns and amounts of proteins and carbohydrates consumed by members of monozygotic twin pairs were remarkably alike, especially the amount of carbohydrates that they ate daily. However, there was no such similarity in food intake by the dizygotic twins, strongly suggesting a genetic influence.

Stout hearts on ice. A study reported in December 1980 shed light on why the Eskimos of Greenland have such a low incidence of acute myocardial infarction, or heart attack. Nutritionists H. Bang, J. Dyerberg, and H. Sinclair of the Clinical Chemical Department, Ålborg Hospital North, Ålborg, Denmark, compared the Eskimos' diet in northwestern Greenland with the diets of Danes, who have a much higher rate of heart attack.

Seal and fish are the major foods in the Eskimo diet. They account for the significantly higher intake of polyunsaturated fatty acids in the Eskimos' diet than in that of the Danes. These fatty acids are associated with decreased risk of heart disease.

Eskimo and Danish diets also differ in the class of polyunsaturated fats that they eat. Eskimos consume significantly more of the linolenic class of fatty acids, while Danes eat more linoleic fatty acids. Eicosapentenoic acid, one of the linolenic fatty acids, forms a substance that hampers blood clot formation. Certain kinds of blood clots in the circulatory system can trigger heart attacks. Moreover, the linoleic acid is the substance from which arachidonic acid is formed. Arachidonic acid is indirectly involved in a process that can cause blood clotting. Thus, a high intake of eicosapentenoic acid and low intake of linoleic acids may account for the Eskimos' low level of heart disease.

Salt in the cellar. In a December 1980 review of 415 natural and artificial food additives that had previously been regarded as safe, the Food and Drug Administration (FDA) found only a dozen or so that required further study to determine their safety. The rest were judged harmless.

The FDA suggested that the long-term effects of caffeine; BHA and BHT, two widely used preservatives; and such nutrient additives as iron, zinc, and vitamins A and D be looked at more closely (see PUBLIC HEALTH).

The biggest loser was salt. The FDA would like to see less salt in the diet because of its role in increasing hypertension, or high blood pressure. An outright ban or restriction on salt as a food additive in processed foods is unlikely, but the FDA is considering such indirect action as requiring more information about the salt content on food labels.   [Judith J. Wurtman]

Oceanography

Experimenters who took part in a series of record-breaking simulated dives at Duke University in 1981 significantly extended the ability of human beings to work deep in the ocean under high pressure. Peter B. Bennett, professor of anesthesiology and director of the F. G. Hall Environmental Laboratory at the Duke Medical Center in Durham, N.C., reported on the dives in May.

Commercial divers Steven Porter and Leonard Whitlock of Oceaneering International Incorporated in Houston, and former United States Navy diver Eric Kramer made the record-breaking Atlantis III simulated dives, which extended the depth to which divers can descend without suffering ill effects, in January and February. Their success depended upon breathing the correct mixture of gases.

Divers breathe compressed air stored under pressure in tanks. A diver takes in more molecules of air per breath from the tank than he would on land. Since the air we breathe is more than three-fourths nitrogen, a diver takes in a great deal of nitrogen. Divers breath-ing ordinary compressed air at great depths can become victims of a condition called nitrogen narcosis.

Until the 1960s, this narcotic effect of large amounts of nitrogen limited divers to depths of less than 60 meters (200 feet). At the increased pressures below this depth, they could not think clearly. Substituting helium for nitrogen in the compressed air mix enabled divers to reach 300 meters (1,000 feet), but also caused high-pressure nervous syndrome (HPNS), a condition that includes tremors, dizziness, nausea, vomiting, sleepiness, fatigue, and loss of muscle control.

Bennett laid the groundwork that led to the Atlantis series of dives. He found in 1973 that he could control the incapacitating effects of HPNS by returning some nitrogen to the divers' breathing mixture. Bennett then simulated dives in a laboratory pressure chamber to determine the most effective breathing mixtures for extended stays in the deep ocean. He experimented until he reduced the worst effects of HPNS. Atlantis I and II divers reached simulated

Wearing a new armored diving suit that protects her from water pressure and has its own air supply, marine botanist Sylvia Earle works at 385 meters (1,260 feet) below the Pacific Ocean surface, tethered only to a submersible. Hers was the deepest solo ocean dive and the first one in a self-sustaining suit with no surface line.

Oceanography

Continued

Small areas containing coral reefs, *above,* in the Caribbean Sea were fenced off for study of the damage that sea urchins do to the reefs. After many years, coral in unfenced area, *above right,* was so eaten away that it resembled giant mushrooms and could be toppled by waves. Loss of coral reefs leaves islands unprotected and removes a haven for many types of marine life.

depths of 460 meters (1,509 feet) and 650 meters (2,132 feet), respectively.

The crucial test of Bennett's theories came in January and February 1981. The divers in the Atlantis III simulated diving series maintained a breathing mixture containing 10 per cent nitrogen for the entire dive, instead of changing mixtures as earlier groups had done. They also took much longer to "descend" than did earlier groups.

The Atlantis III experimenters increased the pressure in the diving chamber over a period of five days to what it would be at a 600-meter (2,000-foot) depth. Atlantis I and II divers had experienced a decline in their ability to work soon after the simulated descent. But the more slowly pressurized Atlantis III group did not have this problem. However, the divers had trouble doing arithmetic problems, which indicated that they had difficulty concentrating.

The diving team spent a total of 11 days in the pressure chamber at simulated depths somewhat greater than 600 meters; 7 days at around 650 me-

ters (2,132 feet); and 1 day at 686 meters (2,250 feet), establishing new world simulated diving records. They also showed that heavy work can be done at these pressures without *dyspnea,* or difficult breathing, and that divers can go deeper and stay longer than scientists had believed possible.

Seeing the deep blue sea. Warren A. Hovis and Dennis K. Clark of the National Oceanic and Atmospheric Administration's (NOAA) National Environmental Satellite Service and their colleagues reported an analysis of *Nimbus-7* scanner images in October 1980. Throughout the 1970s, scientists had worked to develop a method that would let them study ocean color as an indicator of the organisms an area of the ocean contains without actually visiting the area by boat. Rather than the usual shades of the sea surface, ocean color refers to the color spectrum of the water just beneath the surface.

The color of this deeper layer of water is determined in great part by its concentrations of phytoplankton—microscopic plants that are the first link in the ocean food chain. Because phytoplankton supports all higher marine life, and therefore affects all commercial fishing efforts, more accurate information about the annual crop may lead to improved methods of using and managing fisheries and checking the excessive phytoplankton.

Hovis and Clark were among the scientists whose work preceded the National Aeronautics and Space Administration (NASA) launch of *Nimbus-7* on Oct. 23, 1978. Still the only satellite designed to study living marine sources, it carries a coastal zone color scanner (CZCS) to measure the concentrations of phytoplankton pigment in the ocean. For two years, the CZCS gathered data from the ocean area off the southwest coast of Florida.

Rocks of ages. Geologists Robert E. Sheridan of the University of Delaware in Newark and Felix Gradstein of the Geological Survey of Canada, working on the drill ship *Glomar Challenger,* reported in December 1980 that they had recovered the oldest rocks yet found in the deep ocean. They estimat-

ed that the rocks, which are buried under 1.6 kilometers (1 mile) of sediment, are 145 million to 155 million years old. This means they were formed at about the time North America began to pull apart from Africa, creating the North Atlantic Ocean.

To obtain the samples, *Glomar* scientists drilled and cored for 60 days about 482 kilometers (300 miles) east of Fort Lauderdale, Fla. Drilling in water 5 kilometers (3 miles) deep required special equipment. Drill bits wore out after grinding only a few hundred meters into the hard sedimentary rock, and the scientists had to devise a way to replace them. They lowered onto the sea floor a surface casing and re-entry cone — a pipe attached to a large metal cone-shaped platform. They also lowered a casing string — a series of several pipes — 521 meters (1,720 feet) long, the longest ever run into the sea floor. The device kept the sides of the drilling hole from caving in and let the scientists lower their coring devices as often as needed. [Feenan D. Jennings and Lauriston R. King]

Physics

Atomic and Molecular Physics. Physicists Stephen R. Lundeen and Francis M. Pipkin of Harvard University in Cambridge, Mass., reported in January 1981 the results of experiments on energy states of atoms that do not completely agree with predictions of quantum electrodynamics (QED). This is the generally accepted theory that describes mathematically the forces between elementary particles such as electrons, positrons (positively charged electrons), and protons, and their interaction with electromagnetic radiation.

According to QED, the distance of an electron's orbit from the nucleus depends upon the atom's energy state — the greater the energy, the higher the orbit. An electron can jump to a higher orbit if it absorbs a sufficient amount of energy from a bundle of radiation called a photon.

The two scientists measured the Lamb-Retherford shift, the energy difference between the second lowest energy state of hydrogen atoms and the third lowest. The Lamb-Retherford shift is proportional to the frequency,

or rate of vibration, of the electromagnetic radiation that causes the electron to jump. Physicists express the value of the shift in terms of this frequency.

Lundeen and Pipkin sought to verify precise calculations made by two theorists. Glen W. Erickson of the University of California, Davis, calculated a value of 1,057.930 megahertz, or millions of cycles per second, in 1971 and Peter J. Mohr of the University of California, Berkeley, computed a figure of 1,057.884 megahertz in 1975. However, the Harvard experimenters' value, which they believe is accurate to 0.001 per cent, was 1,057.845 megahertz.

The Harvard researchers used a sophisticated atomic beam method to determine this frequency so that they could calculate the shift. They created a beam of hydrogen nuclei, which are single protons, and boosted their energy in an accelerator to levels of either 55,100 or 106,800 electron volts. This proton beam then passed through a chamber filled with nitrogen gas. Some of the positively charged protons pulled negatively charged electrons away from the nitrogen molecules, thus becoming hydrogen atoms — assemblies of one proton and one electron.

Many of these new atoms were in the second-lowest energy state, from which they cannot easily return to the lowest state. The atoms in this state then passed through a chamber where photons of two precisely tuned fields of microwaves moved some of the atoms to an energy state where they were no longer trapped.

Next, the researchers indirectly measured how effectively this particular microwave frequency energized atoms. Rather than measure the energized atoms, they measured the atoms that the microwaves had not energized.

To do this, they sent the energized and nonenergized atoms through an electrical field that allowed the nonenergized atoms to leave their trapped state by radiating photons. The amount of energy radiated depended upon the number of nonenergized atoms. Lundeen and Pipkin measured the energy and calculated the number of nonenergized atoms that had ra-

diated it, and then repeated the experiment at various frequencies.

Finally, they identified the frequency that left the least amount of atoms nonenergized, leading to the least amount of radiation — in other words, the frequency that energized the greatest number of atoms. The small differences between their value and the numbers that Erickson and Mohr had calculated theoretically indicate a possible flaw in QED, but the results are not accurate enough to be conclusive.

Fine structure. West German physicists Klaus von Klitzing of the University of Würzburg and G. Dorda of Siemens Research Laboratory in Munich, and British physicist M. Pepper of Cambridge University in England published results of a promising new technique for measuring the fine structure constant in August 1980. Physicists may soon use the technique to make more accurate measurements of this number, which enables scientists to calculate such things as small differences in atoms' energy levels and the charge on the electron.

Universal cross-beamed apparatus at Lawrence Berkeley Laboratory has a laser (in box at left) and a molecular beam generator (cylinder at right) aimed precisely at a point inside a machine that measures molecular masses. This provides information on chemical reactions that occur when beams collide.

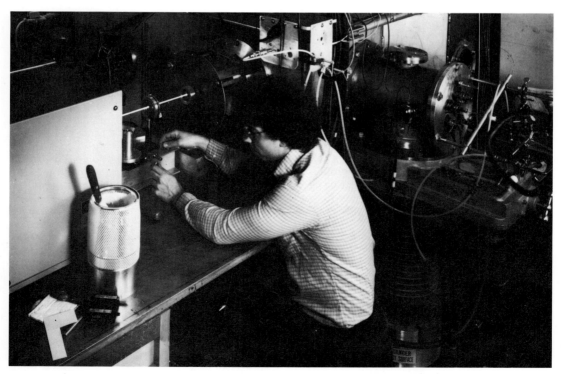

Physics

Continued

Von Klitzing and his colleagues experimented with two electromagnetic phenomena known as Hall voltage and the quantum energy behavior of a two-dimensional electron gas, a thin layer of electrons. Hall voltage results from passing an electrical current through a conductor in a magnetic field perpendicular to the conductor. Hall voltage is perpendicular to both the current and the magnetic field. The quantum energy behavior of a two-dimensional electron gas is its tendency to gain and lose energy in quanta, or bundles. That is, the energy level increases and decreases in sharp steps, rather than gradually.

Von Klitzing and his group used the electrons on the surface of a metal-oxide-semiconductor field effect transistor (MOSFET) as their electron gas. They connected electrodes to the ends of the MOSFET and switched on electrical coils that generated a strong magnetic field perpendicular to the MOSFET. Next, they applied a voltage across the electrodes, causing a current of one-millionth of an ampere to flow through the electron gas along the MOSFET surface.

Ordinarily, the flowing electrons that make up the current would travel almost directly from one electrode to the other under the influence of the electrode voltage. However, the strong magnetic field pushed the electrons to one side of the MOSFET, establishing a Hall voltage. The researchers gradually raised the electrode voltage, thus increasing its influence over electron flow by overcoming the effect of the magnetic field and changing the paths of the electrons that flowed along the MOSFET surface. Although the scientists increased electrode voltage uniformly, the resulting change in flow paths decreased the Hall voltage in steps, because of the quantum energy behavior of the two-dimensional electron gas. The scientists then applied the values of the Hall voltage and the current to an equation that enabled them to calculate the fine structure constant. Their preliminary value agreed with the generally accepted value of the fine structure constant. If improved experiments are successful, these researchers will obtain an even more accurate value. [Karl G. Kessler]

Elementary Particles. After nearly a decade of stunning new discoveries and rapid advances in theory, particle physics enjoyed a breathing spell during the year ending in May 1981. The new picture of subatomic matter holds that most so-called elementary particles, including the protons and neutrons found in atomic nuclei, are not really elementary after all. Instead, they are composed of smaller units called quarks that are linked together by a force transmitted by "messenger" particles known as gluons. The year's most significant experiments merely confirmed these theories.

No surprises. A team of 67 physicists from eight universities in the United States, experimenting at the Cornell Electron-Positron Storage Ring (CESR) at Cornell University in Ithaca, N.Y., announced in July 1980 that they had evidence for the existence of the first combinations of the b quark, with the u and d varieties of quark that are the building blocks of protons and neutrons. A spokesman for the group, reporting on the discovery, emphasized that "the most surprising thing is that there are no surprises."

The b quark was discovered in 1977 as a component of the upsilon particle. The upsilon consists of a b linked to its own antimatter opposite, an anti-b. This kind of combination of a quark with its own antiquark is easy to create at rings like CESR that produce head-on collisions of electrons with their antimatter opposites, positrons. The electron and positron annihilate each other in a flash of pure energy, and much of this energy then changes back into particles that include such a quark-antiquark pair.

But this kind of pair can be difficult to study, because quark and antiquark also annihilate each other quickly, converting their mass to energy before they have had a chance to reveal the properties that make them different from other quarks. When quark and antiquark are of different types, however, they cannot annihilate each other until one changes to match the other's type.

The theory of quark behavior holds that a b quark rapidly converts itself into a c quark. The c must convert itself into an s quark, and the s to a u, as its antimatter partner becomes an anti-u, before annihilation can take place. The CESR experiment gave indications that these reactions had occurred.

News from PETRA. "No surprises" was also the word during the year from the world's foremost facility for studying electron-positron collisions, the PETRA accelerator at the DESY Electron Synchrotron Laboratory near Hamburg, West Germany. PETRA produces head-on collisions with a combined energy of nearly 40 billion electron volts (GeV), the most powerful reaction of this type in the world.

No more than a few times per hour, an electron and positron in PETRA annihilate each other, thus producing quarks, antiquarks, and gluons. These particles never emerge by themselves because strong forces quickly link them together into composite particles. In experiments during the year, PETRA physicists proved conclusively that quarks are electrically charged particles whose diameter is at most 0.1 per cent as large as a proton's diameter.

But even more significant were PETRA's findings on the properties of gluons. Scientists cannot observe these particles directly. Instead, they observe the effects when the energy of a gluon is converted to mass in the form of particles moving in almost the same direction as the original gluon. The particles form a jet of tracks in particle detectors, and physicists can reconstruct the approximate motion of the gluon by examining these jets.

Proof of the existence of gluons rested on a mere dozen examples of this process in 1979, but the sample grew to more than 2,000 by the summer of 1981, enough to test many of the detailed properties of gluons. For example, PETRA researchers had determined by the fall of 1980 that gluons are polarized in a manner similar to ordinary light. This is a crucial discovery, because the theory that predicted their existence also insists that they resemble photons, particles of light.

Quark light. A new technique for probing quark behavior emerged from experiments conducted between 1979 and 1981 at the Intersecting Storage Ring (ISR) at the multinational European Center for Nuclear Research (CERN) near Geneva, Switzerland, and at Fermi National Accelerator

Laboratory (Fermilab) in Batavia, Ill. At the ISR, intense beams of protons collide nearly head-on at combined energies of up to 62 GeV. These colliding beams produce the most powerful proton collisions available at any laboratory, including Fermilab, where 400-GeV proton beams strike stationary targets.

These collisions produce a variety of particles, including photons. The new technique for studying quarks is based on observing these photons. The photons are similar to those of ordinary visible light but have several billion times more energy.

Physicists believe that protons contain three quarks, each of which carries a fractional electrical charge. When two protons collide, they are subject to such violent forces that any particle carrying an electrical charge will radiate photons of light.

The quarks themselves cannot emerge from the collision, because the gluons bind them in an unbreakable grip. But the photons escape, and scientists can measure their energy and direction with particle detectors to learn about the motions of the quarks that produced them. This gives valuable information about the nature of the gluon force.

A multinational team of physicists led by L. Resvanis of the University of Athens in Greece developed the technique at the ISR in 1979. A group of physicists from Fermilab and Johns Hopkins University in Baltimore observed such photons at Fermilab in April 1981.

Are protons immortal? Japanese and Indian investigators reported in April 1981 that they might have seen evidence of proton decay. One of the most important unanswered questions in physics is whether protons, the basic building blocks of nuclei, are immortal or whether they simply live to a fantastically ripe old age. Some theorists have suggested that protons, like radioactive nuclei, are unstable, with a half-life of 10^{31} years. This means that half the protons presently in the universe would have disappeared within 10^{31} years.

This half-life would not affect the stability of matter over any familiar time scale. The universe itself is estimated to be only 10^{10} years old, so nearly all the protons created at its

Physics

Continued

Photomultiplier tubes mounted on poles inside one of the units of the Fly's Eye array of cosmic-ray detectors in Utah amplify light reflected from a mirror at the bottom of the detector. The mirror collects the faint fluorescence from nitrogen atoms that is triggered by cosmic rays.

beginning are still with us, according to these theorists. But one proton in several tons of matter could disintegrate each year, releasing about a hundred times as much energy as any known form of radioactivity.

Experiments to test this prediction must be conducted in mines or tunnels deep in the earth, because the incessant hail of cosmic rays at ground level would produce false signals that would mask the disintegration of a proton. The joint Japanese-Indian detector buried 2,440 meters (8,000 feet) deep in the fabled Kolar Gold Fields of southern India produced a tantalizing hint that this prediction might be true. S. Miyake of the University of Tokyo announced that, in four months of observation, this 137-metric-ton (150-short-ton) "sandwich" of steel and particle detectors had recorded three unexplained signals whose energy roughly coincided with that expected from proton disintegration.

This detector's picture of these signals is much too crude for physicists to identify them clearly as products of proton decay. And in any event, few physicists would be ready to accept the theory of proton instability on the basis of just three examples. So Miyake does not claim to have discovered proton decay, but merely a tantalizing hint that the theory might be true.

To prove that the proton is unstable would be momentous, because the theory that predicts this instability rests on two very significant assumptions. One is that quarks are truly pointlike objects, with no size. The other holds that all of the forces that operate inside the atom are simply different forms of a single master force. Thus, proof of proton instability could spell the realization of two of science's most cherished goals — to find the ultimate building blocks of matter, and to understand the forces that create them and link them together.

Several larger U.S. and European detectors are under construction, so we should know within a few years whether this goal has at last been realized, or whether it remains an impossible dream.　　　　[Robert H. March]

Physics

Continued

Nuclear Physics. Physicists Ingo Sick of the University of Basel in Switzerland and Donal Day and James S. McCarthy of the University of Virginia in Charlottesville reported in September 1980 that they used beams of high-energy electrons at the Stanford Linear Accelerator Center (SLAC) in California to determine the momentum of nucleons—neutrons and protons—in the helium nucleus. No scientist had ever before measured the distribution of momentum—mass times velocity—of nucleons within the nucleus so precisely. The distribution of momentum in a nucleus is determined by the so-called strong force between nucleons, so the measurements made by these scientists provide valuable new insight into this nuclear force.

The generally accepted theory of the nuclear force matches experimental evidence showing that there is a weak attractive force between two nucleons a long distance from each other. However, no theory explains the strongly attractive force at closer distances, comparable with the average separation between nucleons within nuclei of ordinary matter. And neither theoreticians nor experimentalists know the strength of the strong force between two or more nucleons that are extremely close. But physicists know that this force must be repulsive. Otherwise, an unopposed attractive force would be able to pull all of the nucleons closer and closer together so that eventually the entire nucleus would collapse.

If the force were sufficiently repulsive at short range, some nucleons would have extremely high momentum. These high-momentum nucleons could be measured experimentally, enabling scientists to deduce the strength of the short-range repulsive force.

To make such measurements, Sick and his colleagues accelerated electrons and directed them at helium-3 nuclei, which have two protons and one neutron. Next, they measured the angles and energies of the electrons that were scattered, or deflected, from the nuclei. Finally, from this information the scientists calculated the distribution of nucleon momentum.

Physics

Continued

Abominable nucleus?
Iron nucleus enters an emulsion (top left) and strikes an atom, losing nucleons – neutrons and protons – thus becoming a chromium nucleus. This collides three more times before leaving as a helium nucleus. Distances between normal collisions (bottom) average about 9 centimeters (3.5 inches), but occasionally there is an extremely short distance (center), as if a collision had changed a nucleus into a huge unknown object.

Experiments such as Sick's are analogous to striking a moving black billiard ball with a white ball. By measuring the energy change in the white ball and the angle at which it is deflected, an observer could calculate the black ball's original velocity.

However, the billiard-ball analogy applies only when the electron transfers a very large momentum to the nuclear target. Experiments that Sick and his colleagues conducted with electrons that had from 3 billion to 10 billion electron volts of energy showed consistent results over a wide range of electron-to-nucleon momentum transfers. These results suggest that the transfer was high enough at these energies to enable the researchers to calculate a valid momentum distribution.

Nuclear physicists express the mass of nucleons in millions of electron volts (MeV) of energy divided by the speed of light squared (c^2), and the nucleon velocity in terms of the velocity of light. Since momentum equals mass times velocity, momentum is expressed in the formula MeV/c.

Sick calculated momentum components as high as 800 MeV/c. These high values clearly indicate the presence of extremely strong repulsive forces at short range. Further analysis of the SLAC experiment and similar measurements on nuclei that have greater numbers of nucleons should significantly improve our understanding of how nuclear interactions at short range prevent nuclei from collapsing.

Gamow-Teller transitions. Experiments at the Indiana University cyclotron in Bloomington reported in June and September 1980 provided the first detailed, systematic measurements of Gamow-Teller transitions. These are reactions that simultaneously change the charge and spin of a nucleon in a target nucleus. A nucleon carries either a positive charge as a proton or no charge as a neutron and it may be thought of as spinning either clockwise or counterclockwise. Scientists previously had observed such transitions only in radioactive beta decays, in which a neutron decays into a proton, an electron, and an antineutrino.

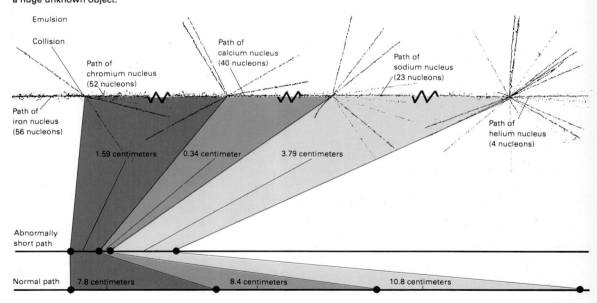

Emulsion

Collision

Path of chromium nucleus (52 nucleons)

Path of calcium nucleus (40 nucleons)

Path of sodium nucleus (23 nucleons)

Path of iron nucleus (56 nucleons)

Path of helium nucleus (4 nucleons)

1.59 centimeters   0.34 centimeter   3.79 centimeters

Abnormally short path

Normal path   7.8 centimeters   8.4 centimeters   10.8 centimeters

The Indiana physicists induced Gamow-Teller transitions by the so-called (p, n) reaction. In this reaction, a nucleus absorbs a proton, emits a neutron, and is left in an excited state — a state of higher energy than its normal state. First, the scientists accelerated protons to an energy of 120 to 160 MeV and collided them with nuclei of various chemical elements. Previous experiments had proved that proton-neutron interactions in this energy range primarily involve changes in spin, so the Indiana physicists did not need to measure the spins of the protons in the beam and the emitted neutrons. But they did need to measure the energy of the excited nucleus after the reaction.

To do this, they measured how long the emitted neutrons took to travel from the target to neutron detectors placed 62 meters (203 feet) from the target. Next, they used these measurements to calculate neutron velocities. Then they used the velocity values to determine the energy of the excited nuclei. This enabled them to determine the relationship between the energy that the protons added to the nuclei and the rate of Gamow-Teller transitions in the nuclei.

The importance of determining this relationship lies in what it teaches us about how nucleons change their charge and spin. For example, theorists A. B. Migdal in Moscow and Raymond F. Sawyer and Douglas J. Scalapino at the University of California, Santa Barbara, predicted independently in 1971 and 1972 that, if nucleons were packed together tightly enough, they would require no additional energy to change their charges and spins. The transition would occur spontaneously, and matter would undergo a transition called *pion condensation,* forming clusters of nucleons of like charge and spin.

The Indiana experiments indicate that spin and charge changes occur at relatively high energies in ordinary nuclei, so pion condensation can occur only at nuclear densities substantially higher than that of ordinary nuclei. Pion condensation is most likely to occur in the interiors of neutron stars, in which gravity can compress nucleons to high density and in certain high-energy head-on collisions between heavy nuclei.　　[John W. Negele]

Plasma Physics. The Energy Research Advisory Board of the United States Department of Energy (DOE) issued an optimistic report in August 1980 on experiments using nuclear fusion to generate electrical power. Experimenters are trying to create reactors that will provide power by controlled fusion of atomic nuclei in a plasma, a gas made up of free electrons and ions. Ions are atomic nuclei that have been stripped of their electrons. Heating a dense plasma to extremely high temperatures makes nuclei fuse and release energy.

A commercially practical reactor would have to heat the plasma to about 100 million°C. At the same time, the *confinement parameter* — fuel density (expressed in ions per cubic centimeter) times the period the plasma is confined (in seconds) — must be greater than 10^{14} (100 trillion). No one has yet achieved this in the laboratory.

The experimenters' immediate goal is to operate a fusion reactor at the break-even point so that the fusion reactions produce as much energy as is required to heat the plasma. Their primary problem is to devise a reliable method of confining the plasma, which is too hot for ordinary containers.

Magnetic fields can control ion paths, so experimental reactors use various arrangements of magnets to confine plasma. The most successful type of reactor, the tokamak, confines plasma in a doughnut-shaped space known as a *torus.* Tokamaks have already operated at a confinement parameter of 3×10^{13} and at temperatures of about 80 million°C. The Tokamak Fusion Test Reactor being built at Princeton University's Plasma Physics Laboratory in New Jersey is expected to perform at break-even levels during the mid-1980s.

The DOE report expressed confidence that scientists can build and operate a reactor that would ignite the plasma. Energy from outside the reactor would initially heat the plasma, causing fusion that would generate more heat. This self-generated heat would cause still more nuclei to fuse, creating even more heat in a self-sustaining controlled reaction. The report recommended building a Fusion Engineering Device (FED), an experi-

Physics

Continued

Electrical transmission lines converge on the target area at the Sandia Laboratories' light-ion accelerator in New Mexico. This research machine is designed to focus so much energy that nuclear fusion will occur, generating at least the same amount of energy as is put into the system.

mental reactor that might be able to ignite plasma.

The advisory board recommended that the government build this reactor by about 1991 at a cost of about $1-billion and establish a Center for Fusion Engineering to oversee the development of fusion technologies' that would lead to the design and construction of an FED. As a result of this report and the DOE endorsement, the U.S. Congress passed the Magnetic Fusion Engineering Act of 1980 in September. The act set the goals of demonstrating the engineering feasibility of magnetic fusion in the early 1990s and operating a fusion demonstration plant by the year 2000. At the same time, a similar advisory committee in Japan recommended building an even more ambitious experimental reactor by the mid-1990s for about $3 billion.

Smoothing the pulses. In July 1980, physicists at the Diverter Injection Tokamak Experiment (DITE) in Culham, England, reported indirect evidence that they have discovered a method of confining plasma while avoiding cer-

tain stresses and heat build-up in mechanical parts of a tokamak reactor.

Tokamaks produce circular magnetic fields that combine to form a spiral field, confining the plasma. One circular field is produced indirectly. A pulsed current in a set of coils creates a pulsating intermediate field that generates a current in the plasma. This plasma current, in turn, produces the circular field that helps to shape the spiral. But such pulses of current in the coils of a full-scale reactor would also generate heat and motion in the reactor's mechanical parts. So scientists are experimenting on ways to provide a plasma current without pulses.

The English scientists directed a steady beam of hydrogen atoms toward the plasma. The atoms were electrically neutral, so they penetrated the magnetic field that confined the plasma. Once inside the plasma, the atoms broke up into charged particles, or plasma, that circulated around the torus. This plasma flow produced plasma heating and a steady current. The scientists suspect that an extremely en-

ergetic electrically neutral beam would provide so much plasma current that they would not need to send a pulsed current through coils.

Similar experiments with the JFT-II tokamak in Tokai, Japan, and at Massachusetts Institute of Technology in Cambridge indicate that radio waves can also create electrical currents in tokamaks. Waveguide antennae near the outer edge of the plasma generate traveling radio waves that push electrons around the torus, as an ocean wave pushes a surfboard toward shore.

In another approach to the steady-current problem, physicists can produce the spiral fields with a magnetic coil that spirals around the outside surface of the torus. This is the stellarator concept developed by astrophysicist Lyman Spitzer, Jr., of Princeton in 1950. The original stellarator device was complicated, with interlocking, twisted coils of wire. Early tests on small stellarators were not promising, but tests reported in July 1980 by physicists Horst Wobig and Günther Greiger at the Institute for Plasma Physics in Munich, West Germany, confined a plasma for 0.02 second with a resulting confinement parameter of 2 × 10^{12}, which is as good as the parameter of comparably sized tokamaks.

Physicists Harold P. Furth, George V. Sheffield, T. K. Chu, and their colleagues at Princeton Plasma Physics Laboratory are simplifying stellarator coil design so that the coils are easier to build and install. They are combining the best features of the stellarator and conventional tokamak.

Another concept that received significant attention during the year was the Elmo Bumpy Torus (EBT), a doughnut-shaped device with about 20 electron-beam rings encircling the plasma inside the torus, like rings on a finger. These rings consist of high-energy electrons driven by powerful microwaves. The rings produce magnetic fields that can confine plasma. In September 1980, the DOE approved the construction of a $100-million EBT project at Oak Ridge National Laboratory in Tennessee. The machine should be ready for operation in 1985, so that physicists can determine whether an EBT can provide the required confinement parameter.   [Dale M. Meade]

Solid-State Physics. Physicist Frank Pobell and colleagues at a research laboratory in Jülich, West Germany, announced in July 1980 that they had cooled about 2 kilograms (4.4 pounds) of thin copper rods to less than 0.00005°C (0.00009°F.) above absolute zero (−273.15°C or −459.67°F.). No one had cooled more than a few grams of material to this temperature.

The less heat energy a material contains, the less its atoms move about. At temperatures near absolute zero, the motions of atoms almost stop. Atoms are surrounded by orbiting electrons. "Free" electrons that are easily detached from the orbits around atoms hold nearly all of a material's heat energy at temperatures near absolute zero. These electrons are the ones that conduct electricity and are therefore called conduction electrons. The West German researchers cooled the copper to such an extremely low temperature by reducing these electrons' energy.

The researchers carried out their experiment in an apparatus called a cryostat that measured 63 centimeters (2.1 feet) in diameter and 2.5 meters (8.2 feet) high. This apparatus contained three cooling chambers, connected so that the experimenters could cool the chambers in groups or individually.

The first chamber contained two isotopes of liquid helium, He-3 and He-4. The second chamber held thin rods made of a compound of praseodymium and nickel (PrNi$_5$), while copper rods were in the third chamber. Powerful electromagnets surrounded the second and third chambers.

The cooling process began in the first chamber, where the lighter liquid He-3 floated on a nearly pure layer of liquid He-4. He-3 is slightly soluble in He-4, though the reverse is not true. The flow of He-3 into the liquid He-4 below can be thought of as evaporation, removing heat from the layer of lighter He-3.

The scientists then pumped the He-3 out of the He-4, liquefied it, and added it back into the He-3 layer. This process continued until the temperature of the three connected chambers reached 0.02°C (0.04°F.) above absolute zero.

Then Pobell and his colleagues switched on the electromagnets around the PrNi$_5$ and the copper to create an effect that would slow the motion of the

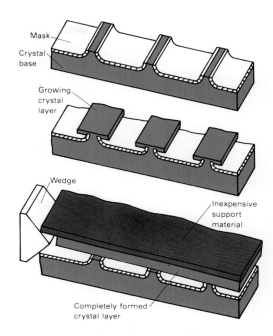

An electronic crystal grows sideways from a rib sticking up from the crystal base, *above,* in a technique that allows a thin layer of expensive crystal to be used with an inexpensive support. A mask that prevents growth is placed on the base, but not on the ribs, *right* (top), so a layer grows from only the ribs (middle). This is then attached to a support and snapped away from the base (bottom).

Mask
Crystal base
Growing crystal layer
Wedge
Inexpensive support material
Completely formed crystal layer

Physics

Continued

conduction electrons by setting up a complex chain of events inside the metal. The sequence began when the resulting magnetic field oriented the magnetic moments of the metal's nuclei, composed of neutrons and protons. The magnetic moments of the individual nuclei of each metal atom can be thought of as tiny bar magnets. They usually point in all directions because of thermal agitation — motion caused by heat.

The scientists' magnetic field eventually overpowered the thermal agitation and forced all of the nuclear moments to line up parallel to one another.

The researchers then disconnected the two lower stages (the $PrNi_5$ and the copper rods) from the helium chamber because these stages had reached the temperature of the helium mixture. Next, they slowly reduced the strength of the electromagnetic field around the $PrNi_5$ to a low value. The $PrNi_5$ neutrons and protons remained aligned. The absence of the powerful magnetic field, along with the orientation of the nuclear moments, made it appear that

the thermal agitation had been sharply reduced, leading to an extremely low temperature of the nuclear moments. This low temperature then cooled the conduction electrons much as an ice cube cools a glass of water. This cooled the $PrNi_5$ which, in turn, cooled the chamber containing the copper rods.

The scientists then disconnected the $PrNi_5$ chamber, slowly reducing the electromagnetic field around the copper rods. This left the copper nuclei cold. These nuclei then cooled the conduction electrons in the copper, just as the $PrNi_5$ nuclei had cooled the conduction electrons in that material. The West German scientists were able to maintain the ultralow temperature for two days.

The prospects for research at such low temperatures are exciting. Scientists expect to find new properties of metals, including properties that can lead to new kinds of superconductors — metals that carry electrical current without resistance.

Polarized hydrogen. Physicists Isaac Silvera and Jook Walraven of the University of Amsterdam in the Netherlands reported in September 1980 that they had produced large numbers of hydrogen atoms that had their electron magnetic moments pointing in the same direction. (Electrons can also be thought of as tiny magnets, though their magnetic moments are more than 1,000 times stronger than nuclear magnetic moments.) This represented a major step toward the creation of a superfluid gas, a "supergas." A superfluid set in motion continues moving forever. Hydrogen atoms that have aligned electron spins cannot combine to form a liquid. So aligned — or polarized — hydrogen may become the first supergas, a gas that would flow without resistance.

The Dutch physicists began by producing a beam of hydrogen atoms in a tube leading to a special container. The beam passed through a magnetic field about 100,000 times stronger than the earth's field. This field aligned the magnetic moments of the electrons. The walls of the container cooled the atoms to 0.27°C (0.49°F.) above absolute zero. The magnetic moments of nearly all the electrons were aligned.

In order to accumulate enough atoms to make a supergas, the researchers must devise a container that will hold the aligned atoms without exerting forces that disorient the electron magnetic moments. Otherwise, hydrogen atoms with opposite electron magnetic moments will combine to form hydrogen molecules, creating a liquid that immediately freezes at these low temperatures.

The Dutch scientists covered the walls of the container with a superfluid liquid helium film. This shielded the aligned hydrogen atoms from forces in the container walls that cause electron magnetic moments to disorient. The physicists kept about 10^{16} (10 million billion) atoms stable in a 1-cubic-centimeter (0.06-cubic-inch) region of the box for 47 minutes, the longest period of observation. They would need to concentrate 10^{19} atoms in a 1-cubic-centimeter volume at 0.20°C (0.36°F.) above absolute zero to create a superfluid gas.   [Raymond Orbach]

Psychology

A first-rate scientific brawl about possible sex-linked differences in mathematical ability between boys and girls began in December 1980. Psychologists Camilla Persson Benbow and Julian C. Stanley of Johns Hopkins University, Baltimore, issued a report on data they had collected about the mathematics courses and the scores on the mathematics section of the Scholastic Aptitude Test (SAT) college entrance examination of 9,927 intellectually gifted students from 1972 to 1979.

The researchers found that boys outperformed girls even when the scores were adjusted to account for the number of previous mathematics courses they had taken. These gifted boys and girls, mostly in the seventh and eighth grades, earned the same average grades in their math classes, but boys averaged 50 points higher on the math section of the SAT test, even though both sexes had received essentially the same mathematical education.

Benbow and Stanley tentatively attributed the differences in SAT scores to "male mathematical superiority, which may in turn be related to greater male ability in spatial tasks." Although the Baltimore researchers cautioned that it was extremely difficult to separate genetic influences on ability from cultural influences, the widespread media coverage the report received touched some raw nerves.

Angry critics challenged the findings. Mathematician Alice T. Schafer of Wellesley College in Massachusetts charged, "There is no evidence that SAT scores are good predictors of creative ability in mathematics." Schafer also pointed out that not a single student identified in the study as mathematically gifted went on to do graduate work in mathematics, although some ultimately received graduate degrees in other fields. Thus, she questioned whether these students actually represented the most gifted student mathematicians. Schafer observed that the study was reported without criticism in the national news media and expressed the fear that it would be virtually impossible to undo the harm that the coverage had done.

Psychology
Continued

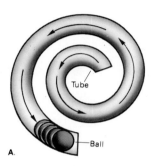

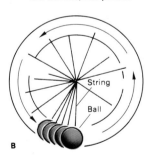

A ball (A) travels through a curved tube, *above;* another (B) swings in a circle on a string, *below.* What path will each take when (A) exits the tube and the string on (B) breaks? For the answer, see p. 306.

Schafer was not alone in criticizing the Benbow and Stanley study. Some researchers challenged the SAT as a measure of mathematical ability, criticized the logic of the study, and pointed out environmental influences that Benbow and Stanley failed to consider, such as mathematics teachers who might encourage boys and discourage girls. Merely eliminating one source of environmental difference – the number of previous math courses – did not, critics believed, prove the existence of a genetic factor.

Benbow and Stanley responded to their critics in April 1981. "We deeply regret that press coverage of our brief report confused the issues, rather than alerting people to the *magnitude* of the sex differences. The situation is far worse than most persons realize. . . . Our search nationwide found another 19 boys but no girls scoring 700 or more. Let's face these dismaying findings squarely and search hard for causes, whatever they may be."

Defying reason. Occult beliefs have increased dramatically in the United States since the early 1960s, psychologists Barry Singer and Victor A. Benassi of California State College at Long Beach reported in January 1981. Although experiments seeking to prove the existence of extrasensory perception (ESP) and occult phenomena have consistently failed, Singer and Benassi pointed out that people continue to believe in them. To see how willing some people are to grasp at weak evidence if it seems to support the existence of ESP, the scientists carried out some experiments with an amateur magician in six college psychology classes.

They had the magician perform psychiclike stunts, such as blindfolded reading; teleportation (the movement of objects by thought); and the bending of a metal rod by thought. In some classes, the visitor was introduced as a psychic; in others, he was introduced as an amateur magician. After watching the magician perform the tricks, students were asked to explain in a questionnaire what they had seen.

Singer and Benassi expected to demonstrate that the students varied in their occult beliefs depending on whether the visitor was introduced as a magician or as a psychic. They found,

instead, that 75 per cent of the students in all the classes believed strongly that the performer was psychic – no matter how he was introduced. Some were even convinced that the performer was an agent of Satan.

In follow-up studies, Singer and Benassi asked students whether magicians could perform such tricks without genuine psychic abilities. Almost all the students said "Yes." Then they asked, "How many people who perform such stunts are likely to be fakes and magicians, instead of genuine psychics?" Students agreed the vast majority were likely to be tricksters and magicians. Finally, the students were asked to re-evaluate the performance they had recently seen, in light of their answers to the previous questions. To Singer and Benassi's astonishment, the students still believed the performer they had seen was a genuine psychic.

Singer and Benassi concluded that students are not troubled by logical inconsistencies as long as there is no penalty for illogical beliefs. "If we had told them that they must reason accurately or be shot in the morning," the psychologists added, "they might have performed better." Singer and Benassi concluded that scientific logic, as taught in today's schools, must not have much impact on students. When no rational explanation seems possible, students fall back on superstition, occultism, and irrational beliefs.

In the mood for memories. Evidence for a long-suspected link between mood and memory was reported in February 1981 by psychologist Gordon H. Bower of Stanford University. In many cases, people cannot remember things they did while in a totally different emotional state.

For example, Sirhan Bishara Sirhan, the convicted assassin of Robert F. Kennedy, did not remember shooting Kennedy after his arrest in 1968. Under hypnosis, Sirhan went into a very emotional, agitated mental state and re-enacted the entire sequence of events leading to Kennedy's death. In his normal state of consciousness, after waking from hypnosis, he could not recall any part of the incident and continued to deny his guilt.

Similarly, people who get very drunk may forget what they did while intoxi-

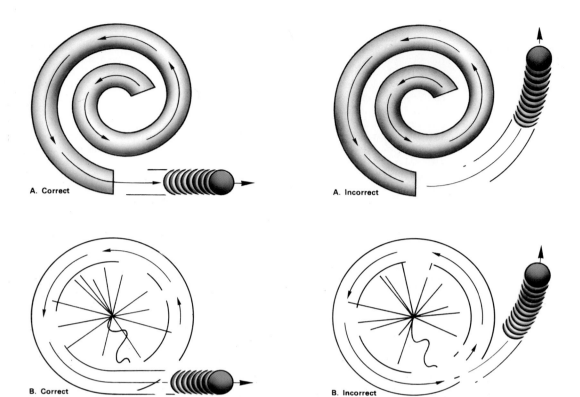

A. Correct

A. Incorrect

B. Correct

B. Incorrect

Psychology

Continued

Both balls will travel in a straight line — (A) when it leaves the tube; (B) when the cord breaks — according to the laws of inertia. More than 50 per cent of the university students tested gave the wrong answer for (A) and 30 per cent for (B). This indicates that many people, including those who have taken physics courses, have misconceptions about the motion of objects.

cated, but may remember it again the next time they drink. This phenomenon is called "state-dependent forgetting." Bower did experiments showing that emotional states, like drug states, can affect memory in this way.

In Bower's experiment, hypnotized students were put into positive or negative mental states. He selected people who were easily hypnotized and, after hypnotizing them, he asked them to get themselves into a happy or sad mood by imagining or remembering a scene in which they had been very happy or very sad. He asked the subjects to maintain each mood for about a minute. During each such period, they were given lists of words to learn.

Later, subjects were again hypnotized and put into happy or sad moods. Bower found that students in a sad mood were much better at recalling words they learned in a previous sad mood, compared with words they learned in a previous happy mood. The opposite was also true. Words learned in a happy mood were recalled better when the subject was again happy.

Bower emphasized that the specific scenes the subjects used to put themselves into a sad or happy mood had no effect on the word recall. In the second mood-setting trial, they imagined scenes that were different from those imagined in the first trial. The differences in recall could not be attributed to associations between the imagined scene and the word lists. Apparently, the differences were due to the mood changes in the individuals.

Mood or emotion, Bower explains, becomes part of a memory, just like other parts of an experience. It can help or harm retrieval, depending on whether a person can reproduce the same mood during recall.

Bower found that mood also influenced free word association. In this test, a subject hears a given word and immediately responds with other words that he or she relates to it. Bower found that a happy subject would associate the word *life* with *love, freedom, fun,* and *joy.* An angry subject was likely to associate the same word with *struggle, toil,* and *compete.* [Russell A. Dewey]

Public Health

By late 1980, public health specialists had made considerable progress in defining toxic shock syndrome (TSS). This newly discovered disease, which most often strikes menstruating women, made headlines throughout the United States during 1980 and 1981. Epidemiologists have identified its potential victims, physicians have studied its symptoms, and others are tracing the biological course of the disease.

New diseases, or important variants of old diseases, often appear suddenly and cause substantial death and disability before medical researchers can identify the causes and learn how to prevent and treat these diseases. TSS is a case in point. In late 1979, preventive medicine specialist Andrew G. Dean of the Minnesota Department of Health notified the Centers for Disease Control (CDC) in Atlanta, Ga., that an unusual illness had recently struck five previously healthy young women in Minnesota. He recognized the disease's symptoms as being similar to those associated with a particular type of the bacterium *Staphyloccocus aureus,* which were first described in 1978.

The CDC released the Minnesota report in early 1980, and new cases were rapidly identified thereafter. The condition occurred almost exclusively in menstruating women, and 80 per cent of the women were under age 30. Of 691 cases reported by early 1981, 10 per cent of the victims died.

Epidemiologist Jeffrey P. Davis and his associates at the University of Wisconsin and the Wisconsin Department of Health and Social Services in Madison described a strict set of diagnostic criteria for the disease in December 1980. To be classified as having TSS, patients must have a temperature above 38.89°C (102°F.); low blood pressure, or a drop in blood pressure after standing up suddenly; a red rash on the palms; redness of the mucous membrane of the throat or vagina; vomiting or diarrhea; impaired kidney or liver function; decreased calcium and phosphorus levels in the blood; and, in severe cases, shock. The diagnosis can be confirmed after laboratory tests rule out other causes.

Most TSS victims were using tampons when the disease struck. When a brand of tampon called Rely was implicated in many TSS cases, the maker promptly removed it from the market.

The researchers do not yet understand the connection between tampons and the disease. Tampon insertion devices may scratch the lining of the vagina, allowing bacteria to enter, or perhaps the tampon itself carries the infection. In addition, while only 10 per cent of menstruating women have *S. aureus* in the vagina, virtually all of the TSS victims harbored this organism. Why *S. aureus* is now associated with TSS is still a mystery.

Medical scientists do not really know why TSS has recently appeared so frequently or, conversely, why it has not occurred even more frequently in view of the fact that roughly 5 million women harbor *S. aureus* in their vaginas. Researchers have not yet identified the specific toxin responsible for TSS, so a specific diagnostic test is not yet available. Removal of the principal offending tampon from the market appears to have reduced the incidence of the disease. The publicity should ensure that physicians will be more alert to the danger of TSS in the future.

Coffee and cancer. Comparing the habits of patients with pancreatic cancer and a control group of cancer-free persons disclosed that cancer patients drank much more coffee than the controls, according to a March 1981 report by epidemiologist Brian MacMahon and his colleagues of the Harvard School of Public Health in Boston. Although the data appear impressive, their interpretation is being challenged by other investigators.

Researchers have been looking closely at many types of environmental agents, such as industrial chemicals and food additives, that are associated with human cancer. Certain groups of people, for example, workers in a specific industry, often show a higher incidence of a particular form of cancer than do other groups. In searching for what causes such an increase, epidemiologists look for factors to which the affected workers are exposed and others are not. These may be environmental triggers for the development of cancer.

This kind of biomedical research must always be viewed cautiously because the mere association of an environmental factor with an increase in a particular disease does not necessarily prove the factor causes the disease. Some other unknown or unrecognized factor may be the true culprit. Absolute proof requires that the agent be experimentally shown to produce the disease.

Obviously, such experiments are not feasible with human cancers. Therefore, medical scientists must rely heavily on epidemiological studies showing an association between a particular factor and a cancer.

Critics of the Harvard study point out that coffee drinkers may have more gastrointestinal complaints in general than noncoffee drinkers. As a result, they may be exposed to more diagnostic procedures that are likely to detect pancreatic cancer. If this is true, the apparent association would merely reflect better cancer detection among the coffee-drinking group. In addition, the risk of cancer does not increase in a straight-line fashion as coffee consumption goes up, according to the Harvard study. There was a high number of cancer cases among subjects drinking five cups of coffee or more per day.

However, those drinking three cups per day had fewer cases than those who drank two cups per day.

This absence of a clear consumption-linked relationship is unusual in cancer produced by an environmental toxin. The issue is unresolved and certain to remain controversial. Pancreatic cancer has become the fourth leading cause of cancer death in the United States and is expected to account for 22,000 fatalities in 1981 – up from 8,952 deaths in 1950.

Hepatitis B vaccine. A test conducted by epidemiologist Wolf Szmuness of the New York Blood Center demonstrated the success of a new vaccine against hepatitis B in October 1980. Hepatitis B, a viral liver inflammation, strikes more than 50,000 persons in the United States every year.

Worldwide, the disease affects millions more, and has been linked to primary hepatocellular cancer, an almost invariably fatal liver cancer. The vaccine should be available in late 1981 or early 1982. See THE OPENING SHOT AT HEPATITIS.   [Michael H. Alderman]

Science
Awards

Six Americans were among the eight scientists awarded Nobel prizes for chemistry, physics, and physiology or medicine in 1980. The awards were presented in formal ceremonies in Stockholm, Sweden, on Dec. 10, 1980. The cash value of each award was about $212,000.

Chemistry. Half the chemistry prize went to Paul Berg, professor of biochemistry at Stanford University in California. The other half was shared by Walter Gilbert, professor of molecular biology at Harvard University in Cambridge, Mass., and Frederick Sanger, professor of molecular biology at Cambridge University in England.

Berg received the prize "for his fundamental studies of the biochemistry of nucleic acids, with particular regard to recombinant DNA." Gilbert and Sanger were honored "for their contributions concerning the determination of base sequences in nucleic acids." Sanger is the second person to win two Nobel prizes in the same category. He won in 1958 for discovering the structure of the insulin molecule. The first

person, John Bardeen of the University of Illinois, won the physics prize in 1956 and 1972.

Berg is one of the principal pioneers of genetic engineering, or gene splicing. This field developed after scientists discovered in the 1970s how to insert genes from one organism into another. Genes pass on the hereditary characteristics of all living things, and this genetic program is coded for by the biochemical deoxyribonucleic acid (DNA). The Royal Academy cited Berg as the first to splice together pieces of DNA from different species – an animal cancer virus called SV-40 with the DNA of a virus that infects bacteria.

Berg is chairman of the Committee on Recombinant DNA Molecules, formed in 1974. At that time, Berg and 10 other distinguished molecular biologists proposed a voluntary, worldwide ban on certain DNA experiments until safeguards could be developed to control potential hazards, such as creating new, deadly strains of bacteria.

Gilbert and Sanger worked independently to develop ways of deter-

Science Awards

Continued

James W. Cronin

Jean Dausset

Frederick Sanger

mining the chemical sequences in DNA strands. Their work was an important step in making possible the process of inserting into bacteria genes that could potentially produce any kind of protein. Already, genes have been inserted into bacteria to produce human insulin and human interferon. Insulin is the hormone needed by diabetics, and interferon is a natural substance that protects cells against viruses and might control the spread of cancer cells.

Physics. James W. Cronin, university professor of physics at the University of Chicago, and Val L. Fitch, Cyrus Fogg Brackett professor of physics and chairman of the Physics Department at Princeton University in New Jersey, shared the Nobel prize in physics for research showing an asymmetry in the behavior of subatomic particles.

Scientists formerly believed in a total symmetry concept called CPT symmetry. CPT consists of charge conjugation (C) – all particles in a reaction can be replaced by their antiparticles and the forces between particles will remain the same; parity (P) – particles coming from a reaction must be mirror images in spin and other right-hand, left-hand properties of those that initiated the reaction; and time reversal (T) – the theory that reactions going forward in time would obey the same physical laws as reactions going backward in time. Scientists had believed that fundamental conservation laws applied to CPT and that the symmetry never varied. CPT symmetry requires that there be an equal amount of matter and anti-matter in the universe. This balance would have to be maintained in all particle physics experiments.

Cronin and Fitch performed their prizewinning experiments in 1964 at the Brookhaven National Laboratory on Long Island, New York. They found that certain elementary particle reactions violated laws of conservation and symmetry. Their experiments specifically showed that the fundamental physical laws do not strictly apply in the theoretical world of reversed time.

Physiology or Medicine. Work extending the frontiers of understanding about the immune response won the Nobel prize for three researchers. Baruj Benacerraf, professor of comparative pathology and chairman of the Pathol-

ogy Department at Harvard Medical School; Jean Dausset of the Blood Disease Research Institute in Paris; and George D. Snell of the Jackson Laboratory in Bar Harbor, Me., shared the award in 1980.

The scientists were honored for research that has led to more successful tissue and organ transplants. A major cause of failure in transplant operations is the body's rejection of donated tissue and organs as foreign. The work of these three scientists resulted in improved methods of "typing" cells, to provide a better match between transplant tissue and the recipient.

Snell started the work in the 1940s, conducting research on mice to determine what genes control whether a transplant is accepted or rejected. He developed strains of mice that were genetically identical except for a single gene. He found that a set of genes, the histocompatibility genes, determine whether tissue grafts are accepted or rejected by the body. Animals with the same histocompatibility genes accept grafts from one another. Those with different histocompatibility genes do not.

When Dausset began his study of human genes, he found a set of genes – called the human leucocyte antigen (HLA) system – in one human chromosome. These histocompatibility genes direct the manufacture of specific. proteins called HLA antigens, which are found on the surface of all human and animal cells. These HLA antigens allow the immune system to recognize tissues as "self" or "nonself."

Benacerraf worked with guinea pigs in his research. He found the immune response (Ir) genes, which control the body's response to some foreign substances. The Ir genes are located in the same region of the chromosome as the histocompatibility genes, and they appear to code for a protein on the surface of white blood cells. Scientists believe that these proteins play a role in the interaction of two parts of the immune system, lymphocytes and macrophages. Lymphocytes are white blood cells that recognize foreign substances, such as bacteria, viruses, and toxins, and attack them. Macrophages are large cells that surround the invaders and digest them.　　[Joseph P. Spohn]

Major Awards and Prizes

Winners of the Nobel prize and their work are treated more fully in the first portion of this section

AAAS-Newcomb Cleveland Prize (oceanography): Fred N. Spiess and 21 others

AAAS Socio-Psychological Prize: Stephen G. Harkins, Bibb Latane, Kipling D. Williams

ACS Award in Petroleum Chemistry: Herman Pines

Amateur Achievement Award (astronomy): George Alcock

American Physical Society (APS) High Polymer Physics Prize: Robert Simha

APS Fluid Dynamics Prize: Hans W. Liepmann

Arctowski Medal (astronomy): Thomas M. Donahue

Arthur L. Day Medal (geophysics): Donald L. Turcotte

Arthur L. Day Prize (NAS) (geology): Gerald J. Wasserburg

Bergey Award: Morrison Rogosa

Bonner Prize (nuclear physics): Bernard L. Cohen

Bowie Medal (geophysics): Herbert Friedman

Brewer Trophy (aviation): Jerome P. Keuper, Florida Institute of Technology

Bruce Medal (astronomy): Riccardo Giacconi

Bucher Medal (geophysics): Jack E. Oliver

Buckley Solid State Physics Prize: David M. Lee, Douglas D. Osheross, Robert C. Richardson

Carski Award (microbiology teaching): Robert J. Brady

Carty Medal (mathematics): Shing-tung Yau

Collier Trophy (astronautics): *Voyager* mission team

Corson Medal (nutrition): Bruce N. Ames

Davisson-Germer Prize (physics): Alexander Dalgarno

Delmer S. Fahrney Medal (telecommunications): Jerome B. Wiesner

Elliott Cresson Medal (chemistry): Riccardo Giacconi

Ewing Medal (geophysics): Manik Talwani

Fisher Award: William Sandine

Fleming Medal (geophysics): Thomas Donahue

Franklin Medal: Avram Goldstein, Lyman Spitzer, Jr.

Freedom Award: Karl Menninger

Gairdner Awards (medicine): Paul Berg, Irving B. Fritz, H. Gobind Khorana, Efraim Racker, Jesse Roth, Michael Sela

Garvan Medal (chemistry): Elizabeth Weisburger

Goddard Astronautics Award: Peter T. Burr, Kenneth J. Frost

Hale Prize (astronomy): J. Paul Wild

Haley Astronautics Award: Gordon Fullerton, Richard A. Truly, Fred Hais

Hazen Award (medicine): William Kunkel

Heineman Prize for Astrophysics: Riccardo Giacconi

Heineman Prize for Mathematical Physics: Jeffrey Goldstone

Horwitz Prize (biology): Cesar Milstein

Howard N. Potts Medal (chemistry): Stanley G. Mason

Ives Medal (optics): Aden B. Meinel

Klumpke-Roberts Award (astronomy): Dietrick Thomsen

Lasker Awards (medical research): Paul Berg, Herbert W. Boyer, Stanley N. Cohen, A. Dale Kaiser

Lawrence Memorial Award (atomic energy): Donald W. Barr, B. Grant Logan, Nicholas P. Samios, Benno P. Schoenborn, Charles D. Scott

Lilly Award (microbiology): Thomas Maniatis

Lomb Medal (optics): David M. Bloom

Longstreth Medal: Leonard T. Skeggs, Jr.

Lounsbery Award (biology, medicine): Philip Leder

Lucian Award (medicine): Solbert Permutt

Luck Award (scientific reviewing): John S. Chipman

Macelwane Award (geophysics): Ronald G. Prinn, David Southwood, Donald J. Weidner

Mackay Trophy (aeronautics): James E. McArdle, Jr.

Maxwell Prize (plasma physics): Thomas H. Stix

Meggers Award (optics): John G. Conway

Michelson Medal (optics): Emil Wolf

NAS Award for Initiatives in Research: Gary D. Patterson

NAS Award in Chemical Sciences: Bruno H. Zimm

NAS Public Welfare Medal: Russell E. Train

Nobel Prize: chemistry, Paul Berg, Walter Gilbert, Frederick Sanger; physics, James W. Cronin, Val L. Fitch; physiology or medicine, Baruj Benacerraf, Jean Dausset, George D. Snell

Oersted Medal (physics teaching): Robert Karplus

Oppenheimer Memorial Prize (physics): Frederick Reines

Penrose Medal (geology): John Rodgers

Perkin Medal (chemistry): Ralph Landau

Pierce Prize (astronomy): Bruce Margon

Priestley Medal (chemistry): Herbert C. Brown

Reed Aeronautics Award: William Sears

Richardson Medal (optics): William T. Plummer, Richard F. Weeks

Robertson Memorial Lecture (cancer research): Stanley Cohen

Russell Lectureship (astronomy): Riccardo Giacconi

R. W. Woods Prize (optics): Anthony E. Siegman

3M Life Sciences Award (biology): Paul E. Lacy

Trumpler Award (astronomy): Richard Kron

U.S. Steel Foundation Award (molecular biology): Ronald W. Davis, Gerald R. Fink

Warner Prize (astronomy): William H. Press

Waterford Biomedical Science Award: Baruj Benacerraf, Henry G. Kunkel

Wetherill Medal: Ralph A. Alpher, Robert Herman

Wolf Prize: Michael E. Fisher, Leo P. Kadanoff, Kenneth G. Wilson

Wright Brothers Memorial Trophy: Olive Ann Beech

Space Exploration

After nearly six earthbound years, United States astronauts returned to orbit on April 12, 1981, in the National Aeronautics and Space Administration's (NASA) space shuttle, *Columbia,* the first reusable spacecraft. John W. Young, 50, and Robert L. Crippen, 43, were the pilots who opened this new frontier in space. Young, a veteran astronaut, flew the first manned *Gemini* mission in 1965 and the *Apollo 16* moon mission in 1972. Crippen, a U. S. Navy pilot, was on his first space flight.

Columbia was the end product of a program that lasted 10 years and cost $9 billion to develop. The shuttle was launched as a rocket and returned as a glider. At launch, the delta-winged *Columbia* orbiter was hitched to a blimp-like propellant tank and two strapped-on solid rocket boosters. *Columbia*'s rocket engines and solid-rocket boosters gracefully lifted a total of 2 million kilograms (4.4 million pounds) off the launching pad at exactly 7 A.M. Eastern Standard Time.

Two minutes into the flight, the solid fuel boosters burned out, were released, and parachuted into the Atlantic Ocean. The boosters were recovered and will be used again. The orbiter's three liquid hydrogen-oxygen engines, burning propellant from the external tank, continued firing to put *Columbia* into orbit. They cut off after 8 minutes 32 seconds, and the 47.4-meter (155-foot) propellant tank, which is not reusable, was dropped toward the Indian Ocean. The crew then fired *Columbia*'s twin orbital maneuvering engines. These engines and 44 attitude-control thrusters performed flawlessly on every maneuvering test.

Except for the loss of 15 of its 31,000 heat-shield tiles and a flight recorder switch failure, no serious malfunctions were reported during the 54 hour 20 minute flight. The tiles, designed to protect the craft from the searing heat of re-entry into earth's atmosphere, were ripped off rear-engine pods during the launch. But their loss did not cause much heat damage during re-entry.

Young and Crippen were delighted with the performance of *Columbia*'s propulsion, navigation, electrical, flight control, and environmental systems. The busy astronauts hardly took time out for meals, and they slept in their ejection seats instead of the more comfortable sleeping bags that operational flight crews will use on future shuttle flights. Their only complaint was that the flight deck became uncomfortably cool both mornings.

On the 36th orbit, Young and Crippen turned *Columbia,* tail first, over the Indian Ocean and fired the maneuvering engines to break it out of its orbit. Nose forward once again, the shuttle entered what is called the sensible atmosphere at 121,951 meters (400,000 feet) over the Pacific Ocean and glided downward. When it crossed the California coast at Big Sur, Young took manual control of the craft and, making a sweeping turn, landed it smoothly on the Rogers Dry Lake runway at Edwards Air Force Base in California's Mojave Desert, 2 days, 6 hours, and 20 minutes after liftoff.

NASA pilots then ferried *Columbia* back to Florida aboard a Boeing 747 jet aircraft for a second orbital test flight that was scheduled for September 30. Never before had a U.S. space vehicle worked so well on a first test flight. NASA had achieved its design objective for the reusable space shuttle — it had built a 20th-century "covered wagon" for the new space frontier.

Russian cosmonauts continued to go aloft in 1980 and 1981 in improved models of the 20-year-old *Soyuz* spacecraft. Their mission was to perform low-gravity manufacturing experiments with alloys, crystals, and pharmaceuticals and to test human endurance in the *Salyut 6* space station. Although Russia reportedly was working on a reusable transport similar to the U.S. shuttle, only modifications of the old-fashioned, expendable *Soyuz* spacecraft appeared during the year.

Valery Ryumin and Leonid Popov set a new record of 185 days in orbit on Oct. 11, 1980, in *Soyuz 35,* breaking the space endurance record of 175 days set by Ryumin and Vladimir Lyakhov in *Soyuz 34* in 1979. During their mission, Ryumin and Popov were visited six times by cosmonauts in *Soyuz* vehicles. Among them were several non-Russians who were trained in the Soviet Union including Hungarian, Vietnamese, Cuban, and Mongolian pilots.

On May 26, 1981, two cosmonauts landed their *Soyuz T-4* in Central Asia

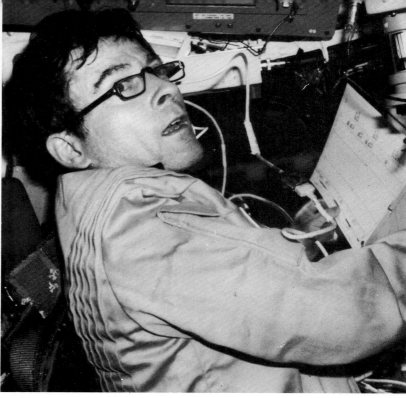

After the space shuttle *Columbia* is launched at 7 A.M. on April 12, 1981, pilot John Young, *above,* begins to make entries in his history-making log of the spacecraft's first successful flight.

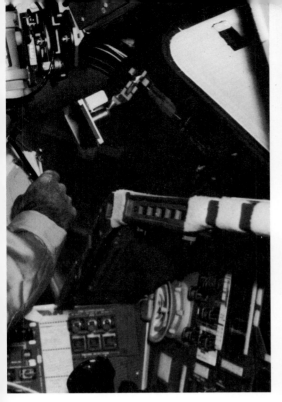

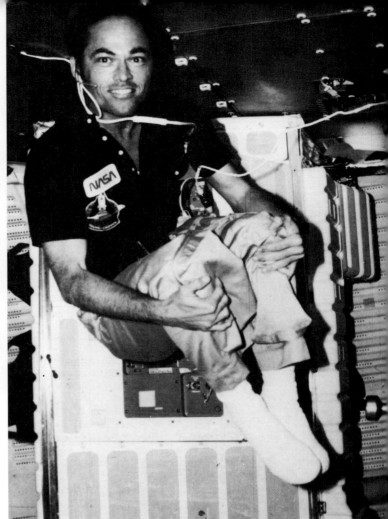

Events logged include co-pilot Robert Crippen's acrobatics; opening cargo bay doors to show lost tiles; and *Columbia*'s triumphant touchdown 2¼ days later.

Space Exploration

Continued

and the Soviet Union announced the successful completion of the program of prolonged flights by Soviet cosmonauts on board *Salyut 6.* The next phase of the Russian program is expected to include orbiting a larger, more complex space station.

Saturn probe. *Voyager 1* passed within 126,000 kilometers (78,000 miles) of Saturn on November 12 and sent back spectacular photos. Along with other measurements, they revealed a much more complex ring system than scientists had expected and confirmed the existence of six new moons. *Voyager 2* was scheduled to fly by Saturn in late August 1981. See FLIGHT TO SATURN.

U.S. satellite launches. NASA launched a Geosynchronous Operational Environmental Satellite (*GOES 4*) from Cape Canaveral, Fla., on Sept. 9, 1980, to monitor atmospheric temperature and moisture. A military communications satellite, second in a series to link U.S. Navy ships with land bases, went up on October 20.

The first satellite to be used exclusively for business communications was placed in geostationary orbit 35,900 kilometers (22,300 miles) high on November 15. A second one, scheduled for launch in April 1981, was delayed. *Intelsat V,* a more powerful communications satellite than any in orbit, was launched on Dec. 10, 1980, for the 102-nation International Telecommunications Satellite Organization. A second machine in the series, scheduled for launch in March 1981, was launched on May 23. NASA launched *Comstar D,* fourth in a series of advanced communications satellites operated by United States Communications Satellite Corporation, on Feb. 19, 1981.

Old, faithful craft. Several long-operating spacecraft continued to return data in 1981. The *Viking 1* spacecraft, orbiting Mars, was turned off on Aug. 8, 1980, after it literally ran out of gas. But the *Viking* lander on the Martian surface continued to return data from its post on Chryse Planitia. *Pioneer 6,* designed to operate for only six months, marked its 15th anniversary on Dec. 16, 1980, continuing to circle the sun and transmit data. And *Copernicus,* an orbiting astronomical observatory equipped to gather data in the ultraviolet range of the electromagnetic

spectrum, was turned off on Feb. 15, 1981, after operating for 8½ years.

Worldwide space activity. *Ariane,* the European Space Agency's (ESA) heavy launch vehicle, failed its second launch test on May 23, 1980, at Kourou, French Guiana. Its first flight in 1979 was successful. A third test is scheduled for June 1981.

ESA delivered the engineering model of *Spacelab* – a nonflying duplicate of the one that will go into orbit – to the Kennedy Space Center at Cape Canaveral on Dec. 15, 1980, so that scientists could become familiar with it. *Spacelab* is being built by Western Europe for use aboard the United States space shuttle. *Spacelab* is set to be carried into orbit in the shuttle's cargo bay in May 1983. Swiss astronomer Claude Nicollier and Dutch physicist Wubbo Ockels began training at the Lyndon B. Johnson Space Center in Houston in 1979 as mission specialists for *Spacelab.*

Asian and South American nations continued to play a part in space exploration. India launched *Rohini,* a 35-kilogram (77-pound) test satellite, on July 18, 1980, from an island north of Madras. China continued to test intercontinental missiles. Brazil announced that it would develop the small solid-fuel *Sonda* rockets, which it has used for suborbital launches, into more powerful launchers for communication and observation satellites.

Program cutbacks. Because of federal budget cuts, NASA canceled its participation in the international solar-polar mission, a joint effort with ESA to fly probes around the north and south poles of the sun. Also delayed were the *Galileo* spacecraft that would probe Jupiter's atmosphere, and *VOIR,* a Venus orbiter carrying radar cameras for photographing that planet's landscape through its dense clouds. NASA also shelved proposals to send a rendezvous mission to Halley's Comet when it reappears in 1986, and deferred work on the Gamma Ray Observatory. Bruce C. Murray, director of the Jet Propulsion Laboratory in Pasadena, Calif., warned the U.S. House of Representatives Subcommittee on Space Science and Applications on March 21, 1981, that budget cuts had hurt the U.S. space program and that it "even may face extinction." [Richard S. Lewis]

Zoology

How do you give a hearing test to an elephant? Physiological psychologists Rickye S. and Henry E. Heffner of the University of Kansas Bureau of Child Research in Lawrence reported in May 1980 that they tested the hearing of Lois, a 7-year-old female Indian elephant at the Ralph Mitchell Zoo in Independence, Kans. Vertebrate animals vary considerably in their ability to hear sounds of different frequencies. Scientists believed elephants hear only low-frequency sounds and the researchers wanted to determine if this was true.

Sound travels in waves, and the number of times per second a sound wave vibrates is termed the frequency. Each vibration per second is one hertz (Hz); 1,000 hertz equal 1 kilohertz (kHz).

Scientists have learned that human beings can hear up to about 20 kHz; dogs, 44 kHz; rats, 72 kHz; and bats, 115 kHz. This suggests that the smaller the animal, the greater its ability to hear high frequencies. However, studies done in the 1960s and 1970s showed that high-frequency hearing ability is actually related to the distance between an animal's ears, not simply to body size. The investigations that led to this theory were based on mammals with small heads and, therefore, relatively short distances between the ears. The Heffners wanted to test this theory on an animal with a very large head.

They trained Lois to start the hearing-test periods by pushing the center button on a three-button panel. If this produced a sound she could hear, she was to push the button on the left. If she heard no sound, she was to push the button on the right.

The researchers at first presented sounds in frequency ranges they knew elephants could hear. These sounds were randomly interspersed with silences. When Lois pushed the correct button in response to either a sound or silence, she was rewarded with a fruit-flavored drink. When she pushed the wrong button, she was not rewarded. After the elephant learned over a two-week period how to obtain the fruit drink, the Heffners began to present sounds of higher and lower frequencies.

A sting ray found on the beach at Port Elizabeth, South Africa, has six gill openings instead of the usual five and several other features so unique that it was given a new family and species name— *Hexatrygon bickelli.* It was named after David Bickell, who found it.

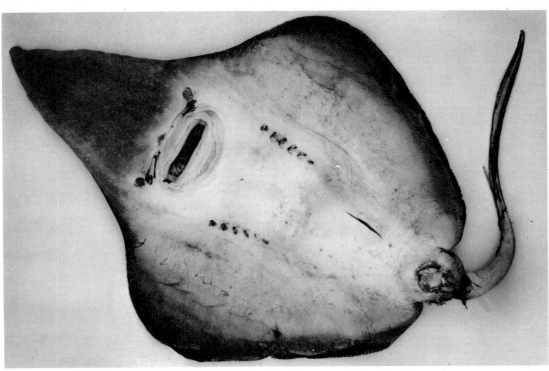

House Reef

You might expect to find more than 400 species of corals, fishes, mollusks, sponges, worms, plants, and other exotic organisms living on a reef in blue ocean waters off some tropical island — but not in a museum. Nevertheless, scientists have managed to re-create a large coral reef with all these living creatures at the Smithsonian Institution's National Museum of Natural History in Washington, D.C.

The reef opened as a public exhibit on Oct. 15, 1980. But it also provides marine scientists with the opportunity to experiment with and observe reef life over long periods, unhindered by the limitations of deep-sea diving.

A tropical reef is a limestone formation built on the seabed by the skeletons of millions of tiny calcified animals and plants. Many of the skeletons are the remains of coral colonies. Over time, these animals build up a reef, a barrier or ridge on the ocean floor. A wide variety of animals and plants live there, including the colorful corals. Large reef communities are found only in warm, clear tropical waters.

Marine biologist Walter H. Adey, the Smithsonian's curator of coralline algae, was the moving force behind the creation of the model coral reef. He began experimenting with maintaining reef organisms in small tanks in 1974, working his way up to the 11,340-liter (3,000-gallon) tank that houses the Smithsonian exhibit.

To simulate the light found on a tropical reef, the museum scientists installed racks of 400-watt and 1,000-watt metal halide lights, positioned over the tank and connected to automatic timers. Different corals are dominant at various depths in a natural reef, and the light varies with depth. All colony-building corals require light because part of their food is provided by algae that live within the corals. The overhead lights provide the appropriate brightness for each depth.

Waves are created in the tank by two dump-trucklike buckets delicately balanced at the upper end of the reef. As water is pumped around the system, it falls into the buckets. Every 10 seconds, one of them tips, creating a wave.

Visitors to the Smithsonian Institution's National Museum of Natural History view one end of its new living coral reef exhibit, *left,* which features such animals as the butterfly fish, *above.*

In order to create a realistic model reef, Adey and his colleagues made detailed studies of several Caribbean Sea reefs. They collected 2.7 metric tons (3 short tons) of dead coral from the Caribbean and shipped it to the Smithsonian to create the necessary bedrock in the tank. They also filled the tank with natural lagoon sand and natural seawater. They collected plants and animals for the reef in the Caribbean during the summer of 1980.

All the species found on a reef could not be packed into an aquarium, but there are more than 50 species of marine algae; 3 of sea grasses; 18 of hard corals; 18 of fishes; 14 of crustaceans; such as crabs and shrimp; 7 of echinoderms, such as sea urchins and starfish; 8 of mollusks; and others, including numerous protozoans.

A natural food chain has been set up in the tank. Small invertebrates — worms, amphipods, and crabs — reproduce quickly, providing a continuous source of food for the *omnivorous* (meat- and plant-eating) and *carniverous* (meat-eating) fish. *Herbivorous* (plant-eating) fish and urchins keep the reef vegetation cropped close.

On a natural reef, plankton — small, floating animals and plants — that comes in from the open ocean with each wave is a major food source. So we add some brine shrimp to the tank to make up for the lack of plankton.

When it is "night" on the coral reef, lights are turned on over flat scrubber tanks lined with algae growing on plastic screens. This allows photosynthesis to occur in the algae, which take up carbon dioxide and nutrients from animal waste materials and release oxygen. The scrubber algae serve the purpose of keeping the enire tank community healthy and stable throughout the day and night.

Adey has even greater plans for the future. He hopes to create an open ocean ecosystem in a tank. Connected to the coral reef tank, its plankton and other organisms would interact with the reef to create an even more realistic underwater world. Not only would this be a delight for tourists visiting the Museum, but it would offer scientists an unprecedented opportunity to study life in the seas and the processes that maintain it.   [Susan H. Brawley]

They determined the thresholds above and below which Lois could hear nothing, and entered their results on a chart called an audiogram. The Heffners' experiment had only one hitch. When Lois could not hear a sound, she pushed the appropriate button and, according to plan, was not rewarded. However, she blamed the uncooperative loudspeaker when no reward appeared and beat upon the speaker with her trunk, probably in hopes of eliciting a sound that would bring her a drink.

The test results showed that elephants cannot hear sounds above 12 kHz, but can hear low-frequency sounds — for example, at 17 Hz — better than any mammal previously tested. This bears out the theory that an animal with wide-set ears can hear low-frequency sounds very well.

The Heffners believe that differences in how well various mammals hear high-frequency sounds is related to how an animal determines the direction from which a sound is coming. When a mammal's ears are close together, each ear receives low-frequency sounds at about the same time and the animal cannot determine the sound's direction. However, faster high-frequency sounds hit one ear slightly before the other, so the animal can tell where they come from. The Heffners concluded that the ability to hear higher-frequency sounds evolved in some mammals to compensate for the small distance between their ears.

Homing in on a new sound. Neurophysiologists Melvin L. Kreithen and Douglas B. Quine of Cornell University's Langmuir Laboratory in Ithaca, N.Y., reported in June 1980 that homing pigeons hear sounds as low as 0.05 Hz, or 1 vibration every 20 seconds.

Even small sounds upset birds and increase their heartbeat rate, so the researchers used this to test pigeon hearing. They monitored pigeons' heartbeats to test their ability to hear the sounds supplied in the laboratory.

The pigeons' ability to hear very low-frequency sound may be related to their ability to navigate. Strong winds, waves breaking on a rocky shore, or winds whistling against a mountain can generate low-frequency sounds. The question now puzzling researchers is whether homing pigeons, and perhaps

Zoology

Continued

Lois, an Indian elephant, gets set to push a button to start a hearing test that proved elephants can hear low-frequency sounds better than any animal previously tested.

other birds, can use infrasound detection to identify coastlines, mountain ranges, or even patches of bad weather.

Low-frequency sounds travel for hundreds of miles with little energy loss, but high-frequency sounds drop off in intensity even over short distances. Kreithen and Quine suspect that birds can determine the direction of an infrasound source while they are flying, and can therefore detect the difference in frequency of the sounds from one place in their flight path to another.

Monkey see, monkey tell. Three wildlife researchers from the Rockefeller University Field Research Center in Millbrook, N.Y., reported in November 1980 that they had studied vervet monkeys to determine how much they use distinct vocal calls to warn other monkeys of danger. Researchers Robert M. Seyfarth, Dorothy L. Cheney, and Peter Marler spent 14 months in Amboseli National Park in Kenya observing three groups of vervet monkeys. Although researchers had extensively studied the ability of captive chimpanzees and gorillas to learn to use signs

when referring to objects, this was the first time researchers had studied the ability of nonhuman primates living in the wild to communicate.

The researchers in Kenya waited until an animal appeared that provoked an alarm call by one of the monkeys. They noted what kind of animal it was and tape-recorded the noise it made and the vocal responses of nearby monkeys. They also noted the monkeys' physical responses and observed which individual monkey sounded the alarm first.

The researchers found that the vervets gave different alarm calls to warn of at least three predators—leopards approaching, eagles, and pythons. They sounded a series of short calls to warn of leopards; a low-pitched, staccato grunt for eagles; and high-pitched calls for pythons.

The researchers reported that on hearing each type of alarm call, the monkeys took the appropriate action. When they heard the leopard alarm, they ran up into trees; at the eagle alarm, the monkeys looked upward or

Zoology

Continued

A 3-day-old cynomolgus monkey is the first to be conceived by a new method in which an egg is surgically removed from the mother's ovary, then inserted into the lower end of the fallopian tube. It is then fertilized by normal mating. Such a method applied to human beings may help women with blocked fallopian tubes to bear children.

ran into dense bushes; and at the python alarm, they looked down at the ground. The researchers also played recordings of the alarm calls through a loudspeaker at times when no leopards, eagles, or pythons were nearby. The monkeys responded to the recorded alarm calls just as they did to the real alarm calls.

The study also showed that adult vervets were more selective in giving alarm calls than younger monkeys and infants. The young ones were likely to sound an alarm on seeing such animals or objects as wart hogs, pigeons, or falling leaves. Even so, the young vervets still followed certain broad categories of warnings. They sounded the leopard alarm mainly for land mammals, the eagle alarm for birdlike objects, and the python call for long, thin objects on the ground.

Vervet mothers recognized the recorded alarm calls of their own offspring and responded to them quicker than did other females. They looked immediately toward the loudspeaker playing the predator noise and moved

toward it as if to attack it or drive it away. Other adult females looked at the appropriate mother when a young monkey sounded an alarm. This suggested to the researchers that all the females in a troop of monkeys know the individual voices of each youngster and its mother.

These studies showed that vervet monkeys living in the wild learn to categorize dangerous objects and situations in their environment and to give calls that warn of each specific danger. This proved that captive primates' ability to learn and use signals to identify objects in laboratory settings stems from their ability to develop survival communication systems while living in the wild.

Froggy went a-courtin'. Zoologist Michael J. Ryan of Cornell University's Langmuir Laboratory reported in July 1980 that he had discovered important elements of frog mating behavior by electronically synthesizing male calling, or mating, songs and studying female responses in the tropical frog *Physalaemus pustulosus*. Ryan meas-

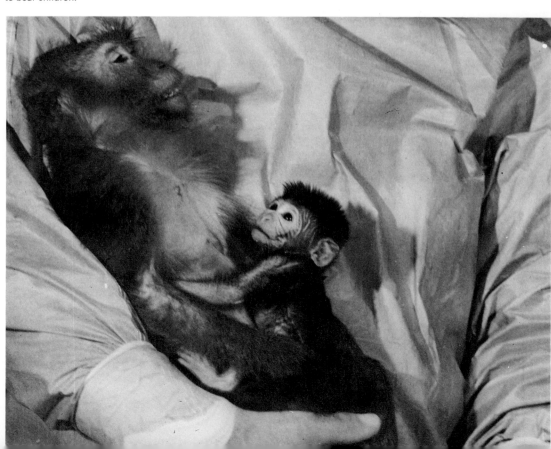

"You realize it's forty years since we crawled out of the water, Edith?"

Zoology

Continued

ured, marked for identification, and then released 185 male frogs captured near a pool on Barro Colorado Island in the Panama Canal Zone. He wanted to determine whether female frogs coming to the pool to breed selected only males that announced their presence with calling songs, or whether they selected males at random.

Ryan compared the size of each male that mated with the average size of all males present on a particular night. Females were usually in the pool only on the night they mated. The results showed that larger males were more likely to acquire mates.

He noted that females selected the larger males before seeing any of the calling frogs. The frogs' mating pattern is such that a female is attracted to the song of an unseen male, then makes her way to him, and mates. Because the female cannot see or touch the male whose song she found to be most attractive until she is quite close to him, Ryan reasoned that there must be something in the song that indicates the size of the male.

Ryan studied the male songs to determine the difference between those of small and large frogs. The basic frog song is composed of a whine followed by several "chucks." He found that small male frogs produce higher-frequency "chucks." To test whether females respond to the sound frequency of "chucks," he synthesized frog songs with identical whines but with "chucks" of different frequencies.

Loudspeakers located at opposite sides of the pool broadcast two synthesized calls simultaneously to an attentive female. All the females Ryan tested responded to the loudspeaker that produced the call with lower-frequency "chucks," indicating that females can discriminate among males of different sizes according to the frequency of this part of the mating call.

Ryan believes female frogs choose large males because they are older and, therefore, have qualities that enable them to survive. Females that mate with these males stand a better chance of passing such genetic benefits on to their own offspring. [William J. Bell]

World Book Supplement

Revised articles on subjects in
science and technology reprinted
from the 1981 edition of *The
World Book Encyclopedia.*

322   Brain

331   Bacteria

334   Radiocarbon

335   Drug Abuse

336   Videodisc

BRAIN

BRAIN is the master control center of the body. The brain constantly receives information from the senses about conditions both inside the body and outside it. The brain rapidly analyzes this information and then sends out messages that control body functions and actions. The brain also stores information from past experience, which makes learning and remembering possible. In addition, the brain is the source of thoughts, moods, and emotions.

In such simple animals as worms and insects, the brain consists of small groups of nerve cells. All animals with a backbone have a complicated brain made up of many parts. Animals that have an exceptionally well-developed brain include apes, dolphins, and whales. Human beings have the most highly developed brain of all. It consists of billions of interconnected cells and enables people to use language, solve difficult problems, and create works of art.

The human brain is a grayish-pink, jellylike ball with many ridges and grooves on its surface. A newborn baby's brain weighs less than 1 pound (0.5 kilogram). By the time a person is 6 years old, the brain has reached its full weight of about 3 pounds (1.4 kilograms). Most of the brain cells are present at birth, and so the increase in weight comes mainly from growth of the cells. During this six-year period, a person learns and acquires new behavior patterns at the fastest rate in life.

A network of blood vessels supplies the brain with the vast quantities of oxygen and food that it requires. The human brain makes up only about 2 per cent of the total body weight, but it uses about 20 per cent of the oxygen used by the entire body when at rest. The brain can go without oxygen for only three to five minutes before serious damage results.

The brain is located at the upper end of the spinal cord. This cable of nerve cells extends from the neck about two-thirds the way down the backbone. The spinal cord carries messages between the brain and other parts of the body. In addition, 12 pairs of nerves connect the brain directly with certain parts of the body. For more information about the nervous system and the brain's place in it, see NERVOUS SYSTEM.

The brain works somewhat like both a computer and a chemical factory. Brain cells produce electrical signals and send them from cell to cell along pathways called *circuits*. As in a computer, these electrical circuits receive, process, store, and retrieve information. Unlike a computer, however, the brain creates its electrical signals by chemical means. The proper functioning of the brain depends on many complicated chemical substances produced by brain cells.

Scientists in various fields work together to study the structure, function, and chemical composition of the brain. This field of study, called *neuroscience* or *neurobiology*, is rapidly increasing our understanding of the brain. But much remains to be learned. Scientists do not yet know how much of the brain's activity can be explained by current laws of physics and chemistry.

This article deals chiefly with the human brain. The last section of the article discusses the brain in various kinds of animals.

The Parts of the Brain

The brain has three main divisions: (1) the cerebrum, (2) the cerebellum, and (3) the brain stem. Each part consists chiefly of nerve cells, called *neurons*, and supporting cells, called *glia*.

The Cerebrum makes up about 85 per cent of the weight of the human brain. A thin layer of nerve cell bodies called the *cerebral cortex* or *cortex* forms the outermost part of the cerebrum. Most of the cerebrum beneath the cortex consists of nerve cell fibers. Some of these fibers connect various parts of the cortex. Others link the cortex with the cerebellum, brain stem, and spinal cord.

The cerebral cortex folds in upon itself and so forms a surface with many ridges and grooves. This folding greatly increases the surface area of the cortex within the limited space of the skull. Some areas of the cortex, called the *sensory cortex*, receive messages from the sense organs as well as messages of touch and tempera-

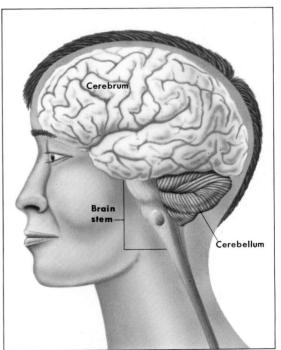

WORLD BOOK diagram by Colin Bidgood

The Human Brain weighs about 3 pounds (1.3 kilograms) and has three major divisions—the cerebrum, cerebellum, and brain stem. The parts of the brain are grayish-pink or white, not the colors used for clarity in the illustrations for this article.

Samuel Bogoch, the contributor of this article, is Associate Research Professor of Biochemistry at the Boston University School of Medicine and Adjunct Associate Professor of Psychiatry at Cornell University Medical College. He is also the author of The Future of the Brain Sciences *and* The Biochemistry of Memory.

ture from throughout the body. Other areas, called the *motor cortex*, send out nerve impulses that control the movements of all the skeletal muscles. However, the largest portion of the cortex is the *association cortex*. The association cortex analyzes, processes, and stores information and so makes possible all our higher mental abilities, such as thinking, speaking, and remembering.

A *fissure* (large groove) divides the cerebrum into halves called the *left cerebral hemisphere* and the *right cerebral hemisphere*. The hemispheres are connected by bundles of nerve fibers, the largest of which is the *corpus callosum*. Each hemisphere, in turn, is divided into four *lobes* (regions). They are (1) the frontal lobe, at the front; (2) the temporal lobe, at the lower side; (3) the parietal lobe, in the middle; and (4) the occipital lobe, at the rear. Each lobe is named after the bone of the skull that lies above it. Fissures in the cerebral cortex form the boundaries between the lobes. The two major fissures are the *central fissure* and the *lateral fissure*.

The Cerebellum is the part of the brain most responsible for balance, posture, and the coordination of movement. It is located below the back part of the cerebrum. The cerebellum consists of a large mass of closely packed *folia* (leaflike bundles of nerve cells). The cerebellum has a right hemisphere and a left hemisphere, which are joined by a finger-shaped structure called the *vermis*. Nerve pathways connect the right half of the cerebellum with the left cerebral hemisphere and the right side of the body. Pathways from the left half connect with the right cerebral hemisphere and the left side of the body.

The Brain Stem is a stalklike structure that connects the cerebrum with the spinal cord. The bottom part of the brain stem is called the *medulla oblongata* or *medulla*. The medulla has nerve centers that control breathing, heartbeat, and many other vital body processes. The major sensory and motor pathways between the body and the cerebrum cross over as they pass through the medulla. Each cerebral hemisphere thus controls the opposite side of the body.

Just above the medulla is the *pons*, which connects the hemispheres of the cerebellum. The pons also contains nerve fibers that link the cerebellum and the cerebrum. Above the pons lies the *midbrain*. Nerve centers in the midbrain help control movements of the eyes and the size of the pupils.

At the upper end of the brain stem are the *thalamus* and the *hypothalamus*. There are actually two thalami, one on the left side of the brain stem and one on the right side. Each thalamus receives nerve impulses from various parts of the body and routes them to the appropriate areas of the cerebral cortex. The thalami also relay impulses from one part of the brain to another. The hypothalamus regulates body temperature, hunger, and other internal conditions. It also controls the activity of the nearby *pituitary gland*, the master gland of the body (see PITUITARY GLAND).

A network of nerve fibers called the *reticular formation* lies deep within the brain stem. The reticular formation helps regulate the brain's level of awareness. Sensory messages that pass through the brain stem stimulate the reticular formation, which in turn stimulates activity and alertness throughout the cerebral cortex.

The Cerebrum The cerebrum consists of a left hemisphere and a right hemisphere. Each hemisphere is divided into four lobes by grooves in the *cerebral cortex*, a layer of nerve cell bodies that covers the cerebrum. This diagram shows the left cerebral cortex and indicates some major functions of each of its parts.

WORLD BOOK diagram by Colin Bidgood

Each part of the motor or somesthetic area of the cerebral cortex is linked to a specific body part. The largest areas of the motor cortex control the body parts that make the most complex movements. The largest areas of the somesthetic cortex receive impulses from the most sensitive body parts.

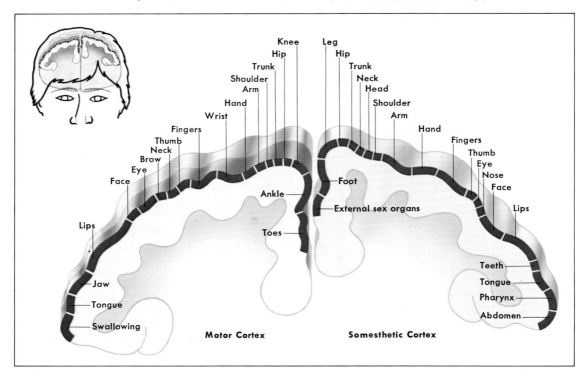

Motor Cortex

Somesthetic Cortex

Brain Cells. The human brain has from 10 billion to 100 billion neurons and a far greater number of glia. The neurons transmit nerve impulses, and the glia surround and so support the neurons. The glia also perform many other important tasks. For example, certain glia keep the brain free of injured or diseased neurons by engulfing and digesting them.

As in all other cells, a thin membrane forms the outermost layer of each neuron. However, a neuron's membrane is highly specialized to carry nerve impulses. Each neuron consists of a cell body and a number of tubelike fibers. The longest fiber, called the *axon*, carries nerve impulses from the cell body to other neurons. Short, branching fibers called *dendrites* pick up impulses from the axons of other neurons and transmit them to the cell body. The point where any branch of one neuron transmits a nerve impulse to a branch of another neuron is called a *synapse*. Each neuron may form synapses with thousands of other nerve cells.

Some axons have a coating of fatty material called *myelin*. The myelin insulates the fiber and speeds the transmission of impulses along its surface. Myelin is white, and tightly-packed axons covered with it form *white matter*. The neuron cell bodies and the axons without myelin sheaths make up the *gray matter* of the brain. The cerebral cortex is made up of gray matter, and most of the rest of the cerebrum consists of white matter.

How the Brain is Protected

The hard, thick bones of the *cranium* (skull) shield the brain from blows that could otherwise seriously

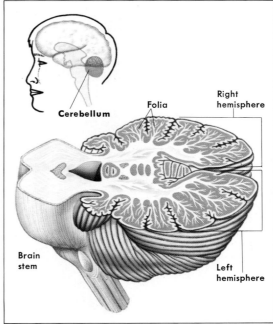

WORLD BOOK diagrams by Colin Bidgood

The Cerebellum is the part of the brain most responsible for balance and coordination. The cross section of the cerebellum clearly shows the *folia*, the leaflike bundles of nerve cells that make up the structure's left and right hemispheres.

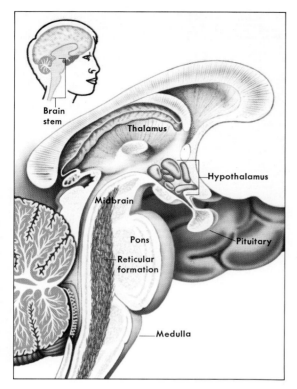

The Brain Stem is a stalklike structure that links the cerebrum with the spinal cord. It contains vital nerve pathways and control centers for many body functions. The larger diagram shows a cross section of the brain stem and the nearby pituitary gland.

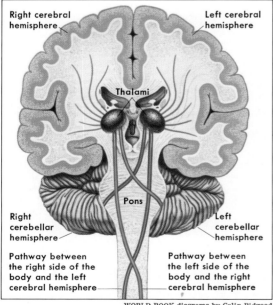

WORLD BOOK diagrams by Colin Bidgood

Nerve Pathways Cross Over as they pass through the brain stem. As a result, each cerebral hemisphere controls the opposite side of the body. Similarly, each side of the cerebrum is linked with the opposite side of the cerebellum.

injure it. In addition, three protective membranes called *meninges* cover the brain. The outermost membrane is the tough *dura mater*, which lines the inner surface of the cranium. A thinner membrane, the *arachnoid*, lies just beneath the dura mater. The delicate *pia mater* directly covers the brain. It follows the folds of the brain's surface and contains blood vessels that carry blood to and from the cerebral cortex.

A clear liquid called *cerebrospinal fluid* separates the pia mater and the arachnoid. This fluid forms a thin cushioning layer between the soft tissues of the brain and the hard bones of the cranium. Cerebrospinal fluid also fills four spaces called *ventricles* within the brain. Tissues inside the ventricles produce the fluid, which flows through small openings into the space between the pia mater and the arachnoid. The cerebrospinal fluid is absorbed into the blood through tiny blood vessels in the arachnoid.

The *blood-brain barrier* safeguards brain tissues from the damage that could result from contact with certain large molecules carried in the bloodstream. Substances in the blood reach body tissues by passing through the thin walls of tiny blood vessels called *capillaries*. Much of this flow occurs through the spaces between the cells that make up the capillary walls. In brain capillaries, the cells are more tightly packed than in other capillaries, and the passage of substances from blood to brain cells is carefully restricted. The brain needs some kinds of large molecules for nutrition, however. The capillary walls have certain enzymes and other properties that enable these particular molecules to pass through.

The Work of the Brain

Most functions of the brain involve the coordinated activity of many brain areas. Scientists have developed numerous methods to study these functions. Experiments on animal brains have revealed a great deal about the workings of various areas of the brain. Studying the human brain is more difficult because of the risk of interfering with its vital functions. However, scientists have learned much about the normal activity of the human brain by studying people with brain damage caused by illness or injury.

Surgeons have mapped the functions of many areas of the cerebral cortex by electrically stimulating the brain during brain surgery. Brain operations do not require that the patients be unconscious because the brain feels no pain directly. Thus, the patients can tell the surgeons what they experience when particular brain areas are stimulated.

Brain surgery has revealed that certain functions of the cerebrum occur chiefly in one hemisphere or the other. Surgeons treat some cases of epilepsy by cutting the corpus callosum, which connects the cerebral hemispheres. This operation produces a condition called the *split brain*, in which no communication occurs between the hemispheres. Studies of split-brain patients suggest that the left hemisphere largely controls our ability to use language, mathematics, and logic. The right hemisphere is the main center for musical ability, the recognition of complicated visual patterns, and the expression of emotion.

In Receiving Sensory Messages. The receiving and interpreting of sensory messages is chiefly the task of the cerebral cortex. Various parts of the body send nerve impulses to the thalamus, which routes them to the appropriate areas of the cerebral cortex. An area of the sensory cortex called the *somesthetic cortex* receives messages that it interprets as bodily sensations, such as touch and temperature. The somesthetic cortex lies in the parietal lobe of each hemisphere along the central fissure. Each part of the somesthetic cortex receives and interprets impulses from a specific part of the body.

Other specialized areas of the cerebrum receive the sensory impulses of seeing, hearing, taste, and smell. Impulses from the eyes travel to the visual cortex in the occipital lobes. Portions of the temporal lobes receive messages from the ears. The area for taste lies buried in the lateral fissure, and the center of smell is on the underside of the frontal lobes. The various areas of the cerebrum interpret the nerve impulses from the sense organs as visual images, sounds, tastes, and smells.

In Controlling Movement. Some reflex actions do not involve the brain. If a person touches a hot stove, for example, pain impulses flash to the spinal cord, which immediately sends back a message to withdraw the hand. However, the brain plays the major role in controlling our conscious movements as well as those we are unaware of. Deep within the cerebrum lie separate collections of neurons called *basal ganglia* or *basal nuclei*. The basal ganglia help control subconscious movements involved in such activities as walking or eating. Areas in the brain stem control the movements of the body's *involuntary muscles*, which line the walls of the stomach, intestines, and blood vessels.

The cerebral cortex and the cerebellum together largely regulate voluntary movements. The motor cortex in each cerebral hemisphere sends nerve impulses to the particular muscles used in an activity, such as writing or throwing a ball. The motor cortex lies in the frontal lobe in front of the central fissure. Each section of the motor cortex controls the movements of a specific part of the body. The largest areas of the motor cortex control those parts of the body that make the most complicated and precise movements. Thus, a large area of cortex controls the lips and tongue, which make complex movements in speaking. Much smaller areas control the relatively simple movements made by such body parts as the back and shoulders.

Because the major motor pathways to the body cross over in the brain stem, the motor cortex of the left hemisphere controls movements on the right side of the body. Similarly, the right motor cortex directs movements on the left side of the body. More than 90 per cent of all people are right-handed because the left motor cortex, which directs their right hand, is dominant over the right motor cortex, which directs their left hand.

The cerebellum coordinates the muscle movements ordered by the motor cortex. Nerve impulses alert the cerebellum when the motor cortex orders a part of the body to perform a certain action. Almost instantly, impulses from that part of the body inform the cerebellum of how the action is being carried out. The cerebellum compares the movement with the intended movement and then signals the motor cortex to make any necessary corrections. In this way, the cerebellum ensures that the body moves smoothly and efficiently.

In the Use of Language. Many parts of the brain are involved in our use of language. The centers of vision and hearing enable us to understand written or spoken words. The motor cortex and the cerebellum order the proper movements of the lips, tongue, and other organs of speech. In addition, two areas of the association cortex are vital in the use of language. They are *Wernicke's area* in the temporal lobe and *Broca's area* in the frontal lobe. Scientists estimate that about 97 per cent of all people have these two areas only in the

The Role of the Brain in the Use of Language

When we read a word, the vision center of the brain converts impulses from the eyes into an image of the word, *below left*. The angular gyrus transforms this visual image into its associated sound pattern, which Wernicke's area then interprets. If we wish to speak the word, Wernicke's area sends impulses to Broca's area, which issues instructions for the necessary muscle movements, *center*. On the basis of these instructions, the motor cortex orders the muscles of the speech organs to move and alerts the cerebellum to coordinate their movement, *right*.

WORLD BOOK diagrams by Colin Bidgood

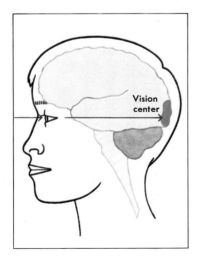
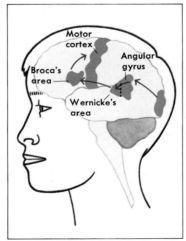
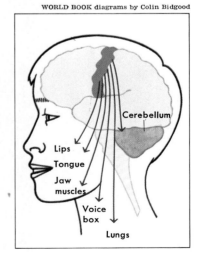

left cerebral hemisphere. The remaining 3 per cent have the language areas in both hemispheres.

When we hear a word, Wernicke's area interprets the meaning of the sound pattern. When we read a word, a brain area called the *angular gyrus* converts the visual image into its associated sound, which Wernicke's area then interprets. Wernicke's area also formulates the sentences we speak. Broca's area supplies detailed instructions for the muscle movements required for speaking a particular word. These instructions are sent to the motor cortex, which orders the movements.

In Regulating Body Processes. The main control centers for body processes are in the brain stem. Nerve centers in the medulla regulate such body functions as breathing, heartbeat, and blood flow. Other areas within the brain stem control swallowing and the movements of the stomach and intestines.

The hypothalamus also has nerve centers that control certain body processes. Most of these centers maintain constant conditions within the body. For example, some centers regulate the amount of water in the body. Certain neurons in various parts of the body detect changes in the level of water and relay this information to the hypothalamus. If the water level is too low, the hypothalamus produces the sensation of thirst, which causes the person to drink water. At the same time, the hypothalamus sends messages that cause the kidneys to reduce the amount of water they remove from the body. If the water level becomes too high, the messages from the hypothalamus eliminate thirst and increase the amount of water removed by the kidneys. Other centers in the hypothalamus operate on the same principle in regulating hunger and body temperature.

A slender stalk of tissue connects the hypothalamus with the master gland of the body, the pituitary. The hypothalamus indirectly regulates many body processes by controlling the pituitary's production and release of chemical messengers called *hormones*. Among other functions, these hormones regulate the body's rate of growth and its sexual and reproductive processes.

In Producing Emotions. The emotions we experience involve many areas of the brain as well as other body organs. A group of brain structures called the *limbic system* plays a central role in the production of emotions. This system consists of portions of the temporal lobes and parts of the hypothalamus and thalamus.

An emotion may be provoked by a message from a sense organ or by a thought in the cerebral cortex. In either case, nerve impulses are produced that reach the limbic system. These impulses stimulate different areas of the system, depending on the kind of sensory message or thought. For example, the impulses might activate parts of the system that produce pleasant feelings involved in such emotions as joy and love. Or the impulses might stimulate areas that produce unpleasant feelings associated with anger or fear.

In Thinking and Remembering. Scientists have only an elementary understanding of the extraordinarily complicated processes of thinking and remembering. Thinking involves processing information over circuits in the association cortex and other parts of the brain. These circuits enable the brain to combine information stored in the memory with information gathered by the senses. Scientists are just beginning to understand the brain's simplest circuits. The forming of abstract ideas

and the study of difficult subjects must require circuits of truly astonishing complexity. Explanations of these types of thinking are still beyond scientists' understanding of the brain.

Scientists also know little about the physical basis of memory. But evidence suggests that memories may be formed through the establishment of new brain circuits or the alteration of existing circuits. Either process would involve changes at the synapses—that is, at the points where impulses pass from one neuron to another. These changes may be controlled by *glycoproteins* or other large molecules at the synapses. Extensive research will be required to verify this general explanation of memory formation and to discover the specific details of the processes involved.

The Chemistry of the Brain

As in all other cells, many complex chemical processes occur within the neurons of the brain. However, some chemical processes occur only within and among neurons. Scientists are especially interested in gaining a fuller understanding of these processes and how they relate to the transmission of nerve impulses.

A nerve impulse is an electrical and chemical process controlled by the nerve cell membrane. The process involves *ions* (electrically charged atoms) of the chemical elements sodium and potassium. The membrane, which has pores, maintains varying concentrations of these ions inside the neuron and in its surrounding fluids. As the membrane selectively allows ions to enter and leave the cell, an electric charge—the nerve impulse—travels along the neuron. For more details about this process, see NERVOUS SYSTEM (How Nerves Carry Impulses). The rest of this section discusses the chemicals that transmit impulses from neuron to neuron.

The Brain's Chemical Messengers. Certain chemicals called *neurotransmitters* make it possible for a nerve impulse to travel from the axon of one neuron to the dendrite of another. An impulse cannot be transmitted electrically across the *synaptic cleft*, the tiny gap between the axon and the dendrite. Instead, when an impulse reaches the end of the axon, it triggers the release of neurotransmitter molecules from the cell. These molecules cross the synaptic cleft and attach themselves to sites called *receptors* on the dendrite of the other neuron. This action alters the electrical activity of the receiving neuron in one of two ways. Some transmitters stimulate the neuron to produce a nerve impulse. Others tend to prevent the neuron from producing an impulse.

The brain produces many kinds of chemicals that are used as neurotransmitters. The most common ones include *acetylcholine, dopamine, norepinephrine,* and *serotonin.* The chemicals are not distributed evenly throughout the brain. Each is found only or primarily in specific areas. For example, the cell bodies of neurons that contain dopamine are in the midbrain of the brain stem. The axons of these cells reach into other areas, including the frontal lobes of the cerebrum and an area near the center of the brain called the *corpus striatum*. These dopamine pathways function in the regulation of emotions and in the control of complex movements.

During the 1970's, researchers discovered that morphine and related drugs relieve pain by attaching to receptors in certain regions of the brain. This discovery suggested the fascinating possibility that the brain produces its own painkillers that attach to these same receptors. Further research led to the discovery of *endorphins* and *enkephalins*, two types of neurotransmitters that bind to these receptors.

Brain Chemistry and Mental Illness. All the brain's functions depend on the normal action of neurotransmitters. An excess or deficiency of any transmitter may lead to a serious disorder in thought, mood, or behavior. For example, studies have suggested that chemical imbalances in the brain play a significant role in several types of mental illness. There is some evidence that the brain produces too much dopamine in a severe mental illness called *schizophrenia*. This excess of dopamine may create emotional disturbances and cause the victim to see things and hear sounds that do not exist.

Disturbances in brain chemistry may also be involved in *manic-depressive psychosis*, another mental illness. A victim of this illness has alternate periods of *mania* (extreme joy and overactivity) and *depression* (sadness). Some research suggests that an excess of dopamine and norepinephrine causes mania and that a deficiency of the same chemicals causes depression.

How Drugs Affect Brain Chemistry. Psychiatrists treat some mental illnesses with drugs that restore the brain's normal chemical activity. For example, many tranquilizers used to relieve the symptoms of schizophrenia work by blocking the brain's receptors for dopamine. Similarly, some drugs used to treat depression increase the level of dopamine and norepinephrine by stopping the action of an enzyme that breaks down the transmitters into smaller, inactive molecules.

Certain drugs produce a feeling of well-being or reduce tension and worry by temporarily altering the normal chemistry of the brain. For example, *amphetamines* increase mental activity by causing brain cells to release an excessive amount of dopamine. Abuse of amphetamines can create mental disturbances like those that occur in some forms of schizophrenia. A person's senses, emotions, thought processes, and judgment can be altered dramatically and dangerously by *hallucinogenic drugs*. These drugs include mescaline, psilocybin, and LSD (lysergic acid diethylamide). Each of these drugs structurally resembles one or more neurotransmitters. Mescaline resembles dopamine and norepinephrine, and LSD and psilocybin resemble serotonin. Scientists think a hallucinogenic drug may produce its effects by combining with the brain's receptors for the natural transmitter that it resembles. Hallucinogenic drugs may produce disturbances in brain chemistry that last long after their contact with the brain.

Disorders of the Brain

Injuries, diseases, and inherited disorders can damage the brain. However, the seriousness of brain damage depends chiefly on the area of the brain involved rather than on the cause of the damage. Disorders that destroy brain cells are especially serious because the body cannot replace the lost cells. In some cases, however, undamaged areas of the brain may eventually take over control of some functions formerly carried out by the damaged areas.

Modern instruments and techniques enable physicians to diagnose brain disorders earlier and more accurately than in the past. For example, an instrument called an *electroencephalograph* (*EEG*) measures the patterns of electrical activity produced by the brain. Differences from the normal EEG patterns may indicate damage to the brain and also help locate the area of the brain involved. Another important technique is *computerized axial tomography*, or *CAT scan* for short. It involves X-raying the brain in detail from many angles. A computer then analyzes the X-ray data and constructs a cross-sectional image of the brain on a television screen.

Injuries are the leading cause of brain damage among people under 50 years of age. A blow to the head may cause temporary unconsciousness without permanent damage. Severe injuries to the head may cause more serious brain damage. Head injuries before, during, or shortly after birth may cause *cerebral palsy*. There are several types of cerebral palsy, all of which involve lack of control of muscle movements.

Stroke is the most common serious disorder of the brain. A stroke occurs when the blood supply to part of the brain is cut off. Nerve cells in the affected areas die, and the victim may lose the ability to carry out functions controlled by those areas. Many stroke victims suffer paralysis on one side of the body. Other symptoms include difficulty in speaking or in understanding language. Most strokes result from damage to the blood vessels caused by *hypertension* (high blood pressure) or *arteriosclerosis* (hardening of the arteries). Some victims of massive strokes die, but many other stroke victims survive and recover at least partially.

Tumors are abnormal growths that can cause severe brain damage. The effects of a tumor depend on its size and location. A tumor may destroy brain cells in the area surrounding it. As the tumor grows, it also creates pressure, which may damage other areas of the brain or at least interfere with their normal function. Symptoms of a tumor include headache, seizures, unusual sleepiness, a change in personality, or disturbances in sense perception or speech. Surgery cures many *benign* (noncancerous) tumors. For *malignant* (cancerous) tumors, physicians combine surgery with treatment with drugs or radiation.

Infectious Diseases. A number of diseases caused by bacteria or viruses can damage the brain. The most common of these infectious diseases are *encephalitis* and *meningitis*, either of which may be caused by bacteria or viruses. Encephalitis is an inflammation of the brain. *Meningitis* is an inflammation of the meninges, the membranes that cover the brain and spinal cord. *Chorea* is a disease of the brain that mainly affects children from 7 to 15 years old. Most cases of chorea occur with rheumatic fever and may be caused by the same bacteria which cause that disease. A virus disease called *poliomyelitis* attacks the brain and spinal cord. A vaccine to prevent polio was developed in the 1950's.

Genetic Disorders. Our *genes* (the hereditary materials in cells) carry instructions for the development of the brain. These instructions are extremely complex, and so errors occasionally occur. These errors can lead to serious defects in the structure and functioning of the brain. Some infants are mentally retarded at birth because genetic errors caused the brain to develop improperly

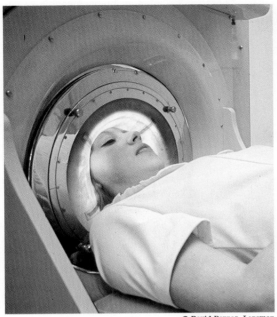

© David Barnes, Lensman

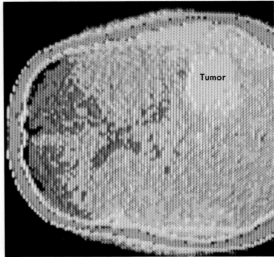

Georgetown University Medical Center

Detecting Brain Tumors is made simpler by the use of an instrument called a *CAT scanner*. This instrument X-rays the brain from many angles, *left*. From the X-ray data, the scanner's computer constructs an image of the brain on a screen, *above*.

during the mother's pregnancy. In *Down's syndrome*, for example, an extra *chromosome* is present. Chromosomes are structures in the cell nucleus that contain the genes. The extra chromosome causes mental retardation as well as physical defects.

Some children suffer severe brain damage after birth because of an inherited deficiency of an enzyme that the body needs to use foods properly. For example, a child who has *phenylketonuria* (PKU) lacks an enzyme needed to convert a certain *amino acid* (protein part) into a form the body can use. This amino acid, *phenylalanine*, accumulates in the blood and damages developing brain tissues. A diet low in phenylalanine can prevent brain damage in PKU victims.

Some genetic errors do not cause damage to the brain until later in life. *Huntington's disease*, for example, strikes most victims during middle age. It causes various areas of the cerebrum to wither away. Involuntary, jerky movements are the main early symptoms of Huntington's disease, but it eventually leads to incurable mental disintegration.

Heredity also plays a role in some types of mental illness. Many children of schizophrenics apparently inherit a tendency to develop schizophrenia. Studies have also revealed an inherited tendency for manic-depressive psychosis. These tendencies may involve inherited defects in brain chemistry. Researchers continue to study these tendencies and how they interact with environmental conditions to produce mental illness.

During the 1970's, geneticists developed techniques whereby specific genes can be added to or removed from an organism. These techniques may make possible new treatments for hereditary diseases of the brain.

Other Brain Disorders include (1) epilepsy, (2) multiple sclerosis (MS), and (3) Parkinson's disease. Scientists do not know the cause of these disorders.

Epilepsy. Victims of epilepsy suffer seizures that occur when many nerve cells in one area of the brain release abnormal bursts of impulses. A seizure may cause temporary uncontrolled muscle movements or unconsciousness. Physicians treat epilepsy with drugs that reduce the number of seizures or prevent them entirely.

Multiple Sclerosis develops when axons in parts of the brain and spinal cord lose their myelin sheaths. As a result, the axons cannot carry nerve impulses properly. Symptoms vary depending on what brain areas are affected, but they may include double vision, loss of balance, and weakness in an arm or leg. Treatment with drugs can relieve some of the symptoms, but no cure is yet known.

Parkinson's Disease is characterized by slowness of movement, muscle rigidity, and trembling. These conditions result in part from the destruction of the nerve pathways that use dopamine as a transmitter. Treatment with the drug L-dopa replaces the missing dopamine and so can relieve the symptoms of Parkinson's disease, though it cannot cure the disease.

The Brain in Animals

Most *invertebrates* (animals without a backbone) do not have a well-developed brain. Instead, they have clusters of nerve cells, called *ganglia*, that coordinate the workings of various parts of the body. All *vertebrates* (animals with a backbone) have some kind of brain. Scientific evidence suggests that the complex brain in higher animals *evolved* (developed gradually) through the ages (see EVOLUTION).

In Invertebrates. The more advanced invertebrates, such as worms and insects, have some type of relatively simple brain. An earthworm, for example, has a large pair of ganglia in its head region, which control the worm's behavior on the basis of information received from the sense organs. An insect has a more complex brain, which consists of three pair of ganglia. The ganglia receive information from the sense organs and control such complex activities as feeding and flying.

BRAIN

Octopuses have the most highly developed brain among invertebrates. It is divided into several parts, the largest of which is the *optic lobe*. The optic lobe processes information from an octopus's eyes, which resemble the eyes of vertebrates in structure and function.

In Vertebrates, the brain can be divided into three main regions: (1) the forebrain, (2) the midbrain, and (3) the hindbrain. The midbrain is the most highly developed region in primitive vertebrates, such as fish and amphibians. In contrast, the forebrain, or cerebrum, makes up only a small part of the brain in these animals. As increasingly complex vertebrates evolved, two major changes occurred in the brain. The size and importance of the cerebrum increased enormously, and the relative size and importance of the midbrain decreased. The hindbrain consists of the medulla and the cerebellum. Its structure and function is basically the same in all vertebrates, though the cerebellum is larger and more complex in advanced animals.

Among fish and amphibians, the midbrain consists chiefly of two optic lobes. These lobes serve not only as the center of vision but also as the major area for coordinating sensory and motor impulses. A fish's cerebrum is composed of two small, smooth swellings that serve mainly as the center of smell. In amphibians, the cerebrum is slightly larger and is covered by a cortex.

In reptiles, some functions of the midbrain have been taken over by the cerebrum. A reptile's cerebrum is larger and more complex than that of a fish or amphibian. Within the cerebrum are basal ganglia. These small bundles of neurons form a major association area, where information is analyzed, processed, and stored. Some advanced reptiles have a small area of cerebral cortex that differs from the cortex in lower vertebrates. This area, called the *neocortex* (new cortex), functions as an important association area.

Birds have a cerebrum larger than that of fish, amphibians, and reptiles. But unlike some advanced reptiles, birds lack a neocortex. Instead, the dominant part of their brain consists of large, highly developed basal ganglia, which fill most of the interior of the cerebrum. The basal ganglia serve as the main association area and give birds an impressive ability to learn new behavior. They apparently also store the instruc-

Some Animal Brains Sharks and other fish have a relatively simple brain in which the cerebrum plays only a minor role. The cerebrum is larger in reptiles and birds, but it reaches its highest development in mammals, such as cats and apes. Of all animal brains, the ape's most closely resembles the human brain.

WORLD BOOK illustrations by Patricia J. Wynne

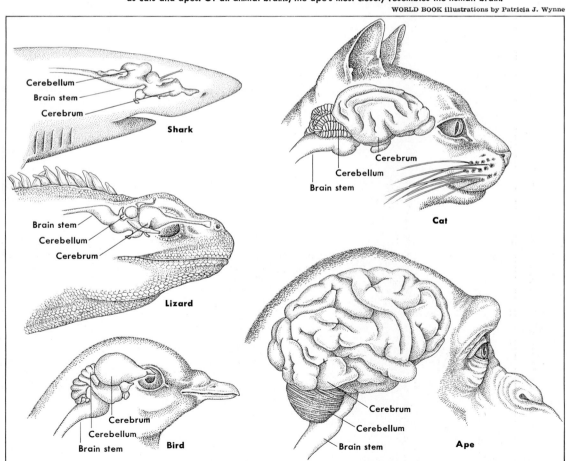

Shark

Lizard

Bird

Cat

Ape

tions for the many instinctive behavior patterns of birds. Birds also have a well-developed cerebellum, which coordinates all the sensory and motor impulses involved in flying.

The brain reaches its highest level of development in mammals. The neocortex forms nearly all the cerebral cortex of the mammalian brain, and the midbrain serves mainly as a relay center. The most primitive mammals, such as moles and shrews, have a relatively small cerebrum with a smooth cerebral cortex. More advanced mammals, such as horses and cats, have a larger cerebrum covered by a cortex with many ridges and grooves. Whales and dolphins have a large, highly developed brain. The brain in chimpanzees and other apes is even more highly developed. It resembles the human brain more closely than does the brain in all other species of animals.

SAMUEL BOGOCH

Related Articles in WORLD BOOK include:

Aneurysm	Epilepsy	Physiological
Aphasia	Huntington's Disease	Psychology
Biofeedback	Meningitis	Poliomyelitis
Cerebral	Mental Illness	Psychosis
Hemorrhage	Mental Retardation	Reflex Action
Cerebral Palsy	Multiple Sclerosis	Schizophrenia
Cerebrospinal	Nervous System	Skull
Fluid	Parkinson's Disease	Sleeping Sickness
Chorea	Penfield, Wilder G.	Stimulant
Electroenceph-	Perception	Stroke
alograph	Phrenology	Tay-Sachs Disease
Encephalitis		

Outline

I. **The Parts of the Brain**
   A. The Cerebrum   C. The Brain Stem
   B. The Cerebellum   D. Brain Cells

II. **How the Brain Is Protected**

III. **The Work of the Brain**
   A. In Receiving Sensory Messages
   B. In Controlling Movement
   C. In the Use of Language
   D. In Regulating Body Processes
   E. In Producing Emotion
   F. In Thinking and Remembering

IV. **The Chemistry of the Brain**
   A. The Brain's Chemical Messengers
   B. Brain Chemistry and Mental Illness
   C. How Drugs Affect Brain Chemistry

V. **Disorders of the Brain**
   A. Injuries   D. Infectious Diseases
   B. Stroke   E. Genetic Disorders
   C. Tumors   F. Other Brain Disorders

VI. **The Brain in Animals**
   A. In Invertebrates
   B. In Vertebrates

Questions

How much does the human brain weigh?
What is the most common serious disorder of the brain?
What is the function of the motor cortex?
What are the three main divisions of the human brain?
Which invertebrates have the most highly developed brain?
How does the blood-brain barrier safeguard the brain tissues?
Which brain areas are vital in the use of language?
How does the hypothalamus regulate the amount of water in the body?
Why are most people right-handed?
Which animals have a brain most similar to the human brain?

BACTERIA are simple organisms that consist of one cell. They are among the smallest living things. Most bacteria measure from 0.3 to 2.0 *microns* in diameter and can be seen only through a microscope. (One micron equals 0.001 millimeter or 0.000039 inch.) Some scientists classify bacteria as plants. Others believe bacteria are neither plants nor animals. These scientists classify bacteria as either *monerans* or *protists* (see MONERA; PROTISTA).

Bacteria exist almost everywhere. There are thousands of kinds of bacteria, most of which are harmless to human beings. Large numbers of bacteria live in the human body but cause no harm. Some species cause diseases, but many others are helpful.

The Importance of Bacteria

Helpful Bacteria. Certain kinds of bacteria live in the intestines of human beings and other animals. These bacteria help in digestion and in destroying harmful organisms. Intestinal bacteria also produce some vitamins needed by the body.

Bacteria that live in soil and water play a vital role in recycling carbon, nitrogen, sulfur, and other chemical elements used by living things. Many bacteria help *decompose* (break down) dead organisms and animal wastes into chemical elements. Without bacterial decomposition, the elements would remain in dead organisms and animal wastes, and all life would soon stop. Other bacteria help change chemical elements into forms that can be used by plants and animals. For example, certain kinds of bacteria convert nitrogen in the air and soil into nitrogen compounds that can be used by plants (see NITROGEN CYCLE).

A chemical process called *fermentation*, used in making alcoholic beverages and cheese and many other foods, is caused by various bacteria. Sewage treatment plants use bacteria to purify water. Bacteria are also used in making some drugs.

Bacterial cells resemble the cells of other living things in many ways, and so scientists study bacteria to learn about more complex organisms. For example, the study of bacteria has helped researchers understand how certain characteristics are transferred through heredity. Most species of bacteria reproduce quickly, enabling scientists to grow large quantities of the organisms for research.

Harmful Bacteria. Some kinds of bacteria cause diseases in human beings. These diseases include cholera, gonorrhea, leprosy, pneumonia, syphilis, tuberculosis, typhoid fever, and whooping cough. Bacteria enter the body through natural openings, such as the nose or mouth, or through breaks in the skin. In addition, air, food, and water carry bacteria from one person to another. Harmful bacteria prevent the body from functioning properly by destroying healthy cells.

Certain bacteria produce *toxins* (poisons), which cause such diseases as diphtheria, scarlet fever, and tetanus. Some toxins are produced by living bacteria, but others are released only after a bacterium dies. A form of food poisoning called *botulism* is caused by toxins from bacteria in improperly canned foods.

Bacteria that usually live harmlessly in the body may cause infections when a person's resistance to

BACTERIA

disease is low. For example, if bacteria in the throat reproduce faster than the body can dispose of them, a person may get a sore throat.

Bacteria also cause diseases in other animals and in plants. *Anthrax* is a bacterial disease that infects many animals, especially cattle and sheep. Plant diseases caused by bacteria include *fire blight*, which occurs in apple and pear trees, and *soft rot*, which decays some fruits and vegetables. Bacteria also cause growths called *crown galls*, which attack various plants.

Protection Against Harmful Bacteria. Many bacteria live on the skin and in the mouth, intestines, and breathing passages. However, the rest of the body tissues are normally free of bacteria. The skin, and the membranes that line the digestive and respiratory systems, prevent most harmful bacteria from entering the rest of the body. When harmful bacteria do enter the body, white blood cells surround and attack them. In addition, the blood produces substances called *antibodies*, which kill or weaken the invaders. Toxins are neutralized by certain antibodies known as *antitoxins*. Sometimes the body cannot make its own antitoxins fast enough. In such cases, a physician may inject an antitoxin from an animal, such as a horse or rabbit, or from another person.

Dead or weakened bacteria are used in making drugs called *vaccines*, which can prevent the diseases caused by those species of bacteria. Vaccines are injected into the body, causing the blood to produce antibodies that attack the bacteria. Some vaccines protect the body from infection for several years or even longer. Drugs called *antibiotics* are made from microorganisms that inhabit the air, soil, and water. Antibiotics can kill or weaken disease-causing bacteria. However, extensive use of antibiotics may cause bacteria to become resistant to the drugs.

People use chemicals called *antiseptics* to prevent bacteria from growing on living tissues. Other chemicals, known as *disinfectants*, are used to destroy bacteria in water and on such items as clothing and utensils. Bacteria can also be killed by heat, and heat is often used to sterilize food and utensils.

The Structure of Bacteria

Nearly all kinds of bacteria are enclosed by a tough protective layer called a *cell wall*. The cell wall gives the bacterium its shape and enables it to live in a wide range of environments. Some species are further enclosed by a *capsule*, a slimy layer outside the cell wall. The capsule makes the cell resistant to destructive chemicals. All bacteria have a *cell membrane*, an elastic, baglike structure just inside the cell wall. Small molecules of food enter the cell through pores in this membrane, but large molecules cannot pass through. Inside the membrane is the *cytoplasm*, a soft, jellylike substance. The cytoplasm contains many chemicals called *enzymes*, which help break down food and build cell parts.

Like the cells of all living things, bacterial cells contain the substance *DNA* (deoxyribonucleic acid). DNA controls a cell's growth, reproduction, and all other activities. The DNA of a bacterial cell forms an area of the cytoplasm called the *nuclear body*. In all other organisms except blue-green algae, the DNA is in the *nucleus*, a part of the cell separated from the cytoplasm by a membrane.

Scientists generally divide bacteria into four groups, according to shape. Round bacteria are called *cocci*, and rod-shaped ones are known as *bacilli*. Bacteria that look like bent rods are known as *vibrios*, and those shaped like spirals are called *spirilla*. Two or more bacteria linked together may be described by the prefixes *diplo-* (pair), *staphylo-* (cluster), or *strepto-* (chain). For example, *streptococci* are a type of round bacteria linked together in chains.

The Life of Bacteria

Where Bacteria Live. Bacteria live almost everywhere, even in places where other forms of life cannot survive. The air, water, and upper layers of soil contain many bacteria. Bacteria are always present in the digestive and respiratory systems and on the skin of human beings and other animals.

Certain bacteria, called *aerobes*, require oxygen to live, but others, known as *anaerobes*, can survive without it. Some anaerobes can exist either with or without oxygen. Other anaerobes cannot live with even a trace of oxygen in their environment.

Some bacteria protect themselves against a lack of food, oxygen, or water by forming a new, thicker cell membrane inside the old one. The cell material surrounding the new membrane dies. The remaining organism becomes inactive and is called a *bacterial spore*. Bacterial spores may live for decades or even longer be-

A Bacterial Cell

A bacterial cell may have up to three protective layers. These layers surround the cytoplasm, which contains the cell's nuclear body. Hairlike flagella extend through the layers and help the bacterium to move.

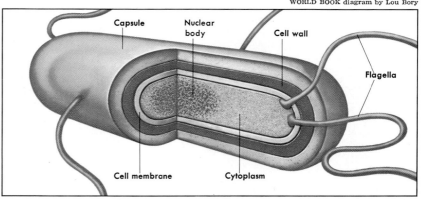

Capsule

Nuclear body

Cell wall

Flagella

Cell membrane

Cytoplasm

The Four Basic Kinds of Bacteria

Scientists classify bacteria according to shape. Cocci are round and are linked together. Bacilli look like rods, and vibrios resemble bent rods. Spirilla have a spiral shape. The type of spirilla shown below is harmless, but the other species illustrated can cause disease.

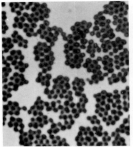

Leon J. Le Beau, U. of Ill.
Cocci

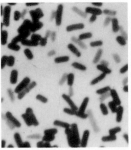

Leon J. Le Beau, U. of Ill.
Bacilli

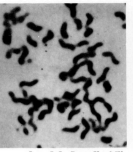

Leon J. Le Beau, U. of Ill.
Vibrios

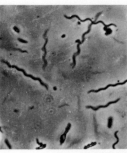

Eric V. Gravé
Spirilla

cause they can resist extremely high or low temperatures and other harsh conditions. If food, oxygen, and water again become available, the spores change back into active bacteria.

How Bacteria Move. Bacteria are carried long distances by air and water currents. Clothing, utensils, and other objects also carry bacteria from one place to another. Various kinds of bacteria have thin hairs, called *flagella*, that enable them to swim. Some species that lack flagella move by wriggling.

How Bacteria Obtain Food. Most kinds of bacteria, called *heterotrophic bacteria*, feed on other organisms. Some species, known as *autotrophic bacteria*, manufacture their own food. For example, *photosynthetic bacteria* make food from carbon dioxide, sunlight, and water. Certain bacteria are both autotrophic and heterotrophic, depending on the food available.

The majority of heterotrophic bacteria feed on dead organisms. Others are parasites. Some parasitic bacteria cause little or no harm to the host organism, but others cause diseases.

How Bacteria Reproduce. Most bacteria reproduce *asexually*—that is, each cell simply divides into two identical cells by a process called *binary fission*. The majority of bacteria reproduce quickly, and some species double their number every 20 minutes. If one of these cells were given enough food, more than a billion bacteria would be produced in 10 hours. Industrial and laboratory processes often produce such enormous numbers of bacteria. In nature, however, such a high rate of reproduction cannot be maintained because the bacteria soon exhaust their food supply.

When bacteria reproduce by binary fission, the DNA in each of the two resulting cells is identical to the DNA in the original bacterium. Some bacteria can exchange DNA by a kind of simple sexual process called *conjugation*. Conjugation involves the direct transfer of DNA from one type of bacterial cell, called a *male*, to another type, called a *female*. DNA also may be transferred from one bacterium to another by viruses. By transferring DNA, bacterial cells also transfer individual traits. For example, bacterial cells that are resistant to certain antibiotics may transfer this characteristic to nonresistant bacterial cells.

History

The first living things on the earth probably included simple forms of bacteria. Some of the oldest fossils ever found were bacteria that lived more than 3 billion years ago. Some scientists believe certain bacteria gradually developed into multicelled organisms that were the ancestors of the more complex plants and animals of today.

Bacteria were first seen in 1676 by Anton van Leeuwenhoek, a Dutch amateur scientist. For many years, scientists believed that bacteria came from nonliving matter. But during the late 1800's, Louis Pasteur, a French chemist, showed that only living things can produce other living things. Pasteur developed the first vaccines and showed that bacteria cause fermentation. Robert Koch, a German physician of the same period, discovered that specific bacteria cause certain diseases. He also developed techniques for isolating and growing pure cultures of bacteria.   DAVID SCHLESSINGER

NASA
Binary Fission occurs when a bacterium divides into two cells, each of which is identical to the original one.

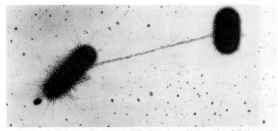

Charles C. Brinton, Jr., and Judith Carnahan, University of Pittsburgh
Conjugation is the transfer of DNA from one bacterium to another through a tube that connects the two organisms.

Radiocarbon Half-Life

Half the radiocarbon in an object *decays* (breaks down by releasing particles) about every 5,700 years. This period is the *half-life* of radiocarbon. Newly cut wood retains most of its radiocarbon. After 5,700 years, half the radiocarbon disappears. After about 11,400 years, a fourth remains.

Newly cut wood

Wood after 5,700 years

Wood after 11,400 years

WORLD BOOK diagrams by Jean Helmer

RADIOCARBON, or CARBON 14, is a radioactive isotope of carbon. It has an atomic weight of 14 and is heavier than ordinary carbon, which has an atomic weight of 12.011. Radiocarbon is used to determine the age of fossils and various other kinds of ancient objects. Researchers also use radiocarbon to study certain biological processes.

In nature, radiocarbon forms when high-energy atomic particles called *cosmic rays* smash into the earth's atmosphere. Cosmic rays cause atoms in the atmosphere to break down into electrons, neutrons, protons, and other particles. Some neutrons strike the nuclei of nitrogen atoms in the atmosphere. Each of these nuclei absorbs a neutron and then loses a proton. In this way, a nitrogen atom becomes a radiocarbon atom.

All living things contain radiocarbon. In the atmosphere, there is about one atom of radiocarbon for every trillion molecules of carbon dioxide gas. Plants absorb radiocarbon from the carbon dioxide in the air. Human beings and other animals take in radiocarbon chiefly from the food provided by plants.

Radiocarbon Dating is a process used to determine the age of an ancient object by measuring its radiocarbon content. This technique was developed in the late 1940's by Willard F. Libby, an American chemist. Archaeologists and geologists have used Libby's method to learn much about prehistoric human beings, animals, and plants that lived up to 50,000 years ago.

Radiocarbon atoms, like all radioactive substances, *decay* (break down by releasing particles) at an exact and uniform rate. Half of the radiocarbon disappears after about 5,700 years. Therefore, radiocarbon has a *half-life* of that period of time (see RADIOACTIVITY [Half-Life]). After about 11,400 years, a fourth of the original amount of radiocarbon remains. After another 5,700 years, only an eighth remains, and so on.

The radiocarbon in the tissues of a living organism decays extremely slowly, but it is continuously renewed as long as the organism lives. After the organism dies, it no longer takes in air or food, and so it no longer absorbs radiocarbon. The radiocarbon already in the tissues continues to decrease at a constant rate. This steady decay of radiocarbon at a known rate—a half-life of about 5,700 years—enables scientists to determine the age of an object.

In one method of radiocarbon dating, scientists burn a piece of the object and convert it to carbon dioxide gas. The carbon dioxide is purified, and the amount of radiocarbon in the purified carbon dioxide is measured with *radiation counters*. These instruments detect the electrons released by the radiocarbon atoms as the atoms change back into nitrogen atoms. The number of electrons emitted indicates the radiocarbon content.

After scientists measure an object's radiocarbon content, they compare it with the radiocarbon in tree-rings whose ages are known (see TREE [diagram: How a Tree Reveals Its History]). This technique enables them to compensate for small variations of radiocarbon content in the atmosphere at different times in the past. By doing so, scientists can convert an object's radiocarbon age to a more precise date.

Radiocarbon in Biology. Radiocarbon is used as a "tracer" to study various complex biological processes. In such research, scientists substitute a radiocarbon atom for an atom of a carbon molecule. Then they use a radiation counter to trace the path of the radiocarbon atom through a chemical reaction in an organism.

The radiocarbon used as a tracer is produced artificially in nuclear reactors. Artificial radiocarbon was first discovered in 1939 by two American chemists, Martin D. Kamen and Samuel Ruben.   RAINER BERGER

Radiocarbon Dating

Scientists determine the age of an ancient object by measuring its radiocarbon content. This process is called *radiocarbon dating.* Two methods of radiocarbon dating are described below.

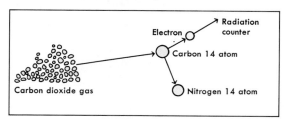

In the Traditional Method, a piece of the object is burned and converted to carbon dioxide gas. Radiocarbon (carbon 14) atoms in the gas release electrons as the radiocarbon changes into nitrogen 14. *Radiation counters* detect the number of electrons given off, which determines the object's radiocarbon content.

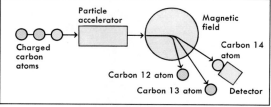

WORLD BOOK diagrams by Arthur Grebetz

In a Newer Method, a *particle accelerator* fires charged atoms from a small piece of the object into a magnetic field. The magnetic field deflects and separates the various carbon atoms. Then a *detector* counts individual carbon 14 atoms to determine the radiocarbon content of the object.

DRUG ABUSE is commonly defined as the harmful, nonmedical use of a mind-altering drug. The continual misuse of one or more such drugs, also called *psychoactive drugs*, can lead to poor health and to personality and behavioral problems. Some experts use the term *drug abuse* to refer only to problems with illegal drugs, also known as *street drugs*. Other authorities include the harmful use of legal drugs, even those prescribed by a physician.

Cultural attitudes about a drug help determine whether its use is considered harmful. For example, both alcohol and marijuana can produce similar intoxication. However, most Americans consider the moderate use of alcohol as acceptable, but many regard any use of marijuana as dangerous. Such cultural attitudes are reflected in a number of drug laws. As a result, the sale of alcohol is legal in most parts of the United States, but the sale of marijuana is not.

Cultural attitudes also make it difficult to distinguish between the accepted use of certain drugs and the abuse of those drugs. Alcoholic beverages have been used by people in many societies for thousands of years. Yet, alcohol ranks as one of the most widely abused drugs.

Commonly Abused Drugs. Many commonly abused drugs are illegal—that is, their possession and sale are forbidden by law. They include marijuana, cocaine, heroin, and such hallucinogenic drugs as LSD, PCP, and mescaline. Other abused drugs can be obtained legally only with a prescription from a doctor. They include amphetamines, barbiturates, morphine, and tranquilizers. Still other abused drugs can be purchased legally without a prescription in most countries. They include alcohol; nicotine, which is present in tobacco; and butyl nitrate and other inhalants, such as fumes from cleaning fluids, gasoline, and model airplane glue.

Why People Abuse Drugs. Many people continually use drugs because they want a pleasurable change in their state of mind. This pleasurable change may range from a mild "lift" to an intense psychoactive effect. Many people use such drugs as alcohol and marijuana to gain *euphoria* (a sense of well-being). This feeling is also called a "high." In larger doses, alcohol and marijuana can completely alter a person's feelings and perceptions. Other drugs that can cause such complete alterations include amphetamines, heroin, and PCP.

Many people start to experiment with drugs out of curiosity, for a thrill, as an expression of rebellion, or because their friends use drugs. Others turn to drugs to escape depression or other personal problems, including difficulties with their schoolwork, job, or family. Regardless of why drug use began, large numbers of individuals continue the practice because they become dependent on a drug.

Effects of Drug Abuse. The regular use of certain drugs causes *psychological dependence*—that is, the use of the drug becomes a hard-to-break habit. The continual use of alcohol, barbiturates, and especially heroin can also lead to *physical dependence*. This condition is usually called *addiction*.

An addict's body needs a drug so badly that pain or sickness results if he or she does not use the drug regularly. Addicts also tend to develop *drug tolerance*, a condition in which they need increasingly larger doses of a drug to achieve the same effect. Drug addiction

WORLD BOOK photo

Drug Education Programs have been started in many schools to help prevent student drug abuse. Police officers often take part by visiting classrooms to talk about the drug problem.

ranks as one of the most serious aspects of drug abuse. For example, alcoholism or heroin addiction can destroy or seriously damage an individual's health and personal life. See DRUG ADDICTION.

The immediate effects of many abused drugs also involve extensive risks. An overdose of alcohol, sleeping pills, or heroin can cause coma or death. Mixing drugs increases the risk of an overdose. For example, the use of alcohol and sleeping pills together can be more dangerous than a double dose of either of those drugs. Many illegal drugs are impure, and different batches have widely varying strengths. An overdose from a batch of great strength can kill the user.

Hallucinogenic drugs cause a person to have *hallucinations*—that is, to see or hear things that do not exist. They also may cause delusions. Users of these drugs may become fearful and harm themselves or others. PCP, a drug that causes users to feel apart from their surroundings, sometimes triggers violent reactions.

Alcohol, marijuana, and tranquilizers decrease mental alertness and muscle coordination. Every year, thousands of traffic deaths and injuries are caused by people who drive under the influence of these drugs, especially alcohol.

The cost of drug abuse in the United States exceeds $60 billion annually. This total includes the expense of hospitalization, property damage, and time lost from work. An even greater cost occurs in the personal and family destruction caused by drug abuse.

Signs of Drug Abuse. Most drugs that are continually misused can influence a person's behavior. In some cases, this influence is obvious. For example, excessive use of alcohol or sleeping pills causes poor muscle coordination, slurred speech, and sleepiness. People who use amphetamines and cocaine become restless and talkative. However, the effects of some drugs, such as tobacco and marijuana, may not be noticed.

Even parents and close friends may not be aware that a person is abusing drugs. Many drug abusers try to keep these activities secret. Long absences from home, school, or work, or a sharp drop in school or job performance, may indicate drug abuse. A sudden change in personality may also be a clue, but such a transformation often occurs without drugs.

Prevention of Drug Abuse. It is easier to prevent drug abuse than to stop the practice after it has started. Most people who abuse drugs begin doing so in their teens or early 20's. Parents of teen-agers should establish reasonable guidelines of behavior and discuss drug abuse openly with their children. Parents also should set an example for their children by not abusing drugs. If a young person develops a drug abuse problem, the parents should seek help from a physician, a professional counselor, or a community organization that provides such assistance.   DAVID C. LEWIS

Related Articles in WORLD BOOK include:

Alcoholism	LSD
Amphetamine	Marijuana
Barbiturate	Mescaline
Cocaine	Methamphetamine
Drug Enforcement	Morphine
Administration	Narcotic
Hallucinogenic Drug	Opium
Hashish	Smoking
Heroin	

See also *Drug Abuse* in the RESEARCH GUIDE/INDEX, Volume 22, for a *Reading and Study Guide*.

VIDEODISC is a flat, round platter on which material has been prerecorded for reproduction on a television set. The word is also spelled *video disk* or *videodisk*. A videodisc is played on a *videodisc player*, which resembles a phonograph. The player can be hooked up to any TV set. Manufacturers prerecord movies, concerts, and educational programs on the disks (or *discs*). Videodisc players cannot record material.

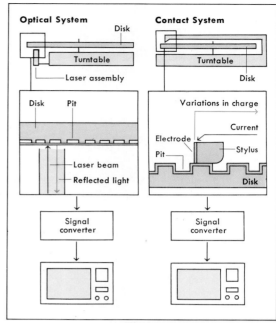

WORLD BOOK diagram by Arthur Grebetz

Videodisc Players convert the material recorded on a disk into television signals. There are two main kinds of disk systems—*optical* and *contact*. An optical player reads a pattern of reflected light. A contact player senses variations in electric charge.

Videodiscs are made of plastic. The surface of the disk is covered with microscopic pits that wind in a coil. The size and arrangement of the pits form a code that represents the recorded pictures and sounds. As the disk spins on the turntable, the player reads the code and converts it into TV signals.

There are two main types of videodisc players—*optical* and *contact*. Each type uses a certain kind of disk and reads it differently. The two kinds of disks differ in the shape and arrangement of the pits and are not interchangeable between the players.

The optical player uses a disk that has a reflective metal coating. The player has a device called a *laser*, which aims a concentrated beam of light at the disk. The light reflects off the pits in a pattern that is read by a light-sensitive device in the player. The player converts the pattern, or code, into TV signals. Disks played on optical players do not wear out because only light touches the surface.

The contact player uses a *stylus* (needle) that rests on the spinning disk. An electrode is attached to the stylus. Electric current flows from the electrode to the disk. The pits on the disk vary in their capacity to hold an electric charge. The player senses these variations and converts the charges into TV signals.

Manufacturers began developing videodisc systems in the early 1970's mainly for use as home entertainment. Some companies are adapting the optical system to store computer information.   PAMELA HAMILTON

Science You Can Use

In areas selected for their current interest, *Science Year* presents information that the reader as a consumer can use in making decisions — from buying products to caring for personal health and well-being.

338 Do You Really Need a Home Computer?

342 Killing Your Ears with the Sound of Music

344 Dressing Your Home for Winter

347 Insulating Yourself Against the Elements

350 Feeling Dry? Humidify

352 Rounding Up Facts About Radial Tires

Do You Really Need a Home Computer?

Home computers are catching on as nothing else has since Alexander Graham Bell introduced the telephone in the 1870s. At the end of 1980, less than 0.5 per cent of the homes in the United States had computers, but communications experts predict that this figure will grow to 25 per cent by 1985.

The main reason for this surge in popularity is a decrease in computer prices. A computer that sells for $200 and weighs 300 grams (10.5 ounces) is as powerful as the massive machines that cost thousands of dollars a few years ago.

Behind this change is a drastic drop in the price of chips — the computer's essential electrical devices. A chip is a slice of silicon crystal smaller than a dime that contains the equivalent of as many as 100,000 components — transistors and their connections.

The computer user communicates with these tiny devices through a keyboard, usually an ordinary typewriter keyboard with special computer keys. In fact, the 300-gram computer looks just like a keyboard on a plastic box that measures 174 millimeters (6.8 inches) wide and 38 millimeters (1.5 inches) high.

Chips in the box contain the computer's main memory, which stores information; the central processing unit (CPU), which performs the arithmetic functions and logic processes; and the control unit, which coordinates the entire machine by regulating the flow of information between the memory and the CPU.

But the box cannot transmit data to the user by itself. Instead, the computer has a cord that plugs into an ordinary TV set so that the picture tube, or cathode-ray tube (CRT), will display the information.

So now imagine that you have paid your $200 and joined the ranks of computer users. The plastic box is sitting on a table at home, hooked up to the TV set and ready to go, except for one problem. A computer cannot work without a program — a set of instructions placed in its memory circuits so that the control unit can tell the CPU what to do. The computer comes without a program, so you have to give it one. But programming a computer through the keyboard would take hours. Moreover, you would have to type the program in a special code, called a computer language, that the box understands.

Must you go through hours of study and programming before using the computer? If this were so, there would be no home-computer revolution.

Today, both computer manufacturers and independent companies sell complete prepackaged programs that let you operate the machine without learning a computer language and without programming. Prepackaged programs come in three kinds of packages — chips mounted in cases that plug into the computer; so-called floppy disks that look like phonograph records 5¼ inches (13.34 centimeters) in diameter and require built-in or *peripheral* (separate) controls and players; and audio cassette tapes or cartridges that use built-in or peripheral players, including an ordinary cassette player that you may already own.

The chip package is the fastest of the three. Inserting this package programs the computer immediately. A disk transmits its program to the computer's memory in seconds, while a tape may take several minutes. Instructions for the simple programs appear on the CRT when the program is completely entered, but you must get directions for complex programs from booklets that come with the chips, disks, and tapes.

These programs do not enable you to do anything that you cannot do without a computer. Rather, they are designed to make certain tasks easier and certain kinds of entertainment more enjoyable.

For example, you do not need a computer to keep track of your household expenses. All you need is a pencil, a calculator, and a pad of ledger sheets.

But you have to write down everything by hand, including your calculations. Analyzing your finances this way requires hours of effort.

You can do elaborate financial arithmetic on a complex electronic calculator. These devices cost as much as $200, can store a small amount of data, and can be programmed. But no matter how complex, a calculator cannot do what a computer can.

A computer will do all of the household mathematics for you, and will also store all of the numbers in its memory. Moreover, you can buy a program that helps you set up a complete household budget. This program lets you select expense categories, records budgeted amounts and actual expenditures, reviews past spending, forecasts future expenses, and identifies trends and patterns in your spending. It even displays bar graphs of expenses on the CRT.

Another prepackaged financial program maintains records of checks and deposits, keeps balances to reconcile with bank statements, and determines expenses by category. Similar packages that organize and compare data can help you with a physical-fitness program or assist you in planning meals.

Another program enables you to record lists, such as the names and addresses of club members, on cassettes or disks.

Most manufacturers also offer computer game packages and programs that educate the user by presenting information and questions on the CRT. Some of these programs use a device that imitates speech. The computer "speaks" to the user, who replies on the keyboard. One manufacturer offers subjects such as algebra, electricity, Spanish, and world history.

A special class of programs lets you compose music, write reports, or draw pictures without the constant marking and erasing that goes with these activities. The computer keyboard replaces the pencil and the CRT replaces the paper. As you type your work, the CRT displays it and the memory stores it. To correct the work, you strike certain keys, changing both the display and the memory. You can avoid having to copy your final results on paper by buying a peripheral printer.

A music program may require the computer memory to store 8,000 letters and other symbols of computer language, while a word-processing program that lets you change words and

A consumer analyzes his household finances by following a prepackaged set of instructions that are displayed on a handheld computer's liquid-crystal array. The cassette in the attached player put the program into the computer memory.

A student ponders a multiple-choice question in an educational program displayed on a desk-top video monitor. The program is contained in an electronic-chip package that has been inserted into the keyboard unit.

punctuation as you type needs 48,000 such characters (called *bytes* in the computer industry). If the basic computer's chips do not have enough memory circuits for a certain program, then you must buy attachments that contain additional circuits. The basic memory of the 300-gram computer, for example, holds 1,000 characters, and an attachment expands this to 17,000 characters.

If you want to use larger programs, then you must buy a more expensive basic computer. These sell for about $400 to $1,200. The major differences in price are in the memory capacity and input and output units. Some of these computers can use the TV set's CRT, while others require special units. The number of characters and the sharpness of detail on the CRT display varies. Not all of these computers can imitate speech. Some can use programmed chip packages, while others are limited to programs on cassettes and disks.

The basic computer sizes vary, but none is much larger than a typewriter keyboard. For example, one popular model is 25.9 centimeters long, 38.1 centimeters wide, and 7.1 centimeters high (10.2 by 15 by 2.5 inches) and weighs less than 2.3 kilograms (5 pounds). You can buy a broad selection of financial, educational, and recreational cassettes for these computers for less than $200.

Many computer owners have joined national computer networks, allowing them to connect their machines through telephone lines to the networks' central banks of large computers. Subscribers can operate these large computers from their own machines. The networks also offer recreational, educational, scientific, and financial programs, and provide CRT displays of information such as news, sports results, financial reports, airline schedules, restaurant menus, and play and movie schedules. Network subscribers

can also use the central computer to arrange trips and send messages. Hourly fees for network use start at about $5. Even though your funds may be limited, you can still use a network to advantage if you do not use it too often.

Serious students of programming can learn the craft on any home computer. The 300-gram computer, for example, includes a manual that introduces you to BASIC (*B*eginner's *A*ll-Purpose *S*ymbolic *I*nstruction *C*ode), the most common language for home computers. Most people can learn BASIC in 2 to 10 hours, depending upon the complexity of the programming that they want to do. Not all home computers use the same form of BASIC, however, and some use different languages. This is something that you should discuss with the owner of your local computer store.

If you want to program at the fundamental level, you can by-pass these high-level languages and learn a machine language. This is a language of bits – the binary digits 0 and 1 – that computers use to store and manipulate data. You can program in bits on a $200 computer with a calculator-style keyboard and display.

Before buying a home computer, you should analyze your needs and plan your purchase systematically. You may discover that you do not need a computer at all. For example, if you simply wish to play video games, then you should buy a programmable TV game. And if you just want something that will do complex mathematics, all you need is a calculator.

But if you decide that you can put a home computer to good use, be sure you know what you want it to do. Match that information against the amount of money you wish to spend — from the $200 lower limit to more than $10,000 for a high-powered computer and a complete set of peripheral units.

Then, welcome to the world of home computers!   [E. Joseph Piel]

A businessman studies stock prices at a desk-top computer in his home through a telephone hookup that connects his machine to an information network. The cassette player contains a prepackaged program that enables him to use his computer in this way.

Killing Your Ears with the Sound of Music

Normal sensory cells in a young guinea pig's ear are arrayed neatly in rows like kernels of corn, *below*. The cells are distorted, jumbled, and broken after exposure to loud music, *bottom*. The sensory cells of the human ear are located in the cochlea, a spiral structure in the inner ear, *below right*.

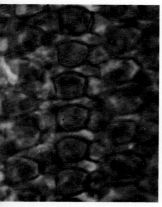

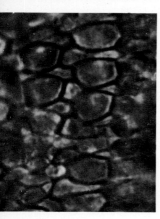

We live in a noisy world — of screaming jet engines, revving motors, honking horns, blaring music, and our own voices straining to be heard over the general din. Environmentalists call it "noise pollution" and it can have severe effects. Excessive noise can cause increased blood pressure and muscle tension, which can lead to fatigue and irritability. But noise reserves its strongest effects for the human ear. It can cause permanent hearing loss.

It is hard for a person to control noise pollution, except perhaps by supporting laws against excessive noise. But the personal approach can work in one area. You can save your hearing by controlling — or avoiding — the excessive amplification of music.

In our Noise Research Laboratory, at the University of Tennessee in Knoxville, we have tested the hearing of hundreds of incoming freshmen. We found that about 2 out of 3 have the kind of hearing impairment that typically results from listening to high-level sound. Some had hearing no better than that of men between the ages of 60 and 69. In effect, these young people were entering their working life with retirement-age ears.

High-intensity sound can cause irreversible damage to two areas in the ear. On rare occasions, sudden, intense noise can burst the eardrum and break apart the *malleus* (hammer), *incus* (anvil), and *stapes* (stirrup), the connected bones in the middle ear, causing hearing impairment. Even less intense noise can destroy some of the irreplaceable sensory cells located in the cochlea, part of the inner ear. These cells — 16,000 in each ear — respond to sound by sending nerve impulses to the brain. Hearing is impaired when some of these cells are destroyed.

The damage takes several forms. Intense sound causes the cells to vibrate

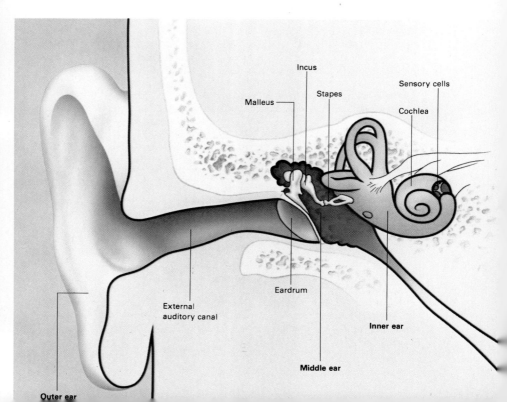

Incus

Sensory cells

Malleus

Stapes

Cochlea

Eardrum

External
auditory canal

Inner ear

Middle ear

Outer ear

so violently that they are dislodged or torn apart. Prolonged noise may cause all the cells to stop functioning.

There are some specific signs of dangerous sound levels to watch out for:

■ If you have to shout directly into someone's ear to talk in the presence of high-level sound, there is great risk that the sound will cause hearing loss.

■ If your ears ring after leaving a noisy area, you have been exposed to dangerous sound levels.

■ If you experience "dullness" of hearing after being exposed to high-level sound, your hearing sensitivity has probably been diminished. This effect is usually temporary, and normal hearing should return. But constant repetition can do permanent damage.

Listening to music — particularly to rock music, which is often highly amplified — has certain risks. Advances in the technology of sound reproduction made it possible for small discothèques to have amplifiers far more powerful than the public-address systems in big outdoor stadiums, and the sound can approach the ear's pain threshold. Sounds as intense as 135 decibels have been measured in discothèques, about the level a jet generates during take-off. Ordinary speech measures about 60 decibels.

Except for the most expensive systems, speaker efficiency limits the amount of sound you can generate at home. Drapes, carpeting, and furniture also absorb some of the sound. Although home speakers can produce enough volume to disturb others, they are only a slight danger to hearing.

Stereo earphones are a very attractive alternative to loudspeakers because the all-encompassing sound makes music come alive for the listener. In addition, listening is more private and will not disturb others. But earphones pose a distinct danger. Because they direct sound into the ear so efficiently, it is possible to produce dangerously intense sound without realizing it. Test the earphones by listening to music at various volume settings and then set a limit for loudness based on your ear's reaction to the sound. If, after listening, you experience ringing in the ears or other signs of excessive noise, turn the volume down.

High sound amplification seems likely to remain popular. But proper precautions can minimize the risk to your hearing. [David M. Lipscomb]

The frenzied music of a rock group is given a sometimes dangerous boost by electronic amplifiers before it finally reaches the fans' ears.

Dressing Your Home for Winter

You may like to think of your home as a snug port in the storm. However, from the viewpoint of thermodynamics, it is just a way station in which heat from your furnace pauses briefly on its way outdoors. Although every precious unit of heat that you buy from the power company will eventually leak out through the walls, windows, and doors of your home, by installing the proper insulation, you can keep it around a little longer.

There are two basic processes involved in the loss of heat: conduction, or heat moving out; and infiltration, or cold moving in. In conduction, heat passes from the warm interior wall, through the space between the walls, and through the exterior wall to the outside. The amount of heat lost through conduction depends on a number of factors: the difference between the inside and outside temperatures, the area of the wall, and the material that the wall is made of. To measure heat loss, we use the formula,

$$Q = \frac{(T_i - T_o)A}{R}$$

where Q is the amount of heat in British thermal units that escapes in one hour; A, the area of the wall in square feet; T_i, the inside temperature in Fahrenheit degrees; T_o, the outside temperature in Fahrenheit degrees; and R, a number that measures the heat resistance of the material in the wall. This measurement, the "R value," is used to rate insulation and is found on the labeling of all insulation. As you can see from the formula, the higher the R value is, the smaller the heat loss becomes. You can also see that if you live in an area where the average outside temperature is close to the inside temperature you find most comfortable, you will not need an insulation with a high R value.

In a thermogram, in which bright colors represent high temperatures, an uninsulated roof is red, *right*, indicating that it is considerably warmer, and thus is losing more heat, than an insulated roof, *opposite page*, which is black.

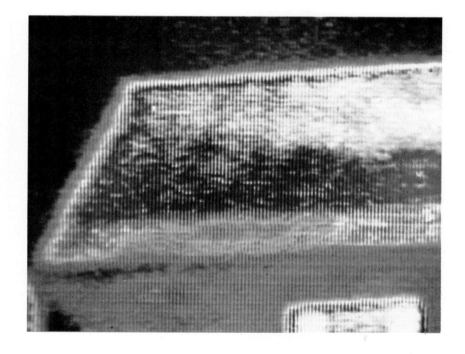

The higher the R value of the insulation, the more heat you can keep inside the house. You can increase the R value of any type of insulation by increasing its thickness. For example, two 3.5-inch layers of fiberglass, each having an R value of 11, have an R value of 22.

The type of insulation you can use depends on the way your house is built. In accessible areas such as attics, basements, and crawl spaces, you can install the insulation yourself. Rolled fiberglass is preferable to shredded materials of insulation for such areas because it is easy to work with and has a higher R value.

Insulating walls as a house is being built is also an easy process. If your home is under construction or if you are remodeling and have torn the interior walls out, fiberglass can be stapled to the wall frames, or studs, before the walls are finished. If you are paneling a room, you can put sheets of polystyrene — a thin material with an R value of 3.5 per inch — behind the paneling.

However, insulating a wall after it is built is much more difficult. Holes must be cut in the outside wall and insulation blown in with special machines. Such a task is probably beyond the capabilities of most homeowners, and should be left to insulation contractors.

There are two types of blown insulation — loose-fill and foam. Loose-fill insulation is just what the name implies, small pieces of material that can be run through a blower easily. All loose-fill insulations have the same drawback — they may settle over time, exposing the upper part of the wall to heat loss. Materials commonly used are fiberglass, with an R value of 2 per inch; rock wool, with an R value of 3 per inch; and cellulose, with an R value of 3 per inch. Cellulose is made from old paper to which fire-retardant chemicals have been added. If you choose the cheapest alternative, cellulose, you should ask the contractor to put a pile of the insulation material on the sidewalk and turn an acetylene torch on it. If it burns, it is not safe to use.

Foams are blown into the wall like shaving cream, and they harden within a few hours. Typical R values for foam insulations are in the 4.5 to 5.5 per inch range. Foams, too, tend to shrink and settle slightly with time. Some foams have been banned because they give off toxic fumes. A reputable insulation contractor will know which are safe.

Windows and doors account for the greatest conduction heat loss in houses. Ordinary single-pane windows have an R value of 1, but thermopane windows or storm windows can raise the R value by 1 point each. Closing drapes and shutters may raise the R value further but, short of boarding up all your windows, there is little else you can do to reduce this heat loss further. Doors have R values of from 1 to 2, and using a storm door can usually increase this value by 1 point.

The second kind of heat loss, infiltration, occurs when cold air from the outside gets into your home through cracks around windows and doors and must be heated to room temperature. About one-third of most heating bills may be spent on heating outside air. No matter how tightly doors and windows are fitted, some infiltration is unavoidable. However, you can control the amount of heat you lose by applying weatherstripping and caulking around the edges.

You can locate excess infiltration simply by checking windows and doors for drafts on a cold day. There are several solutions for the leaks you may find inside window frames and around doors. You can install storm windows and storm doors; plug holes in frames with puttylike sealers that can be squeezed into cracks; and apply adhesive-backed foam-rubber strips or wood or metal weatherstripping to fill gaps around door and window frames.

Caulking is the best solution for leaks around windows. After checking the seams where the windows join the house, scrape out loose caulking and replace it with new caulking. Silicone caulks are the best and most expensive. They are easy to install and last a long time because they do not shrink or crack. However, they cannot be painted. Latex-acrylic and butyl-rubber caulks, which can be painted, also can be applied easily. Butyl-rubber caulk is more flexible, but it has a greater tendency to shrink than latex caulk.

Although it is difficult to predict the severity of the next few winters, it is certain that fuel prices — and home-heating costs — will continue to rise. Considering the added comfort of a warm snug home, the tax breaks currently allowed for insulation, and heat savings, improving your home insulation could be one of the best investments you can make. [James S. Trefil]

There are several ways to add to the R value, or resistance to heat loss, of different areas in a house. Caulking windows boosts their R value 0.3 to 0.5; installing storm windows adds 1. Weather stripping adds 0.5 to the R value of a door. Fiberglass insulation increases the R value of a wall by 11, and injected foam, by 4.5.

Insulating Yourself Against the Elements

The commuters huddle at the bus stop, bracing themselves against the icy January wind. They are outfitted in heavy wool jackets, billowing goose-down parkas, ankle-length furs, and padded overcoats. They have chosen varied ways of keeping warm, yet each of their coats insulates them in much the same way — by retaining heat generated by the body in layers of trapped air and fabric surrounding it.

How well a coat — or any other garment — traps body heat is measured in units called *clos*. Researchers at the United States Army Research Institute of Environmental Medicine in Natick, Mass., developed a procedure for measuring *clo* values using a heated anodized copper mannequin.

At Kansas State University in Manhattan, we have adopted this procedure, using "Sam the Copper Man" to determine clo values of various articles of clothing. Sam is a life-sized manne-quin that generates heat in much the same way as people do. He has a black anodized copper "skin" that is heated by electric wires and outfitted with heat-measuring devices called thermistors. We place Sam in a cooled chamber, dress him in the garment to be measured, and record the amount of electrical power needed to keep his skin temperature at 33°C (92°F.), the average skin temperature of most humans. The less power used, the higher the garment's clo value. A heavy tweed blazer has a clo value of approximately 0.49, while a light shirt has a clo value of 0.22.

The clo value of a coat depends on several factors, among them length, fit, lining, and outer fabric. The longer a coat is, the warmer it will be because it insulates more of the body's surface. Thus, a long wool coat with a hood will have a higher clo value than a short wool jacket.

The author, *below left*, studies a computer tape showing the amount of power needed to maintain a constant "skin" temperature on Sam, an electrically heated anodized copper mannequin that she has dressed in winter clothing, *below*. The less electrical power used, the higher the "warmth rating" of Sam's outfit will be.

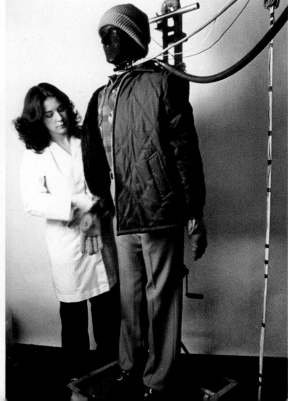

Adjustable closures that can regulate the fit — such as snaps, zippers, or ties at the wrists, neck, waist, and hood — allow us to adjust a coat's clo value according to changes in temperature.

Linings, which are layers of fabric on the inside of the coat, create more air pockets and increase the amount of trapped air. The more layers of lining, the warmer the coat will be. For this reason, detachable linings are also excellent features for adjusting the warmth of a coat.

The insulation value of outer fabrics depends more on the thickness than on the type of fiber or construction, because most fabrics have the same clo value — 1.6 clos per centimeter (4 clos per inch) of thickness. Of course, with compression the thickness decreases and the insulation value of fabrics is reduced. Sitting and other pressures of daily wear can compress a fabric and, consequently, enable body heat to pass through it more rapidly. Fabrics made of resilient fibers, such as wool and polyester, will spring back more readily and maintain their thickness — and their insulating properties — longer than nonresilient fibers such as cotton and linen will.

Fabrics with a pile such as corduroy, velour, or synthetic fur; a napped finish such as flannel; or high bulk yarns of wool or acrylic all have "hairy" surfaces that supplement the fabric's thickness by trapping air. These fabrics are good insulators when used as the shell, lining, or inner lining of a coat.

Although all thick fabrics trap body heat, it is difficult to achieve thickness without adding weight when layers of such fabrics are used in coats. Consequently, many people prefer coats made of quilted fabrics. These coats usually contain lightweight, fluffy fillings of either polyester fiberfill or goose down sandwiched between two sheets of lightweight fabric. The fabric covers are sewn together in lines, squares, or decorative patterns that also prevent the filling from shifting. Most heat loss in a quilted coat occurs at the points where the layers are sewn together.

Polyester fiberfill is an excellent insulation choice because it is lightweight, resilient, inexpensive, washable, water repellent, odor-free, and nonallergenic.

Goose down, which is more expensive than polyester fiberfill but lighter in weight, can be compressed into a smaller space and has superior loft, or

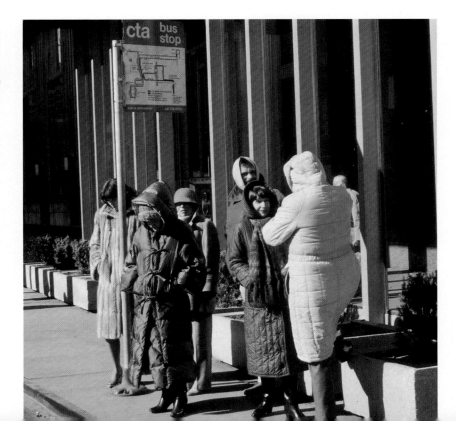

Commuters huddled at a bus stop have chosen varied ways of keeping warm, including a luxurious fur coat, a trim wool jacket, and lightweight, yet bulky, polyester and down-filled parkas.

ability to expand and trap air. However, unlike polyester, down absorbs moisture and becomes useless as an insulator when wet. High-quality down affords the greatest thickness per unit weight of any known insulating material. Unfortunately, many garments labeled "down-filled" do not contain this quality of down or contain down mixed with other materials.

The outer fabric shell of a coat or jacket should be windproof and water repellent to keep warm air trapped. It may be made of tightly woven fabrics or treated with special finishes and coatings. Unfortunately, some of these fabrics do not allow perspiration to evaporate, so it may accumulate and condense in the clothing, making the wearer feel cold and clammy. However, a new coating called Gortex film provides a one-way passage out for moisture. Made of expanded polytetrafluoroethylene with microscopic pores, it keeps water from penetrating while allowing perspiration to escape.

New fabrics that provide more insulation for a given weight and thickness have recently been developed for use in outdoor garments. These include Thinsulate, which is made of 35 per cent polyester and 65 per cent polyolefin, and Sontique, which is 100 per cent polyester. Both fabrics consist of large numbers of very fine fibers, which capture air molecules on their surfaces, increasing the amount of heated air the fabric can hold.

The type of coat you choose will, of course, depend upon several factors — including the climate in which you live, how you want to look, and how much you want to spend. You may want to sacrifice the trim fit of a wool overcoat in favor of the lighter weight and greater warmth of a bulky down parka.

To economize, you may pass up the lightweight down coat in favor of its slightly heavier look-alike filled with polyester fibers. Or, you may be more concerned with a coat's adaptability — features such as adjustable closures and zip-out linings that make it possible to regulate the amount of warmth a coat provides.

Whatever your priorities, it will pay to shop for a coat with its insulation value in mind. For although fashion, prices, and even the weather may vary from season to season, the principles of insulation are certain to remain the same. [Elizabeth A. McCullough]

Materials used to insulate coats trap heated air in several ways. Down filaments, *below left* (magnified 5 times), catch air molecules on tiny hairs; polyester fibers, *below*, form air pockets; and the dense network in Thinsulate, *bottom*, traps air on, as well as between, fiber surfaces (magnified 500 times).

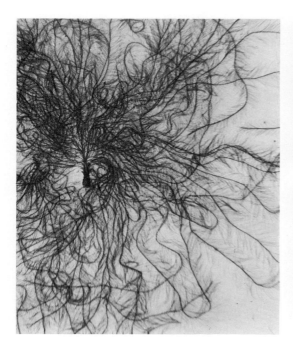

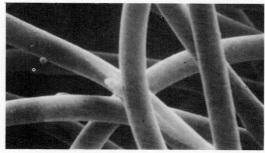

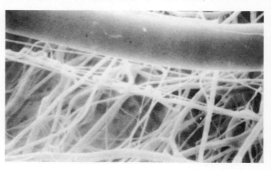

Feeling Dry?
Humidify.

Dry warm air in your house or apartment during winter can rob you of moisture needed for health and comfort. People, pets, plants, and furniture will suffer the effects of drying unless you use a humidifier, a machine that adds water vapor to the air.

Dry air actually pulls moisture from your sinuses, throat, skin, and eyes. This parching leads to inflamed noses, scratchy throats, chapped lips and skin, and irritated eyes. These discomforts are particularly hard on infants, older people, and the chronically ill. Pets and plants that are kept indoors are affected, too.

Heated air's insatiable thirst also dries out wood and leather furniture, shrinks and cracks the house's wooden structural beams, and causes annoying static electricity to build up.

How can you tell how much humidity — the water vapor content of air — you need? We measure relative humidity as a ratio between the amount of water in the air and the greatest amount that could be there. Completely dry air has 0 per cent relative humidity, while saturated air contains all the water vapor it can hold; it has 100 per cent relative humidity.

Temperature determines the amount of water vapor that the air can hold. Warm air can contain more water vapor than cold air. As the air in a room cools, its relative humidity increases. When cold winter air enters a heated home, it warms up and its relative humidity drops. This air absorbs moisture, and everything in the home dries out.

If your home is well insulated and well heated in winter, the relative humidity may be as low as 10 to 30 per cent. But the American Society of Heating, Refrigeration, and Air Conditioning Engineers recommends maintaining a standard of 30 to 60 per cent relative humidity.

You may already know that your home is too dry. Or you can measure its relative humidity with a hygrometer, an instrument similar to a thermometer. If you find that the relative humidity is below the recommended standard, you should consider buying a humidifier for your family's comfort and health, and also to lower your heating bills. Tests have shown that people feel warmer in a room with adequate relative humidity. For example, air heated to a temperature of 21°C (70°F.) that has a relative humidity of only 10 per cent feels like a chilly 17°C (63°F.). But when the relative humidity is raised to 60 per cent, the 21°C air feels like 19°C (67°F.) — a difference that matters at a time when we are turning down thermostats to save fuel.

Engineers point out that the air must be in motion — a very slight motion, like a faint breeze — for water vapor to mix completely with air. Many people try to humidify their homes by setting out pans of water. This works well only if you place a fan so that it blows across the pan, causing ripples so the water will evaporate into the air. The important factor is to make the water easily accessible to the dry air.

A humidifier automatically provides all the aids to evaporation. You can choose from two basic kinds, portable or central. A portable humidifier comes in two sizes, tabletop or console. The unit sits on the floor or on a piece of furniture. It has a conveyor belt that passes through a tank of water, soaking up moisture and carrying it up in front of a fan, which blows water vapor out through vents into the air. A central humidifier is connected to the central heating system in houses with forced-air heating systems. In most of those, a shallow revolving drum lifts water from a tank. The unit is positioned in the ductwork so that the hot air from the furnace flows past the revolving drum picking up moisture from it.

What size humidifier do you need? A portable tabletop humidifier circulates about 3.8 to 19 liters (1 to 5 gallons) of water per day and costs about $35. A portable console humidifier circulates

A console humidifier is filled by hand, *left.* A central humidifier, attached to a forced-air furnace, *below left,* receives water through copper tubing connected to the home water system.

about 38 to 57 liters (10 to 15 gallons) per day and retails for about $85. A built-in central humidifier circulates up to 95 liters (25 gallons) per day and costs about $200, plus installation.

The better insulated your house is, the less moisture you will need to place in the air. In a poorly insulated house, the air to which moisture has been added escapes easily, to be replaced with new air with less moisture. A well-insulated two-story house with about 276 square meters (3,000 square feet) of floor space will only need about 46 to 53 liters (12 to 14 gallons) of water per day. A poorly insulated house of the same size could drink up 98 liters (26 gallons) per day.

The size and layout of your house or apartment, your life style, and the amount you want to spend on a humidifier are factors to consider in selecting the system that is best for you. If you live in a studio apartment, or in a larger place but are at home mainly in the evening, and the heat is kept fairly low during the day, a small tabletop model may be sufficient. You can move a small humidifier from the living room to your bedroom as the evening unfolds so that the humidity will be raised only in the rooms you are using.

But if there is plenty of traffic in the house all day and the temperature is kept at a fairly high level, you may want a larger console model that can supply moisture throughout the house from one location. If doors are kept closed and parts of a house are closed off, it may be necessary to have console models on each floor, or several tabletop models to move around as needed. Only if you have forced-air heating, with air-distribution ducts throughout the house, will you be able to make use of a central humidifier.

Whether your home is small or spacious, a humidifier is definitely a worthwhile investment in your comfort and health.   [Pasquale M. Sforza]

Rounding Up Facts About Radial Tires

When I was a boy in the 1930s, I traveled about 60 miles (97 kilometers) by car one day from New York City to a small Connecticut town. On the way, we had to repair three flat tires.

Now I drive thousands of miles per year without a flat, largely because tire quality and durability has improved greatly. Flat tires are rare, especially on cars with radial tires.

But buying tires has become confusing. There are more than 2,000 different passenger-car models of tires to choose from. However, these fall into only three main categories — bias-ply, bias-belted, and radial. In addition, a Uniform Tire Quality Grading Code that became effective in 1980 makes impartial test data and tire-quality information readily available.

The best way to learn about tire types is to look at how they are put together. The rubber tread — the grooved surface that rolls on the road — is held on the wheel rim by the side walls. Inside the tread are the plies, layers of nylon, rayon, or polyester fabric that give the tire strength. Steel wires — the beads — run around the tire wall edge to keep it in place on the rim.

Bias-ply tires are so named because the cords of the fabric in the plies run at an angle of about 35 degrees to the tire's center line. The cords of each ply run at right angles to the cords adjacent to it. A bias-ply tire may have two or more plies to give the tread a firm base and make the side walls rigid. Bias-ply tires flex easily and provide a smooth ride. However, their treads tend to squirm, or swivel from side to side, as the tire rolls. This scuffs off tread rubber and makes bias-plies run hotter, thus shortening their life.

Bias-belted tires have, in addition to bias body plies, two or more belts or layers of fabric or steel wire between the body plies and the tread. These belts run parallel to the tire's circumference. They help to prevent punctures and make the tread stiffer so the tires squirm and scuff less and give

better traction on both dry and wet surfaces. The treads also wear longer.

Radial tires are the most popular type because of their superiority in a wide range of areas: tread life; traction; car handling; and resistance to cuts, punctures, and other road hazards. They also help save gasoline.

These advantages result mainly from radial-ply construction. The radial body plies run perpendicular to the tire's circumference, so the side walls do not flex like bias-plies. Radial cords bend together; they do not work against one another like the crisscrossing bias-plies do. Their side walls tend to work like shock absorbers, generating less heat than do bias-plies. And while bias-plies act like one-piece tires, radials act like two-piece systems. There is no reaction in the tread when the side walls flex because stabilizing belts hold the treads in place, reducing tread squirm and scuffing.

Unlike bias-ply tires, the treads on a radial are not squeezed inward as the tire rolls. The tread grooves stay open and road contact is not diminished. This provides better traction and long tread wear because there is less hard rubbing against the road.

Another advantage is that radial tires have less rolling resistance — the force a tire encounters as it rolls. So less horsepower is needed to keep the tire rolling and this saves gasoline.

While radials are superior in performance and last longer than other types of tires, they are also more expensive. The average price of a radial is about $73, according to *Modern Tire Dealer* magazine, compared with $42 for a bias-ply tire and $50 for a bias-belted model. Tires belted with fiberglass or aramid — a synthetic fiber that is stronger than steel — cost about 75 per cent as much as steel-belted ones.

How do you select the right tire for your car when you have to take all these facts into consideration? Tires may vary in price by $30, yet offer the same performance. The United States

Radial tire, *above,* is safer in rainy weather than bias-ply tire, *top,* because its tread is not squeezed together. As a result, tread grooves can dissipate water on road faster, lowering the danger of hydroplaning.

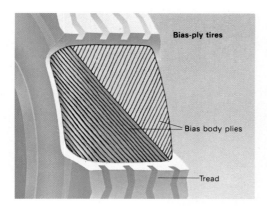

Bias-ply tires

Bias body plies

Tread

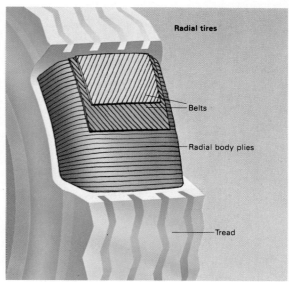

Radial tires

Belts

Radial body plies

Tread

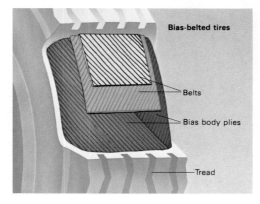

Bias-belted tires

Belts

Bias body plies

Tread

Bias-ply tires, *top left,* with fabric cords in the plies at a 35-degree angle to the center, have a tread that squirms. It does not wear as well as tread on bias-belted tires, *left,* where belts under the tread add firmness. Radial tires, *above,* wear the best and provide excellent steering control.

Department of Transportation (DOT) recommends that you make your own comparisons of tire quality, and the agency provides a grading system to help you. The system was devised by the National Highway Traffic Safety Administration (NHTSA).

Manufacturers are now required to grade their tires on tread-wear life; wet-traction performance; and high-temperature resistance, which reveals high-speed capability. These grades are molded onto the side wall, along with information on tire size, type, brand, maximum inflation pressure, cord composition, number of side wall and tread plies, and the symbol DOT. The symbol indicates the tire meets federal motor vehicle safety standards.

The codes grade tires. Wet-traction performance and high-temperature resistance are graded from best to worst — A, B, or C.

Tread-wear life is rated on a scale starting at 10 and increasing in increments of 10. Each 10 points on the scale equals 3,000 miles (4,827 kilometers) of tread life as measured on an official government test course in San Angelo, Tex. For example, a tire rated 100 would have an expected tread life of 30,000 miles (48,270 kilometers).

However, the tire may not actually last that long because tread life varies according to the type of roads the tires run on and the way the motorist drives. For example, continual "jack rabbit" starts drastically reduce tread life, as does driving on underinflated tires.

Although NHTSA believes that the tire-quality grading system increases your chances of getting the most for your money, most tire makers dispute that claim. Nevertheless, the system provides the only measurable quality data available to tire buyers. You have to decide how much money you want to spend on a tire, then select one with the highest rating you can get for the price you want to pay. [Herbert Shuldiner]

People in Science

A medical career has many faces and can take unexpected turns. This section, which describes the lives of special scientists, talks about two in the medical world. One is a seasoned veteran who has contributed to a field that only recently has been recognized as a medical specialty. The other is still undergoing training and just beginning to have those special experiences that will help to shape her career.

356 **J. Robert Cade** by Noel D. Vietmeyer
This kidney specialist has applied his training
and interests to health problems that range
from athletic performance to mental health.

370 **The Making of a Doctor** by Sherry Baron
The author, a third-year medical student, describes
the hard work and long hours that go into preparing
for one of the most rewarding of careers.

J. Robert Cade

By Noel D. Vietmeyer

Inventor of a thirst-quenching soft drink, this kidney specialist has contributed many ideas toward better human health and welfare

Mention the name Robert Cade in Gainesville, Fla., and people smile. Walk along the street with Cade and you hear greetings called out from all sides. Parents bring their children up to meet him. People treat him with the warmth and respect once reserved for the popular horse-and-buggy doctor of the 19th century, before medical practice and research lost much of the human touch.

Robert Cade, professor of renal medicine at the University of Florida, has become one of the best-known personalities in his state. Some Floridians know him as a skilled physician; others as an endearing teacher. He is probably best known as the inventor of a unique soft drink that is sold from coast to coast, and in other countries as well. But few people — even his colleagues and close friends — fully appreciate the many interests of this remarkable scientist.

A chance encounter in the coffee shop of the University of Florida Medical Center during the

1965 football season was a major turning point in Robert Cade's life. Dwain Douglas, assistant coach of the freshman team, leaned across the table and asked: "Dr. Cade, why don't the players need to urinate during a football game?"

Most renal physiologists, or kidney specialists, would have brushed the question aside with a trite answer. Obviously, the players were sweating out their fluids under the hot Florida sun. But Cade is a scientist. He began to wonder how much sweat a player loses during a game and what effect this has on the body. To find out, he devised a rubber sleeve, and coaxed several players to wear it during practice. Having collected and measured the perspiration, he then set about to identify its constituents.

"Once we learned what was leaving the body, it took us only three minutes to formulate a drink to replace it," he says.

Cade concocted a mixture of sodium and potassium phosphates and citrates. He also added glucose for quick energy. He formulated this fluid to duplicate exactly the structure of blood so that it would pass quickly from the stomach into the bloodstream. Coach Douglas served this "sugared perspiration" to his players during a scrimmage with the Varsity B team. During the game's first half, the freshmen were pushed all over the field and fell 14 points behind. But in the fourth quarter they began to run through the opposition, eventually winning the game — an almost incredible upset.

That evening, head football coach Ray Graves asked Cade to make up more of his drink for the next day's varsity game against Louisiana State University (LSU). Cade remembers it well. "It was October 2, 1965. I went back to the lab and made up 100 liters of the drink. I was out of glucose, and had to raid labs across the Medical School."

The next day was a scorcher — 38°C (104°F.) on the playing surface. Fifteen years later, Cade can still recite most of the plays. "The Gators kicked off and were desperately lucky to stop the resulting LSU drive on their own 20-yard line. Two linebackers — Larry Gagner and Jim Benson — came off the field. I handed them a glass of the concoction. Gagner tasted a little, made a crude remark, and poured the rest on his head.

"At half-time, LSU was 13 points up and the statistics were terribly lopsided. Meanwhile, the team members had been sipping the drink, since it was the only liquid on the sideline. Larry Gagner told me that he was beginning to like the taste. The third quarter was played evenly and ended with LSU leading 13 to 7. Then, in the fourth quarter, the Gators began to run through the powerhouse LSU team. In the final minute they scored a touchdown and won 14 to 13."

And that became the pattern game after game for the Gators during the next few years. The scoring seemed to indicate that the University of Florida players were in far better physiological shape during the fourth quarter than their opponents. For example, the 1965 team was outscored 50 points to 30 during first quarters, but outscored the

The author:
Noel D. Vietmeyer is a professional associate of the U.S. National Academy of Sciences. He wrote "An Ancient Animal in the Modern World" for the 1980 edition of *Science Year.*

opposition a whopping 80 points to 7 during fourth quarters. The Gators finished the season by beating Georgia Tech in the Orange Bowl in Miami.

The University of Florida coaching staff used so much of the drink that Cade, with the help of a laboratory technician, began making it up at home. James Free, one of Cade's colleagues, suggested calling the elixir "Gatorade," because it was an "aid to the Gators."

Of course, anything that helps win football games cannot be kept secret, and soon the word about Cade's drink began to trickle out. Cade soon found himself manufacturing gallons of Gatorade, packing jugs of the concentrate in cardboard and sending them by Greyhound bus to Florida high schools as far away as Key West. When Notre Dame University lost to Gatorade-drinking Purdue University in 1967, the Fighting Irish put in an order for the drink the following Monday. Before long, amateur athletes, from Little League to college, and many professional football, baseball, basketball, and hockey teams were using it. Even Canadian and U.S. Olympic athletes started drinking Gatorade.

Commercial production began after Kent Bradley, one of Cade's former students, joined the faculty of the University of Indiana. At a Christmas party in 1967, Bradley met the son-in-law of Alfred J. Stokely, president of Stokely-Van Camp, Inc., a leading canner of pork-and-beans. Subsequently, Stokely-Van Camp negotiated manufacturing rights to Cade's "flavored perspiration" and put corporate merchandising muscle behind it. In the late 1960s, Gatorade became one of the hottest new products in the United States. Today, it is sold in supermarkets nationwide and in 12 foreign countries. It is a major profit earner for Stokely-Van Camp.

Before Gatorade — and drinks like it — five to ten football players in the United States died each year from acute dehydration and heat exhaustion, especially in the South where the heat during early season games is usually brutal. Today, such deaths are rare. The drink has brought other medical benefits. Pediatricians use Gatorade to treat infant diarrhea and now rarely have to hospitalize babies for dehydration — once a common occurrence.

When Gatorade royalties began flowing in, Cade, with characteristic generosity, set up a trust that includes the technicians and graduate students who helped him refine and perfect the drink. In 1981, they and the University of Florida were sharing a reported income of about $160,000 a month.

Cade uses part of his share to finance his medical research. He works out of a tiny basement office beneath the gigantic University of Florida Medical Center, at the end of a rabbit warren of narrow stairs and corridors. To find his office, you have to squeeze past filing cabinets and secretaries' cubicles. A plainly dressed Cade sits in a straight-backed chair behind an inexpensive steel desk. Scattered round him are the paraphernalia of his various careers — Gray's

A soft drink, *above,* developed for perspiring football players, launched physician Robert Cade's career as an inventor. His creative mind has also served sports safety, with a shock-absorbing football helmet, *below left,* and nutrition, with a protein-enriched ice stick, *below right.*

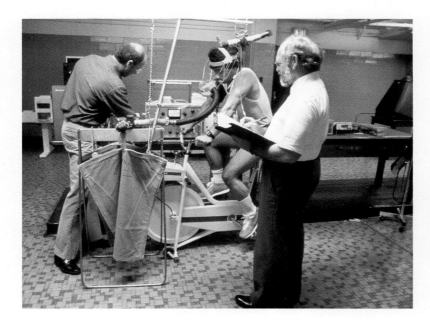

Cade and physiologist Christian Zauner work with a student volunteer to study how oxygen is carried to the muscles during heavy exercise.

Anatomy, textbooks on the kidney, samples of new drugs left by pharmaceutical salesmen, and recent copies of the *American Journal of Medicine* and *Sporting World* magazine. Tropical fish swim lazily in a big tank along one wall end. Above the tank is a framed copy of the prayer of Maimonides, court physician to the Sultan Saladin at the time of the Crusades in the 1100s. It begins: "Grant that I may be filled with love for my art and for my fellowmen. May the thirst for gain and the desire for fame be far from my heart."

Cade swivels around and leans forward to greet his visitor. A calm, direct gaze glints through his bifocals. Introductions seem superfluous — somehow you already feel he is a long-time friend. He is a small man with a thin thatch of light-colored hair above a round, kindly face that is adorned with a beard. There is gentleness in his manner. He speaks without gesturing in a soft voice, pulling together scattered fragments of ideas so that you absorb and understand technical complexities almost effortlessly.

James Robert Cade was born in San Antonio, Tex., in 1927 and grew up in that city. "I was a terrible student," he recalls. "I finished high school with a D average and an 'incomplete' in English." After finishing high school in 1945 he joined the Navy and became a pharmacists mate. After completing service, he was admitted to the University of Texas. He completed his four-year undergraduate program in two years taking as many as 30 credit hours per semester. He then went to the University of Texas Medical School.

Cade's medical research began at Cornell University Medical School in New York City in 1958. He had begun studies of how the lungs function, especially how they maintain the optimum balance

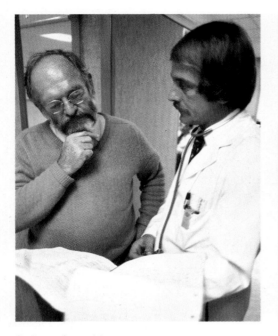

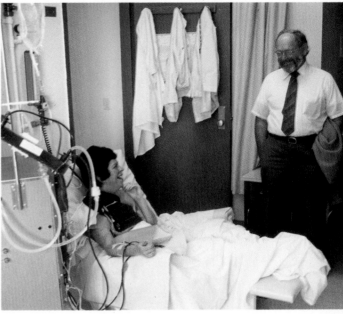

Cade confers with a University Hospital resident, *above,* on the progress of star patient Linda Cook, *above right,* whom he has treated successfully for schizophrenia by dialyzing her blood.

between acids and salts in the blood, at Southwestern Medical School in Dallas. At Cornell, he undertook to learn about the kidney, the other organ that regulates acid-base balance. Cade's investigations introduced him to renal research, because kidneys help maintain the optimum level of blood acidity. It also led him to his medical specialty — treating patients with kidney disease. He moved to the University of Florida in 1961.

The success of Gatorade in 1965 did not quench Cade's own thirst for new challenges. During early experiments with the drink, one of the football players received such a severe concussion during a game that he lost his memory for ten days. Concerned about such injuries, Cade decided to try to redesign the football helmet. The standard plastic helmet transfers much of the energy of a blow to the head it is supposed to protect. An improved helmet should absorb and dissipate this energy before it reaches the player's head — in less than one hundredth of a millisecond. Springs make good shock absorbers, but they act relatively slowly and require more distance to compress than there is space between head and helmet.

Cade's alternative was simple. ("That's the only kind of idea I'm capable of," he says.) Applying basic engineering principles, he designed a helmet containing rubber bags filled with liquid. The bags are connected so that one hangs down inside the helmet on each side of the player's head. A blow to one side of the helmet squeezes liquid through small tubes that slow the flow of liquid into the bag on the other side. The impact is thus cushioned and the shock is spread out. The liquid gives almost instant resistance, and the expanding rubber

A popular and gifted teacher, Cade discusses some techniques for simplifying concepts for fourth-year medical students with one of his fellow professors, *top*. He always finds time to counsel a student, whether the problems be personal or academic.

bags provide the slow-acting effect of a compressing spring. In his earliest models, Cade filled the bags with olive oil. But after watching a televised game between the Minnesota Vikings and the Dallas Cowboys in −30°C. (−16°F.) weather in Minneapolis, Minn., in 1972, he decided to switch to antifreeze.

He tested the helmets by putting a 5-kilogram (11-pound) weight inside one and dropping it upside down onto a plate. The plate's movement from the impact was measured electronically, indicating the amount of energy transferred to the inside of the helmet. Cade's helmets absorbed so much shock that they transmitted less energy when dropped from a height of 3.4 meters (8 feet) than conventional helmets did when dropped from 1.3 meters (4.5 feet).

Cade donned one of his helmets and had 6 foot 7 inch tackle Jim Yarborough bop him over the head with a two-by-four. Yarborough, who later played for the Detroit Lions, hit him gently at first, and Cade did not feel it. Yarborough then hit him more vigorously, still with no effect. Finally, the player lashed out with a mighty blow and the sound of the impact echoed across the football stadium. One of the bags ruptured and the liquid inside ran down Cade's face. "Oh my God," screamed an alarmed Yarborough. "Did I kill you?"

"But I wasn't hurt at all," Cade recalls.

Although Cade patented his helmet design, he has not tried to market it himself. Since 1971, however, thousands of similar helmets have been manufactured by a sports equipment company in Florida. They are now used by college and professional players — particularly those who have suffered head injuries. One of these, Willie Lanier, former linebacker for the Kansas City Chiefs, has called it, "the greatest helmet ever invented."

Although he is busy with his clinical practice and research in renal diseases, Gatorade and football helmets have made Cade an expert in sports medicine. In 1979, he plunged into the problem of body fluids and how they accumulate and disappear during vigorous exercise. "We wanted to find ways to deliver more oxygen to the tissues so our athletes could win more gold medals at the Olympics," he says.

This idea for helping healthy athletes came to him as an extension of his work with desperately sick patients. The case of Richard Goldkamp, a middle-aged man with kidney failure, got Cade started. He made some blood tests and noticed that as the level of phosphate in Goldkamp's blood went up — because the kidneys were not getting rid of it — the red blood cell count, or hematocrit, went down proportionately. There seemed to be a connection between the amount of phosphate and the number of red blood cells, which carry oxygen to the tissues. With this and other information, Cade theorized that higher phosphate levels permitted each cell to carry more oxygen. He believed that by manipulating the amount of phosphate, he could influence the amount of oxygen being transported to the muscles through the bloodstream.

With the 1980 Olympic Games in mind, he used Gatorade royalties to hire as guinea pigs several nationally ranked athletes who were attending the University of Florida. These included four-minute-miler Mike Conti and world class pole-vaulter Dave Roberts. During a series of tests, Christian Zauner, professor of exercise physiology at the University of Florida, added tablets to the athletes' diet, using a double-blind strategy so that neither the athletes nor Cade knew when or to whom phosphate was being given.

The results demonstrated that tablets containing about the same amount of phosphate found in a quart of milk, taken for three days in a row, increase the amount of oxygen delivered to the tissues by about 20 per cent. Each blood cell does more work and acquires more oxygen. The effects seem to be even greater in highly trained athletes.

This research may prove valuable in other areas of medicine. For example, phosphate tablets might help surgical patients get more oxygen to their muscles before and after an operation. Also, the results have shown that with extra phosphate in the blood, the heart not only supplies more oxygen but also beats more slowly. This could become extremely important for cardiac patients. "It's sort of like getting the heart into overdrive," says Zauner.

When Gatorade began to be marketed commercially, both the University of Florida and the federal government demanded royalties because Cade had used university facilities and federal funds to develop the drink. This led to a highly publicized legal battle.

Thus, Robert Cade is no stranger to controversy. Probably nothing has been more controversial than his research on schizophrenia, a severe mental disorder that disrupts the victim's feelings, thoughts, and relations to the outside world. A conspicuous symptom of many schizophrenics is hallucinations; in one form they hear voices that they believe are real.

Cade considers schizophrenia to be one of the world's greatest health problems. The disease affects more than one per cent of the population in the United States alone. It destroys the life of the victim and often that of his family, and it frequently requires extremely costly hospital care, even a lifetime in a mental institution.

For decades, psychiatrists have considered schizophrenia to be an exclusively psychological disorder. However, Cade studied literature indicating that the disease might have a genetic connection and be caused by abnormalities in enzymes — chemicals involved in the production of proteins. He reasoned that the disease might be treated by filtering compounds produced by the abnormal enzymes out of the blood. This could be done by hemodialysis, one of the major tools of renal medicine in which the patient's entire blood supply is routed through a special filtering machine.

In 1972, 29-year-old Linda Cook, a schizophrenic, was sent to Cade to be treated for hypertension before being committed to a mental institution. Cade spent four hours just to complete a routine

Cade and his son Stephen contemplate the remains of several old Studebakers, *above,* that hard work and loving care can make into one beautifully restored vehicle, *above right.*

physical examination of the patient. "Every time I asked a question she had to consult with her voices, and her answers were mostly irrelevant," he recalls. "The psychiatrists had given up on her. She was terribly ill and it was clear we had nothing to lose. One Wednesday, we put her on dialysis. When she came off the machine, she was not hallucinating and did not seem to be having delusions. It was remarkable. But the voices came back the following Sunday. So we put her on the machine once a week for 16 weeks; then, once a month. In the last eight years with this treatment, there's been no recurrence of hallucinations."

This was an incredible discovery. Linda Cook had spent 15 years in an asylum, seven of them in a locked ward. She had been treated by innumerable psychiatrists. "It seemed a miracle of Biblical proportions," says one of Cade's colleagues.

Cade treated other schizophrenics with dialysis. He could hardly believe the improvement in some of them and did not report it until he became more sure. By the summer of 1981, he and colleague Dr. Herbert Wagemaker had treated 34 schizophrenics with dialysis. About 65 per cent of the women and some 20 to 30 per cent of the men treated have been cured or improved markedly. "These patients were chronic schizophrenics," Cade said. "They didn't respond to any other treatment."

Despite the early promise of Cade's results, schizophrenia researchers, such as Solomon H. Snyder of Johns Hopkins University, remain skeptical. They are concerned that undue optimism about this treatment may lead to cruel disappointment for schizophrenics and their families. Robert Cade, they point out, is so personable, that his patients may be responding more to him than to the dialysis. This may prove to be true. In one test conducted at the National Institutes of Health in Bethesda, Md., in 1980, not one of the eight schizophrenics in the program responded to dialysis.

People who know Cade well say that you cannot be with him for long without getting introspective thoughts yourself . . . about the

A family trio — Cade and daughter Emily on violin, wife Mary at the piano — practices a Beethoven sonata.

way you handle your own life, your relations with children, neighbors, friends, and colleagues. You react to him because he is completely unpretentious. Indeed, many people describe him as an oddball, the neighborhood crackpot who once felled a tree onto his house by mistake, and who has been known to tie bicycles up in trees as a Halloween stunt. He likes the oddball description.

Some of the University of Florida administrators, however, think differently about Cade. They admire him as a person and appreciate the honor and research funds that he has brought to the institution. But the administrative headaches caused by his unconventional ways often dismay them. And Cade's notion that schizophrenia is, at least in part, a biochemical disease that can be treated with dialysis met with resistance. "The administrators wouldn't provide funding," says Cade, "so I support much of the work myself." For almost 10 years he has paid most of the hospital bills of his schizophrenic patients. Some of the campus sororities and fraternities have paid the rest out of funds raised at dance marathons.

Cade jogs daily and once a week he runs at least 5 kilometers (3 miles) with the Florida Track Club. Much of his thinking is done while running. He often takes his students with him, and they swap a variety of ideas and plan experiments while pounding the campus sidewalks.

"I was a flunky helping out with laboratory analyses for my own gratification," admits Mike Conti, now one of Cade's graduate students. "But Dr. Cade and I run together and one evening the phosphate idea came up. Dr. Cade said 'Gee Mike, that'd be a good subject for a masters in exercise physiology.' And that's how I got into the phosphate program; now I hope to end up in medicine."

The ability to see the peace and beauty in a camellia complements the character of a man whose busy life has profoundly affected those around him.

"Bob's strongest points," reports Thomas Fuller, head of the Department of Nephrology at the University of Florida, "are his unique ideas, his teaching, and his exceptional ability to inspire others. He was inspiring enough to make me change my career from cardiology to nephrology."

Cade mainly teaches fourth-year medical students. He has the ability to make complicated subjects simple – sometimes too simple, according to a colleague. "He's a little theatrical and very sensitive to the needs of the audience," says Fuller. "Nobody leaves his lectures early and the students remain very quiet – no coughing or rustling of papers." Cade has won several "most popular professor" and "best teacher" awards at the University of Florida Medical School.

Cade's life style is unpretentious. He and his wife, Mary, have raised their six children in an attractive but unspectacular house on an average-sized lot beneath the slash pines in a Gainesville suburb populated largely by university professors.

Cade and his sons – especially Stephen who is a mechanic – like to tinker with old cars. He rents a nearby garage to give them a place to work. With his income you might think he would specialize in expensive antiques, but, true to character, his interest is in 1950s Studebakers. At any one time he has 16 or more: musty-smelling, acned with rust, their fenders crumpled and the upholstery split. He buys them for $25 or so, and renovates them – replacing, rewelding, and rebuilding broken parts. It gives him an outlet for the tensions that can build up teaching and practicing medicine. One day he hopes to race one of the cars.

Cade loves music. He once built his own violin, and for years he played it in the University of Florida Symphony Orchestra. The whole Cade family is musically inclined. Eldest son Michael, 26, is a guitarist, eldest daughter Martha, 24, graduated summa cum laude in music from Appalachian State University in North Carolina in 1980. Celia, 22, plays harp and piano; Stephen, 20, plays cello; Emily, 19, plays violin; and Phoebe — a senior in high school — is an accomplished pianist. Mary Cade is also a pianist and she and her husband sometimes play Beethoven sonatas together. They met in 1952 when he was a medical student at the Children's Hospital in Dallas and she was the floor nurse. "We met over the ruptured liver of a young boy who'd been kicked by a horse," recalls Cade. "That was the luckiest day of my life!" They were married in 1953.

Another Cade invention is a nutritious food that uses whey, the liquid residue from cottage cheese, much of which is dumped into rivers. In 1967, Cade mixed whey and powdered egg into ordinary milk to make "Gator-Go," an exceptionally nutritious, protein-fortified drink now manufactured by Farmbest Dairy in Jacksonville and sold throughout Northern Florida. "It doesn't make sense to have a protein-hungry world and throw away tons and tons of lactalbumin," he says. Lactalbumin is the milk protein that stays in the whey when the other proteins are precipitated from the milk when it is made into the cheese.

Following the success of this protein-fortified milk, Cade began experimenting in 1975 with making a protein-rich orange juice. This proved unsuccessful, but the work led to the development of "Ten-Plus," a protein-enriched ice stick. The first successful ice sticks were made in 1977. They are manufactured in Ocala, Fla., by the Goldbond Company, makers of ice cream products. They are available in vending machines in about 40 elementary and high schools in the Miami area and "are doing quite well so far." Cade would like to see Ten-Plus served in school lunches. "Ten-Plus and Gator-Go are ideal for elementary schools," he says. "At least half of each lunch — the mashed potatoes and everything else on the hot tray — now goes into the garbage, but kids eat their ice cream and desserts. Gator-Go and the ice stick supply the same amount of nutrition as the rest of the meal and cost only one-fourth as much."

Cade welcomes young people into his home life. "He's one of the few people who you feel really cares about what you're doing," says Ken Adams, an admirer, who worked in Cade's laboratory while a teen-ager. Adams also spent so much time at Cade's home that he became like a member of the family. Now on the staff of the U.S. Geological Survey in Washington, D.C., Adams sums up Robert Cade this way: "Dr. Cade's a special person — someone you want to pattern yourself after. Heck, I'd like to be as smart!"

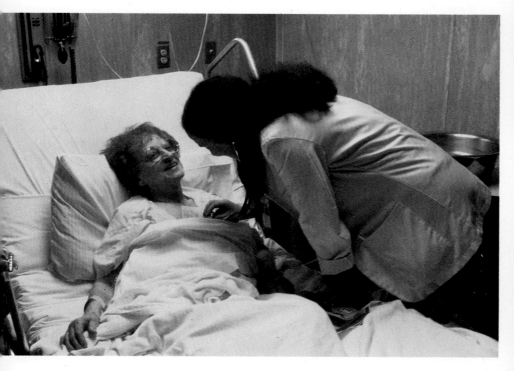

The Making
of a Doctor

By Sherry Baron

**A medical student discusses the rigors as well as the
rewards of her experience as a physician in training**

It was one of my first nights on duty as a medical student in the hospital emergency room, and it was the first time I had ever treated such extensive wounds. The police brought in a woman who had attempted suicide by slashing her wrists. I injected a local anesthetic into her wrists and then — under the supervision of a physician — began on the more than 20 stitches the wounds required.

It took me two hours to complete the task, much longer than it would have taken an experienced doctor. But it gave me an opportunity to talk to the woman about her life and why she had attempted suicide. She kept apologizing for causing so much trouble.

She had cut part of a wrist tendon, so I put a stitch in it and made a follow-up appointment for her two weeks later in the orthopedic clinic, where doctors could check on whether the tendon was healing properly. I just happened to be in the orthopedic clinic on the day of her follow-up appointment. She looked much better, she was not as depressed, and she remembered me right away. I must admit, it gave me a very nice feeling to see that I had done something toward helping someone get well.

As a third-year medical student at Case Western Reserve University (CWRU) School of Medicine in Cleveland, I am beginning to feel the personal satisfaction that can come from a career in medicine. But I have also found that the life of a medical student is far from the glamorous one of the physician portrayed in TV dramas. Medical education is a grueling combination of academic study and a kind of on-the-job training in hospitals.

The first and second years are spent mainly in laboratories and lecture halls. During the first year, medical students study such subjects as physiology and anatomy and examine tissue through microscopes to learn about the human body in its normal, healthy condition. At the end of the first year and throughout the second year they study pathology — disease states — and how diseases cause normal bodily states to change.

For me, the first two years of medical school were similar to being in college. I would get to school about 8 A.M. I and my classmates would either have lectures or spend the morning in a laboratory looking at slides or dissecting cadavers. My afternoons were taken up by laboratory work or elective studies in areas that particularly interested me, such as preventive medicine. The rest of the day and part of the night I spent studying in the library or at home.

Howeover, we did have some contact with patients during the first two years. Medical students work with patients in hospitals that are owned by or affiliated with the medical school. For example, CWRU School of Medicine is affiliated with six hospitals in the Cleveland area and requires first-year students to spend several nights at one of these hospitals observing childbirth. In fact, I was helping with deliveries the first month I was in school. I will never forget my first experience in the delivery room. After the obstetrician delivered the baby, she gave it to me to hold while she cut the umbilical cord. It was a very positive experience for me as a beginning doctor. The mother had just given birth to a healthy baby, and there was something easy that I could do.

In addition to simply observing births, each first-year student at CWRU Medical School is assigned to follow the progress of a pregnant woman. After the woman gives birth, the student, under the supervision of a doctor in the hospital's outpatient clinic, takes care of the baby for about two years. For example, I functioned as the doctor for the mother and baby to whom I was assigned. If the baby had a problem such as a cough, or was just crying too much, the mother would call me. I gave the baby his routine checkups and his immunization shots. Of course, I worked closely with an experienced physi-

The author:
Sherry Baron is a third-year medical student at Case Western Reserve University School of Medicine in Cleveland.

cian, who discussed every aspect of the case with me and advised me on how to handle any problems that arose.

Medical students must also learn how to give physical examinations. So during my second year I spent one afternoon a week with a physician in a hospital doing physical exams on patients.

But the amount of time spent caring for patients was very limited during the first two years. I always believed it is important for a good doctor to be able to relate well with people, especially patients. Yet I spent most of my first two years of medical school with books and classes. Studying in a library for long hours is important, and medical students have to do that. But it was very hard for me.

Many of my classmates felt the same way. Some had special problems, however. My friend, Rita Egan, has a Ph.D. in biochemistry and returned to school for an M.D. because she believed the training would be of help in her future research projects. "One of my greatest problems," she says, "is being an older student. At the age of 30, I'm just not used to going to class and studying."

Michael Fine, a second-year student, found it difficult to realize that he could never learn all there is to know about medicine. "Each student must learn to set comfortable limits and draw a line between studying enough and finding time to do other things," he says. "But it is very easy for me to feel guilty — there is always something else I could be reading."

Many medical students find physical activity useful in helping them relax. Some like to play basketball and run or jog. One of my favorite sports is swimming, so during my first two years, I swam laps every day at noon in one of the university pools.

I managed to get involved in other situations and activities that took me away from my studies. For example, I lived off campus in a large house with five other people, none of whom were medical students. Sometimes I went to the movies or out to dinner with my housemates or other friends. I also did volunteer work as a women's counselor at a free clinic in Cleveland.

Almost every medical student feels great pressure and tension, even though administrators and instructors convey the idea that a student who is accepted into medical school will become a doctor. I know many students fall by the wayside in premedical and other college programs, but medical schools choose so carefully and make such a large investment in each medical student that perhaps 1 person in an average class of 140 will not finish. Of course, there were times I was sure I would be that one student. I was greatly relieved that the formal classwork ended after my second year.

In the third year of medical school, students begin working full time in the affiliated hospitals. There they serve what are called clerkships for one to three months in each of the five major areas of medicine: internal medicine, which covers all the basic diseases that occur in the body; pediatrics, which deals with children; obstetrics

A skeleton appears to eavesdrop on class as
first-year students listen to an instructor
in one of CWRU medical school's lecture halls,
above. In a nearby laboratory, an instructor shows
specimens of healthy and diseased kidneys to
second-year students, *left*, while other
students study tissue with microscopes, *below*.

and gynecology, which involves births and problems with women's reproductive organs; psychiatry, which deals with mental illness; and surgery. Most clerkships are a combination of seminars in special topics and working with patients.

The students are not expected to master the subjects taught in the clerkships, but to get an understanding of these various specialty areas. Under the guidance of physician instructors, they learn how to deal with routine cases, such as uncomplicated childbirth, but they also learn when a complex case must be referred to a specialist. In addition, serving clerkships gives students an opportunity to consider which specialty area they might want to enter.

Fourth-year students in most schools also serve clerkships, but they elect one or more of the five areas they wish to study further. At CWRU, we also spend two months in outpatient clinics in the Cleveland area where we see a wide range of less severe illnesses than we encountered during our hospital clerkships. Fourth-year students spend the rest of their time going into further depth in any field they choose, such as heart disease, kidney disease, neurology, or special laboratory research.

I first had a sense of the fact that I am becoming a doctor when I began serving my third-year clerkships in the fall of 1980. During the various clerkships, medical students learn to do procedures on patients — how to stitch wounds, insert feeding tubes, draw blood, and set up transfusions. There is a saying in medical school: watch one, do one, teach one. And that is exactly how it is. You watch someone do a procedure, then you do it with them watching you and helping you, and eventually you teach someone else how to do it.

Two first-year students discuss a problem in public health care with a medical school professor as part of their elective studies.

My first clerkship was in surgery and I was very nervous. I arrived at the hospital having no idea of what they would expect of me. Soon the surgeon in charge of the students on that clerkship appeared and took me to a room where a surgical team was doing an operation. "Put on your scrubs [sterile operating-room clothes] and go in and watch," he said. Within the first hour, I was in the operating room watching a blood vessel graft on a patient with diseased arteries in his abdomen and legs.

At first, I just stood in the back of the room, feeling lost. But later on that day I actually took part in an operation. The patient had an abscess near his pancreas. The surgeons opened him up and drained the infection.

The role of a medical student in surgery is always a minor one. We hold the scissors and cut the threads or grasp the retractors that pull back the skin around an incision. So my fears of what they might expect of me were unfounded. All I did that first day was snip sutures, and that was no problem. I have been sewing since I was 5 years old, so I thought to myself, "I can cut a thread."

In the surgical clerkship, my day usually started at 6:30 A.M. The medical students go along with the interns, who are first-year doctors, and a resident, who has been out of medical school two or three years, to check on the patients. For example, we checked for fever and examined incision sites for signs of infection in patients recovering from surgery.

At 7:30 A.M. we went into the operating room and stayed there until between 2 P.M. and 5 P.M., depending on how busy things were. After that, we went around again to see the patients. Every third night I was on call — that is, I stayed at the hospital all night to handle any problems that might come up.

My internal medicine clerkship was quite different. We began visiting patients at 8 A.M. At 9:30 A.M., the medical students got together with all the doctors working on the floor to discuss either a medical topic or particular patients. I spent the rest of the day talking to my patients and doing various tests and procedures, such as taking blood or urine samples or inserting intravenous tubes.

During my clerkship in internal medicine, I discovered that physicians cannot always cure people. Many of the patients I saw were older people with chronic illnesses, such as arthritis, lung or bone diseases, or some other degenerative condition. Doctors can give these patients medication and try to improve the quality of their lives. But there is not much that physicians can do to cure them. As a medical student with high expectations of helping people, this was very difficult for me to accept.

All medical students must spend a certain amount of time in hospital emergency rooms during their clerkships. For two weeks in the fall of 1980 I worked 24-hour shifts there every other day. In the emergency room, students have the opportunity to see everything from accidents to shootings to heart attacks. In the morning, we

Baron and the doctor in charge of her internal medicine clerkship listen to a patient describe her symptoms, *below*. Later they review the medical history of the patient, *below right*, that Baron has prepared.

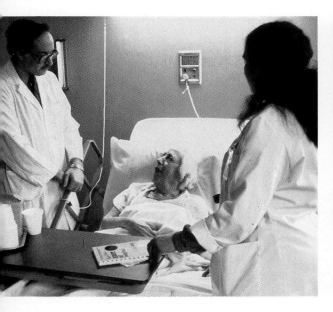

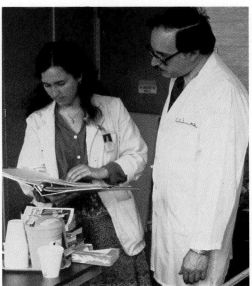

As part of her training in internal medicine, Baron sorts out the microscopic components of a urine sample under the guidance of a hospital intern.

generally removed stitches from patients we had treated a week or so before. During the day, any kind of emergency case could come in — kids with broken arms, factory workers with fingers cut off, people burned in fires, housewives who hurt their backs lifting heavy objects; even people with serious infections. At night we tended to have more traffic accident victims, perhaps because there are more drunk drivers on the streets at night. And between 1 A.M. and 2 A.M., we saw people who had been in gunfights, knifefights, or fistfights, along with other victims of violence.

In the emergency room, I sometimes found my professional responsibilities and attitudes challenged by my personal feelings toward a patient. The role of the physician is to help people, not to judge their characters. But we occasionally took care of people who had been picked up by the police after a gunfight or some other violent incident. Often these patients gave me a hard time, especially if they were drunk. In the early hours of the morning when I was tired from almost 24 hours of work, it was difficult to remember that a doctor delivers quality care no matter who the patient is. Sometimes I would get very angry and think, "Look, I don't have to do this for you. I'm here because I want to help you." Nevertheless, I learned to remind myself it was not the patient's fault that I had been up so long and was so tired.

However, most of my patients are very nice. In fact, one of the most enjoyable aspects of my medical education is just sitting and talking to them. In my third year, I am beginning to feel as though I am doing something for them. Also, I feel I am beginning to understand medicine. All the bits of facts that formed a big information blur before are finally beginning to come into focus at this point in my medical training.

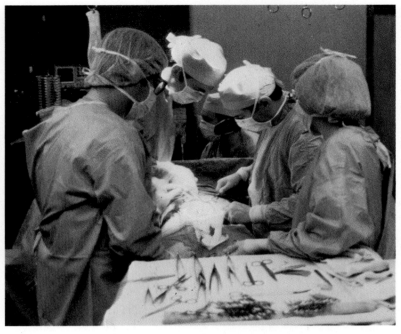

A surgeon points out
X-ray evidence of
disease, *above*, to
a student in the
surgical clerkship.
While surgeons and
residents repair a
ruptured hernia, *right*,
the student, foreground,
stands ready to lend
a hand if needed.

As of 1980, there were approximately 64,000 medical students in the United States. According to the Association of American Medical Colleges, about 16,000 students enter their 122 member schools each year. Approximately 36,000 persons apply.

Some medical students enroll in an M.D., Ph.D. program geared toward a career in research and teaching. However, most students work toward an M.D. degree with the intention of practicing clinical medicine after they graduate.

The kinds of people who study medicine have changed greatly over the past 10 years. In 1970, almost all medical students in the United States were white males. As of 1980, 25 per cent were females, and 7 per cent were members of minority groups. We come from a wide variety of ethnic and economic backgrounds.

I was born in 1955 in Irvington, N.J., near Newark. Most of my early life was spent with my mother, father, and older brother in little northern New Jersey towns just outside of New York City. My father, an immigrant from Israel, has his own small leather-goods company. My mother started working with my father in his company about 10 years ago and now designs pocketbooks, wallets, and other things for various leather companies.

My parents always wanted me to be a doctor. But I did not realize I had a talent or even a liking for science until my last years in high school, when a physics teacher whom I admired very much sparked my interest in science. Then I had an experience during the summer before my senior year of high school that finally made me decide on a

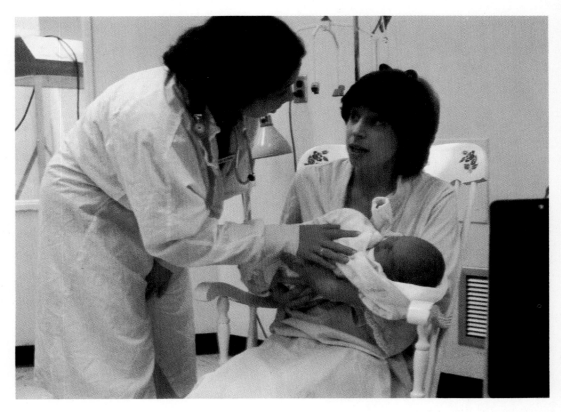

A student serving her clerkship in obstetrics and gynecology counsels a new mother about the care of her infant.

career in medicine. The National Science Foundation was sending gifted high school students to various colleges for intensive summer science courses. My high school physics teacher helped me get into a physics program at Cornell University in Ithaca, N.Y., during the summer of 1972.

A major flood hit New York State that summer, and I volunteered to help in a flood-relief program. Along with a busload of other students, I went to the disaster area to move furniture from flooded houses and help people relocate. Coming back on the bus, I began to think about this. I had not been very happy sitting in the lectures and laboratories, but I enjoyed being out that day working with people. Yet I also liked the intellectual challenge of science. Right then, the idea of becoming a doctor seemed to make a lot of sense. It combined the two things that were important to me: I could do science and also be involved with people.

In 1973, I enrolled in Radcliffe College in Cambridge, Mass. I did not go into a standard premedical program. Instead, I majored in the history of science, concentrating on the history of medicine. I felt that it was extremely important for me to have a broad educational background. I was very interested in history and political thought, and I knew I was going to be spending many years in the future

During her psychiatric
clerkship, Baron
helps a patient learn
how to cope with such
ordinary tasks as
doing laundry, *right*.
A student in the
pediatrics clerkship,
below, learns to calm
fears and win trust
from his young patient.

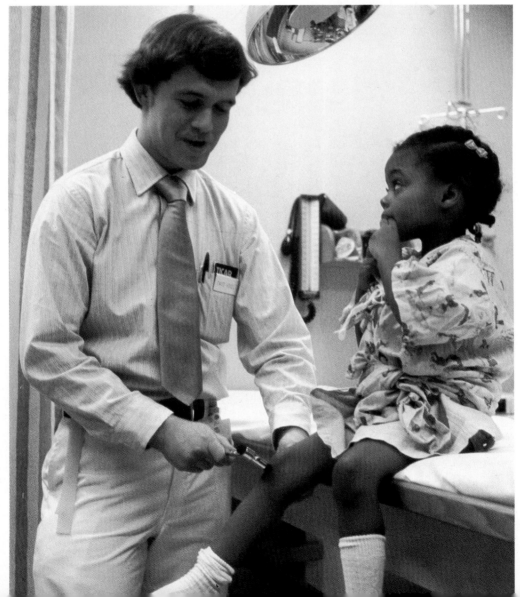

studying medicine. Therefore, I saw no reason to begin that study in college. So I just took the courses that are required to qualify for medical school — a year of basic biology, a year of basic physics, a year of inorganic chemistry, a year of organic chemistry, and a year of math, which some schools require.

People have different theories on the best course of college study to prepare for medical school. I would recommend that anyone thinking about medical school just take a few science courses. The medical school will start from the beginning and teach you all you need to know. However, other medical students say they are glad they took a lot of basic science courses in college, because it made medical school easier for them.

Applying to medical school can be expensive. The first step is taking the Medical College Admission Test (MCAT). Since most medical schools participate in the American Medical College Application Service (AMCAS), applicants need only fill out one form, include their MCAT scores, and check the schools to which they want the form sent. The basic application fee is $20 and there is an additional charge of $5 for each school to which the application is sent. The students I know applied to between 15 and 20 schools. Most of the medical schools require an additional $10 to $25 for processing their own secondary application.

Then applicants must visit the schools they want to attend and which have expressed interest in them. They must pay their own transportation, but the schools usually help them find places to stay. Occasionally, a school will hold regional interviews, especially in large cities. High school or college students interested in medical school can consult a guide published by the AMCAS each year. It lists all the medical schools and their requirements and is generally available in undergraduate college libraries.

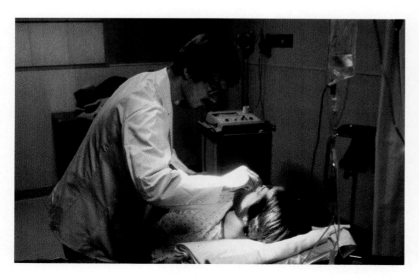

While intravenous fluids help stabilize the condition of an auto-accident victim, a medical student in the hospital emergency room quickly but gently cleans a deep cut on the injured man's head.

Medical school tuition costs vary. In 1981, they ranged from about $1,000 at some state schools to $15,000 a year at Georgetown University. CWRU School of Medicine is close to the average at $6,000 a year. But other expenses must be considered in addition to tuition. Rent, food, clothing, instruments, and books bring my total costs to between $10,000 and $12,000 a year.

Each school has financial-aid officers to help students finance their education. Financing ranges from ordinary bank loans to special government programs. For example, I am committed to three years' service in the National Health Service Corps, a federal government program designed to place doctors in areas that have a shortage of physicians. In exchange, the government pays my tuition and gives me a stipend of $480 a month. However, many medical school administrators fear that financing a medical education will become increasingly difficult in the future, because the federal government is cutting back on funds for loans and other forms of financial aid for medical students.

A doctor's training just begins with medical school. Most new doctors decide to specialize in pediatrics, obstetrics and gynecology, psychiatry, surgery, or internal medicine. After choosing a field, they enter a residency. The time served in residency varies depending on the field. For general surgery, it is five years; for pediatrics and internal medicine, three years. Residents work in a hospital taking care of patients under the guidance of attending physicians, who have already completed their residency.

Residents function as physicians, but they are under fairly close supervision. A great deal of teaching goes on during residency. The attending physicians teach the residents and interns in addition to the medical students. After completing residency, a doctor can either

An evening of lively conversation among housemates and friends provides Baron with a welcome break from the rigors of medical study.

Before calling it a day, Sherry Baron takes a moment in her room to try catching up on her medical reading material, a task that seems to have no end.

begin practicing medicine or go on for further study in a specialty, such as neurology or cardiology.

I will have to find a residency during my fourth year of school. A complex system that is exactly like computer dating has been set up for this purpose. Students list the institutions they prefer for their residencies, and the institutions list the students they prefer on the basis of applications and interviews. One day in March they hold "the match." Each applicant gets a letter naming the institution with which he or she was matched.

I am interested in doing my residency in occupational diseases, which are caused by conditions in the workplace. There is not much we can do about many diseases, but I believe society should start doing something to prevent the ones society is causing. I hope to work in a community clinic, rather than for a particular industry, and try to combine taking care of people with educating them about the hazards of occupational diseases.

The residencies recently set up specifically to train doctors in occupational diseases involve a three-year program of internal medicine plus an additional year devoted to occupational diseases caused by chemicals or other kinds of poisons. During the last year, residents study ways to monitor and prevent the diseases and learn research techniques that will help them to determine which diseases are environmentally caused.

Although my career plans do not include laboratory research, I may do some work in another important research area that involves documenting cases in an effort to determine the causes of specific diseases. This kind of statistical research is called epidemiology. Epidemiological researchers try to determine why certain groups of people develop certain kinds of diseases. For example, statistics might show that people living in a particular area have a high incidence of a rare form of cancer. Most of these cancer victims work at a local chemical plant. Researchers may then be able to trace the cause of these cancers to a particular chemical in the plant and devise ways of protecting workers from the effects of the chemical.

I have already undertaken projects in this area. I am the chairperson of the occupational health task force of the American Medical Students Association (AMSA). AMSA has some 25,000 members and about 12 task forces covering special interest areas that expose students to problems not encountered in school. My task force sponsors workshops on environmentally caused diseases and develops summer work programs for students interested in this field.

I look forward to my future work as a physician and have never really regretted choosing medicine as my career. But there are several things regarding medical education that disturb me. I believe that the training system in the United States produces highly competent doctors. But I also think these doctors have some negative feelings about their medical education. Almost everyone I have talked to — students, interns, and residents — sees this period as a necessary but very difficult part of their life. First they endured long hours of study, then long hours of work in the hospitals from the third year of medical school through residency. There is a standard joke in medical school: A student asks, "How often should I be on call?" The instructor answers, "Well if you're only on call every other night, you miss half the cases." Yes, doctors trained this way come out qualified, but I think they also come out somewhat dehumanized. Medical educators are becoming concerned about this. Personally, I do not believe there has to be such intense pressure and such long working hours in the hospitals.

Medical school, internship, and residency do not mark the end of a medical education. Doctors must comply with a continuing education program to stay licensed. Usually medical schools operate these programs. Medicine is constantly changing, and physicians need to be aware of and keep learning about new medications, treatment methods, and theories of diseases. So in a sense, a doctor's training never ends.

Anyone considering medicine as a career should take the time to find out exactly what is involved. Work in a hospital or be a volunteer. See if a local physician needs a part-time office helper. In addition, talk to some doctors and other health-care professionals about their feelings and experiences to get a good sense of the kinds of demands that go along with the challenging, satisfying aspects of the profession. Then think carefully about your choice. If you choose medicine, you will find that very heavy demands are made on your life, and you will have to make many sacrifices, especially during your training. However, there are many attractive aspects to a medical career, including not only a secure income and a respected role in society, but perhaps more importantly, the opportunity to combine a love of science with the chance to work with and help other people.

Index

This index covers the contents of the 1980, 1981, and 1982 editions of *Science Year,* The World Book Science Annual.

Each index entry is followed by the edition year in *italics* and the page numbers:

Cyclone: hurricane, *Special Report, 81*–88;
  meteorology, *82*–279, *80*–304.
This means that information about cyclones begins on the page indicated for each of the editions.

An index entry that is the title of an article appearing in *Science Year* is printed in boldface italic letters: ***Archaeology.***
An entry that is not an article title, but a subject discussed in an article of some other title, is printed: **Plutonium.**

The various "See" and "See also" cross references in the index are to other entries within the index. Clue words or phrases are used when the entry needs further definition or when two or more references to the same subject appear in *Science Year.* These make it easy to locate the material on the page.

***Neuroscience, 82*–286, *81*–306, *80*–311.**
  See also **Brain.**

The indication *"il."* means that the reference is to an illustration only, as:

Butterfly fish, *il., 82*–316

Index

A

Absorption lines: cosmology, *81*-246; interstellar medium, *81*-160; X-ray astronomy, *82*-141
Acid rain: *Close-Up, 81*-276
Acne: drugs, *82*-240; medicine, *80*-299
Addiction: alcoholism, *Special Report, 82*-112; drugs, *81*-261
Adenovirus 2: split genes, *81*-200
Advanced X-ray Astrophysical Facility: X-ray astronomy, *82*-151
Aegyptopithecus, 81-232
Aging: medicine, *82*-270, *81*-297
Agriculture, 82-210, *81*-226, *80*-226; chemistry, *80*-260; environment, *82*-255; microbiology, *80*-310; Negev, *Special Report, 80*-127; archaeology, *82*-216, *81*-233, 237; acid rain, *81*-276; water buffalo, *80*-77. See also *Botany; Chemical Technology; Climate; Food; Nutrition.*
Air pollution: transportation, *81*-332. See also *Automobile; Climate; Environment; Pollution.*
Alcohol: *Special Report, 82*-112
Alcoholics Anonymous, *82*-124
Alfvén waves: solar wind, *80*-21
Allogenic effect factor (AEF): immunology, *81*-292
Aluminum: energy, *82*-248
Amateur astronomy, *81*-389
Amazon River Basin: plant chemicals, *Special Report, 82*-131
American Sign Language, *81*-325
Ames test: animal welfare, *82*-89
Amino acids: anthropology, *81*-232; chemical ecology, *81*-18; chemistry, *81*-258; split genes, *81*-199
Ammonia: Saturn, *82*-15
Amoco Cadiz: oil spill, *81*-71
Amphetamine, *81*-137
Amplified music, *82*-342
Anastomosis: surgery, *80*-300
Angina pectoris: drugs, *82*-238
Angiotensin: drugs, *82*-239
Anhedonia: alcoholism, *82*-116
Animal behavior: animal welfare, *82*-85; ecology, *80*-271, *Close-Up, 81*-266; navigation, *81*-114; psychology, *81*-325; rhinoceros, *82*-27; swimming, *81*-28; water buffalo, *80*-77; zoology, *82*-315, *81*-333, *80*-349
Animal welfare: *Special Report, 82*-85
Anode: chemistry, *82*-232
Ant: chemical ecology, *Special Report, 81*-20; zoology, *81*-333
Anthropology, 82-213, *81*-230, *80*-229; *Books of Science, 82*-228; Mead, Margaret, *Close-Up, 80*-232; museum, *81*-146. See also *Archaeology.*
Antibiotics: anthropology, *82*-214; biochemistry, *80*-249; drugs, *81*-263
Antibodies: hepatitis, *82*-154; immunology, *82*-266, *81*-293; inflammation, *81*-59; monoclonal antibodies, *Special Report, 82*-167; neuroscience, *82*-287
Anticyclone system: hurricane, *81*-91
Antifeedant, *82*-133
Antigenic determinant: immunology, *82*-267; *Special Report, 82*-168
Antigens: hepatitis, *82*-154; inflammation, *81*-59; monoclonal antibodies, *82*-167
Antimatter: cosmology, *81*-246; physics, *82*-295, *80*-323
Antiquarks: physics, *82*-295, *81*-315, *80*-323
Apes: anthropology, *81*-231; psychology, *81*-325
Archaeology, 82-215, *81*-233, *80*-237; *Books of Science, 80*-253; Negev, *80*-131; New World, *82*-217, *81*-235, *80*-237; Old World, *82*-215, *81*-233, *80*-234; *Special Report, 80*-99; sunken treasure, *82*-97. See also *Anthropology; Geoscience.*
Arctic Ocean: oceanography, *81*-310; paleontology, *81*-288
Aromatics: catalysts, *82*-204
Arrhythmia: surgery, *82*-276
Artificial blood: *Close-Up, 81*-295
Artificial food coloring, *81*-326
Artificial gene. See Recombinant DNA.
Artificial insemination, *80*-336
Artificial skin: surgery, *82*-277
Artificial spine: surgery, *81*-298
Ash, volcanic: agriculture, *82*-210; Mount Saint Helens, *82*-76
Aspirin: drugs, *81*-262, *80*-267
Astronomy: amateur, *81*-389; awards, *81*-406, *80*-392; *Books of Science, 82*-228, *80*-253; *Close-Up, 81*-242;* cosmology, *82*-226, *81*-245, *80*-247; Einstein, Albert, *80*-408; extraterrestrial life, *80*-57; high-energy, *82*-224, *81*-243, *80*-245; interstellar medium, *81*-156; Jupiter, *81*-41; planetary, *82*-219, *81*-238, *80*-240; Saturn, *82*-12; solar wind, *80*-13; star birth, *80*-99; stellar, *81*-240, *80*-243; X-ray astronomy, *82*-139. See also *Space Exploration.*
Atherosclerosis: cell receptors, *80*-44; nutrition, *81*-308
Atmosphere. See Climate; Meteorology; Weather.
Atmospheric pressure, *82*-219
Atomic and molecular physics. See *Physics* (atomic and molecular).
Atomic reactor. See Nuclear power plants.
Atwater, Tanya: biography, *80*-356
Audio cassette tape, *82*-338
Australia: anthropology, *81*-231
Australia antigen: hepatitis, *82*-154
Australopithecines, *80*-229
Autoimmune diseases: immunology, *80*-293; inflammation, *81*-68
Automated DNA synthesizer, *82*-282
Automatic defibrillator, *82*-276
Automobile: catalysts, *82*-203; chemical technology, *80*-257; energy, *82*-248; *Special Report, 80*-141.* See also *Air pollution; Transportation.*
Aversion therapy, *82*-125

Aviation: collision research, *Special Report, 80*-150; technology, *80*-345
Awards and Prizes, 82-308, *81*-402, *80*-386

B

B-DNA: biochemistry, *81*-249; molecular biology, *82*-285
B-lactamase: biochemistry, *81*-250
B-lymphocytes: immunology, *82*-266; monoclonal antibodies, *82*-167
B quark, *82*-295, *81*-316
Background radiation, *82*-226
Bacteria: agriculture, *81*-226; biochemistry, *81*-250, *80*-249; drugs, *81*-263; inflammation, *81*-58; microbiology, *80*-308; oceanography, *81*-311; *World Book Supplement, 82*-331
Bacteriology. See Bacteria; Biology; Microbiology.
Barnard's Star, *80*-58
Barosaurus: Close-Up, 81-290
Barrier beach: ecology, *82*-241
Baryon, *81*-174
Base: molecular biology, *82*-282
BASIC: *Consumer Science, 82*-341
Batteries: energy, *82*-248; physics, *80*-330; transportation, *81*-331
Beach: ecology, *82*-241
Bedouins: *Close-Up, 81*-322
Bee: animal navigation, *81*-116
Beetle, bombardier, *80*-12
Beginner's All-Purpose Symbolic Instruction Code, *82*-341
Behavior: See Animal behavior.
Bernoulli's principle, *81*-35
Beta-blockers: drugs, *82*-238
Bias-belted tires, *82*-352
Bias-ply tires, *82*-352
Bicycle: energy, *Close-Up, 82*-249
Big bang: cosmology, *82*-226, *81*-245, *80*-247; interstellar medium, *81*-158; X-ray astronomy, *82*-140
Bighorn Medicine Wheel, *80*-108
Binary pulsar, *81*-241
Binary star: astronomy, *82*-223, *81*-242; interstellar medium, *81*-161
Biochemistry, 81-247, *80*-249; chemistry, *80*-262; *Close-Up, 80*-250; extraterrestrial life, *80*-62; genetics, *80*-282; nutrition, *80*-314; nutrition and the brain, *80*-87; schizophrenia, *81*-134. See also *Amino acids; Biology; Chemistry; DNA; Enzymes; Hormone; Plant.*
Biological clock, *81*-124
Biology: awards, *81*-405, *80*-390; *Books of Science, 82*-228, *81*-251, *80*-253; cell receptors, *80*-42; embryo transplants, *80*-185; extraterrestrial life, *80*-57; interferon, *80*-115; molecular, *82*-281; split genes, *81*-197. See also *Biochemistry; Botany; Cell; Ecology; Enzymes; Genetics; Microbiology; Zoology.*
Birds: animal navigation, *81*-116; birdsong, *80*-28; oil spill, *81*-79; paleontology, *82*-265, *80*-292; zoology, *81*-337

Birdsong: *Special Report, 80*-28
Birth defects: dentistry, *82*-268
Bit: *Consumer Science, 82*-341
Bitumen: tar sands, *81*-188
Blastocyst: genetics, *82*-255
Blindness: surgery, *81*-299
Blister: *Consumer Science, 81*-345
Blocking drug, *82*-238
Blood: anthropology, *82*-214;
  forensic science, *81*-107; hepatitis,
  82-154; inflammation, *81*-58;
  medicine, *81*-295; nutrition, *80*-314
Blood clots: nutrition, *82*-290
Blood markers: hepatitis, *82*-165
Blood pressure: medicine, *82*-269;
  nutrition and the brain, *80*-97
Blood sugar: internal medicine,
  82-270, *81*-296
Blood transfusion: hepatitis, *82*-155
Body identification, *81*-111
Bombardier beetle, *81*-12
Bond, chemical: catalysts, *82*-197
Bone destruction: dentistry, *81*-294
Bone fractures, *81*-297, *80*-301
Bone grafts: medicine, *82*-271
Bone tools: archaeology, *82*-217
Books of Science, *82*-228, *81*-251,
  80-253
Botany, *82*-230, *81*-253, *80*-255;
  agriculture, *80*-226; chemistry,
  80-260; ecology, *80*-270; museum,
  Special Report, 81-146. See also
  Agriculture; Plant.
Bowie Medal, *82*-310, *81*-404, *80*-388
Brachiopod: paleontology, *82*-265
Brain: nutrition, *80*-87; schizophrenia,
  81-130; *World Book* Supplement,
  82-322. See also **Neuroscience;**
  Psychology.
Brain damage: birdsong, *Special*
  Report, 80-41; *il., 80*-312
Breast cancer, *81*-351
Breast feeding: nutrition, *82*-288;
  Close-Up, 80-314
Breeding: agriculture, *82*-212;
  embryo transplants, *80*-185
Brontosaurus: *Close-Up, 81*-290
Bronze Age: sunken treasure, *82*-99
Bruce Medal, *82*-310, *81*-406, *80*-392
Buckley Prize, *82*-310, *81*-403, *80*-388
Buffalo, water: *Special Report, 80*-73
Buprenorphine: drugs, *81*-261
Butterfly: zoology, *81*-336
Butterfly fish, *il., 82*-316
Byte: *Consumer Science, 82*-340

C

Cadaver-bone grafts, *82*-271
Cade, J. Robert: biography, *82*-356
Calcareous microplankton, *82*-44
Calcium: internal medicine, *81*-297
Calcium-blockers: drugs, *82*-238
Camarasaurus: *Close-Up, 81*-290
Camera: *Consumer Science, 81*-346;
  Special Report, 82-56; X-ray
  astronomy, *82*-143
Canals, Mayan: archaeology, *82*-217
Cancer: chemistry, *82*-234;
  Consumer Science, 81-351; drugs,
  81-261, *80*-267; electronics, *81*-270;
  environment, *82*-253; hepatitis,

82-161; immunology, *81*-293;
  inflammation, *81*-68; interferon,
  80-115; internal medicine, *82*-273,
  81-297; monoclonal antibodies,
  82-167; public health, *82*-307
Capillaries, *80*-89
Capuchin monkey: *Close-Up, 80*-332
Carbohydrate oxidation, *81*-281
Carbohydrates: nutrition, *82*-290
Carbon: geochemistry, *81*-281; radio
  dating, *Close-Up, 80*-236
Carbon dioxide: botany, *81*-254;
  environment, *81*-278; meteorology,
  82-278, *81*-301
Carbon dioxide laser probe, *81*-299
Carcinogens. See **Cancer.**
Cardiovascular. . . . See headings
  beginning **Heart. . . .**
Caries: dentistry, *80*-295; *il., 81*-294
Carrier, disease: hepatitis, *82*-155
Cascade Range, *82*-72
Cassini's division: Saturn, *82*-21
Cassiopeia-A, *82*-144
CAT scan, *81*-208
**Catabolite gene-activating protein
  (CAP):** molecular biology, *82*-285
Catalyst: chemistry, *82*-233; *Special*
  Report, 82-195
Catalytic converter, *81*-332
Catalyzed reaction: catalysts, *82*-196
Catatonic schizophrenia, *81*-131
Catchment areas: Negev, *80*-134
Cathode-ray tube (CRT): *Consumer*
  Science, 82-338; electronics, *80*-244
Cattle: agriculture, *80*-229; animal
  welfare, *82*-91; embryo transplants,
  80-186; water buffalo, *80*-73
Caulking: *Consumer Science, 82*-346
Cave painting: archaeology, *82*-216
Cell: genetics, *82*-257; internal
  medicine, *82*-273; microbiology,
  81-304; monoclonal antibodies,
  82-167; shock, *Close-Up, 80*-250;
  split genes, *81*-200. See also **Amino**
  acids; Blood; Cancer; DNA;
  Enzymes; Genetics; Virus.
Cell receptors: inflammation, *81*-66;
  schizophrenia, *81*-135; *Special*
  Report, 80-42
Cellulose: *Consumer Science,*
  82-345; energy, *82*-250
Central processing unit (CPU), *82*-338
Cerebral cortex, *80*-311
CERN: physics, *82*-296, *81*-317,
  80-322
Charge, theory of, *81*-171
Charon (Pluto): astronomy, *82*-219
Chediak-Higashi syndrome, *81*-68
Chemical bonding: chemistry, *82*-235
Chemical dating: Old World
  archaeology, *82*-215
Chemical ecology: *Special Report,*
  81-12; zoology, *81*-336
Chemical industry: environment,
  81-274, *80*-280
Chemical Technology, *80*-257
Chemistry, *82*-232, *81*-255, *80*-260;
  awards, *82*-308, *81*-402, *80*-386;
  catalysts, *82*-195; *Close-Up, 81*-256;
  forensic science, *81*-113;
  geochemistry, *80*-284; plant
  chemicals, *82*-128; schizophrenia,
  81-129. See also **Biochemistry;**

Chemical Technology;
  Geochemistry.
Chemotaxis, *81*-64
Chemotherapy: drugs, *81*-261
China: anthropology, *82*-213;
  Close-Up, 80-339
Chip, computer: *Consumer Science,*
  82-338; electronics, *82*-244
Chlorine: environment, *82*-254
Chlorpromazine, *81*-130
Cholera: drugs, *Close-Up, 81*-263
Cholesterol: cell receptors, *80*-44;
  nutrition, *82*-288, *81*-308
Choline, *80*-89
Chromosomes. See **Cell; Genetics.**
Chronic granulomatous disease:
  inflammation, *Special Report, 81*-68
Cigarette smoking: drugs, *80*-266;
  public health, *81*-327
Circadian rhythms: animal
  navigation, *Special Report, 81*-124
Circulatory system. See **Blood; Heart**
  disease.
Cirrhosis: alcoholism, *82*-119;
  hepatitis, *82*-161
Clam: paleontology, *82*-265
Clay tokens: archaeology, *81*-234
Cleft lip and palate, *82*-268
Climate: environment, *81*-278;
  extinction, *82*-46; meteorology,
  82-278, *81*-301, *80*-307;
  oceanography, *81*-310. See also
  Weather.
Clo value, *82*-347
Clone: genetics, *82*-255;
  immunology, *80*-294; molecular
  biology, *82*-281; monoclonal
  antibodies, *Special Report, 82*-168;
  neuroscience, *82*-287
Close binary star: astronomy, *82*-223
Closed universe, *82*-149
Cloud seeding: hurricane, *81*-98
Coal: acid rain, *81*-276; catalysts,
  82-202; energy, *82*-248, *81*-271; tar
  sands, *81*-186
Codon: biochemistry, *81*-247; split
  genes, *Special Report, 81*-199
Coffee: public health, *82*-307
Colds: interferon, *80*-120
Colitis: surgery, *82*-275
Color: quantum chromodynamics,
  Special Report, 81-178
Color deficiency: probability, *82*-184
Color vision: chemistry, *81*-256;
  neuroscience, *81*-306
Columbia (space shuttle): space
  exploration, *82*-311, *81*-329, *80*-342
Combination reaction, *82*-197
Comet: amateur astronomy, *81*-390;
  planetary astronomy, *82*-219
Communications, *81*-259, *80*-264;
  birdsong, *80*-28; ecology, *80*-271;
  extraterrestrial life, *80*-65; fiber
  optics, *80*-212; space exploration,
  82-314; zoology, *82*-318, *81*-334.
  See also **Computer; Electronics.**
Compass: animal navigation, *81*-119
Complement system: inflammation,
  Special Report, 81-59
Composite dome: Mount Saint
  Helens, *Special Report, 82*-83
Computed tomography (CT) scanner,
  82-248

Computer: *Close-Up, 80*-274; communications, *81*-260; *Consumer Science, 82*-338; electronics, *81*-268, *80*-272; Fourier Transforms, *81*-213; technology, *80*-345
Computerized axial tomography (CAT): Fourier Transforms, *81*-208
Condensation: botany, *82*-230
Conduction, *82*-344
Conductor electrons, *82*-302
Confinement parameter: plasma physics, *82*-300
Congenital defects, *81*-306
Conservation: rhinoceros, *82*-28; sunken treasure, *82*-110; **See also** *Agriculture;* **Air pollution;** *Ecology; Environment;* **Petroleum; Pollution;** *Public Health; Zoology.*
Continental drift: geology, *80*-287; geophysics, *82*-262; geoscience, *Close-Up, 82*-260. See also **Plate tectonics; Sea-floor spreading.**
Continents, formation of, *82*-258
Controlled Ecosystem Pollution Experiment (CEPEX), *81*-311
Convection zone: solar wind, *80*-14
Copernicus satellite: interstellar medium, *Special Report, 81*-165
Copia gene, *81*-278
Coral reef, *il., 82*-292; zoology, *Close-Up, 82*-316
Core, earth: geochemistry, *82*-258
Cornell Electron Storage Ring: elementary particles, *82*-295, *81*-316
Corona: solar wind, *80*-13
Coronary. . . . See headings beginning **Heart. . . .**
Cosmic radiation: cosmology, *82*-226, *80*-247; high-energy astronomy, *82*-224
Cosmology, 82-226, *81*-245, *80*-247; *Books of Science, 82*-228, *81*-251, *80*-253; X-ray astronomy, *82*-139
Coxsackie virus: medicine, *80*-296
Crater: Mount Saint Helens, *82*-75
Crater density: Saturn, *82*-17
Craving: alcoholism, *82*-115
Cretaceous Period: extinction, *82*-42; paleontology, *81*-288
Crime investigation, *81*-101
Cro molecule, *82*-285
Crop residues: energy, *82*-250
Crust, earth: geochemistry, *82*-259; geophysics, *81*-286
Cryostat: solid-state physics, *82*-302
Crystal, *il., 82*-303; solid-state physics, *81*-321, *80*-329
C-T boundary: extinction, *82*-42
Curvature of the spine, *82*-275
Cyclic adenosine monophosphate (cAMP), *82*-285
Cyclone: hurricane, *Special Report, 81*-88; meteorology, *82*-279, *80*-304
Cytomegalovirus infection: interferon, *80*-121; internal medicine, *81*-298; microbiology, *81*-306

D

D-phenylalanine (DPA), *80*-259
Dancing: medicine, *Close-Up, 82*-272

Dane particle: hepatitis, *82*-156
Darwinism: macroevolution, *80*-200
Data processing. See **Computer.**
David, Hurricane, *81*-94
Deafness: birdsong, *Special Report, 80*-35; *Consumer Science, 82*-342
Deaths of Notable Scientists, 82-236, *81*-409, *80*-394
Deceleration, *80*-142
Decomposition: catalysts, *82*-197
Decompression sickness, *82*-101
Deep-sea animals: Lake Baikal, *Special Report, 80*-157
Deep-sea drilling, *81*-313
Defensive chemicals: chemical ecology, *Special Report, 81*-12
Defibrillator: surgery, *82*-276
Deformed nucleus: physics, *81*-318
Deimos: planetary astronomy, *81*-239
Delirium tremens, *82*-115
Density, stellar: physics, *81*-319
Dentistry, 82-268, *81*-294, *80*-295; forensic science, *81*-107
Deoxyribonucleic acid. See **DNA.**
Dependence: alcoholism, *82*-115
Depression: neuroscience, *80*-311
Desert life: botany, *82*-230; heat absorption, *Close-Up, 81*-322
Deuterium: cosmology, *80*-247
Diabetes: cell receptors, *Special Report, 80*-50; genetics, *80*-282; medicine, *82*-269, *81*-296, *80*-296; nutrition, *81*-310, *80*-313
Diabetic retinopathy: surgery, *81*-300
Diagnosis: electronics, *80*-275; medicine, *Close-Up, 80*-298; neuroscience, *80*-311
Dialysis: Cade, J. Robert, *82*-365; technology, *80*-346
Diamonds: geophysics, *82*-263
Diarrhea: public health, *81*-327
Diatomaceous earth, *81*-194
Dictation machine, *81*-269
Diet: ecology, *80*-269; nutrition and the brain, *80*-87; swimming, *81*-39. See also **Food;** *Nutrition.*
Diffusion equation, *81*-212
Dihydrofolate reductase, *81*-304
Dimer: molecular biology, *82*-285
Dinosaur: *Close-Up, 81*-290; extinction, *82*-42; oceanography, *81*-310; paleontology, *81*-291
Diplodocus: dinosaur, *81*-290
Directed blast: Mount Saint Helens, *Special Report, 82*-70
Disabled persons, *80*-332
Disco felon: medicine, *82*-272
Disease: agriculture, *81*-226; alcoholism, *82*-112; anthropology, *82*-214; biochemistry, *82*-249; hepatitis, *82*-153; immunology, *80*-293; interferon, *80*-115; medicine, *80*-298; monoclonal antibodies, *82*-167; nutrition, *81*-308; plant chemicals, *82*-128; schizophrenia, *81*-138. See also *Medicine;* names of specific diseases.
Dispersed repeated gene families: genetics, *81*-278
Diving, exploratory: sunken treasure, *Special Report, 82*-101
Diving, simulated, *82*-291

Dizygotic twins: alcoholism, *Special Report, 82*-123; nutrition, *82*-290
DNA (deoxyribonucleic acid): biochemistry, *81*-247, *80*-249; drugs, *81*-263; genetics, *82*-257, *81*-279; *il., 80*-252; immunology, *82*-266; microbiology, *81*-304, *80*-308; molecular biology, *82*-282; monoclonal antibodies, *82*-178; split genes, *81*-197. See also **Cell;** *Genetics;* **RNA; Virus.**
Dog: animal welfare, *Special Report, 82*-94; ecology, *Close-Up, 81*-266
Dopamine: schizophrenia, *81*-134
Doppler effect, *80*-320; interstellar medium, *Special Report, 81*-161
Double clusters: astronomy, *82*-225
Down-filled garments, *82*-349
Downstream molecule, *82*-284
Draize test: animal welfare, *82*-88
Drinking water: environment, *82*-252
Drought: Negev, *80*-131
Drug abuse: alcoholism, *82*-112; *World Book* Supplement, *82*-335
Drug resistance: biochemistry, *81*-250, *80*-251; microbiology, *81*-304
Drugs, 82-238, *81*-261, *80*-266; *Close-Up, 81*-263; dentistry, *82*-268; interferon, *80*-115; medicine, *82*-269, *81*-298; monoclonal antibodies, *82*-174; plant chemicals, *82*-126; public health, *80*-337; schizophrenia, *81*-129. See also **Antibiotics; Brain; Cancer; Hormone;** *Medicine.*
Dry farming: Negev, *80*-127

E

Earphones, *82*-343
Earth sciences. See *Agriculture; Geoscience; Meteorology; Oceanography.*
Earthquakes: Atwater, Tanya, *80*-363; geology, *81*-284, *80*-286; geophysics, *81*-288, *80*-289; Mount Saint Helens, *Special Report, 82*-69
East Pacific Rise: geophysics, *81*-286; oceanography, *81*-312
Eclipse: shrinking sun, *81*-242
Ecology, 82-240, *81*-264, *80*-269; acid rain, *81*-276; *Close-Up, 81*-266; Lake Baikal, *80*-155; oil spill, *81*-71; rhinoceros, *82*-27. See also *Environment;* **Pesticide; Pollution; Waste;** *Zoology.*
Edison, Thomas: *Close-Up, 80*-345
Education: *Close-Up, 80*-339. See also **Learning.**
Eggs, insect: zoology, *81*-336
Egypt, ancient: archaeoastronomy, *80*-112; archaeology, *82*-216
Eicosapentenoic acid, *82*-290
Einstein, Albert, *80*-397
Electric power: energy, *82*-251; plasma physics, *82*-300
Electric ray (fish), *80*-352
Electric vehicles: energy, *82*-248, *81*-274; transportation, *81*-331
Electricity: chemistry, *82*-232, *80*-260; electronics, *82*-246; energy,

82-248, 81-273; solid-state physics, 81-321; surgery, 82-275. See also **Electronics.**
Electroencephalograph (EEG), 82-287
Electromagnetic radiation: physics, 82-293, 81-314
Electromagnetic radiation spectrum: interstellar medium, 81-160; X-ray astronomy, 82-140
Electromagnetic waves, 80-172
Electromagnetism: chemistry, 81-257; fiber optics, 80-214
Electron: atomic and molecular physics, 82-293; chemistry, 81-255; elementary particles, 82-295, 80-322; nuclear physics, 81-318; solid-state physics, 81-324, 80-329; synchrotron, 80-171
Electron accelerator, 81-318
Electron neutrinos: physics, 81-316
Electronics, 82-244, 81-268, 80-272; biofeedback, Close-Up, 80-274. See also **Astronomy** (high energy); **Communications; Computer; Magnetism; Physics** (solid-state).
Electrophoresis, 81-108
Electrostatic mirror: physics, 81-320
Elementary particles: See **Physics** (elementary particles).
Elephant: zoology, 82-315
11-cis-retinal: chemistry, 81-256
Elmo Bumpy Torus (EBT): plasma physics, 82-302
Embryo transplants: genetics, 82-255, 80-283; transplants, 80-185
Emission lines: cosmology, 81-246; astronomy, 82-222, 225; interstellar medium, 81-160; X-ray astronomy, 82-141
Emulsion: artificial blood, 81-295; Sauce Béarnaise, 81-256
Encke's division: Saturn, 82-21
Energy, 82-248, 81-271, 80-276; acid rain, 81-276; agriculture, 81-230; atomic and molecular physics, 82-293, 81-314; Books of Science, 81-251; catalysts, 82-197; chemical technology, 80-258; chemistry, 81-255; Close-Up, 82-249; electronics, 82-246; nuclear physics, 81-318; nutrition, 82-289; plasma physics, 82-300, 81-320; synchrotron, 80-171; tar sands, 81-184; technology, 80-347; transportation, 80-347; X-ray astronomy, 82-140
Energy loss spectrometer, 81-319
Entomology: chemical ecology, 81-12
Environment, 82-252, 81-274, 80-279; acid rain, 81-276; alcoholism 82-123; Books of Science, 82-228, 81-251; Consumer Science, 82-342; energy, 80-277; oil spill, 81-71; public health, 82-307; tar sands, 81-192; transportation, 80-347; water buffalo, 80- 83. See also **Air pollution; Ecology; Public Health; Waste; Water pollution.**
Enzymes: catalysts, 82-196; drugs, 81-263; nutrition, 82-289
Eosuchian reptile, 82-264
Epidemic: drugs, Close-Up, 81-263
Epoxide: chemistry, 82-234

Equilibrium: catalysts, 82-197
Eruption, volcanic: agriculture, 82-210; extinction, 82-45; Mount Saint Helens, 82-70
Escherichia coli: hepatitis, 82-159; public health 81-328
Eskimos: nutrition, 82-290
Ethanol: alcoholism, 82-112; catalysts, 82-199; chemical technology, 80-258; energy, 82-250
Ethylene: botany, 82-230
Eucaryotes: molecular biology, 82-283; split genes, 81-198
Europa: Jupiter, 81-42
European Space Agency (ESA): space exploration, 82-314, 81-329
Evolution: anthropology, 81-321; geochemistry, 81-281; macroevolution, Special Report, 80-197; paleontology, 82-265
Excavation: sunken treasure, 82-99
Exercise: neuroscience, 81-307; swimming, Special Report, 81-38
Exon: biochemistry, 81-249; split genes, Special Report, 81-206
Extinction: macroevolution, 80-197; paleontology, 82-266; rhinoceros, 82-29; Special Report, 82-41
Extragalactic object, 82-224
Extrasensory perception, 82-305
Extraterrestrial life, 80-57
Eye: chemistry, 81-256; surgery, 81-299, 80-300

F

Fast Fourier Transform (FFT), 81-215
Fast-twitch muscle fibers, 81-37
Fat: nutrition, 82-288, 81-308; Close-Up, 82-289
Fatty acids: nutrition, 82-290
Feingold diet: psychology, 81-326
Felon (disorder): medicine, 82-272
Fertilization: genetics, 82-255
Fetal brain: neuroscience, 81-306
Fetus: embryo transplants, 80-185
Fiber optics: communications, 81-259; Special Report, 80-210
Fiberglass, 82-345
Fibroblasts: chemistry, 81-258; interferon, 80-116; medicine, 82-273; molecular biology, 82-281
Filament: Close-Up, 80-345
Film: photography, 81-347
Fine structure constant: atomic and molecular physics, 82-294
Fingerprints, 81-106
Firefly: chemical ecology, 81-24
Fireplace: Consumer Science, 81-341
Fischer-Tropsch process, 82-201
Fish: Lake Baikal, 80-165; oil spill, 81-83; zoology, 80-350
Fishing: archaeology, 80-237
Floods: ecology, 82-242; hurricane, 81-99; Negev, 80-130
Fluid mechanics: swimming, 81-30
Fluorocarbons, 81-295
Foam insulation, 82-345
Folk medicine: plant chemicals, 82-126; rhinoceros, 82-30
Food: archaeology, 82-216; nutrition

and the brain, 80-87; water buffalo, 80-79. See also **Agriculture; Nutrition.**
Food additives: nutrition, 82-290
Food chain: extinction, 82-50; zoology, Close-Up, 82-317
Food coloring, artificial, 81-326
Football: Cade, J. Robert, 82-358
Force: nuclear physics, 82-298; quantum chromodynamics, 81-181
Forecasting, weather: hurricane, 81-99; meteorology, 82-278
Forensic science: Special Report, 81-101
Forest: ecology, 82-242, 80-271
Fossils: anthropology, 82-213, 81-230, 80-229; extinction, 82-42; geology, 81-286; paleontology, 82-264, 81-289, 80-291. See also **Anthropology; Archaeology.**
Fourier, Jean Baptiste, 81-220
Fourier Transforms, 81-208
Franklin Medal (physics), 82-310, 81-405, 80-386
Fraternal twins: alcoholism, 82-123; schizophrenia, 81-133
Frederic, Hurricane, 81-98
Freezing: embryo transplants, 80-193
Frequency response, 81-349
Freshwater research: ecology, 81-266; Lake Baikal, 80-155
Frog: ecology, 80-271; zoology, 82-319
Fruit fly: genetics, 81-278; neuroscience, 81-308
Fruit trees: Negev, 80-134
Fuel: catalysts, Special Report, 82-203; chemical technology, 80-258; chemistry, 82-233; energy, 82-248, 80-278. See also **Oil.**
Fungus: microbiology, 82-305
Fusion: nuclear physics, 81-319; plasma physics, 82-300, 81-320
Fusion Engineering Device, 82-300

G

Gairdner Awards (medicine), 82-310, 81-404, 80-389
Galapagos Rift Valley: geophysics, 81-286; oceanography, 81-311, 80-318
Galaxy: cosmology, 82-227, 81-245, 80-248; extraterrestrial life, 80-57; stellar astronomy, 82-223; X-ray astronomy, 82-146. See also **Astronomy; Quasar.**
Galilean satellites: Jupiter, 81-41
Game preserve: rhinoceros, 82-32
Gamma globulin: hepatitis, 82-163
Gamma rays: astronomy, 82-224
Gammarids: Lake Baikal, 80-158
Gamow-Teller transitions, 82-299
Ganglion: neuroscience, 82-287
Ganymede (satellite): astronomy, 80-242; il., 80-241; Jupiter, 81-42
Gas chromatograph, 81-113
Gasification, coal: energy, 81-271
Gasohol: chemical technology, 80-258; energy, 82-250, 80-278; transportation, 80-348

Index

Gasoline: catalysts, *82*-203
Gate delay: electronics, *82*-244
Gatorade: Cade, J. Robert, *82*-359
Gene transplants: genetics, *80*-283;
microbiology, *81*-304
General circulation models, *81*-302
Genetic disease, *80*-49
Genetic engineering: agriculture,
80-226; biochemistry, *80*-251;
botany, *80*-256; microbiology,
80-308
Genetics, *82*-255, *81*-278, *80*-282;
alcoholism, *82*-123; anthropology,
82-214; biochemistry, *80*-249;
microbiology, *81*-306; molecular
biology, *82*-281; neuroscience,
80-311; nutrition, *82*-290, *80*-313;
probability, *82*-184; psychology,
82-304; public health, *80*-336;
schizophrenia, *81*-132; science
policy, *80*-339; *Special Report,*
81-197. See also ***Biochemistry;***
Cell; DNA; RNA.
Geochemistry, *82*-258, *81*-281, *80*-284
Geology, *81*-283, *80*-286; Atwater,
Tanya, *80*-363; extinction, *82*-42;
geoscience, *82*-260; Mount Saint
Helens, *82*-69. See also
Oceanography.
Geophysics, *82*-262, *81*-286, *80*-289;
Atwater, Tanya, *80*-356; Mount
Saint Helens, *Special Report,* *82*-69.
See also ***Oceanography.***
Geoscience, *82*-258, *81*-281, *80*-284;
awards, *81*-404, *80*-388; *Books of
Science,* *81*-251; *Close-Up,* *82*-260;
geochemistry, *82*-258, *81*-281,
80-284; geology, *81*-283, *80*-286;
geophysics, *82*-262, *81*-286, *80*-289;
paleontology, *82*-264, *81*-288,
80-291. See also ***Climate; Ecology;***
Meteorology; Oceanography;
Weather.
GOES satellite, *82*-314
Geothermal energy, *82*-248
Glands. See **Hormone.**
**Global Atmospheric Research
Program:** meteorology, *81*-304
Globular clusters, *82*-223
Glomar Challenger: oceanography,
82-293, *81*-313, *80*-316
Glucocorticoids: shock, *80*-250
Glucose, *81*-296
Gluons: physics, *82*-296, *81*-315,
80-322; quantum chromodynamics,
Special Report, *81*-171
Glycogen: swimming, *81*-37
Goddard Astronautics Award,
82-310, *81*-406, *80*-392
Gonorrhea: drugs, *Close-Up,* *81*-263
Goose down, *82*-348
Gossamer Penguin: energy, *82*-251
Gossyplure, *80*-260
Graham, Ronald L., *81*-373
Graphite fibers, *81*-331
Grassland: ecology, *82*-241;
rhinoceros, *Special Report,* *82*-32
Gravitation, *80*-397
Gravitational star collapse, *81*-319
Gravitational tidal forces, *81*-239
Gravitational waves: astronomy,
80-243; Einstein, *80*-408
Gravitropic response: botany, *82*-230

Great Pyramid, *80*-112
Great Red Spot: Jupiter, *81*-45
Greenhouse effect, *81*-278
Ground water: environment, *82*-252
Growth: agriculture, *82*-211, *81*-227;
botany, *82*-230
Gypsy moth: chemistry, *82*-234

H

HA protein: monoclonal antibodies,
Special Report, *82*-176
Haber process: catalysts, *82*-197
Hadron: quantum chromodynamics,
Special Report, *81*-174
Hall voltage, *82*-295
Halley's comet: astronomy, *82*-219
Hallucination: schizophrenia, *81*-131
Hand: neuroscience, *82*-286
Handicapped: communications,
81-261; psychology, *80*-332
Hangover: alcoholism, *82*-115
Harmonic tremor, *82*-82
HB$_s$AG. See **Hepatitis B surface
antigen.**
Health: interferon, *80*-115
Hearing: zoology, *82*-315
Hearing loss, *82*-342
Heart disease: drugs, *82*-238, *81*-262;
medicine, *80*-299; nutrition, *82*-288,
290, *81*-308; surgery, *82*-275
Heat absorption, *Close-Up,* *81*-322
Heat conduction, *81*-211
Heat transfer, *Consumer Science,*
82-344; fireplace, *81*-341;
geochemistry, *82*-259
Heavy chain molecule, *82*-266
Heavy quark, *81*-181
Hebephrenic schizophrenia, *81*-131
Helium (He): geochemistry, *80*-285;
planetary astronomy, *81*-238
Hemoglobin: anthropology, *82*-214;
synchrotron, *Special Report,* *80*-180
Hepatitis: alcoholism, *82*-119;
interferon, *80*-121; *Special Report,*
82-153
Hepatitis B: hepatitis, *Special Report,*
82-154; public health, *82*-308
Herbicide: agriculture, *81*-227,
80-228; environment, *80*-280;
microbiology, *81*-305
Herculaneum: archaeology, *81*-233
Heredity: alcoholism, *82*-123;
macroevolution, *80*-197; nutrition,
80-313; probability, *82*-184
Herpes: internal medicine, *81*-298
Heterogeneous catalyst, *82*-200
Hexon protein: split genes, *81*-200
Hi-fi components, *81*-348
High blood pressure: drugs, *82*-239;
medicine, *81*-294, *80*-297; nutrition,
81-310
High-Energy Astronomy, *82*-224,
81-243, *80*-245
**High Energy Astronomy Observatory
(HEAO):** high-energy astronomy,
82-224; space exploration, *81*-331,
80-343; X-ray astronomy, *82*-139
High-intensity sound, *82*-342
High-level language, *82*-341

**High-pressure nervous syndrome
(HPNS):** oceanography, *82*-291
High-pressure system, *81*-91
Hodgkin's disease: medicine, *82*-273
Homing pigeon, *81*-118
Hominid: anthropology, *82*-213,
80-229; archaeology, *82*-215
Homo erectus: anthropology, *82*-213
Homogeneous catalyst: catalysts,
Special Report, *82*-199
Homosexuals: hepatitis, *82*-159
Honeybee: animal navigation,
81-116; zoology, *80*-349
Hormone: agriculture, *81*-229;
botany, *82*-230, *80*-256; drugs,
80-266; embryo transplants, *80*-190;
microbiology, *80*-308
Horticulture. See ***Agriculture;***
***Botany;* Plant.**
Horwitz Prize, *82*-310, *81*-405, *80*-390
Hot spots, *82*-263, *81*-287
Hubble expansion effect, *81*-245
Human fibroblast interferon, *82*-281
Human fossils: anthropology, *82*-213
Human leucocyte antigen:
monoclonal antibodies, *82*-179
Human leucocyte interferon:
molecular biology, *82*-283
Human-powered vehicle (HPV):
energy, *Close-Up,* *82*-249
Humidifier, *82*-350
Humpback whale, *81*-311
Hungarian komondor, *81*-266
Hunting, prehistoric: New World
archaeology, *82*-218
Hurricane: *Special Report,* *81*-87
Hybridization, in situ, *81*-278
Hybridoma, *82*-167
Hydralazine: drugs, *82*-239
Hydrocarbons: catalysts, *82*-204;
fossil fuels, *81*-185; oil spill, *81*-77
Hydrogen: chemistry, *82*-233, 235,
81-255; energy, *80*-278; interstellar
medium, *81*-162; physics, *82*-304;
81-313; technology, *80*-347
Hydrogen cyanide: Saturn, *82*-19
Hydrogen isotopes: physics, *80*-327
Hydronium ion, *81*-257
Hydroquinones, *81*-16
Hydrothermal vents, *81*-311
Hydroxide ions, *81*-255
Hyperactivity, *81*-326
Hyperion: Saturn, *82*-16
Hypertension: drugs, *82*-239;
medicine, *81*-294, *80*-297; nutrition,
81-310
Hyperthermia: electronics, *81*-271
Hypnotism: psychology, *82*-305
Hypogammaglobulinemia, *81*-67
Hypotension: medicine, *82*-269
Hypothermia: medicine, *82*-270

I

Iceland Plateau, *81*-285
Identical twins: alcoholism, *82*-123;
schizophrenia, *81*-132
IgM antibody: immunology, *81*-293
Igneous rock: geology, *81*-286

Ileal endorectal pull-through: surgery, *82*-275
Imaging device, *82*-143
Immune deficiency disease, *81*-67
Immune system: hepatitis, *82*-157; immunology, *82*-266; inflammation, *81*-58; interferon, *80*-116; internal medicine, *81*-297; molecular biology, *82*-281; monoclonal antibodies, *82*-167
Immunization: public health, *81*-329
Immunology, *82*-266, *81*-292, *80*-293
Implant, brain tissue, *81*-306
In situ hybridization: genetics, *81*-278
Indium phosphide crystal, *82*-232
Inertia: swimming, *81*-30
Inertia confinement: plasma physics, *81*-321
Infection: interferon, *80*-115; medicine, *82*-273. See also **Disease.**
Infectious hepatitis: hepatitis, *82*-154
Infiltration, *82*-344
Inflammation: *Special Report,* *81*-57
Influenza, *82*-176
Infrared radiation, *81*-260
Inner cell mass (ICM): genetics, *82*-255
Insecticide: agriculture, *81*-226; plant chemicals, *Special Report,* *82*-133
Insects: chemical ecology, *81*-12; plant chemicals, *82*-133; zoology, *81*-334, *80*-349
Insulation, *82*-344, 347
Insulin: genetics, *80*-282; medicine, *82*-270, *81*-296, *80*-296
Intelligence: psychology, *82*-304
Intelsat satellite, *82*-314
Interferon: botany, *81*-253; chemistry, *81*-258; medicine, *81*-297; molecular biology, *82*-281; monoclonal antibodies, *82*-179; *Special Report,* *80*-115
Internal Medicine, *82*-269, *81*-294, *80*-296
Interplanetary dust: interstellar medium, *Special Report,* *81*-156
Interstellar bubble, *81*-240
Interstellar medium: cosmology, *81*-246; *Special Report,* *81*-156; X-ray astronomy, *82*-146
Intestinal surgery, *82*-275, *80*-300
Intron: biochemistry, *81*-248; split genes, *Special Report,* *81*-206
Iron: geochemistry, *82*-258, *81*-281; nutrition, *80*-314; physics, *81*-319
Irrigation: agriculture, *82*-211, *81*-230; archaeology, *82*-217
Isotope: chemistry, *80*-261; geochemistry, *82*-258, *80*-285; radio dating, *Close-Up,* *80*-236; solid-state physics, *81*-323

J

Jaundice: hepatitis, *Special Report,* *82*-153; medicine, *80*-302
Jesus Christ: radio dating, *80*-236
Jojoba plant: agriculture, *82*-210
Josephson junction device: electronics, *82*-244
Jovian system: Jupiter, *81*-42

Jupiter: planetary astronomy, *80*-240; space exploration, *81*-330, *80*-342; *Special Report,* *81*-41

K

Kelp: ecology, *82*-242
Kidney transplant, *81*-298
Kimberlites: geophysics, *82*-263
Kinetically directed reaction, *82*-199
Kintraw: archaeoastronomy, *80*-102
Klystron: atomic and molecular physics, *81*-315; synchrotron, *Special Report,* *80*-177
Komatiite: geochemistry, *81*-283
Komondor: ecology, *81*-266

L

Lactalbumin: Cade, J. Robert, *82*-369
Lactic acid: swimming, *81*-38
Laetoli: anthropology, *81*-230, *80*-229
Lake: ecology, *81*-264
Lake Baikal: *Special Report,* *80*-155
Lake Rudolf: anthropology, *81*-230
Lamb-Retherford shift: atomic and molecular physics, *82*-293
Land reclamation: ecology, *82*-240
Language: birdsong, *Special Report,* *80*-28; electronics, *80*-275; psychology, *81*-325
Large-scale integration (LSI): electronics, *81*-268
Lasers: atomic and molecular physics, *81*-315, *80*-320; communications, *81*-259; Einstein, Albert, *80*-405; electronics, *80*-275, *79*-272; fiber optics, *80*-216; plasma physics, *80*-329; surgery, *81*-299; technology, *80*-345
Lasker Awards (medicine), *82*-310, *81*-405, *80*-300
Lava: geochemistry, *81*-283; Mount Saint Helens, *Special Report,* *82*-70. See also **Volcano.**
LD-50: animal welfare, *82*-89
Lead-acid battery, *81*-331
Lead isotope: geochemistry, *82*-258
Learning: birdsong, *Special Report,* *80*-30; neuroscience, *82*-288, *81*-308; psychology, *82*-304, *81*-325; swimming, *Special Report,* *81*-28
Lecithin: *Special Report,* *80*-89
Leeches: neuroscience, *82*-286
Leucocyte: interferon, *80*-116; molecular biology, *82*-281; monoclonal antibodies, *82*-169
Leukemia: chemistry, *82*-234; *il.,* *82*-284; public health, *80*-335
Lift, principle of: swimming, *81*-35
Light: atomic and molecular physics, *81*-315; chemistry, *81*-255; fiber optics, *Special Report,* *80*-210
Light Amplification by Stimulated Emission of Radiation. See **Lasers.**
Light bulb: *Close-Up,* *80*-345; energy, *81*-274
Light chain molecule, *82*-266

Light-emitting diode (LED): communications, *81*-259; fiber optics, *Special Report,* *80*-216
Light sensitivity, *81*-256
Light wave measurement, *81*-215
Limb replantation: surgery, *81*-300
Limbic system: schizophrenia, *Special Report,* *81*-138
Linear predictive coding: electronics, *81*-268
Lining (garment), *82*-348
Linoleic fatty acids: nutrition, *82*-290
Lipoprotein: cell receptors, *80*-45
Liquefaction, coal: energy, *81*-272
Liquid-crystal display (LCD), *82*-245
Liquid fluorocarbon: artificial blood, *Close-Up,* *81*-295
Liquid junction solar cell, *82*-232
Lithospheric plate: geology, *81*-283; geophysics, *81*-288
Liver: alcoholism, *82*-119; drugs, *80*-267; hepatitis, *82*-153
Livestock: animal welfare, *82*-91; embryo transplants, *80*-186; water buffalo, *80*-73
Loess (soil): Negev, *80*-128
London: archaeology, *80*-235
Loose-fill insulation, *82*-345
LORAN-C: communications, *81*-261
Love Canal, *81*-274, *80*-280
Low-density lipoprotein, *80*-45
Low-pressure system: hurricane, *Special Report,* *81*-91
Lucibufagin, *81*-25
Lumpectomy: breast cancer, *81*-352
Lung disease: public health, *81*-327
Lupus erythematosus: drugs, *82*-239
Lutalyse: agriculture, *81*-229
Lymphoblast: chemistry, *81*-258
Lymphocytes, *81*-292, *80*-293; inflammation, *81*-58; medicine, *81*-297; monoclonal antibodies, *82*-167
Lymphokine: inflammation, *81*-59
Lysosome: shock, *Close-Up,* *80*-250

M

Macroevolution: *80*-197
Macrophage: immunology, *81*-293; inflammation, *81*-58
Magma: geology, *81*-285; geophysics, *81*-286; Mount Saint Helens, *Special Report,* *82*-70
Magnetic bubble memory, *80*-272
Magnetic field: planetary astronomy, *82*-220, *81*-238; solar wind, *80*-14; physics, *82*-303
Magnetic fusion: physics, *82*-301
Magnetic mirror device, *81*-320
Magnetic moment: physics, *82*-303
Magnetism: animal navigation, *81*-116; zoology, *80*-349
Magnetite, *81*-125
Magnetosphere: Jupiter, *81*-46; astronomy, *81*-238
Main-memory, *82*-338
Malaria: anthropology, *82*-214; immunology, *81*-293; monoclonal antibodies, *Special Report,* *82*-175
Mammoth: archaeology, *82*-217; Earthwatch, *80*-371

Index

Manic-depressive psychosis: schizophrenia, 81-131
Mantle: geochemistry, 82-258; geology, 81-283; geophysics, 81-288; Mount Saint Helens, 82-70
Marijuana: drugs, 81-261; neuroscience, 80-311
Marine life: ecology, 82-242; oceanography, 81-310; oil spill, 81-72; zoology, 82-316
Mars: astronomy, 82-221, 81-239
Maser: Einstein, Albert, 80-405
Mass, neutrino: cosmology, 82-226; physics, 81-316
Mastectomy: breast cancer, 81-352
Mathematics: *Books of Science,* 82-228, 80-254; electronics, 80-274; Fourier Transforms, 81-208; Graham, Ronald L., 81-373; probability, 82-180; psychology, 82-304
Mating patterns: zoology, 82-319
Maunder Minimum: astronomy, 80-243
Maya: archaeology, 82-217, 81-236
Mead, Margaret, 80-232, 80-395
Mean density: Saturn, 82-17
Meat production, 82-91
Medical school, 82-371
Medicine, *82*-268, 81-294, 80-295; alcoholism, 82-112; awards, 82-309, 81-404, 80-389; *Books of Science,* 80-254; cell receptors, 80-42; *Close-Up,* 82-272, 81-295, 80-298; dentistry, 82-268, 81-294, 80-295; drugs, 80-266; electronics, 81-270, 80-275; genetics, 80-282; immunology, 80-293; interferon, 80-115; internal, 82-269, 81-294; medical school, 82-371; monoclonal antibodies, 82-167; plant chemicals, 82-128; public health, 80-335; rhinoceros, 82-30; surgery, 82-275, 81-298, 80-300; technology, 80-346. See also **Disease;** *Public Health.*
Medicine man, 82-129
Medicine wheel, 80-108
Medieval seafaring, 82-110
Meltdown: energy, 80-276; environment, 80-279
Memory: neuroscience, 82-288; psychology, 82-305, 80-331
Memory (computer), 82-338
Menopause: medicine, 81-297
Mental illness: schizophrenia, 81-129
Meson: elementary particles, 81-315; quantum chromodynamics, 81-174
Messenger RNA: biochemistry, 81-247, 80-251; immunology, 82-267; microbiology, 80-308; molecular biology, 82-281; split genes, *Special Report,* 81-200
Metabolism: drugs, 80-266; nutrition, *Close-Up,* 82-289
Metal electrides: chemistry, 81-257
Metal-oxide-semiconductor field effect transistor: physics, 82-295
Metal sulfide: geophysics, 81-287
Meteorites: extinction, *Special Report,* 82-44; geology, 80-288
Meteorology, *82*-278, 81-301, 80-304; agriculture, 80-228; hurricane, 81-88. See also **Climate; Weather.**

Methane: astronomy, 82-219
Methanol: catalysts, 82-203
Methotrexate (MTX), 81-304, 80-251
Mexico: archaeoastronomy, *Special Report,* 80-110; geology, 80-289; geophysics, 80-289
Microbiology, 81-304, 80-308
Microcircuits, *il.,* 81-269; synchrotron, *Special Report,* 80-183
Microtubules: inflammation, 81-67
Microwave energy: physics, 82-294; electronics, 81-270
Migration: animal navigation, 81-116
Mimas: Saturn, *Special Report,* 82-16
Mind. See **Brain;** *Psychology.*
Mind-altering drugs, 82-114
Mining: ecology, 82-240; tar sands, *Special Report,* 81-183
Mirror magnet reactor: plasma physics, 81-320
Mitochondria, biochemistry, 81-247, *Close-Up,* 80-250; genetics, 82-257
Molecular biology, 82-281, 282
Molecule: physics, 80-320
Momentum: nuclear physics, 82-298
Monarch butterfly, 81-336
Monazite: physics, 81-323
Mondrian display, 81-307
Monkey: psychology, *Close-Up,* 80-332; zoology, 82-318
Monoclonal antibodies, 82-172; neuroscience, 82-287
Monozygotic twins: alcoholism, 82-123; nutrition, 82-290
Mood: psychology, 82-305
Moog synthesizer, 81-221
Moons of Jupiter: Saturn, 81-50
Moons of Saturn, 82-12
MOSFET: physics, 82-295
Mount Saint Helens: agriculture, 82-210; *Special Report,* 82-69
Multiple Mirror Telescope Observatory, 80-244; *il.,* 80-243
Multiple myeloma, 81-298
Multiple sclerosis, 81-293
Muon neutrino, 81-316
Muscle: swimming, 81-37
Museum, 81-141; zoology, 82-316
Music: *Consumer Science,* 82-342
Mutation: anthropology, 82-214; drugs, 81-263; macroevolution, 80-200; molecular biology, 82-283
Myocardial depressant factor, 80-250

N

Nabataean Empire: Negev, 80-132
Naloxone: internal medicine, 82-269
NANB. See **Non A/non B hepatitis.**
Narrow-line quasar: astronomy, 82-225
National Aeronautics and Space Administration (NASA): Saturn, *Special Report,* 82-12; science policy, 80-337; space exploration, 82-311, 81-329, 80-343
National computer network, 82-340
National Institutes of Health: animal welfare, *Special Report,* 82-90
Natural gas: science policy, 80-338; tar sands, *Special Report,* 81-186

Natural history: *Books of Science,* 82-229, 81-251, 80-254; museum, *Special Report,* 81-141
Natural selection, 80-200
Navigation: animal behavior, 81-114; communications, 81-261
Neanderthal Man, 82-214
Nebula, 81-242
Neem tree, *il.,* 81-226; 82-137
Negev Desert: *Special Report,* 80-127
Neptune: astronomy, 81-238
Nerve impulses, *il.,* 81-298; neuroscience, 82-286
Nervous system. See **Brain; Neuroscience.**
Neuroleptics: schizophrenia, 81-130
Neuron, 80-311; nutrition and the brain, *Special Report,* 80-86
Neuroscience, 82-286, 81-306, 80-311. See also **Brain.**
Neurosis: schizophrenia, 81-131
Neurotransmitter: alcoholism, 82-116; nutrition and the brain, 80-87
Neutrinos: cosmology, 82-226; elementary particles, 81-316; nuclear physics, 81-319
Neutron: physics, 82-299, 81-315
Neutron star: physics, 82-300; stellar astronomy, 81-241; X-ray astronomy, 82-146
Neutrophil: inflammation, 81-58
N-15 isotope: agriculture, 82-211
Niagara Falls: environment, 81-274
Nitrates: acid rain, *Close-Up,* 81-276
Nitrogen: ecology, 81-264
Nitrogen conversion, 80-310
Nitrogen fixation, 82-211, 80-227
Nitrogen narcosis, 82-291
NMR spectroscopy: biochemistry, 80-252; chemistry, 81-257
Nobel prizes: chemistry, 82-308, 81-402, 80-386; medicine, 82-309 81-404, 80-389; physics, 82-309, 81-403, 80-386
Noise pollution, 82-342
Non A/non B hepatitis: *Special Report,* 82-164
Norepinephrine, 80-97
Nova: amateur astronomy, 81-399
Nuclear energy: Einstein, 80-407
Nuclear fusion: energy, 80-277; plasma physics, 82-300, 80-327
Nuclear magnetic resonance (NMR): biochemistry, 80-252; chemistry, 81-257
Nuclear moment: physics, 82-303
Nuclear physics. See *Physics.*
Nuclear power plants: chemical technology, 80-259; environment, 80-279
Nuclear reactor: energy, 80-276; science policy, 80-338
Nuclear Regulatory Commission: environment, 80-279; science policy, 80-341
Nucleon: physics, 82-298, 81-319
Nucleotide: genetics, 82-257
Nucleus: genetics, 82-255; nuclear physics, 82-298
Nutrients: ecology, 81-264; oceanography, 81-311, 80-318

Nutrition, 82-288, 81-308, 80-313; and the brain, 80-87; *Books of Science,* 80-254; Cade, J. Robert, 82-369; *Close-Up,* 82-289, 80-314; ecology, 80-269; medicine, 80-298; pets, 81-338; zoology, 80-352

O

Obesity, 82-289, neuroscience, 80-311; nutrition, 81-309, 80-313
Ocean crust: geology, 81-283; oceanography, 81-312, 80-316
Ocean pollution: environment, 81-276; oil spill, 81-72
Oceanography, 82-291, 81-310, 80-316; Atwater, Tanya, 80-356; Earthwatch, 80-385; extinction, 82-46; paleontology, 81-288. See also *Geoscience; Ocean pollution; Plate tectonics.*
Odontology: forensic science, 81-106
Odor: neuroscience, 81-308
Off-road vehicle: ecology, 82-241
Oil: energy, 82-248; geology, 80-289; science policy, 80-338; tar sands, *Special Report,* 81-182
Oil spill: environment, 81-276; *Special Report,* 81-71
Olefins: catalysts, 82-204
Ontong Java-Manihiki Plateau: geology, 81-286
Open universe, 82-149
Optical fibers: communications, 81-259; electronics, 80-210
Optically active epoxides, 82-234
Organ transplant: monoclonal antibodies, *Special Report,* 82-179
Orion, *il.,* 81-393
Osteoporosis: medicine, 81-297
Otter: ecology, 82-242
Ovulation, 80-190
Oxygen: artificial blood, 81-295; chemistry, 82-233, 81-255; extinction, 82-51; geochemistry, 81-281

P

Pacific Ocean: geophysics, 81-286
Pacific Plate: geology, 81-284; *il.,* 82-73
Paleontology, 82-264, 81-288, 80-291; *Close-Up,* 81-290; Earthwatch, 80-372; extinction, 82-41. See also *Anthropology; Archaeology.*
Pancreas: internal medicine, 82-269; public health, 82-307
Parabola: Fourier Transforms, 81-210
Paraffins: catalysts, 82-204
Paranoid schizophrenic, 81-131
Parkinson's disease, 81-306; schizophrenia, 81-138
Particle accelerator: elementary particles, 82-296, 81-315; synchrotron, 80-171

Particle physics. See *Physics* **(elementary particles).**
Pauli exclusion principle, 81-319
PC 1 Duarte: neuroscience, 80-311
PCBs. See **Polychlorobiphenyls.**
Pecked cross, 80-110
Peking Man: anthropology, 82-213
Penicillin, 81-250
Pentagonal dodecahedron, 82-235
Peptide, 81-258
Perception: neuroscience, 81-306
Perfluorinated decalin: artificial blood, 81-295
Periodic curves: Fourier Transforms, *Special Report,* 81-212
Periodontal diseases, 81-294
Permian Period: paleontology, 82-265
Personality: alcoholism, 82-121
Perspiration: heat absorption, 81-322
Pertussis: public health, 81-328
Pesticide: agriculture, 81-226
PETRA: physics, 82-296, 81-315
Petroleum: tar sands, 81-182
Pets: animal welfare, 82-85; diet, 81-338
Pharmacology. See *Drugs.*
Phenytoin: dentistry, 82-268
Pheromone, 82-234, 80-263
Philosophy of science: *Books of Science,* 82-229, 81-252, 80-254
Phobos: planetary astronomy, 81-239
Phoebe: Saturn, 82-25
Phosphate: Cade, J. Robert, 82-364
Phosphorus: ecology, 81-264
Photoelectric effect: Einstein, Albert, 80-404
Photoelectronics, 81-259
Photography, 82-54, 81-346
Photons: atomic and molecular physics, 82-293; elementary particles, 82-296, 80-322; quantum chromodynamics, 81-173; X-ray astronomy, 82-140
Photosphere: astronomy, 80-244; solar wind, *Special Report,* 80-14
Photosynthesis: Botany, 81-254, 80-255; geochemistry, 81-281
Photovoltaics: energy, 82-251
Phreatic eruption: Mount Saint Helens, *Special Report,* 82-76
Physical dependence, 82-115
Physical fitness: swimming, 81-37
Physics: atomic and molecular, 82-293, 81-313, 80-320; astronomy, 82-220; awards, 82-309, 81-403, 80-388; *Books of Science,* 82-229, 81-252, 80-254; *Close-Up,* 81-322; Einstein, Albert, 80-397; elementary particles, 82-295, 81-171, 315, 80-322, Fourier Transforms, 81-210; nuclear, 82-298, 81-318, 80-325; plasma, 82-300, 81-320, 80-327; solar wind, 80-13; solid-state, 82-302, 81-321, 80-329; synchrotron, 80-171; X-ray astronomy 82-139. See also **Lasers; Nuclear power plants.**
Physiology: awards, 82-309; collision research, 80-142; nutrition, 80-314; shock, 80-250. See also **Biology; Medicine.**
Phytosaur: paleontology, 82-264
Picture element: electronics, 82-245

Pigeon: animal navigation, *Special Report,* 81-118; zoology, 82-317
Piltdown fossil hoax, 80-233
Pion condensation: physics, 82-300
Pioneer: astronomy, 81-238, 80-242; Jupiter, 81-42; Saturn, 82-14
Pistachio: Negev, 80-138
Pixel: electronics, 82-245
Planet: amateur astronomy, 81-391; Saturn, 82-12
Planetary Astronomy, 82-219, 81-238, 80-240; extraterrestrial life, 80-57; Jupiter, 81-41; Saturn, 82-12
Planetary waves, 82-278, 80-304
Plankton: oil spill, 81-81
Plant: agriculture, 82-210; botany, 82-230, 81-253, 80-255; ecology, 82-240, 81-268, 80-270; *Special Report,* 82-128. See also *Agriculture; Botany.*
Plasma clouds: astronomy, 82-223
Plasma confinement: physics, 81-320
Plasma physics. See *Physics* **(plasma).**
Plasmodium: immunology, 81-293; monoclonal antibodies, 82-175
Plastics: chemical technology, 80-257; transportation, 80-347
Plate tectonics: Atwater, Tanya, 80-362; geology, 81-283, 80-286; geophysics, 82-262, 81-286, 80-289; geoscience, 82-260; Mount Saint Helens, 82-72; oceanography, 81-312; paleontology, 81-288
Platinum: chemistry, 81-255
Pluto: astronomy, 82-219, 80-242
Pneuman, Gerald: solar wind, 80-24
Pneumonia: *Close-Up,* 81-263
Polarization spectroscopy, 80-321
Polarized hydrogen: physics, 82-303
Pollution: oceanography, 81-310, 80-319; transportation, 80-347. See also **Air pollution;** *Ecology; Environment;* **Ocean pollution; Water pollution.**
Poloidal Divertor Experiment (PDX): plasma physics, 81-321
Polyester fiberfill, 82-348
Polyethylene glycol (PEG), 82-110
Pompeii, 81-233
Positron: physics, 82-295, 80-322
Potassium: geochemistry, 81-282; medicine, 81-294; nutrition, 82-289
Poultry: animal welfare, 82-92
Praseodymium-nickel compound (PrNi₅), 82-302
Predation, 81-12; zoology, 81-337
Pregnancy, 81-296
Prehistoric people: archaeology, 82-216, 217
Pressure chamber: oceanography, 82-291
Priestley Medal, 82-310; 81-402, 80-386
Primary hepatocellular cancer (PHC): hepatitis, *Special Report,* 82-161
Prime number: electronics, 80-274
Probability: *Special Report,* 82-180
Product testing: animal welfare, 82-88
Program: *Consumer Science,* 82-338
Proinsulin synthesis, 80-308
Promoter sequence, 82-283

Index

Propulsion: swimming, *81*-30
Prostaglandin: agriculture, *81*-229; chemistry, *81*-258
Protein: biochemistry, *81*-247; chemistry, *81*-256; nutrition, *82*-290; split genes, *81*-198
Proton: atomic and molecular physics, *82*-293; cosmology, *81*-247; elementary particles, *82*-296, *81*-315; nuclear physics, *81*-318
Psychiatry: schizophrenia, *81*-130
Psychoactive drug, *82*-112
Psychology, *82*-304, *81*-325, *80*-331; alcoholism, *82*-121; *Books of Science,* *81*-252; *Close-Up, 80*-332; schizophrenia, *81*-130. See also **Brain;** *Environment.*
Psychosis: schizophrenia, *81*-131
Pterosaur: paleontology, *82*-266
Public Health, *82*-307, *81*-327, *80*-335; alcoholism, *82*-125; drugs, *81*-263; environment, *82*-253, *80*-280; hepatitis, *82*-153. See also **Cancer;** *Medicine;* **Vaccines; Virus.**
Puffin: oil spill, *81*-79
Pulltrouser Swamp, archaeology *81*-237
Pulsars: stellar astronomy, *81*-241, *80*-243; X-ray astronomy, *82*-146. See also ***Astronomy* (high-energy).**
Pulsed current: physics, *82*-301
Pumice: Mount Saint Helens, *82*-80
Purkinje nerve cell, *81*-307
Pus: inflammation, *81*-58
Pyramid: archaeoastronomy, *80*-112

Q

QCD force, *81*-172
QED theory: physics, *82*-293
Quantum chromodynamics (QCD): physics, *80*-322; *81*-171
Quantum energy behavior, *82*-295
Quantum theory, *81*-314, 318, *80*-404
Quarks: elementary particles, *82*-295, *81*-315, *80*-322; quantum chromodynamics, *81*-172
Quasar: astronomy, *82*-224, *80*-244; cosmology, *81*-245, *80*-247; Einstein, Albert, *80*-403; X-ray astronomy, *82*-149
Quassin: chemistry, *82*-234
Queuing problems: probability, *Special Report, 82*-189
Quilted garments, *82*-348
Quinones: chemical ecology, *81*-16

R

R-loop technique: split genes, *81*-201
R-plasmids: drugs, *Close-Up, 81*-263
R value: *Consumer Science, 82*-344
Radial tires, *82*-352
Radiation: astronomy *82*-224; chemistry, *81*-257; cosmology, *82*-226, *80*-247; extinction, *82*-52; physics, *81*-314; public health, *80*-335; synchrotron, *80*-171; X-ray astronomy, *82*-139

Radiation belts: Jupiter, *81*-45
Radio: communications, *81*-261; stereo, *Consumer Science, 81*-349
Radio astronomy: astronomy, *80*-244; cosmology, *82*-226; Fourier Transforms, *81*-221; geophysics, *82*-262; interstellar medium, *81*-162; X-ray astronomy, *82*-141
Radio frequency (rf) radiation, *81*-270
Radio telescope: cosmology, *82*-226; extraterrestrial life, *Special Report, 80*-67; geophysics, *82*-262
Radio waves: astronomy, *82*-224; geophysics, *82*-262; Jupiter, *81*-45; plasma physics, *82*-302, *81*-320
Radioactive waste disposal, *81*-323, *80*-277
Radiocarbon, *82*-334
Radiometer, *81*-270
Rainfall: acid rain, *81*-276; Negev, *80*-128; paleontology, *81*-291
Ram pressure stripping, *82*-147
Ramapithecus: anthropology, *82*-213
Ramsey theory, *81*-382
Random numbers: probability, *Special Report, 82*-191
Rasmussen Report, *80*-279
Reactive schizophrenic, *81*-131
Receptor cells, *il., 82*-273
Receptors: inflammation, *81*-66
Recombinant DNA: hepatitis, *Special Report, 82*-159; microbiology, *80*-308; science policy, *80*-339
Record players: stereo, *81*-349
Red blood cell markers: anthropology, *81*-107; hepatitis, *82*-154
Red blood cells, *81*-294
Red shift: astronomy, *82*-224, *81*-245; Einstein, Albert, *80*-403
Relative humidity, *82*-350
Relativity: Einstein, Albert, *80*-397
Renal medicine: Cade, *82*-356
Renin: drugs, *82*-239
Replantation: surgery, *81*-300
Reproduction: agriculture, *81*-229; embryo transplants, *80*-185
Reptile, prehistoric, *82*-264
Research safety vehicles, *80*-149
Reserve, wildlife: rhinoceros, *82*-32
Resist: electronics, *82*-244
Resistance, electrical: physics, *81*-321
Resistance genes: biochemistry, *80*-249; drugs, *Close-Up, 81*-263; microbiology, *81*-304
Restriction enzyme: biochemistry, *80*-250; split genes, *81*-200
Retina: chemistry, *81*-256
Retinex theory: neuroscience, *81*-307
Retinopathy, diabetic: surgery, *81*-300
Reverse transcriptase: molecular biology, *82*-283
Rf hyperthermia: electronics, *81*-271
Rheumatoid arthritis, *80*-297
Rhinoceros: *Special Report, 82*-27
Rhizobacteria: agriculture, *81*-227
Ribonucleic acid. See **RNA.**
Ribosome: molecular biology, *82*-281; split genes, *81*-199
Ribulose-biphosphate carboxylase/oxygenase, *81*-254

Rice: agriculture, *82*-211
Ring: Jupiter, *81*-46; planetary astronomy, *81*-238; Saturn, *82*-21
Rivera Submersible Experiment (RISE): geophysics, *81*-286; oceanography, *81*-312
RNA (ribonucleic acid): interferon, *80*-117; microbiology, *80*-308; molecular biology, *82*-281; split genes, *81*-199. See also **Cell; DNA;** *Genetics;* **Virus.**
RNA polymerase, *82*-283
Root systems: ecology, *82*-243
Rotation, planetary: astronomy, *82*-219, *81*-238; hurricane, *81*-91; Jupiter, *81*-44
Runoff agriculture: Negev, *80*-127
Russia: Lake Baikal, *80*-155; science policy, *80*-338; space exploration, *80*-343
Ruthenium: catalysts, *Special Report, 82*-205; chemistry, *82*-233, *81*-255
Rydberg atom: atomic and molecular physics, *81*-314

S

Safety: collision research, *Special Report, 80*-141; environment, *80*-279; science policy, *80*-339
St. Augustine (Fla.): New World archaeology, *82*-218
Salt: botany, *82*-230; nutrition, *82*-290, *81*-310
Salyut 6, *82*-311, *81*-329, *80*-343
Satellite: astronomy, *81*-238, *80*-242; Jupiter, *81*-41; space exploration, *82*-314; X-ray astronomy, *82*-139
Saturn: planetary astronomy, *81*-238; space exploration, *81*-331; *82*-12
Sauce Béarnaise: chemistry, *81*-256
Sauropod: dinosaur, *81*-290
Sawfly: chemical ecology, *81*-24
Scanning electron microscope (SEM): forensic science, *81*-103
Schistosomiasis, *82*-133
Schizophrenia: Cade, J. Robert, *82*-365; *Special Report, 81*-129
Scholastic Aptitude Test, *82*-304
Science Policy, *80*-337; *Close-Up, 80*-339. See also *Ecology; Space Exploration; Transportation.*
Scoliosis: surgery, *82*-275
Sea-floor spreading: Atwater, Tanya, *80*-362; geology, *81*-283; geoscience, *82*-260. See also **Continental drift; Plate tectonics.**
Sea otter: ecology, *82*-242
Sea urchin: ecology, *82*-242
Seat belts: collision research, *80*-146
Secondary hypertension: internal medicine, *81*-294
Sedimentary rock: extinction, *82*-42
Semiconductors: chemistry, *82*-232
Sencor: agriculture, *81*-227
Sensory cell, *il., 82*-343
Sensory perception: neuroscience, *81*-306
Sepsis: internal medicine, *82*-269
Sequenator: chemistry, *81*-258

Serotonin: nutrition and the brain, *Special Report, 80*-89
Serum, blood: hepatitis, *82*-154; inflammation, *81*-58
Serum hepatitis: *82*-154
Sex-linked learning ability: psychology, *82*-304
Sex-linked trait: probability, *82*-185
Seyfert galaxy: astronomy, *82*-225
Shale oil: energy, *82*-248
Shear stress: geophysics, *81*-288
Sheep: agriculture, *82*-212
Shigella: drugs, *Close-Up, 81*-263
Shingles: interferon, *80*-121
Shipbuilding, ancient: sunken treasure, *Special Report, 82*-98
Shipwreck, ancient: archaeology, *81*-234; sunken treasure, *82*-97
Shock, *81*-257, *80*-250
Shroud of Turin: *Close-Up, 80*-236
Siberia: geology, *80*-287; Lake Baikal, *Special Report, 80*-155
Sickle cell anemia, anthropology, *82*-214; *il., 82*-238; microbiology, *81*-305
Silicon: chemistry, *81*-256; electronics, *82*-244
Sine wave: Fourier Transforms, *81*-210
Single-lens reflex camera, *81*-347
Skin: disorders, *81*-344; drugs, *82*-240; surgery, *82*-276
Skylab: solar wind, *80*-15; space exploration, *81*-330, *80*-342
Slow-reacting substance (SRS), *81*-257
Slow-twitch muscle fibers, *81*-37
Smoking: drugs, *80*-266; public health, *81*-327
Smooth-arm galaxy: *82*-223
Sociobiology: neuroscience, *81*-307
Sodium: geochemistry, *81*-282; Lake Baikal, *80*-164; medicine, *81*-294
Sodium fluorosilicate, *81*-256
Sodium-potassium-ATPase, *82*-289
Soil: *82*-240, 242, 255
Solar cells: chemistry, *82*-232, *81*-256, *80*-260; electronics, *82*-246; energy, *82*-251
Solar Challenger: energy, *82*-251
Solar constant: astronomy, *82*-222
Solar energy: agriculture, *81*-230; chemistry, *81*-255; electronics, *82*-246; energy, *82*-251, *81*-272
Solar flares: astronomy, *82*-222
Solar Maximum Mission Observatory satellite: space exploration, *81*-331; stellar astronomy, *82*-222
Solar nebula: Saturn, *82*-24
Solar neutrino, *81*-316
Solar system: Jupiter, *81*-41; Saturn, *82*-12
Solar tracking: botany, *82*-231
Solar wind: Saturn, *Special Report, 82*-24; *Special Report, 80*-13
Solid-State Physics, 82-302, *81*-321
Sound frequency: zoology, *82*-315
Sound spectrography, *80*-31
Soyuz, 82-311, *80*-343
Space Exploration, 82-311, *81*-329, *80*-342; Saturn, *82*-12; X-ray astronomy, *82*-139. See also *Astronomy* (planetary).

Space shuttle: space exploration, *82*-311, *81*-329, *80*-342
Space station. See *Space Exploration.*
Spacelab, 82-314, *80*-342
Speaker, stereo, *81*-349
Speaker-activated video-display terminal: electronics, *81*-270
Spectral lines: astronomy, *82*-219
Spectrometer: nuclear physics, *82*-318; X-ray astronomy, *82*-143
Spectrum, electromagnetic, *82*-140
Speech: birdsong, *80*-28
Speech recognition device, *81*-269
Speech synthesis: electronics, *81*-268
Sphincter muscle: surgery, *81*-299
Spine: surgery, *82*-275, *81*-298
Spiral galaxies, *82*-223 *81*-245, *80*-247
Split genes: *Special Report, 81*-197
Spodoptera worm, *82*-134
Sports medicine: Cade, *82*-356
Staphyloccocus aureus, *82*-307
Star: amateur astronomy, *81*-390; extraterrestrial life, *80*-57; high-energy astronomy, *80*-245; interstellar medium, *81*-158; nuclear physics, *81*-319; stellar astronomy, *82*-222; X-ray astronomy, *82*-144
Stellar Astronomy, 82-222, *81*-240, *80*-243; *Special Report, 81*-156
Stellar wind: astronomy, *81*-240; interstellar medium, *Special Report, 81*-167; *Special Report, 80*-27
Stellarator: plasma physics, *82*-302
Stereo system, *82*-343, *81*-348
Sterols: botany, *81*-253
Stone tools: archaeology, *82*-215
Stonehenge: *Special Report, 80*-101
Stop-action photography, *82*-54
Storm: hurricane, *81*-87
Streptomycetes, *82*-214
Strobe light: photography, *82*-54
Stroke: nutrition, *81*-308
Strong force: nuclear physics, *82*-298
Subatomic matter: physics, *82*-295, *80*-322; quantum chromodynamics, *Special Report, 81*-172
Subconjunctival hemorrhage, *82*-272
Subduction: Atwater, Tanya, *80*-362; geology, *81*-283; geophysics, *80*-289
Subliminal perception, *81*-327; *80*-331
Sulfate respiration, *81*-281
Sulfur dioxide: acid rain, *81*-276; Jupiter, *81*-54
Sun: animal navigation, *81*-119; astronomy, *82*-222, *80*-243; shrinking sun, *81*-242; solar wind, *80*-13. See also headings beginning Solar . . . .
Sunspots: astronomy, *80*-243; solar wind, *Special Report, 80*-15
Superconductors: physics, *81*-321
Superfluid gas: physics, *82*-304
Superfund: environment, *82*-254
Supernova: amateur astronomy, *81*-399; astronomy, *80*-245; interstellar medium, *81*-168; physics, *81*-319; X-ray astronomy, *82*-144
Supernova remnant, *81*-242
Superovulation: agriculture, *82*-212; embryo transplants, *80*-190

Superoxide ion: chemistry, *82*-235
Superstition: psychology, *82*-305
Support: catalysts, *82*-201
Surface antigen: hepatitis, *82*-157
Surface mining: ecology, *82*-240
Surgery: breast cancer, *81*-351; medical school, *82*-375. See also *Medicine* (surgery).
Swamp forest: ecology, *82*-242
Swimming: *Special Report, 81*-27
Symbiosis, *il., 82*-231
Synchrotron: *Special Report, 80*-171
Synthesis gas: catalysts, *82*-201

T

T lymphocytes: immunology, *81*-292; interferon, *Special Report, 80*-116
Tampons: public health, *82*-307
Tandem mirror concept (TMC): plasma physics, *81*-320
Tar sands: *Special Report, 81*-182
Tardive dyskinesia: nutrition and the brain, *80*-92; schizophrenia, *81*-138
Targeted drug therapy, *82*-174
Tau: elementary particles, *81*-316
Technology, 80-345; *Books of Science, 82*-229; *Close-Up, 80*-345; forensic science, *81*-102
Telephone: communications, *81*-259; fiber optics, *Special Report, 80*-212
Telescope: amateur astronomy, *81*-392; X-ray astronomy, *82*-139
Teletext, *81*-261, *80*-266
Television: communications, *81*-261, *80*-264; electronics, *82*-244
Tellico Dam, *81*-281
Teotihuacán, *80*-110
Termites: chemical ecology, *81*-18
Tertiary Period: extinction, *82*-42
Tetracycline: anthropology, *82*-214; dentistry, *81*-294
TGA codon: biochemistry, *81*-248
Tharsis (Mars): astronomy, *82*-221
Thermistor: electronics, *81*-271
Thermonuclear reactor, *81*-327
Thigmomorphogenesis, *82*-230
Three Mile Island: energy, *80*-276; environment, *80*-279; public health, *80*-335; science policy, *80*-341
Thunderstorm, *il., 82*-279
Tidal forces, gravitational, *81*-239
Tires: *Consumer Science, 82*-352
Titan: Saturn, *Special Report, 82*-19
Toe: surgery, *81*-299
Tokamak: energy, *80*-277; plasma physics, *82*-300, *81*-320, *80*-327
Tolerance: alcoholism, *82*-115
Tomato: agriculture, *81*-226, *80*-226
Tool, prehistoric, *il., 82*-215; archaeology, *82*-215, 217
Tooth decay, *81*-294, *80*-295
Topsoil: ecology, *82*-240
Torus: plasma physics, *82*-300
Total Harmonic Distortion, stereo, *81*-349
Toxic shock syndrome, *82*-307
Toxic waste disposal: environment, *82*-252, *81*-274, *80*-280
Toxicity tests: animal welfare, *82*-88

Index

Transcription: molecular biology, *82*-281; split genes, *81*-198
Transfusion hepatitis, *82*-154
Transistor: electronics, *81*-268
Transplantation: surgery, *81*-299
Transportation, *81*-331, *80*-347; collision research, *80*-141
Transposon: biochemistry, *80*-249
Triazine: agriculture, *81*-227
Tris-(bipyridine) ruthenium (II) di-cation: chemistry, *82*-233
Tritium: physics, *81*-321
Trophectoderm (TE) cell: genetics, *82*-255
Tropical depression: hurricane, *Special Report, 81*-88
Tropical reef: extinction, *82*-48; zoology, *82*-316
Tryptophan: biochemistry, *81*-248; nutrition and the brain, *80*-89
Tubulin: inflammation, *81*-67
Tumor: botany, *80*-256; electronics, *81*-270; immunology, *81*-293; inflammation, *81*-68; medicine, *81*-297; microbiology, *81*-304; monoclonal antibodies, *82*-167
Turbine: energy, *82*-248, *81*-273
Turin shroud: *Close-Up, 80*-236
Turntable: stereo, *81*-349
Twins: alcoholism, *82*-123; nutrition, *82*-290; schizophrenia, *81*-132
2-dinitrochlorobenzene, *82*-178

U

Ulcerative colitis: surgery, *82*-275
Ultraviolet radiation: animal navigation, *81*-121; heat absorption, *81*-322; interstellar medium, *81*-164
Underwater research: archaeology, *80*-238; oceanography, *82*-291; sunken treasure, *82*-97
Universe: cosmology, *81*-245, *80*-247; Einstein, Albert, *80*-409; X-ray astronomy, *Special Report, 82*-140
Upsilon, *82*-295, *81*-316
Upstream molecule, *82*-283
Uracil: split genes, *81*-199
Uranium: Geochemistry, *82*-258
Urban-cowboy rhabdomyolosis: medicine, *Close-Up, 82*-272
Urinary bladder: surgery, *81*-299

V

Vaccines: hepatitis, *82*-153; public health, *82*-308, *81*-328
Vacuum fluorescent (VF) tube, *82*-244
Variable star: astronomy, *81*-396
Vasopressin: neuroscience, *82*-288
Veal production, *82*-91
Venus: geochemistry, *80*-286; planetary astronomy, *81*-240, *80*-242; space exploration, *80*-342
Verapamil: drugs, *82*-239
Veronica: plant chemicals, *82*-133
Very Long Baseline Interferometry (VLBI): geophysics, *82*-262
Videodisc, *82*-336
Virus: botany, *81*-253; chemistry, *81*-258; drugs, *80*-268; *ils., 81*-219; hepatitis, *82*-153; inflammation, *81*-59; interferon, *80*-116; medicine, *82*-273, *81*-297, *80*-296; microbiology, *81*-306; molecular biology, *82*-281; monoclonal antibodies, *82*-176. See also **Cancer;** *Microbiology;* **Vaccines.**
Visual-display language translator: electronics, *81*-268
Vitreous humor, *81*-300, *80*-300
Voice recognition device, *81*-268
Volcano: agriculture, *82*-210; astronomy, *81*-221, *80*-240; Atwater, Tanya, *80*-362; geochemistry, *82*-258, *81*-283; geophysics, *82*-263, *81*-286; Jupiter, *81*-53; Mount Saint Helens, *82*-69; oceanography, *81*-312, *80*-316
Voyager: astronomy, *81*-238, *80*-240; Jupiter, *81*-41; Saturn, *82*-12; space exploration, *82*-314, *81*-330, *80*-342

W

Waste: environment, *82*-252, *81*-274, *80*-280; oceanography, *81*-311; solid-state physics, *81*-323
Water: botany, *82*-230; chemistry, *81*-255
Water pollution: acid rain, *81*-276; environment, *82*-252; Lake Baikal, *80*-155; oil spill, *81*-71. See also *Ecology;* **Ocean pollution; Pollution.**
Weaning: nutrition, *82*-288

Weather: hurricane, *81*-87; solar wind, *80*-26. See also **Climate;** *Meteorology.*
Weed control: agriculture, *81*-226
Whale: oceanography, *81*-311; paleontology, *82*-264
White blood cell: immunology, *81*-292; inflammation, *81*-58; medicine, *81*-297; monoclonal antibodies, *82*-167
Wildlife conservation: rhinoceros, *Special Report, 82*-28
Wind, solar: *Special Report, 80*-13
Wind turbine: energy, *81*-273
Winds of Saturn: Saturn, *82*-16
Withdrawal syndrome: alcoholism, *Special Report, 82*-115
Wolstenholme Town, *81*-235
Word-processing, *82*-339
Writing: archaeology, *81*-234

X

X-ray astronomy: astronomy, *81*-241, 243, *80*-245; *Special Report, 82*-139;
X-ray crystallography, *82*-285
X-ray telescope, *82*-139
X rays: astronomy, *82*-224; electronics, *81*-270; energy, *82*-248; Fourier Transforms, *81*-216; public health, *80*-335; synchrotron, *80*-172; X-ray astronomy, *82*-139
Xenon: geochemistry, *80*-285; solid-state physics, *80*-330

Y

Young, William G.: deaths, *82*-237
Yrast curve: nuclear physics, *80*-327

Z

Z-DNA: molecular biology, *82*-285
Zeolite: catalysts, *82*-204
Zoology, *82*-315, *81*-333, *80*-349; birdsong, *80*-28; museum, *81*-146; rhinoceros, *82*-27
Zooplankton: oceanography, *81*-311

Acknowledgments

The publishers of *Science Year* gratefully acknowledge the courtesy of the following artists, photographers, publishers, institutions, agencies, and corporations for the illustrations in this volume. Credits should be read from top to bottom, left to right, on their respective pages. All entries marked with an asterisk (*) denote illustrations created exclusively for *Science Year*. All maps, charts, and diagrams were prepared by the *Science Year* staff unless otherwise noted.

Cover

© Jonathan Blair, Woodfin Camp Inc.

Advisory Board

7　University of Pennsylvania; Harvard University; Cornell University; Argonne National Laboratory; Harvard University; California Institute of Technology; Duke University Medical Center

Special Reports

10　© Jonathan Blair, Woodfin Camp Inc.; Mohamid Amin, Bruce Coleman Inc., Phil Renaud*
11　Steve Hale*; Alan E. Cober*; Jet Propulsion Laboratory
12-19　Jet Propulsion Laboratory
20　NASA; Jet Propulsion Laboratory
21-24　Jet Propulsion Laboratory
26　Mohamid Amin, Bruce Coleman Inc.
29　The Cultural Relics Bureau, Beijing and The Metropolitan Museum of Art, New York City; Bettmann Archive
30　K. Ross, JACANA; J. Robert, JACANA
31　G. Schaller, Bruce Coleman Inc.; Milwaukee Public Museum; Daphne Sheldrick
34　© Robert Frerck; Joe McDonald, Bruce Coleman Inc.; Andrew Laurie, Orion Press
35　Leonard Lee Rue III, Bruce Coleman Inc.; David C. Fritts, Animals Animals; Clem Haagner, Bruce Coleman Inc.; J. M. Labat, JACANA
37　Bob Campbell, Bruce Coleman Inc.; Bob Campbell, Bruce Coleman Inc.; Norman Owen-Smith
38　Andrew Laurie, Orion Press
40-46　Phil Renaud*
48　Erle Kauffmann
49-51　Phil Renaud*
54-55　Harold E. Edgerton and John Guenette, Massachusetts Institute of Technology
56-58　Harold E. Edgerton, Massachusetts Institute of Technology
59　Harold E. Edgerton, Massachusetts Institute of Technology; Dennis Shute
60　Harold E. Edgerton, Massachusetts Institute of Technology
61　Calvin Campbell, Massachusetts Institute of Technology; Harold Moffitt; Harold E. Edgerton, Massachusetts Institute of Technology
62　Harold E. Edgerton, Massachusetts Institute of Technology
63　© Robert A. Tyrrell; Harold E. Edgerton, Massachusetts Institute of Technology
64　Fike Metal Products Corporation; Boeing
65　William Hyzer, Amoco Oil Company, from *Photo Methods*, November, 1980
66　William Hyzer, Amoco Oil Company; William Hyzer, Amoco Oil Company; Andrew Davidhazy, Rochester Institute of Technology; Andrew Davidhazy, Rochester Institute of Technology; William Hyzer, Amoco Oil Company
67　William Hyzer, Amoco Oil Company; George Suyeoka*; William Hyzer, Amoco Oil Company; William Hyzer, Amoco Oil Company
68　Royal Ontario Museum, Toronto
69　Peter W. Lipman, U.S. Geological Survey
71　Michael Lawton; Gary Rosenquist, Earth Images; Gary Rosenquist, Earth Images; Gary Rosenquist, Earth Images
73-75　Gregory Manchess*
76　Peter W. Lipman, U.S. Geological Survey
77　Ralph Perry
78　Roger Werth
79　Gregory Manchess*; Bill Thompson, Earth Images
80　Gary Braasch
81　D. May, U.S. Geological Survey
82　Ralph Perry

84　Michael Fox, Institute for the Study of Animal Problems
87　Peter Menzel, Stock Boston; Woodfin Camp Inc.; Susan McElhinney, Woodfin Camp Inc.; H. S. Owen, Black Star; H. S. Owen, Black Star; H. S. Owen, Black Star
90　Michael Fox, Institute for the Study of Animal Problems; Temple Grandin; Temple Grandin
91　Michael Fox, Institute for the Study of Animal Problems; Peter Menzel, Stock Boston
92　Carlos Sanuvo, Bruce Coleman Inc.; John J. Dommers, Humane Society of the United States; W. D. Marshall
94　N. deVore III, Bruce Coleman Inc.
96　© Jonathan Blair, Woodfin Camp Inc.
99　George Suyeoka*; © Jonathan Blair, Woodfin Camp Inc.; Donald A. Frey
100　Donald A. Frey; R. C. M. Piercy; Donald H. Keith
102　George Suyeoka*
103　Donald A. Frey
104　George Suyeoka*
105　George Suyeoka*; Donald H. Keith
106-108　Donald A. Frey
113　Steve Hale*; John Downs*; John Downs*
116　John Downs*; Steve Hale*
117　John Downs*
118　John Downs*; Steve Hale*
119　Steve Hale*; John Downs*
120　John Downs*
121　© Mark Reinstein, Lensman; John Downs*
122　John Downs*; Steve Hale*
123　"Computer Tomography Scans of Alcoholics: Cerebral Atrophy?" P. L. Carlen et al, *Science*, © June, 1979, by the American Association for the Advancement of Science
126　Leon V. Kofod
129　Topkapi Palace Museum, Istanbul, Turkey (Esin Atil); © Derek Fell
130　Leon V. Kofod
132-134　Isao Kubo
135　© Martin Rogers, Woodfin Camp Inc.; © Nathan Benn, Woodfin Camp Inc.; © Nathan Benn, Woodfin Camp Inc.; Isao Kubo
136　Isao Kubo
138　© Smithsonian Institution
142　Phillip Shaffer*
143　Phillip Shaffer*; COS-B Collaboration; © Smithsonian Institution; Edward B. Jenkins, Princeton University; NASA; Robert D. Gehrz, Gary L. Grasdalen, John A. Hockwell, Wyoming Infrared Observatory, University of Wyoming
145　Phillip Shaffer*; TRW
148　Rob Wood*; C. Jones, Harvard-Smithsonian Center for Astrophysics
149　C. Jones, Harvard-Smithsonian Center for Astrophysics
150　Rob Wood*; E. Schreies, Harvard-Smithsonian Center for Astrophysics; © Smithsonian Institution; F. Seward, Harvard-Smithsonian Center for Astrophysics
152　Merck Sharp & Dohme
158　© Robert Frerck
159　Baruch S. Blumberg, M.D.
160-161　Merck Sharp & Dohme
164　Robert R. McElroy, *Newsweek*
166-171　Alan E. Cober*
172　© David Scharf
173　Alan E. Cober*
174　A. Cochrane, R. Nussenzweig, M.D., and E. Nardin
175　B. Ballou, G. Levine, T. R. Hakala, and D. Soltor
177　Alan E. Cober*
181-184　Steve Hale*
188　Pauline Cary Family Photo Collection; (Mime) Steve Hale*
190-192　Steve Hale*
194-203　James Conahan*

Science File

208 Randa Bishop, Du Pont; U.S. Department of Energy; D. F. Malin, UK Schmidt Telescope Unit
209 Sandia Laboratories; Jon W. Gordon, Yale University; Chuck Nicklin, Ocean Films, Ltd.
210-212 U.S. Department of Agriculture
213 William Breen Murray
214 Margaret Keith, University of Massachusetts
215 Donald C. Johanson
216 Phillip Shaffer*, Luke Powell, City of David Society
217 Jet Propulsion Laboratory
218 Archaeology Laboratory, University of South Dakota and U.S. Army Corps of Engineers
219 Mullard Radio Astronomy Observatory, Cambridge, England
220 Jet Propulsion Laboratory
221 Goddard Space Flight Center
222 Sidney Harris, *American Scientist*
223 Mullard Radio Astronomy Observatory, Cambridge, England
227 D. F. Malin, UK Schmidt Telescope Unit
231 Vernon Ahmadjian, Clark University and Jerome B. Jacobs, St. Vincent Hospital and University of Massachusetts Medical School
232 Lawrence Livermore National Laboratory
233 Drawing by Lorenz; © 1980 The New Yorker Magazine, Inc.
235 Goodyear Tire & Rubber Company
236-237 Wide World
238 Weizman Institute of Science, Rehovot, Israel
239 F. P. Ottensmeyer, Ontario Cancer Institute
241 U.S. Department of Energy
243 Oak Ridge National Laboratory
244 British Telecom
245 Drawing by H. Martin; © 1981 The New Yorker Magazine, Inc.
246 International Business Machines Corporation
247 Zelex Corporation
249 Paul Van Valkenburg
250 Randa Bishop, Du Pont; Nordskog Industries
251 General Electric
253 H. Martin, *Audubon*
254 Battelle, Pacific Northwest Laboratories
255 Jon W. Gordon, Yale University
256 *Cell*; Phillip Shaffer*
257 Sidney Harris, *American Scientist*
259 A. Gow and T. Williamson, USA CRREL
260 International Stop Continental Drift Society
262 Kenneth R. Lajoie, U.S. Geological Survey
264 Louisiana State University
265 Sankar Chatterjee, Royal Society of London; Phillip Shaffer*
266 Wolfgang Suter. Reprinted by permission from Nature, Vol. 286, No. 5772, p. 486 by Olivier Peppel. © 1980 Macmillan Journals
268 Lee E. Pinckney, M.D., Children's Medical Center, Dallas, Texas from *Radiology*, May, 1980
269 Franklin Lim, et. al., Medical College of Virginia, Virginia Commonwealth University
270 Sidney Harris, *American Scientist*
271 Johns Hopkins University
273 Dean A. Handley, M.D., Cynthia M. Arbeeny, M.D., Larry D. Witte, M.D. and Shu Chien, M.D., College of Physicians and Surgeons, Columbia University
274 Gerald S. Williams
276 University of Utah
277 Calvin Campbell, Massachusetts Institute of Technology
279-280 National Center for Atmospheric Research
281 Computer Graphics Laboratory, University of California, San Francisco
284 Peter P. H. De Bruyn and Sonia Michelson, University of Chicago
286 National Institute of Health
287 Drawing by Lorenz; © 1980 The New Yorker Magazine, Inc.
291 Chuck Nicklin, Ocean Films, Ltd.
292 Haris Lessios, Smithsonian Tropical Research Institute
294 Lawrence Berkeley Laboratory, University of California
297 University of Utah
298 Sidney Harris, *American Scientist*
299 Erwin Friedlander, Lawrence Berkeley Laboratory, University of California; Lawrence Berkeley Laboratory, University of California
301 Sandia Laboratories
303 C. O. Bozler, Massachusetts Institute of Technology; Phillip Shaffer*
305-306 Drawings adapted from *Science,* © 1980, by the American Association for the Advancement of Science, from study done at Department of Psychology, Johns Hopkins University; Phillip Shaffer*
309 University of Chicago; Wide World; Wide World
312-313 NASA
315 R. E. Stobbs, J. L. B. Smith, Institute of Ichthyology, Grahamstown, South Africa
316 Smithsonian Institution
318 Rickye Heppner, University of Kansas
319 National Institute of Child Health and Human Development
320 Drawing by Ross; © 1980 The New Yorker Magazine, Inc.

Science You Can Use

339-341 Steve Hale*
342 University of Tennessee; Leonard Morgan*
343 © Annie Leibovitz, Contact
344-345 Mineral Insulation Manufacturers Association
346 Leonard Morgan*
347 Kansas State University*
348 Steve Hale*
349 The 3M Company
351 Steve Hale*
353 Leonard Morgan*

People in Science

354 Steve Hale*; Daniel D. Miller*; Steve Hale*
355 Daniel D. Miller*; Steve Hale*; Daniel D. Miller*
357-368 Steve Hale*
370-383 Daniel D. Miller*

Cyclo-teacher® The easy-to-use learning system

Features hundreds of cycles from seven valuable learning areas

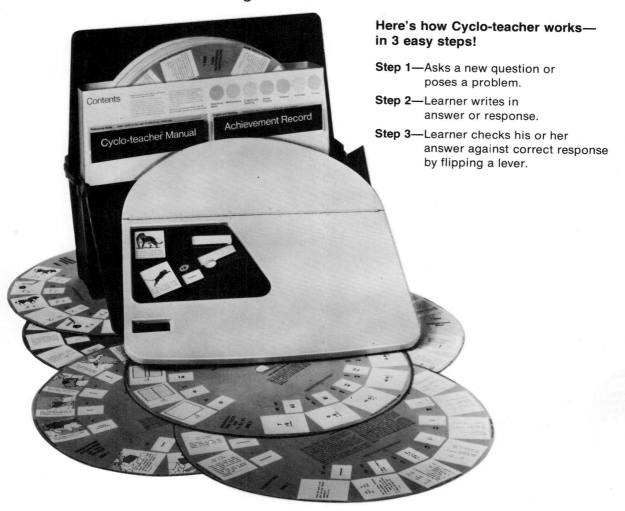

Here's how Cyclo-teacher works— in 3 easy steps!

Step 1—Asks a new question or poses a problem.

Step 2—Learner writes in answer or response.

Step 3—Learner checks his or her answer against correct response by flipping a lever.

Cyclo-teacher —the remarkable learning system based on the techniques of programmed instruction —comes right into your home to help stimulate and accelerate the learning of basic skills, concepts, and information. Housed in a specially designed file box are the Cyclo-teacher machine, Study Wheels, Answer Wheels, a Manual, a Contents and Instruction Card, and Achievement Record sheets.

Your child will find Cyclo-teacher to be a new and fascinating way to learn —much like playing a game. Only, Cyclo-teacher is much more than a game —it teaches new things

. . . reinforces learning . . . and challenges a youngster to go beyond!

Features hundreds of study cycles to meet the individual needs of students —your entire family —just as *Science Year* is a valuable learning aid. And, best of all, lets you track your own progress —advance at your own pace! Cyclo-teacher is available by writing us at the address below:

Science Year
Post Office Box 3737
Chicago, IL 60654

These beautiful bookstands-

specially designed to hold your entire program,
including your editions of *Science Year*.

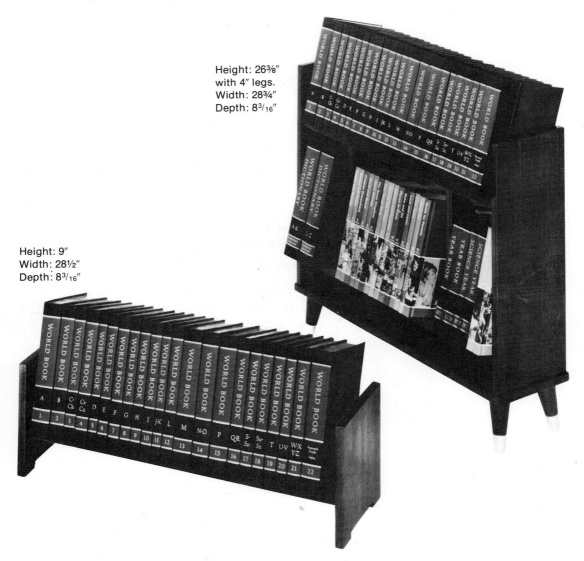

Height: 26⅜"
with 4" legs.
Width: 28¾"
Depth: 8³/₁₆"

Height: 9"
Width: 28½"
Depth: 8³/₁₆"

Most parents like having a convenient place to house their *Science Year* editions and their *World Book Encyclopedia*. A beautiful floor-model bookstand —constructed of solid hardwood —is available in either walnut or fruitwood finish.

You might prefer the attractive hardwood table racks, also available in either walnut or fruitwood finish. Let us know by writing us at the following address:

Science Year
Post Office Box 3737
Chicago, IL 60654